IRISH HOTELS FEDERATION

13 Northbrook Road, Dublin 6, Ireland
Telephone +353 1 497 6459   Fax: +353 1 497 4613

Be Our Guest

2003

Featuring over 1,000 Hotels & Guesthouses

as well as details on Golfing, Angling, Conference Facilities
and Touring Maps

irelandhotels.com
log on and book in

Book online at: www.irelandhotels.com

The Irish Hotels Federation does not accept any responsibility for errors, omissions or any information whatsoever in the Guide and members and users of the Guide are requested to consult page 22 hereof for further information.

N.B. Some telephone / fax numbers and codes will change during 2003, if you experience difficulty, please contact the operator
When dialing Ireland from abroad, please use the following codes:
Republic of Ireland: 00 353 + local code (drop the 0)
Northern Ireland: 00 44 + local code (drop the 0)
If dialling Northern Ireland directly from the Republic of Ireland replace the prefix code 028 with the code 048.

Printed & Published by The Wood Printcraft Group, Greencastle Parade, Malahide Road Industrial Park, Malahide Road, Dublin 17. Tel: +353 1 847 0011. Fax: +353 1 847 5570.
Design & Origination by Printcraft Imaging, Unit 95 Malahide Road Industrial Park, Malahide Road, Dublin 17.

BE OUR GUEST

GUINNESS.

CONTENTS
Page No.

FACILITIES

- Total number of rooms
- Number of rooms with bath/shower and toilet
- Direct dial facilities
- TV in all bedrooms
- Elevator/Lift
- Can be booked through travel agent / tourist office and commission paid
- Childrens playground
- Childrens playroom
- C Price reduction for children
- Babysitter service
- CM Childrens meals
- CS Creche
- Garden for visitors use
- Indoor swimming pool
- Outdoor swimming pool
- Sauna
- Gym
- Leisure Complex (including sauna / swimming pool / gym)
- Tennis court - hard / grass

- Games room
- Squash court
- Horse riding/pony trekking on site or nearby
- 9-hole golf course on site
- 18-hole golf course on site
- Angling on site or nearby
- Evening Entertainment
- P Car parking
- Facilities for pets
- S Price reduction for senior citizens excl. July/August and subject to availability
- Wine Licence only
- Dispense Bar Service only
- Licensed to sell all alcoholic drink
- alc À la carte meals provided
- Tea/coffee making facilities in bedroom
- Facilities and services are accessible to disabled persons
- Suitable for disabled persons, with the assistance of one helper
- Inet Modem access in room
- FAX Fax machine in room
- Special Offer

 Denotes that premises are members of the Irish Hotels Federation as at 18 September 2002. Denotes that premises are members of the Northern Ireland Hotels Federation as at 18 September 2002.

ACTIVITY SECTIONS
Green symbols Illustrated below denote that the hotel or guesthouse is included in a particular activity section. Further details of the facilities available and the arrangements made on behalf of guests for participation in these activities are shown on pages 417 to 465.

 Golf   Angling   Conference

MARKETING GROUPS
Many of the hotels and guesthouses in the guide are members of Marketing Groups. Those properties which are members of a Marketing Group will have the name of the group displayed within their entry. Some of these groups operate a central reservation system and can make reservations for you.

GUINNESS

SELECTING YOUR HOTEL AND GUESTHOUSE

REGIONS

Begin by selecting the region(s) you wish to visit. This guide divides into eight separate Regions – East Coast, Midlands & Lakelands, South East, South West, Shannon, West, North West and North – and they are represented in that order.

COUNTIES

Within each region, counties are presented alphabetically.

LOCATIONS – CITIES, TOWNS, VILLAGES

Within counties, locations are also presented alphabetically, see Index Pages 4 & 6.

PREMISES

Hotels and guesthouses are also presented in alphabetical order, see Index Pages 489 to 507.

	COUNTIES	REGION	PAGES
1	DUBLIN	East Coast	Page 31 to 95
2	LOUTH	East Coast	Page 95 to 99
3	MEATH	East Coast	Page 99 to 104
4	WICKLOW	East Coast	Page 104 to 115
5	CAVAN	Midlands & Lakelands	Page 117 to 120
6	KILDARE	Midlands & Lakelands	Page 120 to 126
7	LAOIS	Midlands & Lakelands	Page 126 to 128
8	LONGFORD	Midlands & Lakelands	Page 128 to 128
9	MONAGHAN	Midlands & Lakelands	Page 129 to 130
10	OFFALY	Midlands & Lakelands	Page 130 to 134
11	WESTMEATH	Midlands & Lakelands	Page 135 to 139
12	CARLOW	South East	Page 141 to 143
13	KILKENNY	South East	Page 144 to 152
14	TIPPERARY SOUTH	South East	Page 153 to 159
15	WATERFORD	South East	Page 160 to 173
16	WEXFORD	South East	Page 173 to 185
17	CORK	South West	Page 187 to 229
18	KERRY	South West	Page 229 to 279
19	CLARE	Shannon	Page 281 to 304
20	LIMERICK	Shannon	Page 304 to 313
21	TIPPERARY NORTH	Shannon	Page 313 to 315
22	GALWAY	West	Page 317 to 354
23	MAYO	West	Page 355 to 367
24	ROSCOMMON	West	Page 367 to 369
25	DONEGAL	North West	Page 371 to 382
26	LEITRIM	North West	Page 382 to 385
27	SLIGO	North West	Page 385 to 389
28	ANTRIM	North	Page 392 to 399
29	ARMAGH	North	Page 400 to 400
30	BELFAST CITY	North	Page 401 to 405
31	DERRY	North	Page 406 to 409
32	DOWN	North	Page 409 to 413
33	FERMANAGH	North	Page 414 to 415
34	TYRONE	North	Page 415 to 415

irelandhotels.com
log on and book in

To view any of the hotels and guesthouses featured in this guide, just log on at

www.irelandhotels.com

And, did you know that you can book many of these hotels and guesthouses online?

Just log on and book in

And while you're there, don't forget to check out our Special Offers Section, Gift Voucher Section or customise your break in the My Preferences Section.

IRISH HOTELS FEDERATION

Be Our Guest

AVOCA

Welcome to the colourful world of Avoca, where our seven magical shops are crammed
with beautiful things, most of which are made exclusively by Avoca. Savour our restaurants
where our delicious lunches are legendary. Visit any one of our shops and be
sure of a warm welcome and an experience with a difference.

Tel: 01 286 7466

Fax: 01 286 2367

Open 7 Days

Kilmacanogue	Avoca Village	Powerscourt House Shop	Molls Gap	Bunratty	Letterfrack	Suffolk St.
Bray, Co. Wicklow	Avoca Co. Wicklow	Enniskerry Co. Wicklow	Killarney, Co. Kerry	Co. Clare	Co. Galway	Dublin 2.

log on and book in

Jim Murphy
President, Irish Hotels Federation

Hotels and Guesthouses in Ireland are very special. The majority are family owned with the proprietor and members of the family there to welcome guests and to extend to them renowned Irish hospitality. Even when they are owned by a company, or are part of a group, they still retain the character and ambience of a family premises - a place where you will be truly welcome.

The Irish hotel is unique, in that more often than not, it acts as a social centre for the community. Hotels offer a lot more than just a bed and a meal - they are fully fledged social, leisure, business and community centres with every imaginable facility and amenity, providing food, accommodation, sports, leisure facilities, entertainment and other attractions.

If you are moving around the country, you'll find that "Be Our Guest" is an invaluable help in choosing your next location.

Ireland's hoteliers and guesthouse owners want to welcome you and want to play their part in ensuring that your stay in Ireland is a happy one. We hope that you will stay with us and that you will use this guide to select the hotel or guesthouse of your choice, so that we can personally invite you to -

Be Our Guest

Ní haon ní coitianta é an Óstlann nó an Teach Lóistín in Éirinn. Is i seilbh teaghlaigh iad a bhformhór acu agus bíonn an t-úinéir agus baill den teaghlach romhat chun fáilte Uí Cheallaigh a chur romhat. Fiú nuair is le comhlacht iad, nó is cuid de ghrúpa iad, baineann meon agus atmaisféar áitreabh teaghlaigh leo – áiteanna ina gcuirfí fíorchaoin fáilte romhat.

Rud ar leith is ea an óstlann in Éirinn agus is dócha ná a mhalairt go bhfeidhmíonn sí mar lárionad sóisialta don phobal. Cuireann an óstlann i bhfad níos mó ná leaba agus béile ar fáil - is lárionad sóisialta,a siamsaíochta, gnó agus pobail ar fheabhas í chomh maith agus gach aon áis faoin spéir aici, a chuireann bia, lóistín, imeachtaí spóirt, áiseanna siamsíochta agus só agus tarraingtí nach iad ar fáil.

Agus tú ag taisteal timpeall na tíre gheobhaidh tú amach go mbeidh "Bí i d'Aoi Againn" an-áisiúil agus an chéad suíomh eile á roghnú agat.

Is mian le hóstlannaithe agus le lucht tithe lóistín na hÉireann fáilte a chur romhat agus a bheith in ann a dheimhniú go mbainfidh tú sult as do sheal in Éirinn. Tá súil againn go bhfanfaidh tú linn agus gó mbainfidh tú leas as an treoir seo

To book online, visit the Be Our Guest web site at the following address: www.irelandhotels.com
Further information on this guide can be obtained from:
IRISH HOTELS FEDERATION
13 Northbrook Road, Dublin 6, Ireland.
Telephone +353 1 497 6459   Fax: +353 1 497 4613.

chun do rogha óstlann nó teach lóistin a aimsiú, i dtreo is go mbeimid in ann a rá leat go pearsanta -

Be Our Guest

Les hôtels et les pensions en Irlande sont d'un caractère particulier.

Ils sont très souvent gérés par le propriétaire et des membres de sa famille, présents pour accueillir les visiteurs et leur faire découvrir la célèbre hospitalité irlandaise. Même s'ils appartiennent à une entreprise ou font partie d'un groupe de sociétés, ils possèdent toujours ce caractère et cette ambiance des lieux familiaux - un endroit où vous serez sincèrement bien accueillis.

L'hôtel irlandais est unique en ce qu'il joue très souvent le rôle de centre social pour la communauté. Les hôtels offrent beaucoup plus qu'un lit et un repas - ce sont, pour la communauté, de véritables centres sociaux, de loisirs et d'affaires, équipés de toutes les infrastructures et installations imaginables. Ils vous proposent le gîte et le couvert, mais aussi activités sportives et de loisir, divertissements et autres attractions.

Si vous voyagez dans le pays, vous trouverez que le guide "Be Our Guest" est d'une aide précieuse pour vous aider à choisir votre prochaine destination.

Les hôteliers et les propriétaires de pensions irlandais veulent vous accueillir et être là pour vous assurer un séjour agréable en Irlande. Nous espérons que vous resterez avec nous et que vous utiliserez ce guide pour sélectionner l'hôtel ou la pension de votre choix, afin que nous ayons le plaisir de vous compter parmi nos visiteurs.

Be Our Guest

Die Hotels und Pensionen in Irland sind von ganz besonderer Art.

Zum größten Teil handelt es sich dabei um private Familienbetriebe, in denen der Besitzer und die Familienmitglieder ihre Gäste mit der vielgerühmten irischen Gastfreundschaft willkommen heißen. Aber auch wenn sich diese Häuser in Unternehmensbesitz befinden oder einer Kette angehören, strahlen sie dennoch den Charakter und die Atmosphäre von Familienbetrieben aus - ein Ort, an dem Sie immer herzlich willkommen sind.

Hotels in Irland sind einzig in ihrer Art und dienen oftmals als Mittelpunkt geselliger Treffen. Hotels haben viel mehr zu bieten als nur ein Bett und eine Mahlzeit - sie sind Gesellschafts-, Freizeit-, Geschäfts- und öffentlicher Treffpunkt mit allen nur erdenklichen Einrichtungen und Annehmlichkeiten, angefangen bei Essen, Unterkunft, Sport und Freizeitmöglichkeiten bis zur Unterhaltung und anderen Anziehungspunkten.

Auf Ihren Reisen im Land werden Sie feststellen, daß Ihnen der "Be Our Guest"-Führer eine wertvolle Hilfe bei der Suche nach der nächstgelegenen Unterkunft leistet.

Irlands Hotel- und Pensionsbesitzer heißen Sie gerne willkommen und möchten ihren Anteil dazu beitragen, daß Ihnen Ihr Aufenthalt in Irland in angenehmer Erinnerung bleibt. Wir hoffen, daß Sie uns besuchen werden und diesen Führer bei der Auswahl Ihres Hotels oder Ihrer Pension zu Rate ziehen, so daß wir Sie persönlich willkommen heißen können.

Be Our Guest

A celebration. A festival.
What the hell, a Wednesday.

There's always a reason to get together and conduct a lengthy
enquiry into this curious business called life.

From early in the Spring to late into the Autumn, up and down the county, from coastal

fishing villages to inland towns, up here people are highly creative at inventing reasons for a

spot of frivolity. Except we use another word for it. Culture.

Donegal *Up here, it's different.*

ALTAN LIVE IN DONEGAL

TOURIST BOARD OFFICES

BORD FÁILTE – IRISH TOURIST BOARD
www.ireland.travel.ie

IRELAND

Dublin
Bord Fáilte - Irish Tourist Board,
Baggot Street Bridge, Dublin 2
Tel: 1850 23 03 30
Fax: 01 - 602 4100

NORTHERN IRELAND

Belfast
Bord Fáilte - Irish Tourist Board,
53 Castle Street, Belfast BT1 1GH
Tel: 028 - 9032 7888
Fax: 028 - 9024 0201

Derry
Bord Fáilte - Irish Tourist Board,
44 Foyle Street, Derry BT48 6AT
Tel: 028 - 7136 9501
Fax: 028 - 7136 9501

If dialling Northern Ireland directly from the Republic of Ireland the code 048 followed by the telephone number is sufficient.

NORTHERN IRELAND TOURIST BOARD
www.discovernorthernireland.ie

Belfast
Northern Ireland Tourist Board,
59 North Street, Belfast BT1 1NB
Tel: 028 - 9023 1221
Fax: 028 - 9024 0960

Dublin
Northern Ireland Tourist Board,
16 Nassau Street, Dublin 2
Tel: 01 - 679 1977
Fax: 01 - 679 1863

TOURISM IRELAND –
EUROPE
www.tourismireland.com

Austria
Tourism Ireland
Libellenweg 1, A-1140 Vienna
Tel: 01 - 501 596000
Fax: 01 - 911 3765
Email: info.at@tourismireland.com

Belgium/Luxembourg
Tourism Ireland,
Avenue Louise 327 Louizalaan
1050 Brussels
Tel: 02 - 275 01 71
Fax: 02 - 642 98 51
E-mail: info.be@tourismireland.com

Britain
Tourism Ireland, Ireland Desk,
Britain Visitor Centre,
1 Regent Street, London SW1Y 4XT
Tel: 0800 039 7000
Fax: 0207 493 9065
Email: info.gb@tourismireland.com

Glasgow
Tourism Ireland
James Millar House
98 West George Street 7th Floor
Glasgow G2 1PJ
Tel: 0800 - 039 7000
Fax: 0141 - 572 4033
Email: infoglasgow@tourismireland.com

Denmark
Tourism Ireland
'Klostergarden', Amagertorv 29B, 3
1160 Copenhagen K
Tel: 806 015 18
Fax: 33 32 44 01
Email: info.dk@tourismireland.com

Finland
Tourism Ireland,
Erottajankatu 7A, PL33, 00130 Helsinki
Tel: 0800 - 41 969
Fax: 09 - 9646 022
Email: info@irlanninmatkailu.com

France
Tourisme Irlandais,
33 rue de Miromesnil, 75008 Paris
Tel: 01 - 70 20 00 20
Fax: 01 - 47 42 01 64
Email: info.fr@tourismireland.com

Germany
Irland Information,
Untermainanlage 7,
D-60329 Frankfurt am Main
Tel: 069 - 66 80 09 50
Fax: 069 - 92 31 85 88
Email: info.de@tourismireland.com

Italy
Turismo Irlandese,
Via Santa Maria Segreta 6, 20123 Milano
Tel: 02 - 482 96 060
Fax: 02 - 869 03 96
Email: informazioni@tourismireland.com

The Netherlands
Ierland Toerisme,
Spuistraat 104, 1012 VA Amsterdam
Tel: 020 - 504 06 89
Fax: 020 - 620 80 89
Email: info.@ierland.nl

Norway
Tourism Ireland,
Postboks 6691, St. Olavs Plass, 0129 Oslo
Tel: 80 03 50 18
Fax: 22 20 26 41
Email: info.dk@tourismireland.com

Spain
Turismo de Irlanda,
Paseo de la Castellana 46,
3TM Planta, 28046 Madrid
Tel: 917 - 456 420
Fax: 915 - 776 934
Email: info.sp@tourismireland.com

Sweden
Tourism Ireland,
Stora Nygatan 40, SE 111 27 Stockholm
Tel: 0200 15 91 01
Fax: 08 233 727
Email: info@irlandsinfo.com

Switzerland
Tourism Ireland
Mettlenstrasse 22, Ch 8142 Uitikon
Tel: 01 21 04 153
Fax: 01 49 21 475
Email: info.ch@tourismireland.com

TOURISM IRELAND –
REST OF THE WORLD

USA
Tourism Ireland
345 Park Avenue, New York NY 10154
Tel: 1800-223 6470
Fax: 212 - 371 9052
Email: info.us@tourismireland.com

Canada
Tourism Ireland
2 Bloor St. West, Suite 1501
Toronto, M4W 3E2
Tel: 1800 - 223 6470
Fax: 416 - 925 6033
Email:info.ca@tourismireland.com

South Africa
Tourism Ireland,
c/o Development Promotions
Everite House, 7th Floor,
20 De Korte Street,
Braamfontein 2001, Gauteng
Tel: 011 - 339 4865
Fax: 011 - 339 2474
E-mail: helenf@dpgsa.co.za

New Zealand
Tourism Ireland,
Level 6, 18 Shortland Street,
Private Bag 92136, Auckland 1
Tel: 09 - 977 2255
Fax: 09 - 977 2256
Email: tourism@ireland.co.nz

Australia
Tourism Ireland,
5th Level, 36 Carrington Street,
Sydney, NSW 2000
Tel: 02 - 9299 6177
Fax: 02 - 9299 6323
Email: info@tourismireland.com.au

Japan
Tourism Ireland, 2-10-7 Kojimachi,
Chiyoda-ku, Tokyo 102 - 0083
Tel: 03 - 5275 1611
Fax: 03 - 5275 1623

TOURIST BOARD OFFICES

GUINNESS.

LOCAL TOURIST INFORMATION OFFICES

The offices below operate throughout the year; approximately one hundred others are open during the summer months.

Antrim
16 High Street
Tel: 028-9442 8331
Email: abs@antrim.gov.uk

Aran Islands
Kilronan
Tel: 099-61263

Armagh
40 English Street
Tel: 028-3752 1800
Email: armagh@nitic.net

Ballycastle
7 Mary Street
Tel: 028-2076 2024
Email: ballycastle@hotmail.com

Ballymena
76 Church Road
Tel: 028-2563 8494
Email: ballymena@hotmail.com

Bambridge
200 Newry Road
Tel: 028-4062 3322
Email: bambridge@nitic.net

Bangor
34 Quay Street
Tel: 028-9127 0069
Email: tic@northdown.gov.uk

Blarney
Towncentre
Tel: 021-438 1624

Belfast
47 Donegall Place
Tel: 028-9024 6609
Email: belfastwelcomecentre@nitic.net

Bundoran
The Bridge
Tel: 071-984 1350

Carlow
Tullow Street
Tel: 059-913 1554
Fax: 059-977 0776

Carrickfergus
Heritage Plaza, Antrim Street
Tel: 028-9336 6455
Email: touristinfo@carrickfergus.org

Clonakility
Ashe Street
Tel: 023-33226

Coleraine
Railway Road
Tel: 028-7034 4723
Email: coleraine@nitic.net

Cookstown
The Burnavon, Burn Road
Tel: 028-8676 6727
Email: burnavon@cookstown.gov.uk

Cork City
Grand Parade
Tel: 021-425 5100
Fax: 021-425 5199

Derry
44 Foyle Street
Tel: 028-7126 7284
Email: info@derryvisitor.com

Dingle
The Quay
Tel: 066-915 1188

Donegal Town
The Quay
Tel: 074-972 1148
Fax: 074-972 2762

Downpatrick
St. Patrick's Centre, 53A
Market Street
Tel: 028-4461 2233
Email: downpatrick@nitic.net

Dublin
Dublin City
Suffolk Street
O'Connell Street
Baggot Street
Dublin Airport
Arrivals Hall
Dun Laoghaire
Ferryport
Tallaght
The Square

Email:
information@dublintourism.ie
Internet:
www.visitdublin.com
For reservations in Dublin
contact Ireland Reservations
Freephone
Tel: 1800 668 668 66

Dungannon / Killymaddy
Ballygawley Road
Tel: 028-8776 7259
Email: killymaddy@nitic.net

Dundalk
Jocelyn Street
Tel: 042-933 5484
Fax: 042-933 8070

Dungarvan
The Courthouse
Tel: 058-41741

Ennis
Arthur's Row
Tel: 065-682 8366
Fax: 065-682 8350

Enniskillen
Wellington Road
Tel: 028-6632 3110
Email: tic@fermanagh.gov.uk

Galway
Forster Street
Tel: 091-537700
Fax: 091-537733

Ireland's Welcoming Tourist Information Network

YOUR GATEWAY
to the Holiday Regions of Ireland

Visit our Tourist Information Offices for detailed information on what to see and do and what's on. Avail of the popular and convenient accommodation booking service.

For your convenience we provide

- Instant confirmed accommodation booking service
- Guide books for sale
- Local and National Information
- Maps – local and national

- Stamps and postcards
- Itinerary and Route planning service
- Display and sale of local craft items
- Souvenirs and gifts

Be sure to follow the Shamrock

Look for the Shamrock sign on all accommodation. It is your assurance that this premises provide accommodation which is inspected and whose standards are fully approved and regulated by agencies supervised by Bord Failte – the Irish Tourist Board.

GUINNESS.

LOCAL TOURIST INFORMATION OFFICES CONTINUED

Gaint's Causeway
Causeway Road, Bushmills
Tel: 028-2073 1855
Email: causewaytic@hotmail.com

Hillsborough
The Square
Tel: 028-9268 9717
Email: hillsborough@nitic.net

Kildare Town
Heritage Centre
Tel: 045-521240

Kilkeel
28 Bridge Street
Tel: 028-4176 2525
Email: kdakilkeel@hotmail.com

Kilkenny
Shee Alms House
Tel: 056-775 1500
Fax: 056-776 3955

Killarney
Beech Road
Tel: 064-31633
Fax: 064-34506

Kinsale
Pier Road
Tel: 021-477 2234
Fax: 021-477 4438

Larne
Narrow Gauge Road
Tel: 028-2826 0088
Email: larnetourism@btconnect.com

Letterkenny
Neil T Blaney Road
Tel: 074-912 1160
Fax: 074-912 5180

Limavady
7 Connell Street
Tel: 028-7776 0307
Email: tourism@limavady.gov.uk

Limerick City
Arthur's Quay
Tel: 061-317522
Fax: 061-317939

Lisburn
Lisburn Square
Tel: 028-9266 0038
Email: lisburn@nitic.net

Magherafelt
The Bridwell, 6 Church Street
Tel: 028-7963 1510
Email: ailishmcpeake100@hotmail.com

Mullingar
Market House
Tel: 044-48650
Fax: 044-40413

Newcastle (Co. Down)
10-14 Central Promenade
Tel: 028-4372 2222
Email: newcastle.tic@downdc.gov.uk

Newgrange
Bru na Boinne Visitor Centre
Donore, Co. Meath
Tel: 041-988 0305

Newtownards
31 Regent Street
Tel: 028-9182 6846
Email: tourism@ards-council.gov.uk

Omagh
1 Market Street
Tel: 028-8224 7831
Email: omagh@nitic.net

Portlaoise
Fintain Lawlor Avenue
Tel / Fax: 0502-21178

Shannon Airport
Arrivals Hall
Tel: 061-471664
Fax: 061-471661

Skibbereen
North Street
Tel: 028-21766
Fax: 028-21353

Sligo
Temple Street
Tel: 071-916 1201
Fax: 071-916 0360

Tralee
Ashe Memorial Hall
Tel: 066-712 1288
Fax: 066-712 1700

Tullamore
Bury Quay
Tel: 0506-52617

Waterford City
The Quay
Tel: 051-875823
Fax: 051-876720

Waterford Crystal
Visitor Centre
Tel: 051-358397

Westport
James Street
Tel: 098-25711
Fax: 098-26709

Wexford
Crescent Quay
Tel: 053-23111
Fax: 053-41743

Wicklow
Fitzwilliam Square
Tel: 0404-69117
Fax: 0404-69118

INTRODUCTION

It is essential that when booking your accommodation you request the "Be Our Guest 2003" Rate

Our Guide features a broad selection of Irish Hotels, including stately Country Houses, luxurious Castles, old-world Inns and homely Guesthouses. The majority of these hotels and guesthouses are members of the Irish Hotels Federation or the Northern Ireland Hotels Federation and we hope that the illustrations and descriptions of these premises and the amenities they offer will help you to choose the most suitable premises for your holiday.

All of the hotels and guesthouses featured in the Guide at the time of going to print (10th Oct 2002) have been registered or are awaiting registration by Bord Failte / Irish Tourist Board or by the Northern Ireland Tourist Board, in accordance with the Statutory Registration Regulations which they administer. (*See also Activity Sections pages 417-465*)

RATES

The only rates featured in this publication relate to Per Person Sharing or a Room Rate.
Per Person Sharing: relates to the cost of Bed & Full Breakfast per person per night, on the basis of two persons occupying a standard double/twin bedded room, most having private bath/shower.
Room Rate: relates to the cost of a standard room per night. There may be a restriction on the number of persons allowed to share the room. It is advisable to check this when making your reservation.
The rates range from minimum to maximum and are those generally in operation throughout the year, but may not apply during special occasions such as Public Holiday Weekends, Christmas and New Year, International Events, Major Festivals and Sporting Fixtures, or on such other occasions as individual premises may decide.
These are guideline rates, please ensure that you contact the premises to vertify the rates applicable to your reservation.
Rates are inclusive of Value Added Taxes at current (2002) rates and Services Charges (if any).
Supplements may be payable for suites or superior / de luxe rooms. Also, where single or double / twin bedded rooms are occupied by one person, a supplement may be payable. Correspondingly, if more than two persons share a family room, special reduced rates may be arranged.
In the case of hotels and guesthouses in the Republic of Ireland, rates are quoted in € (Euro).
Whereas in Northern Ireland rates are quoted in STG£.

STANDARD SPECIAL OFFERS (Per Person Sharing) ☺

Many of the hotels / guesthouses in the Guide feature special offers :
- **Weekend Specials** include 2 nights' accommodation, 2 Breakfasts and 1 Dinner.
- **Midweek Specials** include 3 nights' accommodation and 3 breakfasts.
- **Weekly Partial Board** includes 7 nights' accommodation, 7 breakfasts and 7 dinners.

Alternative Special Offers may also be featured

HOTEL CLASSIFICATION

ONE STAR ★

Here you can enjoy the comforts of a pleasantly simple hotel where a warm welcome prevails. These premises offer all the mandatory services and facilities to a satisfactory standard, which are necessary for a most enjoyable and relaxed visit. Some guest rooms have a private bathroom with a bath or a shower.

TWO STAR ★★

These are more likely to be family operated premises, selected for their charm and their comfortable facilities.

All guest rooms have a telephone and most have a private bathroom with a bath and / or shower. Full dining facilities are available, representing excellent value and good wholesome food.

Dúchas Heritage Card

...the way to explore Ireland's heritage

Buy a Hertiage Card from any
site under Dúchas care and
enjoy unlimited access to over
65 of Ireland's finest castles,
gardens, nature reserves, historic
houses, abbeys and monuments

For more information...

email: heritagecard@ealga.ie
web: www.heritageireland.ie
Tel: +353 1 647 2461
Fax: +353 1 661 6764

An Roinn Comhshaoil
agus Rialtais Áitiúil
Department of the Environment
and Local Government

Dúchas The Heritage Centre Service
Education and Visitor Service
6, Ely Place Upper, Dublin 2

Images from top: Casino Marino, Dublin 3 • Lough Veagh Co. Donegal
• Muchross, Co. Kerry • Hill of Tara, Co. Meath • Céide Fields, Co.Mayo

THREE STAR ★★★

These range from small, family operated premises to larger, modern hotels. Guest rooms are well decorated with the emphasis on comfort and all have a private bathroom with a bath and/or shower. Some hotels may also have colour TV, direct dial phones, hairdryers, tea/coffee facilities and room service. Many hotels also have leisure facilities, car parking, safety deposit boxes.

Restaurants offer high standards of cuisine in relaxed and hospitable surroundings. Table d'hôte and / or à la carte dinner menus are available.

FOUR STAR ★★★★

These include contemporary hotels of excellent quality and charming period houses renovated to very high standards complete with all modern comforts. All guest

accommodation is luxurious with suites and half suites available in most cases. Restaurant facilities provide excellent cuisine and service for the discerning diner. Table d'hôte and / or à la carte lunch and dinner menus are available.

FIVE STAR ★★★★★

These include Ireland's most luxurious hotels, all of which are of high international standard. They range from elegant, stately castles to prestigious country clubs and top class city hotels catering for both the business and tourist visitor. All guest accommodation is luxurious and spacious suites are also available.

These fine hotels boast of some of the country's best restaurants and offer table d'hôte and / or à la carte lunch and dinner menus. Exceptional service and a personalised welcome are the norm in these hotels.

GUESTHOUSE CLASSIFICATION

ONE STAR ★

These premises meet all the mandatory requirements for guesthouses and offer simple accommodation, facilities and services to a satisfactory standard. Restaurant facilities are available in some guesthouses.

TWO STAR ★★

Half or more of the guest rooms have private bathroom with bath and / or shower. Guesthouse facilities include a reading / writing room or lounge area for residents' use. Restaurant facilities are available in some guesthouses.

THREE STAR ★★★

All guest rooms have private bathroom with bath and / or shower and direct dial telephone. Guesthouse facilities include a TV lounge, travellers cheques are exchanged and major credit cards are accepted. Restaurant facilities are available in some guesthouses.

FOUR STAR ★★★★

This is the top classification for guesthouses in Ireland. Guest accommodation includes half suites and all guest rooms have private bathroom with bath and / or shower, direct dial telephone, colour TV and radio. Room service offers full breakfast. Many premises provide dinner, with table d'hôte and / or à la carte menus. Guesthouse facilities include car parking, safety deposit boxes, fax.

OPENING DATES

Some of the premises featured in the guide were not open at the guide print date (10 October 2002). The planned date of opening as supplied by these premises is displayed.

Hotels and Guesthouses may have the symbols: U, N, R, P, CR for the following reasons:

U Under the terms of the classification scheme a premises may opt to remain unclassified and will be shown U in this guide. Of course these premises meet all the mandatory requirements for hotel/guesthouse registration.

N These are premises that have recently registered with Bord Fáilte / Northern Irish Tourist Board but, at the time of going to print, have not been long enough in operation for their standards to be fully assessed.

R These premises were undergoing major refurbishment at the time of printing this guide. Their classification will be assessed when the work is completed.

P Applied to Bord Fáilte/Northern Ireland Tourist Board for registration at time of going to print.

CR Classification Rescinded - At the time of going to print (10 October 2002) the classification of these properties had been rescinded and the registration was under review by Bord Fáilte.

Ireland's Gaeltacht

A search for Ireland's culture and heritage, peace and tranquillity, stunning scenery or holiday activities must inevitably bring you to the Gaeltacht.

Here the Irish language is an everyday community language for many of the inhabitants, reflecting a rich Gaelic heritage...

...a heritage of hospitality, great music, song and dance.

For family holidays or short breaks, the Gaeltacht has it all. Spectacular scenery, world class activities including golf, walking, fishing, horse riding, language and culture courses not to mention the best of restaurants, pubs, music and a range of quality accommodation to suit all budgets.

Information on a wide range of special offer accommodation and activity packages available.

Éire i mbláth a maitheasa !

GaelSaoire
SCÍTH SA GHAELTACHT
HOLIDAYS IN IRELAND'S GAELTACHT

For further information on holidays in any of the 7 Gaeltacht regions contact Gael Saoire at:

Freephone Ireland:	**1800 621 600**
Freephone UK:	**0800 7835708**
International:	**+353 66 9152423**
Fax:	**+353 66 9152429**
Email:	**info@gaelsaoire.ie**

GAELTACHT AREA

RESERVATIONS

Courtesy Onward Reservations

If you are moving around the country, the premises in which you are staying will be delighted to help you select your next accommodation from the Be Our Guest Guide and make your reservation.

The following are other ways in which a booking can be made :

1. Advance enquiries and reservations may be made directly to the premises by phone, fax, e-mail or letter and details of the reservation should be confirmed by both parties. A deposit should be forwarded if requested.

2. Book your accommodation **online** at:

**which features all premises
listed in the Be Our Guest guide.**

www.irelandhotels.com

3. Some of the hotels and guesthouses in the Guide participate in a Central Reservations system which may be indicated in their entry.

4. Travel Agent - your travel agent will normally make a booking on your behalf without extra charge where the premises pays travel agents' commission (this is indicated by the symbol ⊤ in the Guide). In other cases, agents will usually charge a small fee to cover the cost of telephone calls and administration.

5. Some Irish Tourist Board offices listed in this guide (see pages 12 - 16) operate an enquiry and booking service and will make an accommodation reservation on your behalf.

COMPLAINTS

Should there be cause for complaint, the matter should be brought to the notice of the Management of the premises in the first instance. Failing satisfaction, the matter should be referred to the Tourist Information Office concerned (see list on pages 12 - 16) or The Irish Tourist Board, Baggot Street Bridge, Dublin 2. In the case of Northern Ireland premises, complaints should be addressed to the Customer Relations Section, Northern Ireland Tourist Board, 59 North Street, Belfast BT1 1NB.

ERRORS AND OMISSIONS

The information contained in the accommodation section has been supplied by individual premises. While reasonable care has been taken in compiling the information supplied and ensuring its accuracy and compliance with consumer protection laws, the Irish Hotels Federation cannot accept any responsibility for any errors, omissions or misinformation regarding accommodation, facilities, prices, services, classification or any other information whatsover in the Guide and shall have no liability whatsoever and howsoever arising to any person for any loss, whether direct, indirect, economic or consequential, or damages, actions, proceedings, costs, claims, expenses or demands arising therefrom.

The listing of any premises in this guide is not and should not be taken as a recommendation from the IHF or a representation that the premises will be suitable for your purposes.

THINK ABOUT INSURANCE

We strongly advise you to take out an insurance policy against accidents, cancellations, delays, loss of property and medical expenses. Such travel and holiday insurance policies are available quite cheaply and are worth every penny for peace of mind alone.

CANCELLATIONS

Should it be necessary to amend or cancel your reservation, please advise the premises immediately, as there may be a cancellation penalty. Please establish, when making a reservation, what cancellation policy applies.

Need money from home?

SAMPLE ENTRY

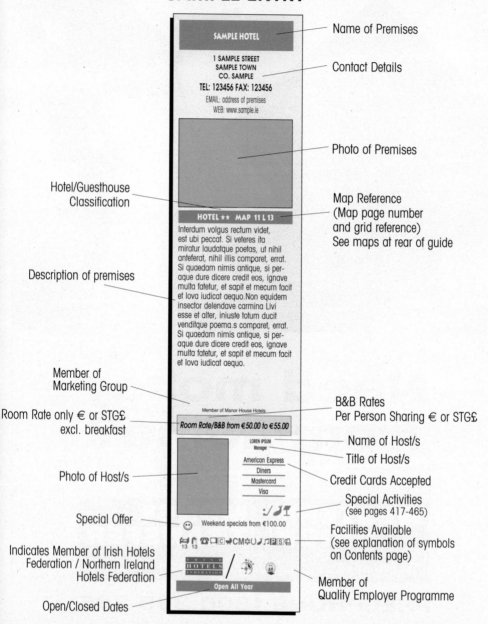

Name of Premises

Contact Details

Photo of Premises

Map Reference
(Map page number
and grid reference)
See maps at rear of guide

Hotel/Guesthouse
Classification

Description of premises

Member of
Marketing Group

Room Rate only € or STG£
excl. breakfast

B&B Rates
Per Person Sharing € or STG£

Name of Host/s

Title of Host/s

Photo of Host/s

Credit Cards Accepted

Special Activities
(see pages 417-465)

Special Offer

Facilities Available
(see explanation of symbols
on Contents page)

Indicates Member of Irish Hotels
Federation / Northern Ireland
Hotels Federation

Member of
Quality Employer Programme

Open/Closed Dates

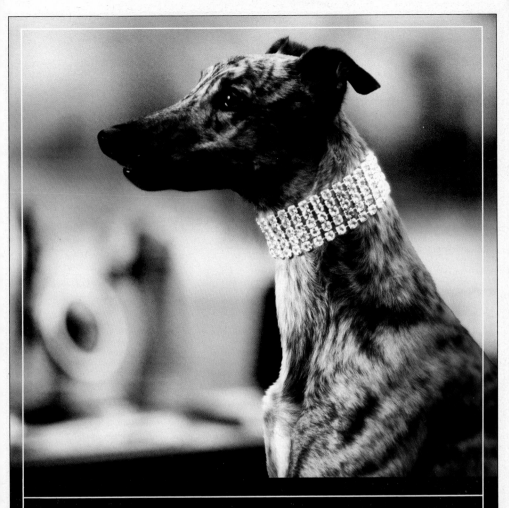

DO YOU COME HERE OFTEN?

Well, with over 15 greyhound stadiums throughout Ireland - in Cork, Dublin, Enniscorthy, Galway, Kilkenny, Lifford, Limerick, Longford, Mullingar, Newbridge, Thurles, Tralee, Waterford and Youghal . . . you're never far from a night at the dogs.

For information contact us at 061 316 788
or check our website www.igb.ie

THE DOGS - ALWAYS TOP FORM

Irish Greyhound Board
Bord na gCon

QUALITY EMPLOYER PROGRAMME SYMBOL AN ASSURANCE TO GUESTS OF THE HIGHEST STANDARDS OF EMPLOYMENT

Readers will notice our Quality Employer Programme (QEP) logo in the right hand corner of a large number of hotel and guesthouse entries throughout this guide. It is an assurance to you, as a guest, that the property you choose offers excellence in all standards of employment and treatment of staff. This ultimately benefits all guests, as the staff in these premises enjoy high job satisfaction, which in turn leads to an enhanced quality of service for you to experience.

The QEP is a defined code of practice with standards set in all areas of employment including; training, personnel relations, rostering and the arrangement of work hours. It also makes recommendations on meals, uniforms and pensions. Once a property has fulfilled all elements of the programme, it faces an annual review to ensure that standards are achieved and maintained. The QEP development by the Irish Hotels Federation is, in effect, a guarantee to you that the accredited properties have reached an important standard in relation to all their employment practices in these areas. It also means that staff are trained to carry out their job to set criteria and receive ongoing training to update their skills. All in all, this means a better service for guests.

The QEP status enjoyed by the properties in this guide also means that they attract the highest calibre of staff. Highly skilled staff in the hospitality sector want to work in the best of hotels and guesthouses, so that they can experience the best conditions of employment and career progression.

So you when you choose a QEP hotel or guesthouse, you can be assured you will experience Irish hospitality and friendliness at its best.

CERT

people in tourism

IRELAND'S
BEST
★★★★★★
SERVICE EXCELLENCE AWARD

Award Winners To Date

Bracken Court Hotel, Balbriggan, Co. Dublin • Buswells Hotel, Dublin
Clontarf Castle Hotel, Clontarf, Dublin • Great Southern Hotel, Dublin Airport
Mespil Hotel, Dublin • Merrion Hotel, Dublin

Hotel Kilkenny, Kilkenny

Ferrycarrig Hotel, Wexford

Maryborough House Hotel, Cork • Carrigaline Court Hotel, Carrigaline, Co. Cork
Lodge & Spa at Inchydoney Island, Clonakilty, Co. Cork • Actons Hotel, Kinsale, Co. Cork
Great Southern Hotel, Parknasilla, Co. Kerry

Renvyle House Hotel, Renvyle, Co. Galway

Atlantic Coast Hotel, Westport, Co. Mayo • Hotel Westport, Westport, Co. Mayo
Knockranny House Hotel, Westport, Co. Mayo • Westport Woods Hotel, Westport, Co. Mayo

Rathmullan House Hotel, Rathmullan, Co. Donegal • Sandhouse Hotel, Rossnowlagh, Co. Donegal

You too can be a winner with Ireland's Best.
For further information call 01 884 7700

NDP
NATIONAL DEVELOPMENT PLA
Your Plan - Your Future

Life's luxuries for less

With great savings at the airport on all your favourite luxuries,
you can now afford to take home the best of Irish and International products.

Travel Value and Duty Free airport shopping, life's luxuries for less.

Aer Rianta Travel Value & Duty Free shopping at Dublin, Cork and Shannon Airports.
www.aerrianta.com

- All travellers can avail of Travel Value Shopping.
- Travelling outside of the EU both Duty Free and Travel Value shopping is available.

DUBL!N™

As one of the oldest cities in Europe, Dublin provides the visitor with a multitude of cultural riches, from the ancient to the avant-garde: from history, architecture, literature, art and archaeology to the performing arts. Monuments in literature and in stone mark the history, writers, poets and people of Dublin. Medieval, Georgian and modern architecture provide a backdrop to a friendly, bustling port which can boast literary giants such as Wilde, Shaw, Joyce, Yeats, Beckett and O'Casey as native sons. Spawned by the need to ford the river Liffey, fortified by the Danes, developed by the Normans, adorned with fine buildings by the Anglo-Irish, the city has grown in stature and elegance over the century.

When it comes to entertainment, Dubliners with their natural friendly and fun-craving attitude, certainly know how to entertain. The quintessential 'Dublin Pub' provides the focal point of Dublin social life, illuminating the vibrant hues of Dubliners and their culture. It is a place where conversations and "craic" flow freely, unleashing the unique atmosphere that is at the heart of Dublin and its friendly people. Just a twenty-minute journey will bring the visitor from the bustling city centre to the charming coastal towns and villages of the county. These towns and villages provide boundless opportunities for craft-shopping, watersports, seafood dining and picturesque walks against the spectacular background of Dublin Bay.

Whatever your heart desires, Dublin provides a superb location for all the above activities and many more besides.

Email: reservations@dublintourism.ie
http://www.visitdublin.com

Reservations and Information may be obtained by visiting one of our Information Centres: - Dublin Tourism Centre, Suffolk St.,
- Arrivals Hall, Dublin Airport,
- Ferry Terminal,
  Dun Laoghaire Harbour,
- Baggot St Bridge,
- O'Connell Street.

GUINNESS®

St. Patrick's Day Festival, Dublin.
March

Kerrygold Horseshow, R.D.S. Dublin.
August

Guinness All-Ireland Hurling Championship Final, Croke Park, Dublin.
September

All-Ireland Football Championship Final, Croke Park, Dublin.
September

Dublin Theatre Festival, Dublin.
October

Event details correct at time of going to press

BRACKEN COURT HOTEL

BRIDGE STREET,
BALBRIGGAN,
CO. DUBLIN
TEL: 01-841 3333 FAX: 01-841 5118
EMAIL: info@brackencourt.ie
WEB: www.brackencourt.ie

HOTEL ★★★ MAP 12 O 12

The newly built Bracken Court Hotel is conveniently located in the seaside town of Balbriggan, 35 minutes north of Dublin City and 15 minutes from Dublin Airport making it an ideal location for access to the city, airport and as a gateway to the north. The 40 bedroom hotel provides luxurious surroundings where comfort and a wide range of facilities combine to satisfy the needs of both business and leisure guest. Ireland's Best Service Excellence Award 2002.

Member of Platinum Hotels

B&B from €69.00 to €99.00

LUKE MORIARTY
OWNER

American Express
Mastercard
Visa

☺ Weekend specials from €169.00

40 40

IRISH
HOTELS
FEDERATION

Open All Year

RADISSON SAS ST HELEN'S HOTEL

STILLORGAN ROAD,
CO. DUBLIN
TEL: 01-218 6000 FAX: 01-218 6010
EMAIL: info.dublin@radissonsas.com
WEB: www.radissonsas.com

HOTEL ★★★★★ MAP 8 O 11

Situated on four acres of parkland with formal gardens to the front and rear. The hotel consists of a historic listed house, blended with a new bedroom wing of 151 bedrooms. The hotel has 2 restaurants, 2 bars and a fitness room, snooker room, health and beauty clinic, extensive meeting rooms and free car parking.

Member of Radisson SAS Hotels and Resorts

B&B from €165.00 to €255.00

ERIC VAN DALSUM
GENERAL MANAGER

American Express
Diners
Mastercard
Visa

151 151
Inet

IRISH
HOTELS
FEDERATION

Open All Year

STILLORGAN PARK HOTEL

STILLORGAN ROAD,
BLACKROCK,
CO. DUBLIN
TEL: 01-288 1621 FAX: 01-283 1610
EMAIL: sales@stillorganpark.com
WEB: www.stillorganpark.com

HOTEL ★★★ MAP 8 O 11

Dublin's premier hotel for the southside. After an investment of €15 million, this contemporary property now boasts 125 en suite fully air-conditioned bedrooms, a new fully equipped conference and banqueting centre catering for up to 500 delegates, a superb Mediterranean style restaurant and a comfortable bar. Located just a few minutes from Dublin's city centre on main N11, parking for 350 cars. 20 minutes from Druids Glen Golf Course. AA 4****. Awarded the hygiene mark.

B&B from €87.50 to €120.00

RONAN DORAN
MANAGING DIRECTOR

American Express
Diners
Mastercard
Visa

☺ Weekend specials from €171.41

125 125

IRISH
HOTELS
FEDERATION

Open All Year

Room rates are per room per night

AIRPORT VIEW

COLD WINTERS,
BLAKES CROSS,
CO. DUBLIN

TEL: 01-843 8756 FAX: 01-807 1949
EMAIL: gerrybutterly@hotmail.com
WEB: www.airportviewguesthouse.com

GUESTHOUSE ★★★   MAP 8 O 11

Airport View newly built luxurious guesthouse situated 4.5 miles from Dublin Airport, on a 7 acre site. Incorporates 4 poster bedroom with jacuzzi, TV lounge, conference room, snooker room, restaurant. All rooms en suite, TV, tea/coffee, fax and computer outlet facilities. Private car park, golf packages available. Airport View is conveniently located 50 yds off the main Dublin-Belfast road. It has all the features of a luxury hotel.

Room Rate from €48.50 to €70.00

GERARD BUTTERLY/ ANNEMARIE BEGGS
PROPRIETOR

Mastercard

Visa

10 10

Closed 24 - 26 December

TUDOR HOUSE

DALKEY,
CO. DUBLIN

TEL: 01-285 1528 FAX: 01-284 8133
EMAIL: info@tudordalkey.com
WEB: www.tudordalkey.com

GUESTHOUSE ★★★★   MAP 8 P 11

An elegant listed manor house with secluded grounds in the heart of Dalkey. Period ambience and personal friendly service are the hallmarks of Tudor House. Bedrooms are individually decorated and enjoy views of Dublin Bay. Dalkey is a charming heritage town with Norman castles and quaint harbours. It has many excellent restaurants and pubs. It is 3km from Dun Laoghaire Ferry Port and offers rapid access to Dublin City.

B&B from €55.00 to €69.00

KATIE HAYDON
OWNER

Mastercard

Visa

6 6

IRISH
HOTELS
FEDERATION

Open All Year

WATERSIDE HOTEL

DONABATE,
CO. DUBLIN

TEL: 01-843 6153 FAX: 01-843 6111
EMAIL: info@thewatersidehotel.com
WEB: www.thewatersidehotel.com

HOTEL U   MAP 12 O 12

Situated only 10 minutes from Dublin Airport and 11 miles from the city centre on the beach. You'll find The Waterside Hotel adorned by 6 beautiful golf courses. Our club house bar offers ambience, comfort and quality service and the new Links Restaurant offers the best of international cuisine from our extensive à la carte menu. Our newly refurbished en suite bedrooms boast spectacular views of Lambay Island, Howth Head and the lush fairways of the adjoining links golf course. Breakfast served till noon. Live music at weekends.

B&B from €45.00 to €75.00

PAULA BALDWIN
PROPRIETOR

Mastercard

Visa

18 18

IRISH
HOTELS
FEDERATION

Open All Year

B&B rates are per person sharing per night incl. Breakfast

GREAT SOUTHERN HOTEL

**DUBLIN AIRPORT,
CO. DUBLIN**

TEL: 01-844 6000 FAX: 01-844 6001
EMAIL: res@dubairport-gsh.com
WEB: www.gshotels.com

HOTEL U   MAP 12 O 11

Situated within the airport complex, just two minutes from the main terminal, the Great Southern Hotel provides a tranquil haven for the busy traveller. The guestrooms have every convenience and allow guests unwind in stylish surroundings. The hotel has a wide range of conference rooms. Bookable worldwide through Utell International or Central Reservations on 01-214 4800.

Room Rate from € 130.00 to € 250.00

EAMON DALY
GENERAL MANAGER

American Express
Diners
Mastercard
Visa

229 229

Closed 24 - 26 December

Room rates are per room per night

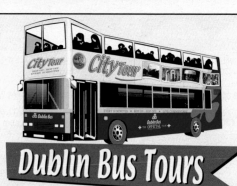

Dublin Bus Tours

Dublin City
Sit back and enjoy all that Dublin has to offer on board this 1 hour 15 mins. fully Guided Tour. There are 16 stops each located at the more popular attractions, you can join the tour at any of these stops. Buses operate every 15 minutes and your "All Day" tour ticket allows you to hop on and off as often as you wish.
Tour operates daily. **Live commentary.**

Coast & Castle
Tour of Dublin's northern coastline, Malahide and Castle, crossing the summit of Howth Head with panoramic views of Dublin Bay.
Tour operates daily.
Admission to Malahide Castle is included.

South Coast
Passing through Dun Laoghaire, Bray and Greystones, the tour travels inland to Kilmacanogue for a visit to the Avoca Handweavers, returning through villages and scenery of Dublin and Wicklow.
Tour operates daily.

The Ghost Bus
The dark romance of a city of gaslight and chilling legends. Your theatrical guide will spirit you away to meet the felons, fiends and phantoms who cross a thousand years of Dublin's history. Tour operates daily except Monday.

**All tours depart from
59 Upr. O'Connell St., Dublin 1.   Tel. 8734222
Buy on line at dublinbus.ie or ticketmaster.ie**

THE OFFICIAL TOUR

Dublin Bus

HOLIDAY INN DUBLIN AIRPORT

DUBLIN AIRPORT,
CO. DUBLIN

TEL: 01-808 0500 FAX: 01-844 6002
EMAIL: reservations-dublinairport@6c.com
WEB: www.dublinairport.holiday-inn.com

HOTEL ★★★★ MAP 12 O 11

A modern hotel located on the airport complex, offering a choice of standard & executive accommodation, 11.27km from the city centre. All rooms offer tea/coffee making facilites, mini-bar, trouser press, hairdryer, TV & pay movies. 24hr courtesy coach to & from the airport. Superb choice of dining options including the Bistro Restaurant, Sampans Oriental Restaurant, Café Express Lounge & 24hr room service. The Bodhran Bar has live music at weekends. Residents may use the ALSAA Leisure Centre swimming pool, gym & sauna.

Member of Six Continents Hotels

Room Rate from € 127.00 to € 291.00

BRIAN THORNTON
GENERAL MANAGER

American Express
Diners
Mastercard
Visa

Weekend specials from €175.00

249 249

Closed 24 - 25 December

AARONMOR GUESTHOUSE

1B/1C SANDYMOUNT AVENUE,
BALLSBRIDGE,
DUBLIN 4

TEL: 01-668 7972 FAX: 01-668 2377
EMAIL: aaronmor@indigo.ie
WEB: www.aaronmor.com

GUESTHOUSE ★★★ MAP 8 O 11

Welcome to Aaronmor, we trust your stay will have pleasant memories. Turn of century home in fashionable Ballsbridge. All rooms en suite, centrally heated, direct dial phones, fax, tea/coffee facilities. Private car park. Convenient R.D.S. showgrounds, Lansdowne Rugby Club, Point Depot, embassies, museums, car ferries, airport, bus/train service. 10 mins city centre. Enjoy our relaxed atmosphere. Traditional Irish breakfast. Lift to all floors. AA ♦♦♦♦

B&B from € 35.00 to € 70.00

BETTY & MICHAEL DUNNE

American Express
Mastercard
Visa

17 17

Closed 24 - 26 December

ABBERLEY COURT HOTEL

BELGARD ROAD,
TALLAGHT,
DUBLIN 24

TEL: 01-459 6000 FAX: 01-462 1000
EMAIL: abberley@iol.ie
WEB: www.abberley.ie

HOTEL ★★★ MAP 8 O 11

The Abberley Court Hotel is a recently built hotel situated at the foothills of the Dublin Mountains, beside The Square Town Centre in Tallaght. The facilities include 40 en suite bedrooms, Kilcawleys Traditional Irish Pub, The Leaf Chinese Restaurant. Conference/meeting/training facilities with private car parking. Activities in the locality include golf, pitch & putt, ten pin bowling, horse riding, pony trekking, fishing, watersports.

Room Rate from € 59.00 to € 124.00

KAREN GARRY & MAIREAD SLYE

American Express
Diners
Mastercard
Visa

40 40

Closed 24 - 27 December

B&B rates are per person sharing per night incl. Breakfast

ABBEY HOTEL

52 MIDDLE ABBEY STREET,
DUBLIN 1

TEL: 01-872 8188 FAX: 01-872 8585
EMAIL: reservations@abbey-hotel.com
WEB: www.abbey-hotel.com

HOTEL ★★ MAP 8 O 11

Small, intimate hotel in the heart of
Dublin city centre. It is close to all
main shopping areas and night life.
The stylish rooms are decorated to a
high standard. The hotel offers a full à
la carte menu daily to 9pm. Only
minutes walk from O'Connell Street
and Temple Bar. Facilities include TV,
telephone, car park, bar, restaurant,
entertainment and lift. 21 rooms all
en suite.

B&B from €58.00 to €115.00

RICHARD MCDERMOTT
OWNER

American Express
Mastercard
Visa

21 21

IRISH
HOTELS
FEDERATION

Closed 24 - 27 December

ABERDEEN LODGE

53 PARK AVENUE, OFF AILESBURY ROAD,
BALLSBRIDGE,
DUBLIN 4

TEL: 01-283 8155 FAX: 01-283 7877
EMAIL: aberdeen@iol.ie
WEB: www.halpinsprivatehotels.com

GUESTHOUSE ★★★★ MAP 8 O 11

Award-winning, 4****, a luxurious
combination of Edwardian grace, fine
food, modern comforts, all that one
expects of a private hotel, aircon
suites with jacuzzi, executive
facilities, landscaped gardens and
guest carpark. Close to city centre,
airport and car ferry terminals by
DART or bus. Accolades - RAC, AAA,
Best Loved Hotels, Green Book,
Johansens. Sister property of Merrion
Hall, Blakes and Halpins Hotel.
USA toll free 1800 617 3178.
UK free phone 0800 096 4748.
Direct Dial 353 1 283 8155.

Member of Relais du Silence

B&B from €45.00 to €90.00

PAT HALPIN
PROPRIETOR

American Express
Diners
Mastercard
Visa

20 20

Inet FAX

IRISH
HOTELS
FEDERATION

Open All Year

Room rates are per room per night

ABRAE COURT

9 ZION ROAD,
RATHGAR,
DUBLIN 6
TEL: 01-492 2242 FAX: 01-492 3944
EMAIL: abrae@eircom.net
WEB: www.abraecourt.com

GUESTHOUSE ★★★ MAP 8 O 11

Built in 1864, family run, 3*** Victorian guesthouse is located in the prestigious residential area of Rathgar, just ten minutes from the heart of Dublin City. Guestrooms are furnished with en suite bathroom, colour TV, direct dial phone and coffee/tea making facilities. Laundry service and a lock up car park are available. Bus routes, a good selection of restaurants, pubs, tourist attractions and various sports.

B&B from €49.50 to €59.00

NEVILLE KEEGAN
OWNER

Mastercard
Visa

🏠♫☎️📺T C U P S
14 14

IRISH
HOTELS
FEDERATION

Closed 22 - 28 December

ACADEMY HOTEL

FINDLATER PLACE,
OFF O'CONNELL STREET,
DUBLIN 1
TEL: 01-878 0666 FAX: 01-878 0600
EMAIL: stay@academy-hotel.ie
WEB: www.academy-hotel.ie

HOTEL U MAP 8 O 11

The natural choice for the discerning visitor to Dublin, we offer the ultimate in comfort & convenience. Located off the city's main thoroughfare, O'Connell Street, only a short stroll from the very best of international shopping, galleries, theatres and the cosmopolitan area of Temple Bar. Our beautifully appointed en suite, air conditioned rooms represent the perfect retreat after a demanding meeting or a hectic day of shopping or sightseeing. Free parking, bar, restaurant & Conference facilities. GDS Access Code: HK

B&B from €49.00 to €99.00

PETER COLLINS
MANAGER

American Express
Diners
Mastercard
Visa

😊 Midweek specials Sun-Thur €49.00
B&B per night

🏠♫☎️📺T C CM♫P S📶
98 98

♿ inet FAX

IRISH
HOTELS
FEDERATION

Open All Year

ADAMS TRINITY HOTEL

28 DAME STREET,
DUBLIN 2
TEL: 01-670 7100 FAX: 01-670 7101
EMAIL: reservations.adamstrinity@indigo.ie
WEB: www.adamstrinity.com

HOTEL ★★★ MAP 8 O 11

What better location in Dublin than the Adams Trinity Hotel? Located midway between Dublin Castle, Grafton Street and Trinity College; it faces the vibrant Temple Bar area. Traditional style bedrooms are finished to an exceptionally luxurious standard. The hotel features the Mercantile Bar and Restaurant, O'Brien's Traditional Bar and café style Brokers Bar. The Adams Trinity Hotel offers all guests that same personal attention and warmth, it has that little something special.

B&B from €65.00 to €110.00

FRAN RYDER/PETER HANAHOE
PROPRIETORS

American Express
Diners
Mastercard
Visa

🏠♫☎️📺T C CM♫ alc inet
28 28

IRISH
HOTELS
FEDERATION

Closed 24 - 27 December

B&B rates are per person sharing per night incl. Breakfast

AISHLING HOUSE

19/20 ST. LAWRENCE ROAD,
CLONTARF,
DUBLIN 3

TEL: 01-833 9097 FAX: 01-833 8400
EMAIL: info@aishlinghouse.com
WEB: www.aishlinghouse.com

GUESTHOUSE ★★★ MAP 8 O 11

Elegant listed family-run Victorian residence, situated in Clontarf, north Dublin's most exclusive suburb. Ideally located only minutes drive from Point Theatre, city centre and Dublin Port, yet only 15 mins from airport. Numerous golf courses nearby and short walk to leisure complex. Tranquil elegant lounge, half acre grounds, child's play area, car park, fax facilities. We offer superb luxury accommodation at affordable prices. A treasure of outstanding quality.

B&B from €45.00 to €55.00

ROBERT & FRANCES ENGLISH
OWNERS

Mastercard

Visa

☺ Midweek specials from €100.00

9   9

Open All Year

ALEXANDER HOTEL

AT MERRION SQUARE,
DUBLIN 2

TEL: 01-607 3700 FAX: 01-661 5663
EMAIL: alexanderres@ocallaghanhotels.ie
WEB: www.ocallaghanhotels.ie

HOTEL U MAP 8 O 11

Contemporary style deluxe hotel ideally located in Dublin city centre beside Trinity College, 5 mins walk from museums, shops and business districts. 102 air-conditioned guestrooms and suites, Caravaggio's Restaurant, Winners Bar, gymnasium and extensive meeting facilities. Free private valet car parking. USA Toll Free Reservations 1800 569 9983 or on line at www.ocallaghanhotels.ie

Member of O'Callaghan Hotels

Room Rate from €219.00 to €335.00

PAUL LEIGHTON
GENERAL MANAGER

American Express

Diners

Mastercard

Visa

☺ Weekend specials from €215.00

102 102

Inet

Open All Year

Room rates are per room per night

AN CUIRT GEORGIAN
GEORGIAN COURT

77-79 LOWER GARDINER STREET,
DUBLIN 1

TEL: 01-855 7872 FAX: 01-855 5715
EMAIL: georgiancourt@eircom.net
WEB: www.ancuirtgeorgian.com

GUESTHOUSE U   MAP 8 0 11

Situated in the centre of Dublin City, 200m from O'Connell Street, Dublin's main shopping street, 50m from the city centre bus station. The 41 bus direct from Dublin Airport stops outside our door. 150m to Connolly rail station. 10 mins walk to Temple Bar. Secure car park available. Built in 1805 and located in a fine Georgian terrace. All rooms are en suite, colour TV, tea/coffee facilities, internal phones, hairdryer, electric iron available.

B&B from €29.00 to €50.00

EILEEN CONROY
OWNER

American Express
Mastercard
Visa

45 45

IRISH
HOTELS
FEDERATION

Closed 24 - 27 December

ANCHOR GUEST HOUSE

49 LOWER GARDINER STREET,
DUBLIN 1

TEL: 01-878 6913 FAX: 01-878 8038
EMAIL: gtcoyne@iol.ie
WEB: www.anchorguesthouse.com

GUESTHOUSE ★★★   MAP 8 0 11

The Anchor Guesthouse is located in the heart of the city centre. It is a tastefully refurbished Georgian house with a modern purpose built bedroom wing attached. Our location is a perfect base for city exploration. Temple Bar, Trinity College, Grafton Street, theatres, galleries and museums are but a stone's throw. We are 2 minutes walk from the central bus station, which has connections to the airport and ferry terminals.

B&B from €32.00 to €51.00

JOAN & GERRY COYNE
PROPRIETORS

Mastercard
Visa

Midweek specials from €96.00

22 22

IRISH
HOTELS
FEDERATION

Open All Year

ANGLESEA TOWN HOUSE

63 ANGLESEA ROAD,
BALLSBRIDGE,
DUBLIN 4

TEL: 01-668 3877 FAX: 01-668 3461

GUESTHOUSE ★★★★   MAP 8 0 11

This is a world-renowned guesthouse of national breakfast award fame. It has been featured on TV in both Ireland and the UK and has won entry in British, Irish, European and American travel guides and journals. It is a fine Edwardian residence of 7 en suite rooms with phone and TV, offering quiet elegance to discerning guests who wish to combine country-style charm with convenience to town. A warm welcome awaits you from your hostess Helen Kirrane and her family.

B&B from €60.00 to €70.00

HELEN KIRRANE
OWNER

American Express
Mastercard
Visa

7 7

Closed 15 December - 08 January

B&B rates are per person sharing per night incl. Breakfast

ARDAGH HOUSE

NO.1 HIGHFIELD ROAD,
RATHGAR,
DUBLIN 6
TEL: 01-497 7068 FAX: 01-497 3991
EMAIL: enquiries@ardagh-house.ie
WEB: www.ardagh-house.ie

GUESTHOUSE ★★★ MAP 8 O 11

Having been recently totally refurbished, Ardagh House is conveniently situated in a premier residential area. This imposing turn of the century premises contains many of the gracious and spacious features of a fine detached residence of that era and yet incorporating modern creature comforts. Within easy distance of the city centre, RDS, etc. This fine property stands on approximately 1/2 acre with ample off street car parking and good gardens.

B&B from € 35.00 to € 65.00

WILLIE AND MARY DOYLE
PROPRIETORS

Mastercard
Visa

Closed 23 - 27 December

Room rates are per room per night

ARIEL HOUSE

50 - 54 LANSDOWNE ROAD,
BALLSBRIDGE,
DUBLIN 4
TEL: 01-668 5512 FAX: 01-668 5845
EMAIL: reservations@ariel-house.net
WEB: www.ariel-house.net

GUESTHOUSE ★★★★ MAP 8 O 11

In the heart of Dublin's embassy belt, just a stones throw from the city centre lies Ariel House. Ideally located for a visit to Dublin, Ariel House boasts 37 magnificent bedrooms and a true Victorian drawing room. Return to a life in the 1850's and make Ariel House your stylish residence in Ballsbridge.

B&B from € 30.00 to € 75.00

DEIRDRE MCDONLAD
MANAGER

Mastercard
Visa

Closed 23 - 27 December

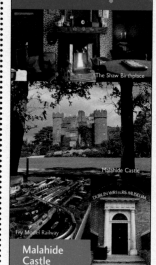

ARLINGTON HOTEL

23/25 BACHELORS WALK,
O'CONNELL BRIDGE,
DUBLIN 1
TEL: 01-804 9100 FAX: 01-804 9152
EMAIL: info@arlington.ie
WEB: www.arlington.ie

HOTEL ★★★ MAP 8 O 11

The most central hotel in Dublin, overlooking the River Liffey at O'Connell Bridge. Dublin's top attractions and shopping districts on your doorstep. 116 en suite bedrooms, free secure underground parking, meeting room. Magnificent medieval Knightsbridge Bar with live Irish music and dancing 7 nights a week all year round (free admission). Carvery lunch and à la carte bar menu available, candle lit Knights Bistro. Perfect base for business or pleasure.

B&B from €55.00 to €100.00

PAUL KEENAN
GENERAL MANAGER

American Express
Mastercard
Visa

116 116

Closed 24 - 26 December

ASHFIELD HOUSE

5 CLONSKEAGH ROAD,
DUBLIN 6
TEL: 01-260 3680 FAX: 01-260 4236
EMAIL: ashfieldguesthouse@eircom.net
WEB: www.guesthouse_dublin.com

GUESTHOUSE U MAP 8 O 11

One of Dublin's friendliest family run guesthouses. Providing comfort and service of a very high standard to the tourist and business sector. Rooms are en suite with TV, direct dial phones, tea/coffee facilities, hairdryer etc. A fax service is available. 10 mins from city centre, RDS, Lansdowne Road, Leopardstown Racecourse, ferry ports etc. Many top class pubs and restaurants adjacent to Ashfield House. We provide off street parking. There is an excellent bus service directly to city centre. Air coach direct to airport is a mere 5 min walk.

B&B from €45.00 to €60.00

FRANK AND OLIVE TAYLOR

American Express
Mastercard
Visa

10 10

Closed 24 - 27 December

ASHLING HOTEL

PARKGATE STREET,
DUBLIN 8
TEL: 01-677 2324 FAX: 01-679 3783
EMAIL: info@ashlinghotel.ie
WEB: www.ashlinghotel.ie

HOTEL ★★★ MAP 8 O 11

Why choose us? Stylish refurbishment. Spacious en suite bedrooms, secure parking, conference/meeting rooms. Under 8 mins by taxi/bus to city cntr/Temple Bar. Lovely quaint pubs, Guinness Brewery, Phoenix Park, other attractions nearby. Easily found location by car/rail/bus. By car take city centre route & briefly follow River Liffey westward. Taxi/airlink bus from airport, Heuston Intercity rail station opposite. For onward journeys we are within easy access of all major roads.

Member of Best Western Hotels

B&B from €53.00 to €105.00

ALAN MOODY
GENERAL MANAGER

American Express
Diners
Mastercard
Visa

☺ Midweek specials from €140.00

147 147

Closed 24 - 26 December

B&B rates are per person sharing per night incl. Breakfast

ASTON HOTEL

7/9 ASTON QUAY,
DUBLIN 2

TEL: 01-677 9300 FAX: 01-677 9007
EMAIL: stay@aston-hotel.com
WEB: www.aston-hotel.com

HOTEL U MAP 8 O 11

A warm welcome awaits you at the Aston Hotel, located in Temple Bar and overlooking the River Liffey. Friendly staff and pleasant surroundings will make your stay a memorable one. All our 27 rooms are en suite and offer every guest comfort including direct dial phone, colour TV, hairdryer and tea/coffee making facilities. A leisurely stroll from the Aston brings you to all Dublin's top attractions and amenities and makes it an ideal base for exploring the capital.

B&B from €32.00 to €85.00

ANN WALSH
MANAGER

American Express
Diners
Mastercard
Visa

Closed 24 - 27 December

AUBURN GUESTHOUSE

OLD NAVAN ROAD, CASTLEKNOCK,
(AT AUBURN ROUNDABOUT),
DUBLIN 15
TEL: 01-822 3535 FAX: 01-822 3550
EMAIL: auburngh@iol.ie

GUESTHOUSE ★★★ MAP 8 O 11

Auburn - is a family run modern guesthouse set on it's own grounds. Landscaped gardens and guest carpark. City centre 15 minutes, M50 adjacent, Dublin Airport 10 minutes. Ideal location for business or holiday. Blanchardstown Complex with shopping and many amenities 5 minutes. Numerous Golf Courses near by. Restaurants within walking distance.

B&B from €41.00 to €46.00

ELAINE COWLEY
MANAGERESS

American Express
Mastercard
Visa

Closed 23 December - 06 January

FINGAL
Dublin – Ireland
Rural Charm at the Gates of Dublin

For further
information contact:

FINGAL TOURISM
Mainscourt, Main St.,
Swords, Fingal, Co. Dublin
Tel: +353 1 8400077
Email: info@fingaltourism.ie
Web: www.fingal-dublin.com

Room rates are per room per night

BAGGOT COURT

92 LOWER BAGGOT STREET,
DUBLIN 2

TEL: 01-661 2819 FAX: 01-661 0253
EMAIL: baggot@indigo.ie

GUESTHOUSE ★★★ MAP 8 O 11

This beautifully refurbished house is situated in the heart of Georgian Dublin and only a 6 minute walk to the city centre. Ideally situated for theatres, museums and art galleries plus a wide selection of fine restaurants and traditional Irish pubs. Our professional and friendly staff pride themselves on providing luxurious accommodation with the personal service of a private residence.

B&B from €65.00 to €85.00

ROXANNE MOONEY
MANAGER

American Express
Mastercard
Visa

☺ Midweek specials from €152.40

🛏️🅽☎️🖥️T❄️P♨️
11 11

Closed 23 December - 06 January

BARRY'S HOTEL

1-2 GREAT DENMARK STREET,
DUBLIN 1

TEL: 01-874 9407 FAX: 01-874 6508

HOTEL ★★ MAP 8 O 11

Barry's Hotel is one of Dublin's oldest hotels built in the later part of the Georgian Period. Situated 300 yds off O'Connell Street. Barry's unique ambience, friendly service assure visitors whether on business or pleasure the warmest of welcomes and special attention. The hotel is within walking distance of the Abbey and Gate Theatres, National Wax Museum, Croke Park and principal shopping districts and major tourist attractions.

B&B from €55.00 to €60.00

SINEAD FAHY
MANAGER

American Express
Mastercard
Visa

🛏️🅽🖥️TCM🎵S🄰🄻🄳🛎️
32 32

Closed 24 - 26 December

BELGRAVE GUESTHOUSE

8-10 BELGRAVE SQUARE,
RATHMINES,
DUBLIN 6

TEL: 01-496 3760 FAX: 01-497 9243

GUESTHOUSE ★★★ MAP 8 O 11

The Belgrave consists of three interconnecting early Victorian buildings overlooking a well matured square. While retaining all the character and charm of its era, the Belgrave has all the conveniences of a modern 3*** guesthouse, each room is en suite and has colour TV, direct dial telephone, tea making facilities. Private car park. Ideally located. We look forward to hosting you and according you a warm welcome for which we are renowned. AA ◆◆◆.

B&B from €45.00 to €88.00

PAUL AND MARY O'REILLY
OWNERS

Mastercard
Visa

🛏️🅽☎️🖥️TCM❄️P🔟7⃣🛎️ Inet
24 24

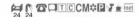

Closed 22 December - 02 January

B&B rates are per person sharing per night incl. Breakfast

BERKELEY COURT

LANSDOWNE ROAD,
BALLSBRIDGE,
DUBLIN 4
TEL: 01-660 1711 FAX: 01-661 7238
EMAIL: berkeleycourt@jurysdoyle.com
WEB: www.jurysdoyle.com

HOTEL ★★★★★ MAP 8 O 11

Luxury, tradition and charm distinguish The Berkeley Court and add a touch of eminence to everything about it. This is why this 5-star hotel is the natural host to international dignitaries and celebrities. Located in the heart of Dublin's fashionable embassy belt, the city is just a short walk away.

Member of Leading Hotels of the World

B&B from € 105.00 to €208.00

JOE RUSSELL
GENERAL MANAGER

American Express
Diners
Mastercard
Visa

188 188

Inet

IRISH
HOTELS
FEDERATION

Open All Year

BEWLEY'S HOTEL BALLSBRIDGE

MERRION ROAD,
BALLSBRIDGE,
DUBLIN 4
TEL: 01-668 1111 FAX: 01-668 1999
EMAIL: bb@BewleysHotels.com
WEB: www.BewleysHotels.com

HOTEL ★★★ MAP 8 O 11

A new stylish concept in a prime location on Merrion Road combining the past with the present. Accommodating you in style with over 220 deluxe bedrooms and 9 purpose built meeting rooms. Enjoy an exciting dining experience in O'Connell's Restaurant. Bewley's Hotels Book on-line www.BewleysHotels.com

Room Rate from €99.00 to €99.00

CLIO O'GARA
GENERAL MANAGER

American Express
Diners
Mastercard
Visa

220 220

 Inet

IRISH
HOTELS
FEDERATION

Closed 24 - 26 December

Christ Church Cathedral, Dublin

OPENING TIMES FOR VISITORS 2002
9.45–17.00 Monday-Friday
10.00–17.00 Saturday and Sunday

Requested Donation: € 3 per Adult/€ 1.50 per Child/Student

Treasures of Christ Church
A permanent exhibition in the cathedral crypt
Opening times:
9.45–17.00 Monday-Friday
10.00–16.45 Saturday
12.30–15.15 Sunday
Last admission is 30 minutes before closing

Admission €3. Group and family entry can be arranged at the Visitor Services area or in advance by telephone the cathedral office

**Telephone: +353 (1) 6778099
Fax: +353 (1) 6798991
Email:
welcome@cccdub.ie**

Room rates are per room per night

BEWLEY'S HOTEL NEWLANDS CROSS

NEWLANDS CROSS,
NAAS ROAD (N7),
DUBLIN 22
TEL: 01-464 0140 FAX: 01-464 0900
EMAIL: res@BewleysHotels.com
WEB: www.BewleysHotels.com

HOTEL ★★★ MAP 8 O 11

A unique blend of quality, value and flexibility for independent discerning guests. Located just off the N7, minutes from the M50, Dublin Airport and the city centre. Our large spacious family size rooms are fully equipped with all modern amenities. Our Bewley's Restaurant offers you a range of dining options, from traditional Irish breakfast to full table service à la carte. Real time on line reservations and availability at www.BewleysHotels.com

Room Rate from € 79.00 to € 79.00

DAMIEN MOLLOY
GENERAL MANAGER
American Express
Diners
Mastercard
Visa

258 258

Closed 24 - 26 December

BLOOMS HOTEL

6 ANGLESEA STREET,
TEMPLE BAR,
DUBLIN 2
TEL: 01-671 5622 FAX: 01-671 5997
EMAIL: blooms@eircom.net
WEB: www.blooms.ie

HOTEL ★★★ MAP 8 O 11

Blooms Hotel is situated at the centre of Dublin's cultural and artistic heart - Temple Bar. The hotel itself is only a few minutes stroll from Grafton Street's shopping and most of the city's best sights. And for those who want to set the town alight, Blooms is on the doorstep of Dublin's most famous nightlife - not least of which is its own nightclub, Club M. Blooms Hotel is a perfect choice for partygoers but not for those planning an early night!

B&B from € 50.00 to € 75.00

BARRY O'SULLIVAN
GENERAL MANAGER
American Express
Diners
Mastercard
Visa

86 86

Closed 22 - 26 December

BROOKS HOTEL

DRURY STREET,
DUBLIN 2
TEL: 01-670 4000 FAX: 01-670 4455
EMAIL: reservations@brookshotel.ie
WEB: www.sinnotthotels.com

HOTEL ★★★★ MAP 8 O 11

Located in the fashionable heart of Dublin City, 3 mins from Grafton St, Temple Bar, Dublin Castle & Trinity College. Brooks is a designer/boutique hotel with high standards throughout, appealing in particular to the discerning international traveller. With superbly appointed air conditioned accommodation, the Butter Lane Bar, residents drawing room, Francesca's Restaurant & the Markets meeting room, Brooks is designed to cater for the sophisticated visitor. Secure parking available opposite the hotel.

B&B from € 110.00 to € 135.00

BERTIE KELLY
GENERAL MANAGER
American Express
Diners
Mastercard
Visa

75 75

Open All Year

B&B rates are per person sharing per night incl. Breakfast

BROWNES TOWNHOUSE & BRASSERIE

22 ST. STEPHENS GREEN,
DUBLIN 2

TEL: 01-638 3939 FAX: 01-638 3900
EMAIL: info@brownesdublin.com
WEB: www.brownesdublin.com

GUESTHOUSE ★★★★ MAP 12 O 11

Overlooking St. Stephen's Green, Brownes Brasserie and Townhouse has the most superb location in Dublin. Brownes - a rare find, striking the perfect balance between traditional comfort and a relaxed contemporary atmosphere. With 12 luxury rooms, it has all of the intimacy, warmth & character of a privately run townhouse, yet corporate guests have the convenience of ISDN, direct personal telephone, fax lines, cable TV and air conditioning.

Room Rate from €190.00 to €470.00

BARRY CANNY
PROPRIETOR

American Express
Diners
Mastercard
Visa

12 12

FAX

HOTELS FEDERATION

Closed 24 December - 03 January

BURLINGTON (THE)

UPPER LEESON STREET,
DUBLIN 4

TEL: 01-660 5222 FAX: 01-660 8496
EMAIL: burlington@jurysdoyle.com
WEB: www.jurysdoyle.com

HOTEL ★★★★ MAP 8 O 11

The Burlington is a Dublin institution, always at the heart of the action and central to the whole whirl of Dublin life. Its lively bars and restaurants and friendly open charm conspire to create an atmosphere that is hard to forget. Ireland's largest conference hotel, it is centrally located - just a 5-minute stroll to the city centre.

B&B from €86.00 to €167.00

JOHN CLIFTON
GENERAL MANAGER

American Express
Diners
Mastercard
Visa

504 504

Inet FAX

HOTELS FEDERATION

Open All Year

DUBLIN'S CITY HALL
The Story *of the* Capital

Multi-media exhibition tracing the history of Dublin. A story of change, highlighting major events that have influenced the growth of the city and civic governance over the past 1,000 years, creating the Dublin we know today.

Admission Times
Monday/Saturday 10am to 5.15pm. Sunday 2.00pm to 5.00pm

Further Information
City Hall Exhibition, City Hall, Dame Street, Dublin 2.
Tel +353 1 672 2204
Fax +353 1 672 2620
Email cityhall@dublincity.ie
www.dublincity.ie

Dublin City Council
Comhairle Chathair Bhaile Átha Cliath

Room rates are per room per night

BUSWELLS HOTEL

23/27 MOLESWORTH STREET,
DUBLIN 2

TEL: 01-614 6500 FAX: 01-676 2090
EMAIL: buswells@quinn-hotels.com
WEB: www.quinnhotels.com

HOTEL U   MAP 8 O 11

One of Dublin's best kept secrets. This elegant Georgian Building provides the highest standards in a relaxing environment. A haven for the discerning traveller. Just minutes walk from St. Stephen's Green and Grafton Street. Our dedicated business suite and dry leisure suite are our newest facilities we have to offer you.

Member of Quinn Hotels

B&B from €65.00 to €110.00

PAUL GALLAGHER
GENERAL MANAGER

American Express
Diners
Mastercard
Visa

69 69

Inet

Closed 24 - 26 December

BUTLERS TOWN HOUSE

44 LANSDOWNE ROAD,
BALLSBRIDGE,
DUBLIN 4

TEL: 01-667 4022 FAX: 01-667 3960
EMAIL: info@butlers-hotel.com
WEB: www.butlers-hotel.com

GUESTHOUSE ★★★★ MAP 8 O 11

An oasis of country tranquillity in the heart of Dublin, Butlers Town House is an experience as opposed to a visit. Opened in March 1997, fully restored to reflect its former glory, but with all modern comforts from air-conditioning to modem points. Butlers Town House is renowned for its elegance and premier guest service. Private secure car park available.

Member of Manor House Hotels

B&B from €95.00 to €107.00

RONAN BRANIGAN
GENERAL MANAGER

American Express
Diners
Mastercard
Visa

19 19

Closed 23 December - 03 January

CAMDEN COURT HOTEL

CAMDEN STREET,
DUBLIN 2

TEL: 01-475 9666 FAX: 01-475 9677
EMAIL: sales@camdencourthotel.com
WEB: www.camdencourthotel.com

HOTEL ★★★ MAP 8 O 11

The Camden Court Hotel is situated in the heart of Dublin within a 5 minute walk of Grafton Street. The hotel comprises of 246 well-appointed bedrooms all en suite with hairdryer, direct dial phone, colour TV, trouser press and tea/coffee making facilities. We also provide excellent conference facilities, restaurant and themed bar. Our state of the art leisure centre consists of a 16m swimming pool, sauna, steamroom, jacuzzi, solarium and a fully equipped gym. Complimentary secure carparking on site.

B&B from €65.00 to €140.00

BRIAN GALLAGHER
GENERAL MANAGER

American Express
Diners
Mastercard
Visa

246 246

Closed 23 - 28 December

B&B rates are per person sharing per night incl. Breakfast

CASSIDYS HOTEL

CAVENDISH ROW,
UPPER O'CONNELL ST.,
DUBLIN 1

TEL: 01-878 0555 FAX: 01-878 0687
EMAIL: rese@cassidys.iol.ie
WEB: www.cassidyshotel.com

HOTEL ★★★ MAP 8 O 11

A little gem in the heart of the city.
Cassidys is a modern 88 bedroomed
townhouse hotel located opposite the
famous Gate Theatre in the city
centre. Cassidys is a short walk from
numerous museums, theatres, bars
and shopping districts. The warm and
welcoming atmosphere of Groomes
Bar lends a traditional air to Cassidys
and fine dining is assured in the
stylish surroundings of Restaurant 6.
Limited parking for guests. Conference
facilities available

B&B from €55.00 to €105.00

MARTIN CASSIDY
GENERAL MANAGER

American Express
Diners
Mastercard
Visa

Midweek 2 B&B + 1 dinner
€105.00pps

88 88

Closed 22 - 27 December

CASTLE HOTEL

2-4 GARDINER ROW,
DUBLIN 1

TEL: 01-874 6949 FAX: 01-872 7674
EMAIL: hotels@indigo.ie
WEB: www.indigo.ie/~hotels

HOTEL ★★ MAP 8 O 11

Elegant Georgian hotel close to
Dublin's main shopping district,
renowned for its friendly service. One
of Dublin's oldest hotels. Authentically
restored the décor and furnishings
offer modern comfort combined with
olde world features: crystal
chandeliers, antique mirrors, marble
fireplaces and period staircases. The
individually decorated rooms offer
private bathroom, satellite TV, direct
dial phone and beverage making
facilities. The hotel has an intimate
residents bar and private parking.

Member of Castle Hotel Group

B&B from €49.50 to €62.50

YVONNE EVANS
MANAGERESS

American Express
Mastercard
Visa

Midweek specials from €150.00

38 38

Closed 24 - 27 December

Room rates are per room per night

CEDAR LODGE

98 MERRION ROAD,
DUBLIN 4

TEL: 01-668 4410 FAX: 01-668 4533
EMAIL: info@cedarlodge.ie
WEB: www.cedarlodge.ie

GUESTHOUSE ★★★★ MAP 8 O 11

Cedar Lodge the luxurious alternative to a hotel. Modern comforts and Edwardian style combine to create a truly unique experience. Our beautifully furnished en suite bedrooms are of international standard. This jewel among guesthouses is located in leafy Ballsbridge, adjacent to RDS, the British Embassy and the Four Seasons Hotel. 10 minutes from the city centre, close to airport and ferry ports. Private car park. AA Premier Selected ◆◆◆◆◆, RAC ◆◆◆◆◆.

B&B from €45.00 to €75.00

GERARD & MARY DOODY
OWNERS

American Express
Mastercard
Visa

🏨 🛏 ☎ 🖥 C ❄ P ♿
16   16

Closed 23 - 28 December

CELTIC LODGE GUESTHOUSE

81/82 TALBOT STREET,
DUBLIN 1

TEL: 01-677 9955 FAX: 01-878 8698
EMAIL: celticguesthouse@eircom.net

GUESTHOUSE N MAP 8 O 11

This gracious Victorian residence is in the heart of the city centre adjacent to the bus and train stations and 15 minutes from the airport. A stroll from our door is the vibrant Temple Bar district with its numerous pubs, restaurants & clubs. Trinity College, Christchurch Cathedral, Dublin Castle & a number of theatres are within a stones throw. All rooms en suite & finished to a very high standard with cable TV & tea/coffee making facilities. Next door a traditional bar with Irish Music seven nights a week, free. Traditional restaurant opening shortly.

B&B from €35.00 to €55.00

NOEL TYNAN
DIRECTOR

Mastercard
Visa

😊 Midweek specials from €95.25

🏨 🛏 📺 T C 🖥
29   29

Open All Year

CENTRAL HOTEL

1-5 EXCHEQUER STREET,
DUBLIN 2

TEL: 01-679 7302 FAX: 01-679 7303
EMAIL: reservations@centralhotel.ie
WEB: www.centralhotel.ie

HOTEL ★★★ MAP 8 O 11

City centre location. Award winning Library Bar, Exchequer Bar and recently refurbished restaurant. Temple Bar, Dublin's Left Bank, one block away. Trinity College, Grafton Street and Christchurch 5 mins from hotel. Rooms en suite include, DD phones, voicemail, hairdryers, tea/coffee making facilities, multi-channel TV. 8 private meeting rooms. Secure parking available nearby.

Member of Best Western Hotels

B&B from €72.00 to €103.00

GUY THOMPSON
OPERATIONS DIRECTOR

American Express
Diners
Mastercard
Visa

🏨 🛏 ☎ 🖥 ⬆ T C 🔌 C M S ♿
70   70

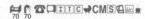

Inet

Closed 24 - 27 December

B&B rates are per person sharing per night incl. Breakfast

CHARLEVILLE LODGE

268-272 NORTH CIRCULAR ROAD,
PHIBSBOROUGH,
DUBLIN 7

TEL: 01-838 6633 FAX: 01-838 5854
EMAIL: charleville@indigo.ie
WEB: www.charlevillelodge.ie

GUESTHOUSE ★★★ MAP 8 O 11

Charleville Lodge, (former home of Lord Charleville), is an elegant terrace of Victorian houses located 15 minutes walk from the city centre, Trinity College & Temple Bar, en route to Dublin Airport and car ferry. The luxurious en suite bedrooms have direct dial phones and colour TV. Rated ◆◆◆◆ by AA and RAC, we are holders of the Sparkling Diamond award. Our car park is for guest use and is complimentary. Let us make your arrangements with local golf clubs. Visit our website.

Member of Premier Guesthouses of Ireland

B&B from €35.00 to €75.00

VAL & ANNE STENSON
OWNERS

American Express
Diners
Mastercard
Visa

 Midweek specials from €99.00

🛏️🔥☎️💻Ⓣ🆑✳️🅿️🆂
30 30

Closed 20 - 26 December

Room rates are per room per night

CHIEF O'NEILL'S HOTEL

SMITHFIELD VILLAGE,
DUBLIN 7

TEL: 01-817 3838 FAX: 01-817 3839
EMAIL: reservations@chiefoneills.com
WEB: www.chiefoneills.com

HOTEL U MAP 8 O 11

Chief O'Neill's Hotel is dedicated to the memory of Francis O'Neill, Chicago Chief of Police & one of the most important individual collectors of Irish traditional music this century. Its theme is Irish traditional music expressed through Ireland's finest contemporary design. Each of the 73 en suite luxury rooms is equipped with a CD/Hi-Fi system, multi-channel TV, direct dial phone & tea/coffee facility. Restaurants & visitor attractions surround the hotel. The Jervis St. Shopping Centre, O'Connell St. are within walking distance.

Room Rate from €180.00 to €380.00

PAT HEVEY
GENERAL MANAGER

American Express
Mastercard
Visa

🛏️🔥☎️💻±Ⓣ🆑🔌CM🎵🎼🅿️🆑ᴬᴮᶜ
73 73

📶 Inet

Closed 24 - 26 December

CLARA HOUSE

23 LEINSTER ROAD,
RATHMINES,
DUBLIN 6
TEL: 01-497 5904 FAX: 01-497 5904
EMAIL: clarahouse@eircom.net

GUESTHOUSE ★★★ MAP 8 O 11

Clara House is a beautifully maintained listed Georgian house with many original features skillfully combined with modern day comforts. Each bedroom has en suite bathroom, remote control colour TV, direct dial telephone, radio/alarm clock, tea/coffee making facilities, hair dryer and trouser press. Clara House is a mile from downtown with bus stops 100 metres away. Bus stop for Ballsbridge/RDS is 200 metres. Secure parking at rear of house.

B&B from €51.00 to €57.00

PHIL & PAUL REID
PROPRIETORS

Mastercard
Visa

13   13

Open All Year

CLARENCE HOTEL

6-8 WELLINGTON QUAY,
DUBLIN 2
TEL: 01-407 0800 FAX: 01-407 0820
EMAIL: reservations@theclarence.ie
WEB: www.theclarence.ie

HOTEL U MAP 8 O 11

Located on the River Liffey, The Clarence Hotel was built in 1852 and was transformed into a boutique hotel in 1996. Many of the hotel's original features have been revived and a unique balance between old and new has been achieved. It's 49 bedrooms and suites, are individually designed in contemporary elegant style. A treatment room is available together with Valet Parking for hotel patrons. The Tea Room Restaurant and Octagon Bar provide a social focus for The Clarence and Dublin City.

Member of Leading Small Hotels of the World

Room Rate from €300.00 to €320.00

ROBERT VAN EERDE
GENERAL MANAGER

American Express
Diners
Mastercard
Visa

49   49

Closed 24 - 26 December

CLARION HOTEL DUBLIN
IFSC

EXCISE WALK, INTERNATIONAL
FINANCIAL SERVICES CENTRE,
DUBLIN 1
TEL: 01-433 8800 FAX: 01-433 8801
EMAIL: info@clarionhotelifsc.com
WEB: www.clarionhotelifsc.com

HOTEL N MAP 8 O 11

New to City Centre the latest in stylish contemporary hotels in a cosmopolitan ambience. Bedrooms are comfortably appointed with modern features. Enjoy a choice of eating experiences - European Cuisine in our Sinergie Restaurant, an exciting twist of Eastern fare in Kudos Bar. Well equipped meeting rooms for small and large conferences. Unwind at Sanovitae Health and Fitness Club including 18m indoor swimming pool, which is complimentary to guests.

Member of Choice Hotels International

B&B from €80.00 to €92.50

BRENDAN CURTIS

American Express
Diners
Mastercard
Visa

160 160

Closed 24 - 27 December

B&B rates are per person sharing per night incl. Breakfast

CLARION STEPHENS HALL HOTEL AND SUITES

THE EARLSFORT CENTRE,
LOWER LEESON STREET,
DUBLIN 2

TEL: 01-638 1111 FAX: 01-638 1122
EMAIL: stephens@premgroup.com
WEB: www.stephens-hall.com

HOTEL ★★★ MAP 8 O 11

3*** deluxe hotel located in the heart of Georgian Dublin on Lower Leeson Street just around the corner from St. Stephen's Green, only minutes walk to fashionable Grafton Street, Trinity College, National Art Gallery, National Concert Hall and National Museum. Clarion Stephens Hall offers all suite accommodation in a relaxed and comfortable setting. All suites consist of spacious living room, fully equipped kitchen, in room fax, modem point, CD player and TV (including movie channel).

Member of Choice Hotels Ireland

Room Rate from €225.00 to €400.00

ANNE BYRNE
GENERAL MANAGER

American Express
Diners
Mastercard
Visa

:/

33 33

Inet FAX

IRISH
HOTELS
FEDERATION

Open All Year

CLIFDEN GUESTHOUSE

32 GARDINER PLACE,
DUBLIN 1

TEL: 01-874 6364 FAX: 01-874 6122
EMAIL: bnb@indigo.ie
WEB: www.clifdenhouse.com

GUESTHOUSE ★★★ MAP 8 O 11

A refurbished city centre Georgian home. Our private car park provides security for guest's cars, even after check-out. All rooms have shower, WC, WHB, TV, direct dial phone and tea making facilities. We cater for single, twin, double, triple and family occupancies. Convenient to airport, ferryports, Bus Aras (bus station) and DART. We are only 5 minutes walk from O'Connell Street. AA and RAC approved.

Room Rate from €60.00 to €140.00

JACK & MARY LALOR

Mastercard
Visa

☺ Midweek specials from €105.00

14 14

IRISH
HOTELS
FEDERATION

Open All Year

CUSTOM HOUSE
Visitor Centre

An exhibition on the history of the building which is over 200 years old and has been heavily involved in the social and political history of the city.

Custom House Quay,
Dublin 1
Telephone: 01 8882538

OPEN
MID-MARCH TO OCTOBER
Monday to Friday
10am to 12.30pm.
Saturday Sunday and Bank
Holidays 2pm – 5pm.

NOVEMBER TO MID-MARCH
Wednesday to Friday
10am to 12.30pm.
Sunday 2pm to 5pm.

PRICE
**Individual €1.00,
Family €3.00,
Groups €0.50 each,
Students Free.**

Room rates are per room per night

CLONTARF CASTLE HOTEL

CASTLE AVENUE,
CLONTARF,
DUBLIN 3
TEL: 01-833 2321 FAX: 01-833 0418
EMAIL: info@clontarfcastle.ie
WEB: www.clontarfcastle.ie

HOTEL ★★★★ MAP 8 O 11

This historic castle, dating back to 1172, is today a luxurious 4**** deluxe, 111 room hotel. Ideally situated only 10 minutes from the city centre and 15 minutes from the airport. With superb facilities including uniquely designed rooms equipped with all the modern facilities. Templar's Bistro specialising in modern international cuisine, 2 unique bars, state of the art conference and banqueting facilities and stunning lobby. Complimentary carparking.

B&B from € 70.00 to € 165.00

ENDA O'MEARA
MANAGING DIRECTOR

American Express
Diners
Mastercard
Visa

Weekend specials from €220.00

111 111

Closed 24 - 25 December

COMFORT INN PARNELL SQUARE

GREAT DENMARK STREET,
OFF PARNELL SQUARE,
DUBLIN 1
TEL: 01-874 1413 FAX: 01-872 8631
EMAIL: info@choicehotelsireland.ie
WEB: www.choicehotelsireland.ie

HOTEL R MAP 8 O 11

The Comfort Hotel Parnell Square, is situated in the heart of Dublin, in a unique blend of Georgian excellence and modern amenities. A perfect base from which to explore shops, theatres, museums and restaurants. Comfort and style are an integral part of this hotel, where the business individual or families are well catered for. Our spacious 96 en suite guestrooms are tastefully decorated to the highest standard with direct dial telephone, multi-channel TV, hairdryer and tea/coffee making facilities. Both family and disabled rooms are available upon request.

Room Rate from € 79.00 to € 195.00

SEAMUS SHAUGHNESSY
GENERAL MANAGER

American Express
Diners
Mastercard
Visa

96 96

Closed 23 - 26 December

COMFORT INN, TALBOT STREET

95-98 TALBOT STREET,
DUBLIN 1
TEL: 01-874 9202 FAX: 01-874 9672
EMAIL: info@talbot.premgroup.ie
WEB: www.comfort-inn-dublin.com

GUESTHOUSE ★★★ MAP 8 O 11

Talbot Street boasts the perfect location, just 2 minutes walk from O'Connell Street. In the surrounding area, you will find many shops, restaurants, pubs, theatres and nightclubs. Temple Bar and Trinity College are just a short stroll away. All rooms are en suite, with colourful modern decor. Full Irish Breakfast available every morning.

Member of Choice Hotels Ireland

Room Rate from € 75.00 to € 190.00

HEATHER WIKTORSKI
GENERAL MANAGER

American Express
Diners
Mastercard
Visa

Midweek specials from €115.00

48 48

Closed 24 - 27 December

B&B rates are per person sharing per night incl. Breakfast

CONRAD DUBLIN

EARLSFORT TERRACE,
DUBLIN 2

TEL: 01-602 8900 FAX: 01-676 5424
EMAIL: dublininfo@conradhotels.com
WEB: www.conraddublin.com

HOTEL ★★★★★ MAP 8 O 11

In the heart of the city providing unsurpassed hospitality to all visitors lies the Conrad Dublin. 191 luxurious guestrooms including 9 suites with colour TV, ergonomic workstation, DD phone, air conditioning, minibars and 24-hour room service. Dining is available in the Plurabelle Restaurant and the hotel is home to one of the most traditional Irish pubs in town, Alfie Byrnes. Fitness centre also available. At the Conrad Dublin service is the secret.

Room Rate from €200.00 to €420.00

LAURENS ZIEREN
GENERAL MANAGER

American Express
Diners
Mastercard
Visa

Weekend specials €240.00
per room, per night

191 191

Inet FAX

IRISH
HOTELS
FEDERATION

Open All Year

DAVENPORT HOTEL

AT MERRION SQUARE,
DUBLIN 2

TEL: 01-607 3500 FAX: 01-661 5663
EMAIL: davenportres@ocallaghanhotels.ie
WEB: www.davenporthotel.ie

HOTEL U MAP 8 O 11

This elegant deluxe hotel is located at Merrion Square in Dublin City centre, beside Trinity College and just a 5 minute walk from the principal business, shopping and cultural districts. Fully air-conditioned with 115 deluxe guestrooms, discreet drawing room bar, fine dining restaurant and extensive meeting facilities, it offers an oasis of tranquillity in the heart of Dublin. Free private valet car parking. USA Toll Free Reservations 1800 569 9983 or on line at www.ocallaghanhotels.ie

Member of O'Callaghan Hotels

Room Rate from €219.00 to €335.00

KEVIN DENNER
GENERAL MANAGER

American Express
Diners
Mastercard
Visa

Weekend specials from €215.00 pps

115 115

Inet

IRISH
HOTELS
FEDERATION

Open All Year

The Book of Kells

'Turning Darkness into Light'

Exhibition and Library Shop
open seven days a week

Admission Times

Monday-Saturday
09.30 - 17.00

Sunday (October to May)
12.00 - 16.30

Sunday (June to September)
09.30 - 16.30

Supported by

WATERFORD
CRYSTAL

**Trinity College Library
Dublin**

Room rates are per room per night

DERGVALE HOTEL

4 GARDINER PLACE,
DUBLIN 1

TEL: 01-874 4753 FAX: 01-874 8276
EMAIL: dergvale@indigo.ie
WEB: www.dergvalehotel.com

HOTEL ★★ MAP 8 O 11

The Dergvale Hotel is located within walking distance of all principal shopping areas, cinemas, museums, Trinity College, Dublin Castle and airport bus. Most bedrooms with showers en suite, colour TV and direct dial telephone. Fully licensed. A courteous and efficient staff are on hand to make your stay an enjoyable one. The hotel is under the personal supervision of Gerard and Nancy Nolan.

B&B from €38.00 to €57.00

GERARD NOLAN
OWNER

American Express
Mastercard
Visa

🛏🛋☎📺TⒸ🛁🆖
20 17

Closed 24 December - 07 January

DONNYBROOK HALL

6 BELMONT AVENUE,
DONNYBROOK,
DUBLIN 4

TEL: 01-269 1633 FAX: 01-269 2649
EMAIL: donnybrookhall@eircom.net
WEB: www.donnybrookhall.com

GUESTHOUSE ★★★ MAP 8 O 11

Situated in the fashionable Donnybrook district of Dublin, this beautifully restored Victorian residence retains many original features. Each of our en suite rooms are of international standard and are individually designed in elegant style. This guesthouse is ideally located just a short walk from the cultural, commercial and entertainment heart of the city. Nearby is the RDS, RTE, UCD, Lansdowne Road, St. Stephens Green and Trinity College.

B&B from €40.00 to €80.00

DOROTHY GLENNON
OWNER

American Express
Mastercard
Visa

🛏🛋☎📺TⒸ✱🜚⚓
7 7

Open All Year

DONNYBROOK LODGE

131 STILLORGAN ROAD,
DONNYBROOK,
DUBLIN 4

TEL: 01-283 7333 FAX: 01-260 4770
EMAIL: info@donnybrooklodge.com
WEB: www.donnybrooklodge.com

GUESTHOUSE ★★★ MAP 8 O 11

Relax in comfortable surroundings in the heart of Dublin's most exclusive area. Ideally situated close to city centre, ferryports and adjacent to RDS, Lansdowne, UCD and RTE. A short stroll from a host of restaurants and entertainment. Recently refurbished, our well-appointed rooms feature en suites, direct dial phone and TV. Private parking available. Enjoy a leisurely breakfast in our elegant dining room, overlooking gardens. A relaxed atmosphere and warm welcome awaits you.

B&B from €35.00 to €75.00

PAT BUTLER

Mastercard
Visa

🛏🛋☎📺TⒸ✱🅿⚓
7 7

Open All Year

B&B rates are per person sharing per night incl. Breakfast

Room rates are per room per night

EGLINTON MANOR

83 EGLINTON ROAD,
DONNYBROOK,
DUBLIN 4
TEL: 01-269 3273 FAX: 01-269 7527

GUESTHOUSE ★★★★   MAP 8 O 11

This gracious red-bricked Victorian Old House which has just been refurbished to the highest standard is situated in the very elegant suburb of Donnybrook. It is very close to the city centre and the RDS. All rooms have a bathroom and tea/coffee makers, TV, radio and direct dial telephones. Private free car parking. 4**** premises with lovely garden. 48 hours is our cancellation policy.

B&B from €64.00 to €82.00

ROSALEEN CAHILL O'BRIEN

American Express
Mastercard
Visa

7   7

Open All Year

FERRYVIEW HOUSE

96 CLONTARF ROAD,
CLONTARF,
DUBLIN 3
TEL: 01-833 5893 FAX: 01-853 2141
EMAIL: ferryview@oceanfree.net
WEB: www.ferryviewhouse.com

GUESTHOUSE ★★★   MAP 8 O 11

Ferryview House is located in the exclusive coastal suburb of Clontarf, 2.5 miles from the city centre on a regular bus route. The recently totally refurbished family run guesthouse is also selected ◆◆◆◆ with the Automobile Association. The House is close to Dublin Port, the Point Theatre, East Point Business Park (2km) and airport 15 minutes. Local facilities include restaurants, coastal walks, Clontarf Rugby Club, tennis and 3 golf clubs.

B&B from €40.00 to €57.00

MARGARET ALLISTER

Mastercard
Visa

8   8

Closed 22 December - 01 January

FITZSIMONS HOTEL

21-22 WELLINGTON QUAY,
TEMPLE BAR,
DUBLIN 2
TEL: 01-677 9315 FAX: 01-677 9387
EMAIL: info@fitzsimons-hotel.com
WEB: www.fitzsimonshotel.com

HOTEL ★★   MAP 8 O 11

The Fitzsimons Hotel situated on the banks of the River Liffey beside the new Millenium Bridge, in the heart of the City's thriving left bank - Temple Bar. It's location offers the visitor doorstep access to this vibrant, colourful, exciting locale and all it has to offer. Theatres, Galleries, Studios, Bars, Restaurants, live music venues and alternative shops. Home to Dublin's top entertainment venue with 3 floors of fun Fitzsimons Bar, Restaurant and the Ballroom Nite Club.

B&B from €55.00 to €100.00

DARINA HOWARD
MANAGER

American Express
Mastercard
Visa

26   26

Closed 24 - 26 December

B&B rates are per person sharing per night incl. Breakfast

FITZWILLIAM

41 UPPER FITZWILLIAM STREET, DUBLIN 2

TEL: 01-662 5155 FAX: 01-676 7488
EMAIL: fitzwilliamguesthouse@eircom.net

GUESTHOUSE ★★★ MAP 8 O 11

Centrally located in the heart of elegant Georgian Dublin, minutes walk from St. Stephen's Green, National Concert Hall and Galleries. Enjoy the charm of this spacious town house. Rooms with en suite facilities, colour TV, direct dial telephone, clock/radios and hair dryers. Overnight car parking available. Excellent restaurants nearby. Our friendly staff will ensure your stay is a relaxed and memorable one.

B&B from €50.00 to €70.00

DECLAN CARNEY
MANAGER

American Express
Diners
Mastercard
Visa

12 12

IRISH HOTELS FEDERATION

Closed 21 December - 04 January

FITZWILLIAM HOTEL

ST. STEPHEN'S GREEN, DUBLIN 2

TEL: 01-478 7000 FAX: 01-478 7878
EMAIL: enq@fitzwilliamhotel.com
WEB: www.fitzwilliamhotel.com

HOTEL U MAP 8 O 11

A modern classic uniquely positioned on St. Stephen's Green, paces away from Grafton Street, Ireland's premier shopping location. Understated luxury, a fresh approach and impeccable service make it the perfect retreat for business and pleasure travellers. Dine in the highly acclaimed Thornton's Restaurant or the fashionable Citron. Facilities include 3 conference rooms, free car parking for residents & Ireland's largest roof garden. Voted by Condé Nast Traveller Magazine as one of the Top 21 Hottest Hotels in the World.

Member of Summit Hotels & Resorts

Room Rate from €280.00 to €380.00

JOHN KAVANAGH
GENERAL MANAGER

American Express
Diners
Mastercard
Visa

130 130

Inet

IRISH HOTELS FEDERATION

Open All Year

FORTE TRAVELODGE

AUBURN AVENUE ROUNDABOUT, NAVAN ROAD, CASTLEKNOCK, DUBLIN 15

TEL: 1800-709709 FAX: 01-820 2151

WEB: www.travelodge.co.uk

HOTEL U MAP 8 O 11

Situated on the N3 route only 5 miles from Dublin City Centre, just off the M50 Dublin ring road and mins from the airport, this superb hotel offers comfortable yet affordable accommodation. Each room is large enough to sleep up to three adults, a child under 12 and a baby in a cot. Price is fixed per room regardless of the number of occupants. Each room has en suite bathroom, colour satellite TV and direct dial phone. Sited next to Little Chef restaurant. Freephone from UK 0800 850 950.

Room Rate from €85.00 to €95.00

BRID LUCKIE

American Express
Diners
Mastercard
Visa

100 100

Open All Year

Room rates are per room per night

FOUR SEASONS HOTEL DUBLIN

SIMMONSCOURT ROAD,
BALLSBRIDGE,
DUBLIN 4

TEL: 01-665 4000 FAX: 01-665 4099
EMAIL: reservations.dublin@fourseasons.com
WEB: www.fourseasons.com/dublin

HOTEL ★★★★★ MAP 8 O 11

The charms of Irish tradition and hospitality combine to provide the stage for Four Seasons Hotel Dublin. Set within the showgrounds of the historic Royal Dublin Society, the hotel brings together 259 exceptional guestrooms and suites with the finest facilities for business and relaxation. Residential in style, the hotel features 15,000 sq ft of meeting and banquet space, fine dining in Seasons Restaurant and an 11,000 sq ft full service spa.

Room Rate from €365.00 to €485.00

JOHN BRENNAN
GENERAL MANAGER

American Express
Diners
Mastercard
Visa

259 259

Open All Year

GEORGE FREDERIC HANDEL HOTEL

16-18 FISHAMBLE STREET,
CHRISTCHURCH, TEMPLE BAR,
DUBLIN 8

TEL: 01-670 9400 FAX: 01-670 9410
EMAIL: info@handelshotel.com
WEB: www.handelshotel.com

HOTEL U MAP 8 O 11

Our secret is out! Centrally located, while situated in the heart of Dublin's vibrant Temple Bar area, the George Frederic Handel Hotel is also within easy walking distance of the city's main tourist attractions and financial districts. We offer a high standard of accommodation combined with a warm Irish welcome - all at a great price. Live online booking system at www.handelshotel.com

B&B from €44.45 to €105.00

SANDRA MACNAMARA
OPERATIONS MANAGER

American Express
Diners
Mastercard
Visa

40 40

Closed 24 - 27 December

GEORGIAN HOTEL

18-22 BAGGOT STREET LOWER,
DUBLIN 2

TEL: 01-634 5000 FAX: 01-634 5100
EMAIL: info@georgianhotel.ie

HOTEL ★★★ MAP 8 O 11

This very comfortable 200 year old house with new extension in the heart of Georgian Dublin, next to St. Stephen's Green and a 5 minute walk to the major sites including Trinity College, galleries, museums, cathedrals, theatres and to fashionable shopping streets and pubs. Bathrooms en suite, TV, ISDN. Perfect location for business or holiday travellers and offers all the amenities of an exclusive hotel. Private car park.

B&B from €57.00 to €105.00

ANNETTE O'SULLIVAN
MANAGING DIRECTOR

American Express
Diners
Mastercard
Visa

47 47

FAX

Open All Year

B&B rates are per person sharing per night incl. Breakfast

GLEN GUESTHOUSE

84 LOWER GARDINER STREET, DUBLIN 1

TEL: 01-855 1374 FAX: 01-855 2506
EMAIL: theglen@eircom.net
WEB: homepage.eircom.net/~theglen

GUESTHOUSE ★★ MAP 8 O 11

The Glen is a beautifully restored and maintained guesthouse. Located in the heart of Dublin City, adjacent to shops, theatres, cinemas, galleries, museums and Dublin's famous night spots. Close to bus and train stations en route to airport. Rooms en suite, TV, direct dial phones, tea and coffee facilities in all rooms.

B&B from €32.00 to €50.00

JOHN MURRAY
MANAGER

Mastercard
Visa

🖐️🛏️☎️💻 T C ♫ P 🍳 S ▤

14 14

Open All Year

GLENOGRA HOUSE

64 MERRION ROAD, BALLSBRIDGE, DUBLIN 4

TEL: 01-668 3661 FAX: 01-668 3698
EMAIL: glenogra@indigo.ie
WEB: www.glenogra.com

GUESTHOUSE ★★★★ MAP 8 O 11

Located opposite the RDS and Four Seasons Hotel, close to city centre, bus, rail, embassies, restaurants, car ferries. Glenogra provides luxury and elegance in a personalised, family run environment. The cosy drawing room is perfect for a restoring afternoon tea. En suite bedrooms are decorated in harmony with a period residence, are all non-smoking with phone, TV, coffee making facilities. Private car parking. AA, RAC ♦♦♦♦.

Member of Premier Guesthouses

Room Rate from €80.00 to €90.00

CHERRY AND SEAMUS MCNAMEE
PROPRIETORS

American Express
Mastercard
Visa

🖐️🛏️☎️💻 T C ❀ P S ▤

12 12

IRISH HOTELS FEDERATION

Closed 20 December - 20 January

GRAFTON CAPITAL HOTEL

STEPHENS STREET LOWER, DUBLIN 2

TEL: 01-648 1100 FAX: 01-648 1122
EMAIL: info@graftoncapital-hotel.com
WEB: www.capital-hotels.com

HOTEL ★★★ MAP 8 O 11

Nestling in the heart of Dublin's most fashionable & cultural areas, your first experience of the Grafton Capital Hotel is that of its traditional Georgian townhouse façade. Thereafter, guests will enjoy the luxury of superb accommodation, affording a wealth of comforts for the discerning guest. Make the most of this prime central location - Grafton St, St Stephens Green and the colourful Temple Bar area, are all a short stroll from the hotel. Restaurants, Cafés Bars & a host of visitor attractions all nearby. Free admission to all Capital Bars/Clubs in Dublin.

Member of Capital Hotels

B&B from €59.00 to €109.00

EIMEAR DOWD
GENERAL MANAGER

American Express
Diners
Mastercard
Visa

🖐️🛏️☎️💻📺 T C 🍷 C M S 🅰️ 🔖 ♿

75 75

inet

IRISH HOTELS FEDERATION

Closed 24 - 26 December

Room rates are per room per night

GRAFTON HOUSE

26-27 SOUTH GREAT GEORGES STREET,
DUBLIN 2

TEL: 01-679 2041 FAX: 01-677 9715
EMAIL: graftonguesthouse@eircom.net

GUESTHOUSE ★★★ MAP 8 O 11

This charming 3*** guesthouse ideally located in the heart of the city within 2 minutes walking distance of Dublin's premier shopping centre Grafton Street, St. Stephen's Green, Trinity College and Dublin Castle. All bedrooms newly decorated with bathroom/shower, direct dial telephone, TV, hairdryers, tea and coffee making facilities. Public car parking close by in enclosed car parks. Grafton House is the ideal location for business or holidays.

B&B from €50.00 to €80.00

BRIDGET COLLINS

Mastercard
Visa

Closed 23 - 30 December

GRESHAM (THE)

23 UPPER O'CONNELL STREET,
DUBLIN 1

TEL: 01-874 6881 FAX: 01-878 7175
EMAIL: info@thegresham.com
WEB: www.gresham-hotels.com

HOTEL ★★★★ MAP 8 O 11

The Gresham, a landmark building in Dublin City Centre, is a four star hotel that has undergone dramatic transformation. You'll enjoy relaxing in our completely renovated and refreshed lobby area & dining in the new contemporary restaurant, 23. The hotel offers 288 bedrooms, including the executive Lavery Wing & 6 penthouse suites. A fully equipped fitness suite and car parking (€10.00 per day) are available at the hotel. Nearby you can enjoy the cultural scene of Temple Bar, the shopping of Grafton Street and Henry Street & a wide variety of restaurants & theatres.

B&B from €85.00 to €165.00

SHAY LIVINGSTONE
GENERAL MANAGER

American Express
Diners
Mastercard
Visa

Weekend specials from €210.00

Open All Year

HARCOURT HOTEL

60 HARCOURT STREET,
DUBLIN 2

TEL: 01-478 3677 FAX: 01-475 2013
EMAIL: reservations@harcourthotel.ie
WEB: www.harcourthotel.ie

HOTEL ★★★ MAP 8 O 11

Centrally located close to Grafton Street and St. Stephen's Green. Once the home to George Bernard Shaw, now more famous for traditional Irish music. All rooms en suite with multi channel TV, direct dial telephone, iron - ironing board & tea/coffee making facilities. Restaurant: Little Ceasars, car parking available locally (chargeable). Self catering apartments also available.

Member of Holiday Ireland Hotels

B&B from €39.00 to €114.00

DANIELLE MCGILL
GENERAL MANAGER

American Express
Diners
Mastercard
Visa

Midweek specials from €177.80

Closed 24 - 26 December

B&B rates are per person sharing per night incl. Breakfast

HARDING HOTEL

COPPER ALLEY,
FISHAMBLE STREET,
DUBLIN 2

TEL: 01-679 6500 FAX: 01-679 6504
EMAIL: harding.hotel@usitworld.com
WEB: www.hardinghotel.ie

HOTEL ★★ MAP 8 O 11

Harding Hotel is a stylish city centre hotel located within Dublin's Temple Bar. This historic area offers the visitor an unrivalled choice of restaurants, cafés, bars and traditional Irish pubs. All 53 en suite rooms have television, direct dial telephone, hairdryer and tea/coffee making facilities. Darkey Kelly's Bar and Restaurant offer exciting array of food and entertainment. Groups and individuals welcome.

Member of USIT Accommodation Centres

Room Rate from €60.00 to €97.00

EDEL KINSELLA
MANAGER

American Express
Mastercard
Visa

Closed 23 - 26 December

HARRINGTON HALL

70 HARCOURT STREET,
DUBLIN 2

TEL: 01-475 3497 FAX: 01-475 4544
EMAIL: harringtonhall@eircom.net
WEB: www.harringtonhall.com

GUESTHOUSE ★★★★ MAP 8 O 11

Harrington Hall with its secure private parking in the heart of Georgian Dublin, provides the perfect location for holiday and business visitors alike to enjoy the surrounding galleries, museums, cathedrals, theatres, fashionable shopping streets, restaurants and pubs. All rooms are equipped to today's exacting standards with en suite, direct dial phone, hospitality tray, trouser press and multi channel TV, access to fax facilities, e-mail and internet. All floors are serviced by elevator. AA ◆◆◆◆ and RAC ◆◆◆◆◆.

B&B from €75.00 to €125.00

HENRY KING
PROPRIETOR

American Express
Diners
Mastercard
Visa

☺ Midweek specials from €200.00

Open All Year

HARVEY'S GUEST HOUSE

11 UPPER GARDINER STREET,
DUBLIN 1

TEL: 01-874 8384 FAX: 01-874 5510
EMAIL: harveysguesthse@iol.ie
WEB: www.harveysguesthouse.com

GUESTHOUSE ★★★ MAP 8 O 11

This fully restored family run Georgian guesthouse provides a friendly atmosphere. Located in the heart of Dublin City and only 700m from O'Connell Bridge and Temple Bar. Conveniently reached by the No 41 or 16 airport bus to Dorset Street and our street, walk back around the corner and up to us on the right after the church. Our en suite facilities include bath/shower and hairdryers. Our car park is free. All rooms have TV and telephone.

B&B from €40.00 to €70.00

EILISH FLOOD
PROPRIETOR

Mastercard
Visa

Closed 23 - 27 December

Room rates are per room per night

HAZELBROOK HOUSE

85 LOWER GARDINER STREET,
DUBLIN 1

TEL: 01-836 5003 FAX: 01-855 0310
EMAIL: hazelbrook@eircom.net
WEB: homepage.eircom.net/~hazelbrook/

GUESTHOUSE U MAP 8 O 11

Hazelbrook House offers superb accommodation with 34 en suite rooms including family rooms. All have remote control TV, iron, tea/coffee facilities and hairdryer. We provide a good Irish breakfast, cater for vegetarians and childrens special needs. Fax/phone on premises. For tourists there are attractions nearby: Trinity College, St Stephens Green and Dublin's trendy Temple Bar area. Our staff are always friendly and, most important, a warm welcome is assured.

B&B from €45.00 to €50.00

DOLORES BURNETT
MANAGER

Mastercard
Visa

🛏️🔥☎️🖥️ T C M P
34 34

Closed 23 - 28 December

HERBERT PARK HOTEL

BALLSBRIDGE,
DUBLIN 4

TEL: 01-667 2200 FAX: 01-667 2595
EMAIL: reservations@herbertparkhotel.ie
WEB: www.herbertparkhotel.ie

HOTEL ★★★★ MAP 8 O 11

Ideally located in Ballsbridge five minutes from the city centre, adjacent to the RDS with spectacular views over 48 acre Herbert Park. All 153 rooms are air-conditioned and appointed to the highest international standards, equipped with mini bar, trouser press, interactive television with internet access and pay per view movies, safe and modem point. The award winning Pavillion Restaurant plays host to live jazz every Sunday. Facilities include cardiovascular gym, meeting rooms, complimentary car parking.

Member of UTELL International

B&B from €80.00 to €175.00

EWAN PLENDERLEITH
DIRECTOR/GENERAL MANAGER

American Express
Diners
Mastercard
Visa

🛏️🔥☎️🖥️ T A C CM❄️ Q U
153 153

🎵 P ♿ aic Inet FAX

IRISH HOTELS FEDERATION

Open All Year

HIBERNIAN HOTEL

EASTMORELAND PLACE,
BALLSBRIDGE,
DUBLIN 4

TEL: 01-668 7666 FAX: 01-660 2655
EMAIL: info@hibernianhotel.com
WEB: www.hibernianhotel.com

HOTEL U MAP 8 O 11

A wonderful red brick Victorian building. This city centre luxury hotel prides itself on the high level of service it offers visitors. A true oasis in which to relax and experience the magic of Dublin. Each bedroom luxuriously appointed with colour multi channel TV, tea/coffee making facilities & exclusive toiletries. Restaurant, full bar & private car parking at hotel. Close to shopping, theatres & museums. Sister hotels McCausland Hotel, Belfast and Woodstock Hotel, Ennis Co. Clare. GDS Acc Code:LX.UK Toll free: 00 800 525 48000

Member of Small Luxury Hotels of the World

B&B from €110.00 to €137.50

BRIEGE DOBBIN
RESIDENT MANAGER

American Express
Diners
Mastercard
Visa

🛏️🔥☎️🖥️ T C CM❄️ U J P S
40 40

♿ aic ♿ Inet

IRISH HOTELS FEDERATION

Closed 24 - 26 December

B&B rates are per person sharing per night incl. Breakfast

HILTON DUBLIN

CHARLEMONT PLACE,
DUBLIN 2

TEL: 01-402 9988 FAX: 01-402 9966
EMAIL: reservations_dublin@hilton.com
WEB: www.dublin.hilton.com

HOTEL U MAP 8 O 11

Overlooking the Grand Canal, the welcoming Hilton Dublin is within walking distance of the main shopping and cultural centre. The Hilton features 189 en suite, well equipped rooms. For that little something extra you can try one of our club rooms, featuring soft bathrobes, mouth-watering chocolates, internet access via the television. Sample our culinary delights in the beautiful surroundings of the Waterfront Restaurant or try Champions Sports Bar. Car parking is available.

Room Rate from €110.00 to €290.00

EOIN LITTLE
OPERATIONS MANAGER

American Express
Diners
Mastercard
Visa

☺ Weekend specials from €176.00

189 189

Inet

IRISH HOTELS FEDERATION

Closed 24 - 27 December

HOLIDAY INN DUBLIN CITY CENTRE

99-107 PEARSE STREET,
DUBLIN 2

TEL: 01-670 3666 FAX: 01-670 3636
EMAIL: info@holidayinndublin.ie
WEB: www.holidayinndublin.ie

HOTEL ★★★ MAP 8 O 11

Located in heart of the city centre, Ireland's first Holiday Inn is within walking distance of Dublin's main tourist attractions, shopping and financial district, Temple Bar, RDS, Point Depot & Lansdowne Road. Featuring 92 beautifully appointed bedrooms, traditional Irish bar, restaurant and 6 conference suites that can accommodate up to 200 people. The hotel boasts a fully equipped residents' gym, and secure underground car parking.

B&B from €64.00 to €100.00

TREVOR SMITH
GENERAL MANAGER

American Express
Diners
Mastercard
Visa

92 92

IRISH HOTELS FEDERATION

Open All Year

HOTEL ISAACS

STORE STREET,
DUBLIN 1

TEL: 01-855 0067 FAX: 01-836 5390
EMAIL: hotel@isaacs.ie
WEB: www.isaacs.ie

HOTEL ★★★ MAP 8 O 11

Situated in the heart of Dublin City, 5 mins by foot from O'Connell Street Bridge, Hotel Isaacs, a converted wine warehouse, is the perfect location for the visitor to Dublin, at the perfect price, close to the shopping & financial centre. All rooms are tastefully furnished & are en suite with telephone, TV, tea/coffee making facilities & iron/ironing board. The restaurant, Il Vignardo, serves great tasting Italian food 7 days a week. Nearby overnight parking available at special rates.

B&B from €55.00 to €95.00

EVELYN HANNIGAN
GENERAL MANAGER

American Express
Mastercard
Visa

☺ Weekend specials from €140.00

58 58

IRISH HOTELS FEDERATION

Closed 23 - 27 December

Room rates are per room per night

HOTEL ST. GEORGE

7 PARNELL SQUARE,
DUBLIN 1

TEL: 01-874 5611 FAX: 01-874 5582
EMAIL: hotels@indigo.ie
WEB: indigo.ie/~hotels

HOTEL U MAP 8 O 11

The historical Hotel St. George is located on Parnell Square at the top of O'Connell Street, Dublin's principal thoroughfare. Within walking distance of the Abbey and the Gate Theatre, Municipal Art Gallery, Dublin's Writers Museum, principal shopping district and other major tourist attractions. Each bedroom is en suite, individually decorated, every modern comfort, including direct dial phone, colour TV and tea/coffee making facilities. Private car park.

B&B from €50.00 to €65.00

JIM STAUNTON
PROPRIETOR

Mastercard
Visa

53 53

HOTELS
FEDERATION

Closed 24 - 27 December

INISHOWEN GUEST HOUSE

199 SOUTH CIRCULAR ROAD,
DUBLIN 8

TEL: 01-453 6272 FAX: 01-454 4564
EMAIL: mcterry1@aol.com

GUESTHOUSE ★★ MAP 8 O 11

Inishowen Guest House, providing comfort and service of a very high standard. Cable TV and secure car park. 10 minutes from city centre. Close to Temple Bar and traditional pubs, excellent restaurants, discos and clubs. Excellent base for exploring Dublin's famed attractions. (Guiness Brewery, Trinity College, Dublin Castle, St. Patrick's Cathedral, Christchurch Cathedral, Kilmainham Museum) buses 19, 121 and 122. We look forward to hosting you and according you a warm welcome.

B&B from €38.00 to €57.00

TERRY MCCABE

Mastercard
Visa

8 4

Closed 20 December - 01 January

IONA HOUSE

5 IONA PARK,
GLASNEVIN,
DUBLIN 9

TEL: 01-830 6217 FAX: 01-830 6732
EMAIL: conradshouldice@btinternet.com

GUESTHOUSE ★★★ MAP 8 O 11

Iona House is a popular 3*** guesthouse near Dublin's City Centre and the Botanic Gardens. We have been under the same management for 40 years and are situated in one of Dublin's tree lined Victorian quarters of charming red brick houses built around the turn of the century. We pride ourselves in presenting rooms of a high standard which are fully en suite, with colour satellite TV and direct dial phone. A comfortable lounge and private garden round off the friendly atmosphere of Iona House.

B&B from €48.00 to €48.00

CONRAD SHOULDICE

American Express
Mastercard
Visa

10 10

HOTELS
FEDERATION

Open All Year

B&B rates are per person sharing per night incl. Breakfast

JACKSON COURT HOTEL

29/30 HARCOURT STREET,
DUBLIN 2

TEL: 01-475 8777 FAX: 01-475 8793
EMAIL: info@jackson-court.ie
WEB: www.jackson-court.ie

HOTEL ★★ MAP 8 O 11

Minutes walk from Grafton Street, Stephens Green and most of Dublin's historic landmarks. Enjoy the combination of local Dubliners and visitors from abroad in our hotel, busy bar and Dublin's hottest night spot, Copper Face Jacks. Rates include full Irish breakfast, night club admission, service and taxes. We look forward to welcoming you!

B&B from € 62.50 to € 62.50

LESLEY-ANNE HAYES
MANAGER

American Express
Mastercard
Visa

Midweek specials available

26 26

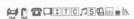

Closed 24 - 28 December

JURYS BALLSBRIDGE HOTEL

PEMBROKE ROAD,
BALLSBRIDGE,
DUBLIN 4

TEL: 01-660 5000 FAX: 01-660 5540
EMAIL: ballsbridge@jurysdoyle.com
WEB: www.jurysdoyle.com

HOTEL ★★★★★ MAP 8 O 11

One of Dublin's top international business hotels, Jurys Ballsbridge is renowned for its genial charm. Luxury accommodation, excellent restaurants and bars, a superb leisure centre and all the charms of the capital close at hand.

TOWERS

LANSDOWNE ROAD, DUBLIN 4
TEL: 01-667 0033 FAX: 01-660 5540
EMAIL: towers@jurysdoyle.com

5 Star Superior hotel adjacent to Jurys Ballsbridge Hotel.

B&B from € 86.00 to € 210.00

RICHARD BOURKE
GENERAL MANAGER

American Express
Diners
Mastercard
Visa

404 404

Open All Year

JURYS GREEN ISLE HOTEL

NAAS ROAD,
DUBLIN 22

TEL: 01-459 3406 FAX: 01-459 2178
EMAIL: greenisle@jurysdoyle.com
WEB: www.jurysdoyle.com

HOTEL ★★★ MAP 8 O 11

Located on the main route from Dublin to the South, the friendly hub of a thriving Dublin South West, Jurys Green Isle is situated away from the hustle and bustle but within comfortable striking distance. Generous rooms, a welcoming bar and restaurant make it the perfect refuge for either the business or leisure guest.

B&B from € 62.00 to € 106.00

JIM FLYNN
GENERAL MANAGER

American Express
Diners
Mastercard
Visa

90 90

Open All Year

Room rates are per room per night

JURYS INN CHRISTCHURCH

CHRISTCHURCH PLACE,
DUBLIN 8

TEL: 01-454 0000 FAX: 01-454 0012
EMAIL: jurysinnchristchurch@jurysdoyle.com
WEB: www.jurysdoyle.com

HOTEL ★★★ MAP 8 O 11

Located in Dublin's oldest quarter in the heart of the city just opposite the historical Christchurch Cathedral, Jurys Inn Christchurch is within easy strolling distance of voguish Temple Bar, St Patrick's Cathedral, Trinity College and fashionable Grafton Street.

Room Rate from €101.00 to €110.00

BOBBY FITZPATRICK
GENERAL MANAGER

American Express
Diners
Mastercard
Visa

182 182

Closed 24 - 26 December

JURYS INN CUSTOM HOUSE

CUSTOM HOUSE QUAY,
DUBLIN 1

TEL: 01-607 5000 FAX: 01-829 0400
EMAIL: jurysinncustomhouse@jurysdoyle.com
WEB: www.jurysdoyle.com

HOTEL ★★★ MAP 8 O 11

Virtually in the shadow of Gandon's magnificent Custom House, from which its named, Jurys Inn Custom House is centrally and attractively located along the river in the International Financial Services Centre. Within easy walking distance are all of the city's main shopping districts and cultural attractions.

Room Rate from €101.00 to €110.00

EDWARD STEPHENSON
GENERAL MANAGER

American Express
Diners
Mastercard
Visa

239 239

Closed 24 - 26 December

JURYS MONTROSE HOTEL

STILLORGAN ROAD,
DUBLIN 4

TEL: 01-269 3311 FAX: 01-269 1164
EMAIL: montrose@jurysdoyle.com
WEB: www.jurysdoyle.com

HOTEL ★★★ MAP 8 O 11

On the main route into the city from Dublin's southside, overlooking the lush grounds of University College Dublin, Jurys Montrose Hotel is just a 10-minute drive from the city centre. Noted for the lively atmosphere and local flavour of its bars and restaurants, its popular appeal is enduring.

B&B from €62.00 to €106.00

CONOR O'KANE
GENERAL MANAGER

American Express
Diners
Mastercard
Visa

179 179

Open All Year

B&B rates are per person sharing per night incl. Breakfast

JURYS TARA HOTEL

MERRION ROAD,
DUBLIN 4

TEL: 01-269 4666 FAX: 01-269 1027
EMAIL: tara@jurysdoyle.com
WEB: www.jurysdoyle.com

HOTEL ★★★ MAP 8 O 11

Along the curve of Dublin Bay with perfect views of the sea and shore, Jurys Tara Hotel is perfectly situated between the city, which is two miles away, and the charming southside villages of Blackrock, Sandycove and Dalkey. A spacious modern hotel, it provides the features and services to make your stay a pleasant one.

B&B from €62.00 to €106.00

GLENN VALENTINE
GENERAL MANAGER

American Express
Diners
Mastercard
Visa

113 113

IRISH HOTELS FEDERATION

Open All Year

KELLYS HOTEL

SOUTH GREAT GEORGES STREET,
DUBLIN 2

TEL: 01-677 9277 FAX: 01-671 3216
EMAIL: kellyhtl@iol.ie
WEB: www.kellyshtl.com

HOTEL U MAP 8 O 11

Situated in the heart of Dublin beside fashionable Grafton Street. A few minutes walk to Trinity College. Temple Bar and many of Dublin's famous pubs and restaurants are on our doorstep. Places of historical, cultural and literary interest are close by. Kelly's is a family run budget hotel of unbeatable value for a city centre location. There is no service charge and our prices include breakfast. Frommers recommended. Parking available in adjacent public multi-storey carpark (for fee). Renovated in 2002.

B&B from €40.00 to €60.00

GERARD LYNAM
PROPRIETOR

American Express
Mastercard
Visa

☺ Midweek specials from €135.00

26 26

IRISH HOTELS FEDERATION

Closed 20 - 26 December

KILRONAN GUESTHOUSE

70 ADELAIDE ROAD,
DUBLIN 2

TEL: 01-475 5266 FAX: 01-478 2841
EMAIL: info@dublinn.com
WEB: www.dublinn.com

GUESTHOUSE ★★★ MAP 8 O 11

This exclusive AA RAC ◆◆◆◆ recommended Georgian House is in a secluded setting, walking distance from St. Stephen's Green, Trinity College, National Concert Hall, Dublin Castle, Cathedrals, St. Patrick's, Christchurch and most of Dublin's historic landmarks. Well appointed bedrooms with private shower, direct dial phone, TV, hairdryers, tea/coffee facilities and quality orthopaedic beds. Commended by New York Times, Beth Byrant, Michelin Guide, Fodors, Frommer & Karen Browns.

Member of Premier Guesthouses

B&B from €44.00 to €76.00

ROSE & TERRY MASTERSON
OWNERS

American Express
Diners
Mastercard
Visa

12 12

IRISH HOTELS FEDERATION

Open All Year

Room rates are per room per night

KINGSWOOD COUNTRY HOUSE

NAAS ROAD,
CLONDALKIN,
DUBLIN 22
TEL: 01-459 2428 FAX: 01-459 2207
EMAIL: kingswoodhse@eircom.net

GUESTHOUSE ★★★ MAP 8 O 11

A warm and welcoming Country House nestling within beautiful walled gardens. Strategically located 3km from the M50 at the beginning of the N7(Naas Road) the gateway to the West and South West. Enjoy the intimate atmosphere of the restaurant which features open fires and sophisticated Irish dishes with a French influence. The seven tastefully decorated bedrooms are all en suite with TV, direct dial phone. Recommended - Egon Ronay, Good Hotel Guide, RAC, AA ◆◆◆◆.

B&B from €60.00 to €74.00

SHEILA O'BYRNE
OWNER/MANAGER

American Express
Diners
Mastercard
Visa

Closed 25 - 26 December

LANSDOWNE HOTEL

27-29 PEMBROKE ROAD,
BALLSBRIDGE,
DUBLIN 4
TEL: 01-668 2522 FAX: 01-668 5585
EMAIL: lanhotel@iol.ie
WEB: www.lansdownehotel.com

HOTEL U MAP 8 O 11

The Lansdowne Hotel is a 3*** Georgian hotel just minutes walk from city centre. We combine olde world charm with modern facilities. Ideally located, with Lansdowne Stadium, RDS, Point Theatre and Dublin's business district just a short stroll. You can relax and enjoy fine Irish cuisine in our Celtic Restaurant or savour the local atmosphere in our Den Bar while enjoying mouth-watering food from our bar menu. We have a fully equipped conference and banqueting hall. Private car park.

Member of MinOtel Ireland Hotel Group

B&B from €62.50 to €105.00

MARGARET ENGLISH
ASSISTANT MANAGER

American Express
Diners
Mastercard
Visa

Closed 23 - 27 December

LE MERIDIEN SHELBOURNE

27 ST. STEPHEN'S GREEN,
DUBLIN 2
TEL: 01-663 4500 FAX: 01-661 6006
EMAIL: shelbourneinfo@lemeridien.com
WEB: www.shelbourne.ie

HOTEL ★★★★★ MAP 8 O 11

Ireland's most distinguished address, provides the ultimate in luxury and service. In the heart of Dublin, overlooking St. Stephen's Green, within walking distance of shopping areas and Dublin's social and cultural life. The hotel has 190 rooms, 2 bars and 2 restaurants. The Lord Mayor's Lounge is a must for afternoon tea. The Shelbourne Club offers exclusive surroundings with fantastic choice of equipment, 18m pool, sauna, steam room, jacuzzi and top class cardiovascular equipment. Strictly over 18s only.
WAP: wap.shelbourne.ie

B&B from €110.00 to €175.00

JEAN RICOUX
GENERAL MANAGER

American Express
Diners
Mastercard
Visa

Weekend specials from €295.00

Open All Year

B&B rates are per person sharing per night incl. Breakfast

LEESON INN DOWNTOWN

24 LOWER LEESON STREET,
DUBLIN 2

TEL: 01-662 2002 FAX: 01-662 1567
EMAIL: leesoninn@iol.ie
WEB: http://www.iol.ie/leesoninn

GUESTHOUSE U   MAP 8 O 11

Located on the fashionable south side of the city centre on the Lesson Street side of St. Stephen's Green. Five minutes from Grafton Street the capital's premier shopping street. Major attractions such as the National Concert Hall, National Gallery, National Museum, Oireachtas (Parliament), Royal Concert Hall, National Gallery, Trinity College, many government buildings, and an abundance of restaurants, theatres, night clubs and bars are all within easy walking distance.

B&B from € 45.00 to € 70.00

DIANA WALDRON
MANAGER

American Express
Diners
Mastercard
Visa

🛏 📞 ▯ T C P ▮ inet
21   21

HOTELS
FEDERATION

Closed 23 - 30 December

LONGFIELDS HOTEL

9/10 FITZWILLIAM STREET LOWER,
DUBLIN 2

TEL: 01-676 1367 FAX: 01-676 1542
EMAIL: info@longfields.ie
WEB: www.longfields.ie

HOTEL ★★★   MAP 8 O 11

Longfield's, a charming and intimate hotel in the heart of Ireland's capital where, with its award winning No. 10 Restaurant, one can relax in oppulence reminiscent of times past. Avid followers of good food guides and well known accommodation publications will have noted numerous accolades bestowed upon this renowned residence. Its central location and its impeccable service make it a must for discerning travellers.

Member of Manor House Hotels

B&B from € 107.00 to € 185.00

CHRIS VOS
GENERAL MANAGER

American Express
Diners
Mastercard
Visa

🛏 📞 ▯ T C ▮ a/c inet
26   26

HOTELS
FEDERATION

Closed 24 - 27 December

LYNAM'S HOTEL

63/64 O'CONNELL STREET,
DUBLIN 1

TEL: 01-888 0886 FAX: 01-888 0890
EMAIL: lynams.hotel@indigo.ie
WEB: www.lynams-hotel.com

HOTEL U   MAP 12 O 11

A boutique style 41 bedroom hotel located on O'Connell Street, close to the GPO and all of Dublin's many attractions. Decorated with elegance and individuality. All rooms are en suite, have direct dial phones and data port. 2 comfortable lounges are provided for guest use and our restaurant offers modern style cuisine. Lynam's Hotel is under the personal management of its owner Mr Gerard Lynam.

B&B from € 60.00 to € 85.00

GERARD LYNAM

American Express
Diners
Mastercard
Visa

☺ Midweek specials from € 149.00

🛏 📞 ▯ T C S ▮ inet
41   41

HOTELS
FEDERATION

Closed 24 - 28 December

Room rates are per room per night

LYNDON GUESTHOUSE

26 GARDINER PLACE,
DUBLIN 1

TEL: 01-878 6950 FAX: 01-878 7420
EMAIL: lyndonh@gofree.indigo.ie

GUESTHOUSE ★★ MAP 8 O 11

Lyndon House is an extremely popular, beautifully restored Georgian guesthouse incorporating modern design. It is excellently located in the heart of Dublin's City Centre off Parnell Square at the top of O'Connell Street & is on 41/41c airport bus route. It is family run, so emphasis is on good value, warm atmosphere and friendly service. Rooms are bathroom en suite, with TV, internal telephone and hospitality tray. Highly Acclaimed AA ◆◆.

B&B from €40.00 to €50.00

CATHERINE CLEARY

Mastercard
Visa

🖐 🕯 ⬜ T C 🛏
9   9

IRISH HOTELS FEDERATION

Open All Year

MAPLE HOTEL

75 LOWER GARDINER STREET,
DUBLIN 1

TEL: 01-874 0225 FAX: 01-874 5239
EMAIL: info@maplehotel.com
WEB: www.maplehotel.com

HOTEL ★★ MAP 8 O 11

The Maple Hotel is situated in the heart of the city, just off O'Connell Street, beside all theatres, cinemas, main railway, bus and DART stations with a direct bus link to Dublin Airport. The hotel is owned and run by the Sharkey Family who have been welcoming guests here for over 38 years. All luxurious bedrooms en suite, colour TV, direct dial phones, hair dryer, coffee/tea facilities. Private car parking.

B&B from €38.00 to €69.85

THE SHARKEY FAMILY

Mastercard
Visa

☺ Midweek specials from €115.00

🖐 🕯 ☎ ⬜ T P S Y
12   12

IRISH HOTELS FEDERATION

Closed 22 December - 16 January

MARIAN GUEST HOUSE

21 UPPER GARDINER STREET,
DUBLIN 1

TEL: 01-874 4129

GUESTHOUSE ★ MAP 8 O 11

Situated in Georgian Dublin, just off Mountjoy Square and five minutes walk from city centre and all principal shopping areas, cinemas, theatres, museums. All our rooms are tastefully decorated, with central heating and all usual amenities are available. There are tea/coffee making facilities. The Marian is family run and you are sure to get a warm welcome. On the 41 bus route from Dublin Airport. Open all year.

B&B from €27.00 to €32.00

CATHRINE MCELROY
OWNER

Mastercard
Visa

🖐 🕯 ⬜ C ✿ P
6   6

IRISH HOTELS FEDERATION

Open All Year

B&B rates are per person sharing per night incl. Breakfast

MCENIFF SKYLON HOTEL

UPPER DRUMCONDRA ROAD,
DUBLIN 9

TEL: 01-837 9121 FAX: 01-837 2778
EMAIL: andrew_hyland@skylon.org
WEB: www.skylon.org

HOTEL ★★★ MAP 8 O 11

A smart hotel on the northern approach, ten minutes from the airport and five from the city centre, McEniff Skylon Hotel has just the right blend of style and informality to make your stay special. Its restaurant and bar are welcoming and just as popular in the neighbourhood as with guests.

Member of McEniff Hotels

Room Rate from €69.00 to €169.00

BRIAN MCENIFF/ANDREW HYLAND
GENERAL MANAGER/DEPUTY MANAGER

American Express
Diners
Mastercard
Visa

☺ Weekend specials from €154.00

88 88

& inet

IRISH
HOTELS
FEDERATION

Closed 24 - 26 December

MERCER HOTEL

MERCER STREET LOWER,
DUBLIN 2

TEL: 01-478 2179 FAX: 01-478 0328
EMAIL: stay@mercerhotel.ie
WEB: www.mercerhotel.ie

HOTEL ★★★ MAP 8 O 11

Luxury boutique style hotel situated in a prime city centre location next to Grafton Street & St. Stephens Green, an ideal base to explore Dublin's main historical sights, theatres, trendy bars and restaurants. 41 superbly appointed en suite rooms. Discreetly blended into the décor is a full complement of modern amenities including individually controlled air conditioning, TV/Video, CD player, trouser press, fax, modem points, DD phone, hairdryer. Conference and restaurant facilities.

Member of Mercer Accommodation Group

B&B from €75.00 to €105.00

DARA MCENEANEY
GENERAL MANAGER

American Express
Diners
Mastercard
Visa

☺ Weekend specials from €180.00

41 41

Inet FAX

IRISH
HOTELS
FEDERATION

Closed 24 - 27 December

MERRION HALL

54 MERRION ROAD,
BALLSBRIDGE,
DUBLIN 4

TEL: 01-668 1426 FAX: 01-668 4280
EMAIL: merrionhall@iol.ie
WEB: www.halpinsprivatehotels.com

GUESTHOUSE ★★★★ MAP 8 O 11

The 4**** Award-winning Merrion Hall offers an elegant combination of Edwardian grace, fine food and modern comforts, all one expects of a private hotel, aircon suites, executive facilities, jacuzzis, 4-poster beds, private carpark & gardens. Adjacent to RDS & Four Seasons Hotel, close to city centre, airport and car ferry terminals by DART or bus. Accolades, AA ◆◆◆◆◆, RAC Property of Year, Times, Bestloved Hotels, Johansens. Sister property of adjoining Blakes, Aberdeen Lodge & Halpins Hotel, Co. Clare. USA toll free 1800 617 3178. UK free phone 0800 096 4748.

Member of Charming Hotels

B&B from €45.00 to €90.00

PAT HALPIN
PROPRIETOR

American Express
Diners
Mastercard
Visa

28 28

alc inet FAX

IRISH
HOTELS
FEDERATION

Open All Year

Room rates are per room per night

MERRION HOTEL

UPPER MERRION STREET,
DUBLIN 2

TEL: 01-603 0600 FAX: 01-603 0700
EMAIL: info@merrionhotel.com
WEB: www.merrionhotel.com

HOTEL ★★★★★ MAP 8 O 11

Dublin's most stylish 5***** hotel is located in the city centre opposite Government Buildings. Created from restored Georgian townhouses, many of the 145 bedrooms and suites overlook 18th century gardens. Bars include The Cellar Bar and the intimate cocktail bar, No 23. Morningtons serves contemporary Irish cuisine while Restaurant Patrick Guilbaud offers formal dining. Other features include an 18m pool, gym, private treatments, steam room and secure private car park.

Member of Leading Hotels of the World

Room Rate from €300.00 to €415.00

PETER MACCANN
GENERAL MANAGER

American Express
Diners
Mastercard
Visa

145 145

I R I S H
HOTELS
FEDERATION

Open All Year

MESPIL HOTEL

MESPIL ROAD,
DUBLIN 4

TEL: 01-667 1222 FAX: 01-667 1244
EMAIL: mespil@leehotels.com
WEB: www.leehotels.com

HOTEL ★★★ MAP 8 O 11

A warm and friendly welcome awaits you at the Mespil Hotel. Situated in the heart of Georgian Dublin overlooking the Grand Canal, offering an ideal city centre location. All 256 en suite guest bedrooms are bright, spacious and tastefully furnished. Relax and unwind in our Terrace Bar or enjoy some tantalising dishes from the Glaze Restaurant. The Mespil is the perfect base from which to discover this bustling capital city.

Member of Lee Hotels

Room Rate from €120.00 to €185.00

MARTIN HOLOHAN
GENERAL MANAGER

American Express
Diners
Mastercard
Visa

256 256

Inet

I R I S H
HOTELS
FEDERATION

Closed 22 - 27 December

MONT CLARE HOTEL

MERRION SQUARE,
DUBLIN 2

TEL: 01-607 3800 FAX: 01-661 5663
EMAIL: montclareres@ocallaghanhotels.ie
WEB: www.ocallaghanhotels.ie

HOTEL ★★★ MAP 8 O 11

The Mont Clare features 74 luxurious fully air conditioned bedrooms, traditional lounge bar, Goldsmith's Restaurant, convention facilities and free private valet parking. Overlooking Merrion Square the Mont Clare Hotel is the ideal city centre location, just a few minutes walk to all major attractions including Trinity College, museums, theatres, exhibition centres and shopping areas. Reservations via UTELL International Worldwide. USA Toll Free Reservations 1800 5699983. On-line bookings: www.ocallaghanhotels.ie

Member of O'Callaghan Hotels

Room Rate from €152.00 to €230.00

LARRY BOWE
GENERAL MANAGER

American Express
Diners
Mastercard
Visa

☺ Weekend specials from €163.00

74 74

Inet

I R I S H
HOTELS
FEDERATION

Open All Year

B&B rates are per person sharing per night incl. Breakfast

MORGAN HOTEL

10 FLEET STREET,
TEMPLE BAR,
DUBLIN 2

TEL: 01-679 3939 FAX: 01-679 3946
EMAIL: sales@themorgan.com
WEB: www.themorgan.com

HOTEL U   MAP 8 O 11

The Morgan is a boutique contemporary hotel offering a lifestyles elegance, with modern chic décor, located in the heart of Dublin's Temple Bar. The Morgan offers a cool modern interior that contrasts from the dynamic street life in the area & provides the ultimate in comfort and luxury for the discerning traveller. All bedrooms including deluxe rooms & suites are individually designed and are equipped with TV/video, mini-hifi, mini bar, voicemail and ISDN lines. On-line bookings, www.themorgan.com

Member of Design & Planet Hotels

Room Rate from €140.00 to €241.00

SANDRA DOYLE
GENERAL MANAGER

American Express
Diners
Mastercard
Visa

61 61

HOTELS
FEDERATION

Closed 24 - 26 December

MORRISON (THE)

LOWER ORMOND QUAY,
DUBLIN 1

TEL: 01-887 2400 FAX: 01-878 3185
EMAIL: info@morrisonhotel.ie
WEB: www.morrisonhotel.ie

HOTEL ★★★★   MAP 8 O 11

One of the most luxurious and sophisticated hotels in Dublin, the Morrison is in the heart of the city overlooking the River Liffey. The 84 superior rooms, 6 stunning suites and the uniquely designed penthouse are decorated in a style which combines the use of natural Irish materials. Features include Halo Restaurant, offering modern European style cooking, the Morrison Bar, Café Bar and Lobo, a late night bar.

Member of Sterling Hotels & Resorts

B&B from €110.00 to €160.00

ANTHONY KENNA
GENERAL MANAGER

American Express
Diners
Mastercard
Visa

94 94

HOTELS
FEDERATION

Closed 24 - 27 December

MOUNT HERBERT HOTEL

HERBERT ROAD,
LANSDOWNE ROAD,
DUBLIN 4

TEL: 01-668 4321 FAX: 01-660 7077
EMAIL: info@mountherberthotel.ie
WEB: www.mountherberthotel.ie

HOTEL U   MAP 8 O 11

This Gracious Victorian residence is 5 mins south of the city centre in Ballsbridge, Dublin's most exclusive area, where most diplomatic embassies are based. Facilities include 185 modern bedrooms, restaurant, licensed bar, coffee bar, sauna, gift shop, conference centre, private car park and picturesque gardens. The Loughran Family has been welcoming guests for over 45 years and it is renowned for its superb value and its warm and friendly atmosphere.

Room Rate from €99.00 to €199.00

MICHELLE SWEENEY
MANAGER

American Express
Diners
Mastercard
Visa

☺ Midweek specials from €150.00

185 185

HOTELS
FEDERATION

Closed 21 - 26 December

Room rates are per room per night

NORTH STAR HOTEL

AMIENS STREET,
DUBLIN 1

TEL: 01-836 3136 FAX: 01-836 3561
EMAIL: norths@regencyhotels.com
WEB: www.regencyhotels.com

HOTEL ★★★ MAP 8 O 11

City centre location directly opposite I.F.S.C., beside Connolly Rail Station & Busarus. Trinity College, St Stephen's Green, main shopping areas & Temple Bar all within walking distance. 90 newly appointed, air-cond. executive bedrooms with 2 luxurious suites. Rooms are en suite with colour TV, DD phone, hairdryer & trouser press. The hotel has been enhanced by a new reception, lobby & restaurant and has excellent meeting facilities with ISDN lines & video conferencing. We have a fully equipped gym with sauna/ changing rooms. 24hr supervised car park.

B&B from €65.00 to €130.00

DAVID KIELY
GENERAL MANAGER

American Express
Diners
Mastercard
Visa

😊 Weekend specials from €105.00

125 125

Inet

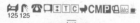

Open All Year

NORTHUMBERLAND LODGE

68 NORTHUMBERLAND ROAD,
BALLSBRIDGE,
DUBLIN 4

TEL: 01-660 5270 FAX: 01-668 8679
EMAIL: info@northumberlandlodge.com
WEB: www.northumberlandlodge.com

GUESTHOUSE ★★★ MAP 8 O 11

Luxurious Victorian house, built in the 1850s, situated in the prestigious embassy belt of Ballsbridge, Dublin 4. Close to the RDS, Shelbourne Park, bus and Dart station city centre. We offer executive accommodation - fully equipped rooms with multi channel TV, DD phone, hairdryer, etc. Secure car parking. A friendly welcome and service is guaranteed.

B&B from €65.00 to €100.00

AVRIL MORDAUNT

Mastercard
Visa

10 10

Open All Year

NUMBER 31

31 LEESON CLOSE,
DUBLIN 2

TEL: 01-676 5011 FAX: 01-676 2929
EMAIL: number31@iol.ie
WEB: www.number31.ie

GUESTHOUSE ★★★★ MAP 8 O 11

An award winning guest house right in the heart of Georgian Dublin. The former home of Ireland's leading architect Sam Stephenson just a few minutes walk from St. Stephen's Green and galleries. An oasis of tranquillity and greenery, where guests are encouraged to come back and relax and feel at home at any time of the day. Vast breakfasts in the dining room or in a sunny plant filled conservatory. Recommended by the Good Hotel Guide, Egon Ronay, Bridgestone 100 Best Places, Fodors.

B&B from €70.00 to €120.00

DEIRDRE & NOEL COMER

American Express
Mastercard
Visa

18 18

Open All Year

B&B rates are per person sharing per night incl. Breakfast

OLD DUBLINER GUESTHOUSE

**62 AMIENS STREET,
DUBLIN 1**

TEL: 01-855 5666 FAX: 01-855 5677
EMAIL: dublinerbb@aol.com
WEB: www.olddubliner.com

GUESTHOUSE ★★★ MAP 8 O 11

The Old Dubliner is a listed Georgian town house that has been completely refurbished to a high standard. All rooms are en suite with TV, phone, hairdryers and tea/coffee making facilities. Situated in the heart of the city close to Connolly Station and central bus station, 10 minutes walk from O'Connell St. and vibrant Temple Bar. Convenient to Point Theatre. Secure car park (limited availability). Our professional and friendly service will ensure a memorable stay.

B&B from €45.00 to €65.00

JOHN O'NEILL

Mastercard
Visa

14 14

IRISH HOTELS FEDERATION

Closed 24 December - 02 January

ORMOND QUAY HOTEL

**7-11 UPPER ORMOND QUAY,
DUBLIN 7**

TEL: 01-872 1811 FAX: 01-872 1362
EMAIL: ormondqh@indigo.ie
WEB: www.ormondquayhotel.net

HOTEL U MAP 8 O 11

Perfectly located overlooking the River Liffey in Dublin City Centre, minutes from Temple Bar and O'Connell Street, the Ormond Quay Hotel is the ideal base for any visitor to Dublin. With 64 en suite rooms, excellent conference & banqueting facilities, stylish Sirens Bar and the Gallery Restaurant, the Ormond Quay Hotel offers you small world charm in the heart of one of Europe's most vibrant capitals.

B&B from €45.00 to €100.00

VERONICA TIMLIN
GENERAL MANAGER

American Express
Mastercard
Visa

64 64

inet

IRISH HOTELS FEDERATION

Open All Year

ORWELL LODGE HOTEL

**77A ORWELL ROAD,
RATHGAR,
DUBLIN 6**

TEL: 01-497 7256 FAX: 01-497 9913
EMAIL: reception@orwelllodgehotel.ie
WEB: www.orwelllodgehotel.ie

HOTEL ★ MAP 8 O 11

The Orwell is a comfortable hotel situated in the leafy garden suburb of Rathgar dating back to the elegant Victorian era. It enjoys a fine reputation for convivial atmosphere and good quality food of an international flavour. Under the personal management of Michael Lynch with friendly qualified staff who ensure that your visit is enjoyable. We serve breakfast, lunch, dinner and bar food. Family and corporate functions are catered for. Off street parking available.

B&B from €65.00 to €95.00

MICHAEL LYNCH
OWNER

American Express
Diners
Mastercard
Visa

10 10

IRISH HOTELS FEDERATION

Closed 23 - 27 December

Room rates are per room per night

O'SHEAS HOTEL

19 TALBOT STREET,
DUBLIN 1

TEL: 01-836 5670 FAX: 01-836 5214
EMAIL: osheashotel@eircom.net
WEB: www.osheashotel.com

HOTEL ★ MAP 8 O 11

O'Sheas Hotel offers a warm and friendly atmosphere and is close to the shopping and cultural centre of Dublin. Its bar and lounge typify everyday life in Ireland offering traditional music seven nights a week. Guests can enjoy a wide and varied menu in our restaurant or bar. Accommodation is en suite with satellite television and we are eager to look after your every need. A new live music venue "Monto" has opened in the refurbished basement at O'Sheas, featuring the best in live, pop, rock music in Dublin.

B&B from € 40.00 to € 50.00

JOHN MCCORMACK
MANAGER

American Express
Diners
Mastercard
Visa

34 34

HOTELS
FEDERATION

Closed 25 December

OTHELLO HOUSE

74 LOWER GARDINER STREET,
DUBLIN 1

TEL: 01-855 4271 FAX: 01-855 7460
EMAIL: othello1@eircom.net

GUESTHOUSE ★★ MAP 8 O 11

Othello is 150m from Abbey Theatre, 200m from Dublin's main O'Connell Street, 50m from central bus station. Number 41 bus direct from Dublin Airport stops outside door. 150m to Connolly Railway Station, 1 mile to ferry terminal, 800m to Point Theatre. Lock up secure car park. All rooms en suite with TV, telephone, tea/coffee making facilities. Trinity College, National Museum, National Library all within walking distance.

B&B from € 45.00 to € 55.00

JOHN GALLOWAY
MANAGER

American Express
Diners
Mastercard
Visa

22 22

HOTELS
FEDERATION

Closed 23 - 26 December

PALMERSTOWN LODGE

PALMERSTOWN VILLAGE,
DUBLIN 20

TEL: 01-623 5494 FAX: 01-623 6214
EMAIL: info@palmerstownlodge.com
WEB: www.palmerstownlodge.com

GUESTHOUSE ★★★ MAP 8 O 11

Prime location adjacent to all amenities and facilities this superb purpose-built property adjoins the N4/M50 motorway. Minutes from the city centre and a mere 12 minutes drive to the airport we offer all the features and standards of a luxury hotel. Each elegant en suite bedroom has individual temperature control, ambient lighting, automated door locking system, phone, TV, etc. Separate tea/coffee and iron/trouser press facilities. Private car park. Golf Packages available.

B&B from € 40.00 to € 60.00

GERRY O'CONNOR
OWNER

Mastercard
Visa

19 19

HOTELS
FEDERATION

Open All Year

B&B rates are per person sharing per night incl. Breakfast

PARAMOUNT HOTEL

**PARLIAMENT STREET & ESSEX GATE,
TEMPLE BAR,
DUBLIN 2**

TEL: 01-417 9900 FAX: 01-417 9904
EMAIL: paramount@iol.ie
WEB: www.paramounthotel.ie

HOTEL ★★★ MAP 8 O 11

Set in the heart of Dublin's Temple Bar, the Paramount is one of the city's most trendy and cosmopolitan hotels. Opened in 1999 the hotel's 66 deluxe en suite bedrooms are a splendid collection of carefully designed, superbly fitted guestrooms with generous space and comfort. Our busy stylish bar, The Turks Head, is open late 7 nights a week and is renowned for its extravagant design, complemented by mosaic and Spanish style architecture. Also contactable at Email: info@turkshead.ie and Website: www.turkshead.ie

B&B from € 99.00 to € 220.00

RITA BARCOE
GENERAL MANAGER

American Express
Mastercard
Visa

66 66

Closed 24 - 28 December

PHOENIX PARK HOUSE

**38-39 PARKGATE STREET,
DUBLIN 8**

TEL: 01-677 2870 FAX: 01-679 9769
EMAIL: info@dublinguesthouse.com
WEB: www.dublinguesthouse.com

GUESTHOUSE ★★ MAP 8 O 11

This friendly AA listed family run guesthouse directly beside the Phoenix Park with its many facilities is ideally located 2 minutes walk from Heuston Station with direct bus service to ferry ports, Dublin Airport, Connolly Train Station and central bus station. Close to the Guinness Brewery, Whiskey Corner, the re-located National Museum and Kilmainham Museum of Modern Art, the popular Temple Bar and numerous pubs and restaurants. Secure car parking available nearby.

B&B from € 35.00 to € 55.00

MARY SMITH & EMER SMITH
PROPRIETORS

American Express
Diners
Mastercard
Visa

25 25

Closed 23 - 28 December

PLAZA HOTEL

**BELGARD ROAD,
TALLAGHT,
DUBLIN 24**

TEL: 01-462 4200 FAX: 01-462 4600
EMAIL: reservations@plazahotel.ie
WEB: www.plazahotel.ie

HOTEL ★★★★ MAP 8 O 11

120 bedrooms, 2 suites. Convenient location on Belgard Road, just off the M50 motorway, 8 miles from the city centre. Secure underground car parking. Extensive conference & banqueting facilities for up to 220 people. Floor one serving food from 9.00am - 10.00pm Mon-Sat. Obar1 music bar. The Playhouse Nightclub. Grumpy McClafferty's traditional pub. 20 minutes from Dublin Airport.

Room Rate from € 100.00 to € 170.00

JIM LAVERY
GENERAL MANAGER

American Express
Diners
Mastercard
Visa

122 122

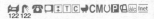

Closed 24 - 30 December

Room rates are per room per night

PORTOBELLO HOTEL & BAR

33 SOUTH RICHMOND STREET,
DUBLIN 2

TEL: 01-475 2715 FAX: 01-478 5010
EMAIL: portobellohotel@indigo.ie
WEB: www.portobellohotel.ie

HOTEL U MAP 8 O 11

This landmark building is located in the heart of Dublin City along the Grand Canal. First opened in 1793, the Portobello Hotel & Bar boasts a long tradition in hospitality and provides guests with luxury en suite accommodation with tea/coffee making facilities, TV, radio, iron & board, direct dial phone & hair dryer. Kostello's night club popular with all ages.

B&B from €50.00 to €65.00

URSULA FOX
MANAGER

American Express
Diners
Mastercard
Visa

FAX

Open All Year

PRINCIPAL HOTEL

19/20 FLEET STREET,
TEMPLE BAR,
DUBLIN 2

TEL: 01-670 8122 FAX: 01-670 8103
EMAIL: bewleyshotel@eircom.net
WEB: www.bewleysprincipalhotel.com

HOTEL ★★★ MAP 8 O 11

Located in the heart of the city. We offer the finest traditions of quality and service from the Principal Hotel. Our location makes us an ideal base for both business or pleasure. Completely refurbished in early 2000. Some bedrooms have air conditioning, all are equipped to the highest standards. A warm welcome awaits you.

B&B from €50.00 to €100.00

PATRICK CARNEY
GENERAL MANAGER

American Express
Diners
Mastercard
Visa

Midweek specials from €130.00

Closed 24 - 27 December

QUALITY CHARLEVILLE HOTEL AND SUITES

LOWER RATHMINES ROAD,
DUBLIN 6

TEL: 01-406 6100 FAX: 01-406 6200
EMAIL: info@charlevillehotel.com
WEB: www.qualitycharlevillehotel.com

HOTEL ★★★ MAP 8 O 11

Located in the bustling area of Rathmines, just over the Grand Canal. A fifteen minute walk will take you to the heart of the city where you can visit Grafton Street, Temple Bar and Trinity College. The hotel is contemporary in style, all rooms have CD player, remote control TV, trouser press, tea/coffee station. Carmines Restaurant is open seven nights, and Tramco Theme Bar offers free admission to residents. Free car parking available.

Member of Choice Hotels Ireland

Room Rate from €69.00 to €220.00

JOANNA DOYLE
GENERAL MANAGER

American Express
Diners
Mastercard
Visa

Midweek specials from €119.00

Inet FAX

Open All Year

B&B rates are per person sharing per night incl. Breakfast

QUALITY HOTEL & SUITES

NAAS ROAD,
CO. DUBLIN

TEL: 01-458 7000 FAX: 01-458 7019
EMAIL: info@qualitycitywest.com
WEB: www.naasqualityhotel.com

HOTEL N MAP 8 O 11

Conveniently located within minutes drive of the M50 Motorway on the N7 Dublin-Cork route and 8 miles from Dublin City Centre. Hotel is a unique concept in hotel and suite accommodation, nestled in the foothills of the Dublin Mountains, adjacent to Christy O'Connor designed Citywest Golf & Country Club. Hotel comprises 7 separate buildings. In addition to spacious bedrooms, the hotel offers one & two bedroom suites with a lounge, dining area & kitchenette. Free car parking, friendly residents' lounge plus Lannigans Restaurant.

Member of Choice Hotels International

B&B from €40.00 to €100.00

PAUL DEMPSEY
GENERAL MANAGER

American Express
Diners
Mastercard
Visa

Midweek specials from €152.00

144 144

Closed 24 - 28 December

RAGLAN LODGE

10 RAGLAN ROAD,
BALLSBRIDGE,
DUBLIN 4

TEL: 01-660 6697 FAX: 01-660 6781

GUESTHOUSE ★★★★ MAP 8 O 11

Raglan Lodge is a magnificent Victorian residence dating from 1861. It is just ten minutes from the heart of Dublin in a most peaceful location. There are seven guest rooms, all of which have bathrooms en suite, colour TV, radio/alarm, telephone and tea/coffee facilities. Several of the rooms are noteworthy for their fine proportions and high ceilings. National winner of the Galtee Irish Breakfast Award. Secure car parking facilities. Recommended by RAC, AA and Egon Ronay. Also, received breakfast award in Georgina Campbell's Jameson Guide 2001.

B&B from €50.80 to €69.85

HELEN MORAN
PROPRIETRESS

American Express
Diners
Mastercard
Visa

7 7

HOTELS
FEDERATION

Closed 22 December - 07 January

RATHMINES CAPITAL HOTEL

LOWER RATHMINES ROAD,
DUBLIN 6

TEL: 01-496 6966 FAX: 01-491 0603
EMAIL: info@rathminescapital-hotel.com
WEB: www.capital-hotels.com

HOTEL ★★★ MAP 8 O 11

Enjoy the best of both worlds, Dublin city 5 minutes by car, whilst guests travelling to/from all major cities nationwide, enjoy easy & direct access from the M50 link road. Regular bus service to the city nearby. Relax in comfortable, spacious accommodation, where a genuinely warm welcome awaits. Experience our stylish cosmopolitan "Savannah" café bar, or explore this lively district with its many bars, restaurants, shops & cafés. RDS exhibition centre, Lansdowne Rd sporting ground & Harolds Cross dog racing - all nearby.

Member of Capital Hotels

B&B from €45.00 to €70.00

FRANCES DEMPSEY
GENERAL MANAGER

American Express
Diners
Mastercard
Visa

54 54

HOTELS
FEDERATION

Closed 24 - 26 December

Room rates are per room per night

RED COW MORAN HOTEL

RED COW COMPLEX,
NAAS ROAD,
DUBLIN 22
TEL: 01-459 3650 FAX: 01-459 1588
EMAIL: reservations@morangroup.ie
WEB: www.redcowhotel.com

HOTEL ★★★★ MAP 8 O 11

4**** Red Cow Moran Hotel combines classic elegance with modern design, situated at the Gateway to the Provinces, convenient to city centre, minutes drive from Dublin Airport. Bedrooms are fully air-conditioned with colour teletext TV, direct dial phones/fax, hairdryer, trouser press & tea/coffee facilities. The complex boasts a choice of lively bars and features two superb restaurants and a carvery restaurant, conference facilities, babysitting service on request. Night Club. Free carparking. AA 4****. A Moran Hotel.

B&B from €60.00 to €125.00

TOM & SHEILA MORAN
PROPRIETORS

American Express
Diners
Mastercard
Visa

123 123

Closed 24 - 26 December

REGENCY AIRPORT HOTEL

SWORDS ROAD,
WHITEHALL,
DUBLIN 9
TEL: 01-837 3544 FAX: 01-836 7121
EMAIL: regency@regencyhotels.com
WEB: www.regencyhotels.com

HOTEL ★★★ MAP 8 O 11

The Regency Hotel is located 3km north of Dublin's city centre on main route to Dublin's International Airport and Northern Ireland. All rooms are en suite with colour TV, DD phone and tea/coffee making facilities. The hotel incorporates 70 executive rooms with hairdryers and trouser press as standard. The hotel features the Shanard Restaurant, the Appian Lounge. Rooks Theme Restaurant is renowned for its steaks, chicken and pasta dishes with seating for 200. The hotel has ample parking.

B&B from €75.00 to €130.00

BRIAN MCGETTIGAN
GENERAL MANAGER

American Express
Diners
Mastercard
Visa

Weekend specials from €105.00

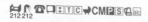
212 212

Open All Year

RIVER HOUSE HOTEL

23/24 EUSTACE STREET,
TEMPLE BAR,
DUBLIN 2
TEL: 01-670 7655 FAX: 01-670 7650
EMAIL: riverhousehotel@compuserve.com

HOTEL U MAP 8 O 11

A downtown Dublin hotel located in Dublin's colourful and exciting Temple Bar area. With its cobbled streets, shops, art galleries, bars, restaurants and lively night life, Temple Bar has become a tourist attraction itself. All of our 29 bedrooms are en suite and have tea/coffee making facilities, remote control TV, radio, hairdryer and direct dial telephone. Hotel facilities include Danger Doyles Bar and the sound proofed The Zazu Nightclub.

B&B from €42.50 to €80.00

SHEELAGH CONWAY
PROPRIETOR

American Express
Diners
Mastercard
Visa

Midweek specials from €90.00

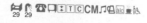
29 29

Closed 24 - 27 December

B&B rates are per person sharing per night incl. Breakfast

ROYAL DUBLIN HOTEL

O'CONNELL STREET,
DUBLIN 1

TEL: 01-873 3666 FAX: 01-873 3120
EMAIL: enq@royaldublin.com
WEB: www.royaldublin.com

HOTEL ★★★   MAP 8 O 11

Located in the heart of the city on Dublin's most famous street, O'Connell Street. Perfect base from which to explore shops, theatres, museums and galleries. Guest rooms include hairdryer, tea/coffee making facilities, direct dial telephone and all are en suite. Relax in the elegant Georgian Room or enjoy the lively Raffles Bar. Excellent food available all day in the Café Royale Brasserie. Secure car park available.

Room Rate from € 120.00 to € 240.00

DARRAGH BRADY
GENERAL MANAGER

American Express
Diners
Mastercard
Visa

117 117

Inet

IRISH
HOTELS
FEDERATION

Open All Year

SACHS HOTEL

19-29 MOREHAMPTON ROAD,
DONNYBROOK,
DUBLIN 4

TEL: 01-668 0995 FAX: 01-668 6147

HOTEL ★★   MAP 8 O 11

Set in a quiet exclusive south city location, yet only a short stroll from the heart of Dublin. A unique blend of Georgian excellence and modern amenities. You will feel the warmth of our welcome and the charm of the traditional decor. Spacious bedrooms individually designed and with en suite, colour TV and direct dial phone. Extensive conference and banqueting facilities.

B&B from € 53.96 to € 95.23

ANN BYRNE
MANAGER

American Express
Diners
Mastercard
Visa

20 20

IRISH
HOTELS
FEDERATION

Open All Year

SCHOOL HOUSE HOTEL

2-8 NORTHUMBERLAND ROAD,
BALLSBRIDGE,
DUBLIN 4

TEL: 01-667 5014 FAX: 01-667 5015
EMAIL: reservations@schoolhousehotel.com
WEB: www.schoolhousehotel.com

HOTEL ★★★★   MAP 8 O 11

Situated in the heart of one of Dublin's most fashionable districts the hotel offers superb accommodation, good food and lively pub. All 31 bedrooms are furnished to the highest international standard, catering for both business and leisure visitors to the capital. Located just a short walk from the commercial, cultural and entertainment heart of the city, the School House Hotel is poised to become one of the city's leading new hotels.

Member of Sweeney Hotels

B&B from € 70.00 to € 125.00

MAUREEN CAFFERKEY
GENERAL MANAGER

American Express
Diners
Mastercard
Visa

☺ 2 nights special B&B from
€170.00 p.p.s.

31 31

Inet

IRISH
HOTELS
FEDERATION

Closed 24 - 27 December

Room rates are per room per night

SHELDON PARK HOTEL & LEISURE CENTRE

KYLEMORE ROAD,
DUBLIN 12

TEL: 01-460 1055 FAX: 01-460 1880
EMAIL: info@sheldonpark.ie
WEB: www.sheldonpark.ie

HOTEL ★★★   MAP 8 O 11

Warm and friendly, the Sheldon Park Hotel is ideally situated just 20 mins from Dublin Airport and 20 mins from the city centre. Just off the M50, we offer easy access to Ireland's most scenic country routes. Spend a relaxing day in our leisure centre, complete with swimming pool, sauna and jacuzzi and finish with a meal in our bistro style restaurant followed by live entertainment.

B&B from €80.00 to €160.00

DONNACHA ROCHE
GENERAL MANAGER

American Express
Diners
Mastercard
Visa

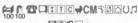
100 100

Closed 24 - 26 December

ST. AIDEN'S GUESTHOUSE

32 BRIGHTON ROAD,
RATHGAR,
DUBLIN 6

TEL: 01-490 2011 FAX: 01-492 0234
EMAIL: staidens@eircom.net

GUESTHOUSE ★★★   MAP 8 O 11

St. Aiden's charming family-run guesthouse is modernised to the highest standard of comfort and elegance while preserving its early Victorian character. Located in one of Dublin's most prestigious areas. 15 mins from city centre on an excellent bus route, 10 mins from the M50 with its links to the airport and national routes, private parking at rear. Hospitality tray and books are provided in lovely drawing room. Under the personal care of Maura O'Carroll and recommended AA ♦♦♦.

B&B from €40.00 to €60.00

MAURA O'CARROLL
PROPRIETRESS

Mastercard
Visa

8 8

Open All Year

ST. ANDREWS

1 LAMBAY ROAD,
DRUMCONDRA,
DUBLIN 9

TEL: 01-837 4684 FAX: 01-857 0446
EMAIL: andrew@dublinn.com
WEB: www.dublinn.com/andrew

GUESTHOUSE ★★★   MAP 8 O 11

Welcome to St Andrews, situated 10 mins from city centre, airport & car ferry. Refurbished to a Bord Failte high standard, we offer a variety of en suite rooms with direct dial phone, multi-channel TV, hairdryer. Hospitality trolley is provided in guests' lounge. Excellent base for exploring the famed attractions of Dublin - Temple Bar, Grafton St, Trinity College, museums, theatres, galleries, etc. Recommended by AA and RAC. Recently awarded the Sparkling Diamond accolade by RAC.

Member of Premier Guesthouses

B&B from €38.00 to €42.00

EILEEN LYNCH
OWNER

Mastercard
Visa

13 13

Open All Year

B&B rates are per person sharing per night incl. Breakfast

STAUNTONS ON THE GREEN

**83 ST. STEPHEN'S GREEN,
DUBLIN 2**

TEL: 01-478 2300 FAX: 01-478 2263
EMAIL: stauntonsonthegreen@eircom.net
WEB: www.stauntons.net

GUESTHOUSE ★★★ MAP 8 O 11

Large Georgian house overlooking St. Stephen's Green, own private gardens. All rooms are en suite and fully equipped with direct dial telephone, TV and tea/coffee welcoming trays, trouser press and hairdryer. It is close to museums, galleries, Grafton Street shopping area and many other major tourist attractions. Stauntons On the Green occupies one of Dublin's most prestigious locations, close to many corporate headquarters and government buildings.

B&B from €70.00 to €83.00

JOANNE NORMAN

American Express
Diners
Mastercard
Visa

🛏️ 📞 ⬛ T C ➡️ ❄️ S ⬛
30 30

Closed 24 - 27 December

STEPHEN'S GREEN HOTEL

**ST. STEPHEN'S GREEN,
DUBLIN 2**

TEL: 01-607 3600 FAX: 01-661 5663
EMAIL: stephensgreenres@ocallaghanhotels.ie
WEB: www.ocallaghanhotels.ie

HOTEL ★★★★ MAP 8 O 11

A shoppers haven, this de luxe boutique hotel is just a 2 minute walk from Grafton Street shops and cafés. The hotel is a splendid craft of Georgian elegance and contemporary style with a four storey glass atrium overlooking St. Stephen's Green. 64 luxurious air conditioned guestrooms and 11 suites, restaurant, traditional bar, gymnasium and business centre. Car parking. USA Toll Free Reservations 1800 569 9983 or online at www.ocallaghanhotels.ie

Member of O'Callaghan Hotels

Room Rate from €219.00 to €335.00

SALLY HUGHES
GENERAL MANAGER

American Express
Diners
Mastercard
Visa

🚩

😊 Weekend specials from €215.00

🛏️ 📞 ⬛ T CM 🅿️ 🔒 alc ⬛
75 75

Inet

HOTELS
FEDERATION

Open All Year

TAVISTOCK HOUSE

**64 RANELAGH ROAD,
RANELAGH,
DUBLIN 6**

TEL: 01-498 8000 FAX: 01-498 8000
EMAIL: info@tavistockhouse.com
WEB: www.tavistockhouse.com

GUESTHOUSE ★★★ MAP 8 O 11

Magnificent Victorian house, tastefully converted retaining all its original plasterwork - very homely. Situated on the city side of Ranelagh Village, on the corner of Ranelagh / Northbrook Roads. We are only 7 mins walk from Stephen's Green in the heart of Dublin, near Helen Dillon's world famous garden. All rooms have colour TV, direct dial phone, hair dryer and tea/coffee making facilities. Private parking. There is a wide variety of restaurants locally. Internet facilities.

B&B from €38.00 to €90.00

MAUREEN & BRIAN CUSACK
CO-OWNERS

American Express
Mastercard
Visa

🛏️ 📞 ⬛ T C ➡️ ❄️ P 🔒 ⬛
6 6

HOTELS
FEDERATION

Open All Year

Room rates are per room per night

CO. DUBLIN
DUBLIN CITY

TEMPLE BAR HOTEL

FLEET STREET,
TEMPLE BAR,
DUBLIN 2
TEL: 01-677 3333 FAX: 01-677 3088
EMAIL: reservations@tbh.ie
WEB: www.templebarhotel.com

HOTEL ★★★ MAP 8 O 11

A Tower Group Hotel - situated in the heart of Dublin's Temple Bar, in close proximity to theatres, shops and restaurants, the Temple Bar Hotel features 129 en suite bedrooms fully equipped with modern facilities. Restaurant. Conference and meeting room facilities for up to 70 people. The Temple Bar Hotel is within easy access of train stations, airport and Dublin port. There is a multi storey car park nearby.

Member of Tower Hotel Group

B&B from €75.00 to €110.00

JOHN CAFFERY
GENERAL MANAGER

American Express
Diners
Mastercard
Visa

129 129

Closed 24 - 26 December

TRINITY CAPITAL HOTEL

PEARSE STREET,
DUBLIN 2
TEL: 01-648 1000 FAX: 01-648 1010
EMAIL: info@trinitycapital-hotel.com
WEB: www.capital-hotels.com

HOTEL ★★★ MAP 8 O 11

Enjoy Dublin City on your doorstep. With a prime central location close to Grafton St, Temple Bar & several places of interest, guests will enjoy the classic contemporary style of this new hotel. Relax in superb accommodation & enjoy our mediterranean style dining menu. Choose the mellow lobby bar for a selection of wines & coffees or the ultimate three-level, themed nightclub adjacent, "Fireworks". Residents avail of complimentary admission to all 12 leading Capital bars and nightclubs.

Member of Capital Hotels

B&B from €59.00 to €109.00

JOSEPHINE PEPPER

American Express
Diners
Mastercard
Visa

82 82

Closed 24 - 26 December

TRINITY LODGE

12 SOUTH FREDERICK STREET,
DUBLIN 2
TEL: 01-679 5044 FAX: 01-679 5223
EMAIL: trinitylodge@eircom.net
WEB: www.trinitylodge.com

GUESTHOUSE ★★★ MAP 8 O 11

Situated in the heart of Dublin, Trinity Lodge offers superb en suite accommodation in a traditional Georgian townhouse. You will find all of Dublin's business, shopping and historic centres right on our doorstep and you are just steps away from Grafton Street, Trinity College and vibrant Temple Bar. Each room, from our singles to our 650 sq' suites, is equipped with air conditioning, personal safe, satellite TV, radio alarm, tea/coffee facilities and trouser press.

B&B from €75.00 to €160.00

PETER MURPHY
MANAGING DIRECTOR

American Express
Diners
Mastercard
Visa

10 10

Closed 23 - 26 December

B&B rates are per person sharing per night incl. Breakfast

UPPERCROSS HOUSE

26-30 UPPER RATHMINES ROAD, DUBLIN 6

TEL: 01-497 5486 FAX: 01-497 5361
EMAIL: uppercrosshotel@ireland.com
WEB: www.uppercrosshousehotel.com

HOTEL ★★★   MAP 8 O 11

Uppercross House is a hotel providing 49 bedrooms of the highest standard of comfort. All with direct dial phone, TV, tea/coffee maker, central heating and all en suite. Uppercross House has its own secure parking and is ideally situated in Dublin's south side 2km from St. Stephen's Green and R.D.S., with excellent public transport from directly outside the door. A fully licensed restaurant and bar opens nightly with a warm and friendly atmosphere.

B&B from €50.00 to €80.00

DAVID MAHON
PROPRIETOR

American Express
Diners
Mastercard
Visa

Closed 23 - 30 December

WALTONS HOTEL

2-5 NORTH FREDERICK, DUBLIN 1

TEL: 01-878 3131 FAX: 01-878 3090
EMAIL: waltonshotel@eircom.net

HOTEL U   MAP 8 O 11

City centre Georgian Hotel, opened in 1998. Fabulous views of the historical Findlater's Church. Offers individually furnished traditional rooms. All rooms en suite with TV, telephone and beverage maker. Secure parking available. This famous building is the home of Waltons Music Store.

Member of Castle Hotel Group

B&B from €50.00 to €70.00

YVONNE EVANS
MANAGERESS

Mastercard
Visa

 Special offers available

Closed 23 - 27 December

WATERLOO HOUSE

8-10 WATERLOO ROAD, BALLSBRIDGE, DUBLIN 4

TEL: 01-660 1888 FAX: 01-667 1955
EMAIL: waterloohouse@eircom.net
WEB: www.waterloohouse.ie

GUESTHOUSE ★★★★   MAP 8 O 11

A warm welcome awaits you at this luxury guesthouse, in the heart of Georgian Dublin. It comprises 2 Georgian houses, refurbished to superb standard, retaining original features, offering unique atmosphere, style, elegance. Minutes from; RDS, St. Stephen's Green, Grafton Street, city centre. Delicious breakfast is served in the dining room, overlooking conservatory & gardens. Lift & carpark. Recommended: Bridgestone 100 Best Places, Alister Sawday's, Michelin Guide and AA ◆◆◆◆◆.

B&B from €59.00 to €99.00

EVELYN CORCORAN
PROPRIETOR

Mastercard
Visa

Closed 23 - 28 December

Room rates are per room per night

WATERLOO LODGE

23 WATERLOO ROAD,
BALLSBRIDGE,
DUBLIN 4

TEL: 01-668 5380 FAX: 01-668 5786
EMAIL: info@waterloolodge.com
WEB: www.waterloolodge.com

GUESTHOUSE ★★★ MAP 8 O 11

Waterloo Lodge is centrally located in Ballsbridge on the south side of Dublin City. Just minutes walk from the city centre, Stephen's Green, Temple Bar, museums, theatres, restaurants and pubs with a bus route outside our door. Our rooms are en suite, tastefully decorated, have direct dial phone, cable TV and hairdryer. Most are non-smoking. Fax and email facilities are available. We assure you of a warm welcome and a pleasant stay.

B&B from €35.00 to €70.00

CATHAL DALY
OWNER

Mastercard
Visa

10 10

Closed 24 - 26 December

WEST COUNTY HOTEL

CHAPELIZOD,
DUBLIN 20

TEL: 01-626 4011 FAX: 01-623 1378
EMAIL: info@westcountyhotel.ie
WEB: www.westcountyhotel.ie

HOTEL ★★ MAP 8 O 11

The West County Hotel, an established family run hotel, located in the picturesque village of Chapelizod. Situated just off the N4 & close to the M50 motorway, which makes it convenient to both Dublin Airport (10 miles) and Dublin City Centre (4 miles). Our hotel comprises 50 en suite bedrooms, which are fully equipped with TV, DD phone, tea/coffee making facilities, ironing board and hairdryer. Food is served all day. A warm and friendly welcome awaits you at the West County Hotel.

B&B from €60.00 to €80.00

VINCENT O'CONNOR
GENERAL MANAGER

American Express
Diners
Mastercard
Visa

50 50

Closed 24 - 26 December

WESTBURY (THE)

GRAFTON STREET,
DUBLIN 2

TEL: 01-679 1122 FAX: 01-679 7078
EMAIL: westbury@jurysdoyle.com
WEB: www.jurysdoyle.com

HOTEL ★★★★★ MAP 8 O 11

Smartly set just off Grafton Street in the very heart of the city, The Westbury can best be described as a truly international 5-star hotel; sophisticated, stylish and at the glamorous hub of Dublin life. Luxury, impeccable service, smart contemporary surroundings with the city at your feet.

Member of Leading Hotels of the World

B&B from €175.00 to €260.00

PARAIC DOYLE
GENERAL MANAGER

American Express
Diners
Mastercard
Visa

204 204

 Inet FAX

Open All Year

B&B rates are per person sharing per night incl. Breakfast

WESTIN DUBLIN

AT COLLEGE GREEN,
WESTMORELAND STREET,
DUBLIN 2
TEL: 01-645 1000 FAX: 01-645 1234
EMAIL: reservations.dublin@westin.com
WEB: www.westin.com

HOTEL ★★★★★ MAP 8 O 11

Situated in the best city location. Ideal for business and leisure travellers. Offering an ambience of warmth and Irish hospitality with the international level of service and amenities that are uniquely Westin. The Exchange Restaurant offers a blend of local and international dishes. The Mint Bar, creatively transformed from the original bank's vaults. The Atrium Lounge housed in the former bank building, with its magnificent glass roof. The Banking Hall, dating from 1863, has been timelessly restored to its original 19th century splendour.

Room Rate from €215.00 to €402.00

ENDA M MULLIN
GENERAL MANAGER

American Express
Diners
Mastercard
Visa

164 164

Open All Year

GLANDORE HOUSE

GLANDORE PARK, LWR MOUNTTOWN,
ROAD, DUN LAOGHAIRE,
CO. DUBLIN
TEL: 01-280 3143 FAX: 01-280 2675
EMAIL: info@glandorehouse.com
WEB: www.glandorehouse.com

GUESTHOUSE ★★★ MAP 8 P 11

Staying at Glandore House allows visitors to take a step back into a more gracious era while at the same time offering the most modern guesthouse facilities. All rooms are en suite with TV, direct dial phone, tea/coffee facilities. Trouser press/ironing centre. A 6 person lift and off street car parking is also available. Situated 5 minutes drive from Dun Laoghaire Ferry Terminal, DART Station and bus terminals, therefore offering easy accessibility to the city centre and surrounding areas.

B&B from €40.00 to €58.00

GRAINNE JACKMAN
MANAGER

Mastercard
Visa

12 12

Closed 19 December - 30 January

Room rates are per room per night

GRESHAM ROYAL MARINE

MARINE ROAD,
DUN LAOGHAIRE,
CO. DUBLIN

TEL: 01-280 1911 FAX: 01-280 1089
EMAIL: info@gresham-royalmarinehotel.com
WEB: www.gresham-hotels.com

HOTEL ★★★ MAP 8 O 11

This elegant 19th century hotel, with panoramic views of Dublin Bay and the picturesque port of Dun Laoghaire, is set in its own landscaped gardens and features 103 bedrooms, including 8 Victorian four-poster suites. The elegant Bay Lounge, Toddy's Bar, and the Powerscourt Room Restaurant provide the ideal location to unwind. Only 20 mins to city centre by rapid rail or bus. Excellent conference facilities. Complimentary car parking. AA, RAC and Egon Ronay recommended.

B&B from €120.00 to €170.00

RONAN WALSH
GENERAL MANAGER

American Express
Diners
Mastercard
Visa

Weekend specials from €135.00

103 103

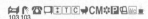

Open All Year

KINGSTON HOTEL

ADELAIDE ST., (OFF GEORGES ST.),
DUN LAOGHAIRE,
CO. DUBLIN

TEL: 01-280 1810 FAX: 01-280 1237
EMAIL: reserv@kingstonhotel.com
WEB: www.kingstonhotel.com

HOTEL ★★ MAP 8 O 11

A delightful 45 bedroomed hotel with panoramic views of Dublin Bay, approximately 15 minutes from city centre. Beside ferryport and DART line. Situated convenient to R.D.S., Point Depot, Lansdowne Road and Leopardstown Racecourse. All rooms are en suite with direct dial phone, TV, tea/coffee making facilities. A family run hotel serving food all day in our lounge/bar and our Haddington Bistro opened nightly.

Member of MinOtel Ireland Hotel Group

B&B from €65.00 to €67.50

JAMES J WALSH

American Express
Diners
Mastercard
Visa

45 45

Closed 24 - 26 December

DEER PARK HOTEL AND GOLF COURSES

HOWTH,
CO. DUBLIN

TEL: 01-832 2624 FAX: 01-839 2405
EMAIL: sales@deerpark.iol.ie
WEB: www.deerpark-hotel.ie

HOTEL ★★★ MAP 12 P 11

14km from Dublin City/Airport on a quiet hillside overlooking the bay, Deer Park enjoys spectacular elevated sea views. Featuring Ireland's largest golf complex (5 courses), 18m swimming pool, sauna and steam room and two all-weather tennis courts. Whether on a golfing holiday or a visit to Dublin you will find Deer Park the ideal choice.

Member of Irish Country Hotels

B&B from €77.00 to €88.00

DAVID & ANTOINETTE TIGHE
MANAGERS

American Express
Diners
Mastercard
Visa

Weekend specials from €147.00

80 80

Closed 23 - 27 December

B&B rates are per person sharing per night

KING SITRIC FISH RESTAURANT & ACCOMMODATION

**EAST PIER,
HOWTH,
CO. DUBLIN**
TEL: 01-832 5235 FAX: 01-839 2442
EMAIL: info@kingsitric.ie
WEB: www.kingsitric.ie

GUESTHOUSE ★★★★ MAP 8 P 11

Est. 1971, Aidan and Joan MacManus have earned an international reputation for fresh seafood in their harbour-side restaurant in the picturesque fishing village of Howth. Now with 8 guest rooms, all with sea views. Wine lovers will enjoy browsing in the atmospheric wine cellar. For leisure pursuits, Howth is the perfect location for golfing, walking and sailing. Dublin City is 20 mins by DART; Dublin Airport 20 mins driving.

Member of Ireland's Blue Book

B&B from €63.00 to €95.00

AIDAN AND JOAN MACMANUS

American Express
Mastercard
Visa

☺ Weekend specials from €165.00

8 8

Closed 21 January - 04 February

FITZPATRICK CASTLE DUBLIN

**KILLINEY,
CO. DUBLIN**
TEL: 01-230 5400 FAX: 01-230 5466
EMAIL: dublin@fitzpatricks.com
WEB: www.fitzpatrickhotels.com

HOTEL ★★★★ MAP 8 P 10

Fitzpatrick Castle Dublin is located in the fashionable suburbs of Killiney and Dalkey, overlooking Dublin Bay. This Castle is only 20 minutes from downtown Dublin. 30 years of tradition in excellence has helped to create the perfect atmosphere at this family owned 18th century Castle. The fitness centre has a 20m indoor pool, jacuzzi, sauna, steam room and gymnasium. Luxurious bedrooms with ISDN lines and in house entertainment system in all rooms. The hotel executive car is available on request. Conference facilities available 4-400.

B&B from €85.00 to €130.00

EOIN O'SULLIVAN
GENERAL MANAGER

American Express
Diners
Mastercard
Visa

113 113

Closed 24 - 26 December

BECKETTS COUNTRY HOUSE HOTEL

**COOLDRINAGH HOUSE,
LEIXLIP,
CO. DUBLIN/KILDARE**
TEL: 01-624 7040 FAX: 01-624 7072
EMAIL: becketts@eircom.net
WEB: www.becketts-leixlip.com

HOTEL ★★★ MAP 8 N 11

Becketts is situated in a quiet scenic area just off the N4 motorway at the Leixlip roundabout close to Dublin's new outer ring with easy access to Dublin Airport and all major road networks. Once home to the mother of Samuel Beckett the completely refurbished Cooldrinagh House is now home to Becketts. There are 4 suites and 6 luxury bedrooms and an elegant restaurant with a reputation for superb cuisine and full bar facilities.

B&B from €52.50 to €70.00

JOHN O'BYRNE
MANAGING DIRECTOR

American Express
Diners
Mastercard
Visa

10 10

Open All Year

Room rates are per room per night

FINNSTOWN COUNTRY HOUSE HOTEL

NEWCASTLE ROAD,
LUCAN,
CO. DUBLIN

TEL: 01-601 0700 FAX: 01-628 1088

EMAIL: manager@finnstown-hotel.ie
WEB: www.finnstown-hotel.ie

HOTEL ★★★ MAP 8 N 11

One of County Dublin's finest country house hotels. Set in 45 acres of private grounds it offers privacy, peace and seclusion yet is only twenty minutes drive from the bustling city centre of Dublin. If it's good old-fashioned hospitality you're after, great food and drink, a relaxed atmosphere and stylish surroundings, you're in the right place! Leisure facilities include an 18 hole-putting course, gym, turkish bath, tennis court and indoor heated swimming pool.

Member of Grand Heritage Hotels

B&B from €89.00 to €115.00

PAULA SMITH
GENERAL MANAGER

American Express
Diners
Mastercard
Visa

Weekend specials from €197.00

53 53

Open All Year

MOAT LODGE

LUCAN,
CO. DUBLIN

TEL: 01-624 1584 FAX: 01-628 1356

GUESTHOUSE P MAP 8 N 11

Exclusive 17th century house, convenient to shops, buses, City Centre. Ideal base for golf and fishing. Off N4, near N7, N3 & M50.

B&B from €30.00 to €35.00

COLETTE EGAN

Mastercard
Visa

10 10

Closed 23 December - 02 January

SPA HOTEL

LUCAN,
CO. DUBLIN

TEL: 01-628 0494 FAX: 01-628 0841

EMAIL: info@lucanspahotel.ie
WEB: www.lucanspahotel.ie

HOTEL ★★ MAP 8 N 11

Situated on the N4, the gateway to the West, and 6km from M50, this elegant hotel is ideally located for convenience, comfort and is exceptionally well appointed with central heating, direct dial phone, colour TV, tea/coffee facilities and ironing board. Our restaurant offers a choice of 3 menus and superb wines. Ideal for conference and weddings alike.

Member of MinOtel Ireland Hotel Group

B&B from €60.00 to €80.00

FRANK COLGAN
DIRECTOR

American Express
Diners
Mastercard
Visa

70 70

Closed 25 December

B&B rates are per person sharing per night incl. Breakfast

CARRIAGE HOUSE

LUSK (NEAR AIRPORT),
CO. DUBLIN

TEL: 01-843 8857 FAX: 01-843 8933
EMAIL: carrhous@iol.ie
WEB: www.iol.ie/~carrhous

GUESTHOUSE U MAP 12 O 12

Carriage House is a family run, warm and friendly guesthouse conveniently situated 10 minutes from Dublin Airport, 20 minutes from city. On main Dublin bus route (33). Relax in our indoor heated swimming pool and sauna. Charming award winning gardens and putting green. All rooms en suite with direct dial phone and colour TV. Tea/coffee making facilities and secure car parking. Semi finalist in Leverclean accommodation awards. Breakfast menu.

B&B from €35.00 to €42.00

ROBERT & GEMMA MCAULEY
PROPRIETORS

Mastercard
Visa

🖐 📞 📺 TV A/C ☀ U P
14 14

Open All Year

GRAND HOTEL

MALAHIDE,
CO. DUBLIN

TEL: 01-845 0000 FAX: 01-816 8025
EMAIL: booking@thegrand.ie
WEB: www.thegrand.ie

HOTEL ★★★★ MAP 12 O 12

The Grand Hotel is situated by the sea in the village of Malahide. Just 10 minutes drive from Dublin Airport and 20 minutes from the city centre, the hotel is ideally situated for guests staying for business or leisure. The conference and business centre is one of Ireland's largest and most successful. All 150 bedrooms have tea/coffee making facilities and fax/modem lines. Most bedrooms have spectacular sea views. Leisure centre includes a 21 metre swimming pool, jacuzzi and fully equipped gymnasium.

B&B from €90.00 to €180.00

MATTHEW RYAN
MANAGING DIRECTOR

American Express
Diners
Mastercard
Visa

☺ Weekend specials from €130.00

🖐 📞 📺 T C CM ☀ 🛏 U
150 150
J P 🅿 alc ♿ Inet FAX

Closed 25 - 27 December

ISLAND VIEW HOTEL

COAST ROAD,
MALAHIDE,
CO. DUBLIN

TEL: 01-845 0099 FAX: 01-845 1498
EMAIL: info@islandviewhotel.ie
WEB: www.islandviewhotel.ie

HOTEL ★★ MAP 12 O 12

Island View Hotel is ideally located for comfort and convenience and just a 10 minute drive from Dublin Airport. Our rooms are all en suite and fully equipped with modern facilities. Oscar Taylors Restaurant is an exclusive 150 seater restaurant with a panoramic view of Lambay Island and Malahide coastline. The restaurant is noted for its excellent cuisine. The menu is extensive and moderately priced.

B&B from €50.00 to €50.00

FEIDHLIM HARDY
GENERAL MANAGER

American Express
Diners
Mastercard
Visa

🖐 📞 📺 T C CM J P 🅿 alc
10 10

Open All Year

Room rates are per room per night

PORTMARNOCK HOTEL & GOLF LINKS

STRAND ROAD,
PORTMARNOCK,
CO. DUBLIN

TEL: 01-846 0611 FAX: 01-846 2442
EMAIL: reservations@portmarnock.com
WEB: www.portmarnock.com

HOTEL ★★★★ MAP 12 O 11

Once the home of the Jameson whiskey family, the Portmarnock Hotel and Golf Links is in a prime location reaching down to the sea, with views over the 18-hole Bernhard Langer designed links golf course. The 19th century character of the ancestral home is retained in the wood panelled walls, marble fireplaces and ornate ceilings of the Jameson Bar. Located just 15 minutes from Dublin Airport and 25 minutes from the city centre.

Member of Summit Hotels

B&B from €95.00 to €150.00

SHANE COOKMAN
GENERAL MANAGER

American Express
Diners
Mastercard
Visa

Golf / Spa specials from €140.00

100 100

Open All Year

WHITE SANDS HOTEL

COAST ROAD,
PORTMARNOCK,
CO. DUBLIN

TEL: 01-846 0003 FAX: 01-846 0420
EMAIL: sandshotel@eircom.net
WEB: www.whitesandshotel.ie

HOTEL ★★★ MAP 12 O 11

Uniquely located facing Portmarnock Strand. A 3*** family run Hotel. 10 minutes from Dublin Airport and 25 minutes from the Dublin City Centre with an abundance of golf courses close by. The Hotel consists of 32 tastefully decorated bedrooms, many with panoramic sea views. The Kingsford Smith Restaurant serves contemporary food with Irish flare. Carvery lunch served daily. Private function & meeting rooms. Extensive free car parking. Cead Mile Failte.

B&B from €75.00 to €110.00

GEORGINA HIGGINS
GENERAL MANAGER

American Express
Diners
Mastercard
Visa

Midweek specials 2 B&B &1 Dinner from €140.00

32 32

Closed 24 - 26 December

CITYWEST HOTEL CONFERENCE, LEISURE & GOLF RESORT

SAGGART,
CO. DUBLIN

TEL: 01-401 0500 FAX: 01-458 8565
EMAIL: info@citywesthotel.com
WEB: www.citywesthotel.com

HOTEL ★★★★ MAP 8 N 11

Nestling peacefully in its own private estate located close to Dublin City Centre and Airport, this luxury 333 bedroom hotel boasts a 5***** Leisure Club with 20m pool, two on-site 18 hole Golf Courses, extensive conference facilities and a Convention Centre boasting a total capacity of 6,500 delegates. The Terrace Restaurant, traditional Grill Room and Carvery offer fine dining, whilst the lively lounges and bars are a popular meeting place for locals and visitors alike. Ample complimentary parking.

B&B from €45.00 to €150.00

JOHN GLYNN
CHIEF EXECUTIVE

American Express
Diners
Mastercard
Visa

333 333

Open All Year

B&B rates are per person sharing per night incl. Breakfast

PIERHOUSE HOTEL

HARBOUR ROAD,
SKERRIES,
CO. DUBLIN
TEL: 01-849 1033 FAX: 01-849 4695
EMAIL: pierhouse@morangroup.ie
WEB: www.morangroup.ie

HOTEL U   MAP 12 P 12

The elegantly refurbished Pierhouse Hotel is situated in the quaint fishing town of Skerries. The hotel is a three star standard property situated only 15 minutes from Dublin Airport and only 30 minutes from Dublin City Centre. Each of the 11 executive en suite rooms has teletext TV, trouser press, tea/coffee making facilities and direct dial telephones. Overlooking the Irish Sea, the hotel's restaurant with its opulent décor is complemented by its imaginative Irish cuisine and array of international dishes. Night Club. A Moran Hotel.

B&B from €40.00 to €60.00

TOM & SHEILA MORAN
PROPRIETOR'S

American Express
Diners
Mastercard
Visa

11 11

Closed 25 - 26 December

REDBANK HOUSE GUESTHOUSE & RESTAURANT

6 & 7 CHURCH STREET,
SKERRIES,
CO. DUBLIN
TEL: 01-849 0439 FAX: 01-849 1598
EMAIL: redbank@eircom.net
WEB: www.redbank.ie

GUESTHOUSE ★★★   MAP 12 P 12

Enjoy the extended hospitality of the McCoy's in Redbank House. The world famous seafood restaurant is the dining room of Redbank House. The seven en suite rooms have the McCoys sense of style and elegance. The area is particularly rich in golf courses and a wide variety of leisure activities includes sea fishing, boat trips, sailing and horse riding. The Chef Proprietor Terry McCoy cooks the catch of the day landed at Skerries Pier specialising in the world famous Dublin Bay prawns.

Member of Premier Guesthouses

B&B from €55.00 to €65.00

TERRY MCCOY
PROPRIETOR

American Express
Diners
Mastercard
Visa

7 7

Closed 24 - 27 December

REDBANK LODGE & RESTAURANT

12 CONVENT LANE,
SKERRIES,
CO. DUBLIN
TEL: 01-849 1005 FAX: 01-849 1598
EMAIL: redbank@eircom.net
WEB: www.redbank.ie

GUESTHOUSE ★★★   MAP 12 P 12

Situated in the picturesque fishing port of Skerries, North County Dublin. Each of the five en suite double bedrooms are elegantly decorated with direct dial telephone and TV. Adjacent to the award-winning Redbank Restaurant, with its famous reputation for superb cuisine (fish dishes our speciality) and a well stocked wine cellar. With easy access to Dublin City & Dublin Airport as well as enjoying local attractions such as Ardgillan Demesne, the nearby Boyne Valley & Newgrange.

Member of Premier Guesthouses

B&B from €45.00 to €60.00

TERRY MCCOY
OWNER

American Express
Diners
Mastercard
Visa

5 5

Closed 24 - 28 December

Room rates are per room per night

MARINE HOTEL

SUTTON CROSS,
DUBLIN 13

TEL: 01-839 0000 FAX: 01-839 0442
EMAIL: info@marinehotel.ie
WEB: www.marinehotel.ie

HOTEL ★★★　MAP 12 P 11

The Marine Hotel 3*** (AA***) overlooks the north shore of Dublin Bay. The two acres of lawn sweep down to the sea shore. All bedrooms are en suite and have trouser press, TV, Direct Dial phone and tea/coffee facilities. The city centre is 6km away and the airport 25 minutes drive. Close by is the DART rapid rail system. The hotel has a heated indoor swimming pool and sauna. Nearby are the Royal Dublin and Portmarnock championship golf courses.

B&B from €82.00 to €150.00

SHEILA BAIRD
GENERAL MANAGER

American Express
Diners
Mastercard
Visa

☺ Weekend specials from €130.00

48　48

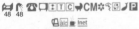

Closed 25 - 27 December

AIRPORT MANOR

NAUL ROAD,
KNOCKSEDAN, SWORDS,
CO. DUBLIN

TEL: 01-840 1818 FAX: 01-870 0010
EMAIL: info@airportmanor.com
WEB: www.airportmanor.com

GUESTHOUSE ★★★★　MAP 12 O 12

Airport Manor is a purposely built property designed to cater for corporate and leisure clientele. Offering the highest standards of services/facilities that can be expected in any 4**** standard establishment. Guestrooms are beautifully decorated with en suite bathrooms, direct dial telephone, satellite TV, tea facilities and hairdryer. Private parking available. The perfect location to enjoy the peace and tranquillity of the countryside yet only 5 minutes from Dublin Airport, 20 minutes from city centre and accessible from all major routes.

B&B from €62.50 to €100.00

CAROLINE KEARNEY

Mastercard
Visa

17　17

Closed 24 - 28 December

CARNEGIE COURT HOTEL

NORTH STREET,
SWORDS,
CO. DUBLIN

TEL: 01-840 4384 FAX: 01-840 4505
EMAIL: info@carnegiecourt.com
WEB: www.carnegiecourt.com

HOTEL P　MAP 12 O 12

The Carnegie Court is a new hotel perfectly located, 5 mins from Dublin Airport, 20 minutes to the city centre and situated in the historic village of Swords. The hotel comprises 36 air-conditioned, en suite rooms, each appointed with TV, DD phone, tea/coffee facilities and all the latest communication technology. Enjoy and relax in our spacious restaurant and uniquely designed bars. We also provide modern conference and banqueting facilities and extensive car parking.

B&B from €62.50 to €82.50

RUDI KRENN
GENERAL MANAGER

American Express
Diners
Mastercard
Visa

36　36

Inet

Closed 24 - 28 December

B&B rates are per person sharing per night incl. Breakfast

FORTE TRAVELODGE

PINNOCK HILL,
SWORDS,
CO. DUBLIN
TEL: 1800-709709 FAX: 01-840 9235

WEB: www.travelodge.co.uk

HOTEL U MAP 8 O 11

Situated only 12.8km from Dublin City Centre on the Dublin to Belfast Road and minutes from the airport, this superb modern hotel offers comfortable, yet affordable, accommodation. Each room is large enough to sleep up to three adults, a child under 12 and a baby in a cot. Excellent range of facilities, from en suite bathroom to colour TV. Unbeatable value for business or leisure. Sited next to Little Chef restaurant. From UK call free: 0800 850 950

Room Rate from €85.00 to €95.00

STEPHANE PEJUS
MANAGER

American Express
Diners
Mastercard
Visa

100 100

Open All Year

GLENMORE HOUSE

AIRPORT ROAD,
NEVINSTOWN, SWORDS,
CO. DUBLIN
TEL: 01-840 3610 FAX: 01-840 4148
EMAIL: rebeccagibney@eircom.net
WEB: www.glenmorehouse.com

GUESTHOUSE ★★★ MAP 12 O 12

Ideally situated just 1km from Dublin Airport and 20 minutes from the city centre, on the main airport/city bus routes, Glenmore House is a spacious family-run guesthouse set in 2 acres of gardens, lawns and private secure carparks. All rooms are beautifully decorated with bathroom, phone, TV, tea/coffee facilities and hairdryer. The warmest of welcomes at a very reasonable cost for business and leisure alike.

B&B from €37.50 to €60.00

REBECCA GIBNEY
PROPRIETOR

Mastercard
Visa

30 30

Closed 24 - 25 December

BEAUFORT HOUSE

GHAN ROAD,
CARLINGFORD,
CO. LOUTH
TEL: 042-937 3879 FAX: 042-937 3878
EMAIL: michaelcaine@beauforthouse.net
WEB: www.beauforthouse.net

GUESTHOUSE ★★★ MAP 12 O 5

Beaufort House, AA ♦♦♦♦♦, listed in Bridgestone, Michelin, Georgina Campbell, a magnificent shoreside residence with glorious sea and mountain views in mediaeval Carlingford Village. Your hosts, Michael & Glynnis Caine, Bord Failte award winners of excellence, will ensure the highest standards. In-house activities include sailing school and yacht charter. Golfing arranged in any of five golf courses within 20 mins of Beaufort House. Private car parking. Dinner by prior arrangement. Small business conference facilities available.

Member of Premier Guesthouses

B&B from €32.50 to €43.00

MICHAEL & GLYNNIS CAINE

Mastercard
Visa

5 5

Open All Year

Room rates are per room per night

CO. LOUTH
CARLINGFORD / CASTLEBELLINGHAM / DROGHEDA

MCKEVITT'S VILLAGE HOTEL

MARKET SQUARE,
CARLINGFORD,
CO. LOUTH

TEL: 042-937 3116 FAX: 042-937 3144
EMAIL: villagehotel@eircom.net
WEB: www.mckevittshotel.com

HOTEL ★★ MAP 12 O 15

McKevitt's Village Hotel is family owned and personally supervised by Kay & Terry McKevitt. At the hotel, pride of place is taken in the personal attention given to guests by owners and staff. Carlingford is one of Ireland's oldest and most interesting mediaeval villages. Beautifully situated on the shores of Carlingford Lough and half way between Dublin and Belfast.

Member of Irish Family Hotels

B&B from €50.00 to €70.00

TERRY & KAY MCKEVITT
OWNERS

Mastercard
Visa

13 13

Open All Year

BELLINGHAM CASTLE HOTEL

CASTLEBELLINGHAM,
CO. LOUTH

TEL: 042-937 2176 FAX: 042-937 2766
EMAIL: bellinghamcastle@eircom.net
WEB: www.bellinghamcastle.com

HOTEL ★★ MAP 12 O 14

Bellingham Castle Hotel is situated close to the pleasant little village of Castlebellingham, Co. Louth, resting in countryside enveloped in history, legend and engaged in beautiful scenery. In the hotel itself, which is an elegant refurbished 17th century castle, you will find all the facilities of a modern hotel, harmonising beautifully with the antique décor and atmosphere of old world splendour.

B&B from €60.00 to €60.00

PASCHAL KEENAN
MANAGER

American Express
Mastercard
Visa

19 19

Closed 24 - 26 December

BOYNE VALLEY HOTEL & COUNTRY CLUB

DROGHEDA,
CO. LOUTH

TEL: 041-983 7737 FAX: 041-983 9188
EMAIL: reservations@boyne-valley-hotel.ie
WEB: www.boyne-valley-hotel.ie

HOTEL ★★★ MAP 12 O 13

Gracious country house on 16 acres of gardens and woodlands, beside historic town of Drogheda, south on the N1. 40km from Dublin and 32km airport. Cellar Bistro with daily supply of fresh fish. Nearby, historic sites of Newgrange, Dowth, Knowth and mediaeval abbeys Mellifont, Monasterboice and Slane. Leisure club with 20m pool, large gym etc. 2 tennis courts. 34 new bedrooms opening September 1st 2003. Large and small conference rooms available.

B&B from €76.50 to €76.50

MICHAEL MCNAMARA
PROPRIETOR/MANAGER

American Express
Diners
Mastercard
Visa

37 37

Open All Year

B&B rates are per person sharing per night incl. Breakfast

WESTCOURT HOTEL

WEST STREET,
DROGHEDA,
CO. LOUTH

TEL: 041-983 0965 FAX: 041-983 0970
EMAIL: reservations@westcourt.ie
WEB: www.westcourt.com

HOTEL ★★★ MAP 12 O 13

At the Westcourt Hotel, our visitors will find the highest standard of courtesy and efficiency coupled with luxurious surroundings in the heart of the historical town of Drogheda. Our bedrooms are all en suite and decorated with television, direct dial phone, tea/coffee making facilities. Our Syzygy Restaurant serving contemporary and traditional cuisine and Bridie Mac's original Irish bar have the finest food, drink, and atmosphere for you to enjoy. We pride ourselves on a highly personalised service and look forward to welcoming you.

B&B from €75.00 to €90.00

VALERIE SHERLOCK
MANAGER

American Express
Diners
Mastercard
Visa

27 27

IRISH HOTELS FEDERATION

Closed 25 - 26 December

BALLYMASCANLON HOUSE HOTEL

DUNDALK,
CO. LOUTH

TEL: 042-9358200 FAX: 042-937 1598
EMAIL: info@ballymascanlon.com
WEB: www.ballymascanlon.com

HOTEL ★★★ MAP 12 O 14

Ballymascanlon Hotel is a Victorian mansion set in 130 acre demesne on the scenic Cooley Peninsula. The hotel while retaining its old world ambience has recently had its facilities modernised. Our leisure centre incorporates a 20m deck level pool, leisure pool, sauna, jacuzzi, steam room, gymnasium and tennis courts. Our 18 hole Parkland golf course surrounding the hotel is both a pleasurable challenge to play and exhilarating to view.

B&B from €72.50 to €75.00

OLIVER QUINN

American Express
Diners
Mastercard
Visa

Weekend specials from €185.00

90 90

IRISH HOTELS FEDERATION

Open All Year

CARRICKDALE HOTEL & LEISURE COMPLEX

CARRICKCARNON,
RAVENSDALE, DUNDALK,
CO. LOUTH

TEL: 042-937 1397 FAX: 042-937 1740
EMAIL: manager@carrickdale.com
WEB: www.carrickdale.com

HOTEL ★★★ MAP 12 O 14

The Hotel, Conference, swimming and leisure complex is situated midway between Dublin and Belfast on the main N1 just 10km north of Dundalk, 8km south of Newry. Our 119 en suite rooms include our newly open 68 deluxe tower block rooms containing 15 fully air-conditioned executive suites with mini bar facilities. Tastefully decorated bar and restaurant serving excellent food and wines. Ideal destination for touring Cooley, Carlingford and all of Northern Ireland's major tourist attractions.

B&B from €65.00 to €65.00

JOHN MCPARLAND
PROPRIETOR

American Express
Diners
Mastercard
Visa

119 119

IRISH HOTELS FEDERATION

Closed 25 - 26 December

Room rates are per room per night

CLANBRASSIL HOTEL

CLANBRASSIL STREET,
DUNDALK,
CO. LOUTH
TEL: 042-933 4141 FAX: 042-932 8779
EMAIL: clanbrassilhotel@hotmail.com

HOTEL ★★ MAP 12 O 14

Ideally situated midway between the two capitals, Belfast and Dublin, in the heart of Dundalk Town, a heavenly location for shopaholics, with an abundance of superb shopping facilities. With six 18 hole golf courses within 10km drive, this area is a golf fanatic's paradise. Carlingford Lough, the Mourne & Cooley Mountains, and the Boyne Valley are just a few of the many famous local tourist attractions waiting to be discovered.

B&B from €50.00 to €60.00

ANITA MCCANN

American Express
Diners
Mastercard
Visa

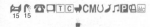
15 15

DERRYHALE HOTEL

CARRICK ROAD,
DUNDALK,
CO. LOUTH
TEL: 042-933 5471 FAX: 042-933 5471
EMAIL: derryhalehotel@eircom.net

HOTEL U MAP 12 O 14

Midway between Dublin and Belfast, Derryhale Hotel is an ideal base for touring the North East of Ireland, Mountains of Mourne, Carlingford, Cooley Peninsula. Bedrooms contain TV and direct dial telephone. Good quality food is a tradition at the hotel. Derryhale Hotel has wedding and conference facilities. Activities close by include fishing, water skiing, sailing, beaches, horse riding and golf.

Member of MinOtel Ireland Hotel Group

B&B from €45.00 to €65.00

LIAM SEXTON
MANAGING DIRECTOR

American Express
Diners
Mastercard
Visa

☺ Weekend specials from €115.00

19 19

Open All Year

FAIRWAYS HOTEL & CONFERENCE CENTRE

DUBLIN ROAD,
DUNDALK,
CO. LOUTH
TEL: 042-932 1500 FAX: 042-932 1511
EMAIL: info@fairways.ie
WEB: www.fairways.ie

HOTEL ★★★ MAP 12 O 14

The Fairways Hotel and Conference Centre is situated 3 miles south of Dundalk, approximately one hour's drive from Dublin or Belfast, and five minutes from the seaside. Facilities include 98 tastefully furnished rooms, a new fully equipped conference and banqueting centre, catering for up to 1,000 delegates. Carvery/grill and Modi's Restaurant serving full meals and snacks throughout the day. Golf can be organised by the hotel on a choice of local golf courses.

B&B from €60.00 to €75.00

BRIAN P. QUINN
MANAGING DIRECTOR

American Express
Diners
Mastercard
Visa

98 98

Closed 24 - 25 December

B&B rates are per person sharing per night incl. Breakfast

HOTEL IMPERIAL

PARK STREET,
DUNDALK,
CO. LOUTH
TEL: 042-933 2241 FAX: 042-933 7909
EMAIL: info@imperialhoteldundalk.com

HOTEL ★★ MAP 12 O 14

Modern hotel in Dundalk Town Centre. Completely refurbished bedrooms, coffee shop, bar and restaurant. Restaurant and coffee shop open daily 8am - 10pm, lunch, high tea and à la carte available. Bar snacks available daily from 12 - 8pm. Secure car parking at no extra cost.

B&B from €60.00 to €60.00

PETER QUINN
MANAGING DIRECTOR

American Express
Diners
Mastercard
Visa

47 47

Closed 25 - 26 December

AISLING HOUSE

DUBLIN ROAD,
ASHBOURNE,
CO. MEATH
TEL: 01-835 0359 FAX: 01-835 1135

GUESTHOUSE ★★ MAP 12 O 12

Situated on one acre of landscaped gardens on the Dublin/Derry Road N2, a mile from Ashbourne Village, only 20 minutes from Dublin City Centre and Airport, convenient to Fairyhouse Racecourse and Tattersalls. Rooms en suite with guest lounge and private car park. Aisling House is an ideal base for business or holiday. Local amenities include golf, horse riding, clay pigeon shooting and fishing in the Boyne River.

B&B from €35.00 to €40.00

NUALA O'CONNELL
PROPRIETOR

Mastercard
Visa

9 9

Closed 24 - 28 December

ASHBOURNE COURT HOTEL

BRIDGE STREET,
ASHBOURNE,
CO. MEATH
TEL: 01-835 9300 FAX: 01-835 9301
EMAIL: info@ashbournecourthotel.com
WEB: www.ashbournecourthotel.com

HOTEL N MAP 12 O 12

Situated in the heart of Ashbourne, 15 minutes from Dublin Airport and 20 minutes from the city centre, this hotel has some of the best quality accommodation in Co. Meath. All bedrooms are decorated and equipped to the highest standard. We pride ourselves on providing luxurious surroundings where comfort and facilities combine with a high level of personal service to satisfy both the business and leisure guest.

B&B from €50.00 to €75.00

MARIAN WILLIAMS
GENERAL MANAGER

American Express
Mastercard
Visa

45 45

Closed 24 - 26 December

BROADMEADOW COUNTRY HOUSE & EQUESTRIAN CENTRE

BULLSTOWN,
ASHBOURNE,
CO. MEATH

TEL: 01-835 2823 FAX: 01-835 2819
EMAIL: info@irelandequestrian.com
WEB: www.irelandequestrian.com

GUESTHOUSE ★★★★ MAP 12 O 12

This exceptional family-run country house is located near Ashbourne Village, only 12km from Dublin Airport and 20km from the city centre. It is set in 100 acres of farmland with a modern purpose-built equestrian centre. All rooms en suite and designed for maximum guest comfort. Private car parking, tennis court and landscaped gardens. Surrounded by numerous golf courses and restaurants. Ideal location for both tourist and business people. Specialists in equestrian packages.

Member of Equestrian Holidays Ireland

B&B from €45.00 to €55.00

SANDRA DUFF
MANAGER

Mastercard
Visa

8 8

Closed 24 - 26 December

OLD DARNLEY LODGE HOTEL

MAIN STREET,
ATHBOY,
CO. MEATH

TEL: 046-32283 FAX: 046-32255
EMAIL: info@olddarnley.com
WEB: www.olddarnley.com

HOTEL CR MAP 11 M 12

This 19th century hotel has been refurbished to the very highest standards. The hotel is a haven of tranquillity and is ideally located. Dublin and Athlone are only one hour's drive away. All bedrooms are en suite and offer a variety of services including, direct dial phone, multi channel TV, trouser press, hair dryers and tea/coffee making facilities. There are plenty of historic landmarks to see and plenty of activities to enjoy, including golf, fishing and horse riding.

B&B from €40.00 to €50.00

SEÁN MANGAN
MANAGER

American Express
Diners
Mastercard
Visa

14 14

Closed 25 - 26 December

NEPTUNE BEACH HOTEL & LEISURE CLUB

BETTYSTOWN,
CO. MEATH

TEL: 041-982 7107 FAX: 041-982 7412
EMAIL: info@neptunebeach.ie
WEB: www.neptunebeach.ie

HOTEL U MAP 12 O 13

Located 25 mins north of Dublin Airport with a spectacular setting overlooking Bettystown Beach. All 38 rooms are elegantly furnished to provide the comfort and facilities expected of a leading hotel. Enjoy fine dining in the restaurant, afternoon tea in the cosy Winter Garden or a relaxing drink in the Neptune Bar. The leisure club facilities include 20m swimming pool, jacuzzi, sauna and fitness suite. Local golf courses: Laytown & Bettystown, Seapoint and Co. Louth.

Member of Select Hotels

B&B from €120.00 to €152.00

DENIS J. REDDAN
PROPRIETOR

American Express
Mastercard
Visa

☺ Weekend specials from €151.00

38 38

Inet

Open All Year

B&B rates are per person sharing per night incl. Breakfast

JOHNSTOWN HOUSE HOTEL

ENFIELD,
CO. MEATH

TEL: 046-954 0000 FAX: 046-954 0001
EMAIL: info@johnstownhouse.com
WEB: www.johnstownhouse.com

HOTEL P MAP 11 M 11

Developed around a 1750s Georgian country estate, in a stunning parkland landscape. This 80 bedroomed hotel is fitted to the highest international standards. Enjoy breakfast in our spacious Atrium Brasserie. The Pavillion Restaurant offers excellent food in an informal atmosphere. Mix with the locals afterwards in the lively Coach House Bar. Our 600-seater conference centre is completed by 12 smaller meeting rooms. The hotel has gained a reputation for attention to detail and the highest standard of customer service.

Room Rate from €120.00 to €300.00

MARTIN FAGAN
ACTING GENERAL MANAGER

American Express
Diners
Mastercard
Visa

Weekend specials from €230.00

80 80

Closed 24 - 27 December

Room rates are per room per night

Meath

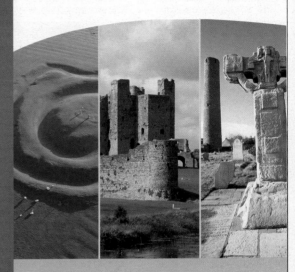

Where Heritage Lives

Just stand for a few minutes on the Hill of Tara and you'll know what we mean. The sight of Trim Castle's monumental ramparts will do it to you as well. Or the mysterious neolithic wonders of Loughcrew and Newgrange at *Brú na Boinne*. Meath's heritage springs to life, grabbing the imagination with vivid images of the past. Discover Meath's living heritage.

For all your tourism needs and services contact Meath Tourism at:

Callsave **1850 300789**
www.meathtourism.ie   info@meathtourism.ie

Meath
Always a visit to treasure

HEADFORT ARMS HOTEL

KELLS,
CO. MEATH

TEL: 046-40063 FAX: 046-40587
EMAIL: headfortarms@eircom.net
WEB: www.headfortarms.com

HOTEL ★★ MAP 11 M 13

Situated in the historical town of Kells, it is 40km from Dublin on the main Derry/Donegal route. This traditional family hotel has 19 bedrooms, with bath/shower, TV, video, etc. We at the Headfort offer a blend of homeliness, good taste & first class management. Conference facilities provided. Available locally: golf, fishing, tennis. Coffee shop / carvery open 7 days until 10pm. New contemporary "Vanilla Pod" Restaurant serving worldwide food. Open from 5.30pm - late, early bird menu available & Sunday lunch. Tel: 046-40084 direct reservations.

B&B from €50.00 to €55.00

VINCENT DUFF
GENERAL MANAGER

American Express
Mastercard
Visa

19 19 📠 ☎ 🖥 T C 🐾 CM ✻ ♋ ♪ 🎵 S 🛄
alc ☕

IRISH HOTELS FEDERATION

Closed 25 December

STATION HOUSE HOTEL

KILMESSAN,
CO. MEATH

TEL: 046-902 5239 FAX: 046-902 5588
EMAIL: info@thestationhousehotel.com
WEB: www.thestationhousehotel.com

HOTEL U MAP 12 N 12

Step off the fast track into a relaxed rural setting where peace and tranquillity exude. Set on 5 acres of gardens. This first class hotel offers many amenities we appreciate today along with much of yesterday's charm. The Signal Suite is unique with four poster bed and whirlpool bath. The award winning Signal Restaurant is open 7 days a week for lunch and dinner. A short drive from Dublin, Trim or Navan. It is a haven at the end of a journey.

B&B from €57.00 to €90.00

CHRIS & THELMA SLATTERY
PROPRIETORS

American Express
Diners
Mastercard
Visa

⛳ 🍴

20 20 📠 ☎ 🖥 T C CM ✻ ♪ 🎵 P S 🛄 alc
☕ 🛏 Inet

IRISH HOTELS FEDERATION

Open All Year

ARDBOYNE HOTEL

DUBLIN ROAD,
NAVAN,
CO. MEATH

TEL: 046-23119 FAX: 046-22355
EMAIL: ardboyne-sales@quinn-hotels.com
WEB: www.quinnhotels.com

HOTEL ★★★ MAP 12 N 13

Situated on the outskirts of Navan, the Ardboyne Hotel is set amidst some of the most famous of Ireland's historical sites. Comprising of 29 luxuriously appointed en suite guest rooms and conference and banqueting suites which can accommodate up to 350 people for a meeting, conference or private banquet, the Ardboyne Hotel will cater for your requirements with the highest standard of service and courtesy.

Member of Quinn Hotels

B&B from €65.00 to €85.00

MICHAEL MCLAUGHLIN
GENERAL MANAGER

American Express
Diners
Mastercard
Visa

🍴

29 29 📠 ☎ 🖥 T C 🐾 CM ✻ ♪ 🎵 P 🛄 alc
☕

IRISH HOTELS FEDERATION

Closed 24 - 26 December

B&B rates are per person sharing per night incl. Breakfast

MA DWYERS GUESTHOUSE

DUBLIN ROAD,
NAVAN,
CO. MEATH

TEL: 046-907 7992 FAX: 046-907 7995

GUESTHOUSE ★★★ MAP 12 N 13

Ma Dwyers guesthouse possesses many of the qualities of a high class hotel, along with a cosy homely feel which is so vitally important. 9 beautiful en suite rooms with a direct dial telephone, TV, hairdryer and tea/coffee facilities with fax and photocopying services available. Ideally located just minutes walk from the town centre and plenty of historic landmarks to see and activities to enjoy including golf, fishing, boating and horseriding.

B&B from €35.00 to €40.00

JOAN O'BRIEN

Mastercard
Visa

🛏🛎☎🖥TC🖐♨🚲🅿🔔
9   9

Closed 24 - 26 December

NEWGRANGE HOTEL

BRIDGE STREET,
NAVAN,
CO. MEATH

TEL: 046-907 4100 FAX: 046-907 3977
EMAIL: info@newgrangehotel.ie
WEB: www.newgrangehotel.ie

HOTEL ★★★ MAP 12 N 13

Located in Navan, the heart of the Royal County. The Newgrange is a modern hotel, designed and inspired by the ancient history of the area. In addition to our 36 elegantly decorated en suite bedrooms, the hotel boasts extensive conference and banqueting facilities, a choice of bars, restaurant and café. Easy access to Dublin City and Airport. Enjoy local attractions including Bru na Boinne, golf, angling and horse racing.

B&B from €63.49 to €88.89

NOEL J O'MAHONY
GENERAL MANAGER

American Express
Diners
Mastercard
Visa

🍸
☺ Midweek specials from €150.00

🛏🛎☎💶C🖐CMU♪🎵🅿🔔
36   36

alc 🍴♿ inet

IRISH
HOTELS
FEDERATION

Closed 25 - 26 December

CONYNGHAM ARMS HOTEL

SLANE,
CO. MEATH

TEL: 041-988 4444 FAX: 041-982 4205
EMAIL: enquiry@conynghamarms.com
WEB: www.conynghamarms.com

HOTEL ★★ MAP 12 N 13

Located in a lovely manor village built c. 1850, this traditional family hotel with 4 poster beds, where you can enjoy good food and friendly service, is an ideal base from which to tour the Boyne Valley - particularly the tomb of Knowth and Newgrange, various abbeys and the birth place of Francis Ledwidge, all within 15 minutes drive. Available locally: 5 golf courses within 25km. Irish Country Hotels reservations Tel: +353-1-295 8900.

Member of Irish Country Hotels

B&B from €50.00 to €80.00

GRAHAM & BERNIE CANNING
PROPRIETORS

Diners
Mastercard
Visa

🛏🛎☎🖥TC🖐CM❄♨🅿🔔
14   14

alc

IRISH
HOTELS
FEDERATION

Open All Year

Room rates are per room per night

HIGHFIELD HOUSE

MAUDLINS ROAD,
TRIM,
CO. MEATH
TEL: 046-36386 FAX: 046-38182
EMAIL: highfieldhouseaccom@eircom.net
WEB: www.highfieldguesthouse.com

GUESTHOUSE ★★★ MAP 11 M 12

Highfield House guest accommodation is a beautiful period residence. Historical building dates back to the early 18th century. It is situated overlooking Trim Castle and the River Boyne just off the main Dublin Road. There are 7 spacious en suite guest rooms with colour TV, DD phone, coffee/tea facilities. Beautiful view from all rooms. 2 mins walking distance to town. Newgrange 30km. Dublin Airport 30 km. Babysitting service & laundry service. Private car parking. We pride ourselves on a highly personalised service & look forward to welcoming you.

B&B from € 32.00 to € 40.00

EDWARD & GERALDINE DUIGNAN
PROPRIETORS

Mastercard
Visa

7 7

Closed 22 December - 05 January

WELLINGTON COURT HOTEL

SUMMERHILL ROAD,
TRIM,
CO. MEATH
TEL: 046-31516 FAX: 046-36002
EMAIL: wellingtoncourt@eircom.net
WEB: www.wellingtoncourthotel.ie

HOTEL ★★ MAP 11 M 12

The Wellington Court Hotel is family owned and offers visitors a warm welcome and old fashioned courtesy along with excellent facilities. Our 18 rooms are all en suite with direct dial phone, colour TV, central heating. Also tea/coffee facilities. Superb accommodation, excellent food, set in Ireland's most historic surroundings with the magnificent mediaeval ruins of King John's Castle, one of the most enduring attractions in the area. Additional Tel. No.: 01-821 3311

B&B from € 50.00 to € 50.00

JOHN & AOIFE CUSACK
PROPRIETORS

American Express
Mastercard
Visa

18 18

Inet FAX

Closed 25 - 26 December

ARKLOW BAY CONFERENCE AND LEISURE HOTEL

ARKLOW,
CO. WICKLOW

TEL: 0402-32309 FAX: 0402-32300
EMAIL: arklowbay@eircom.net
WEB: www.arklowbay.com

HOTEL ★★★ MAP 8 O 8

Nestled in the heart of Co. Wicklow, a warm welcome awaits your arrival. Overlooking Arklow Bay with panoramic views of the Garden of Ireland, the hotel boasts 92 en suite rooms. Enjoy excellent cuisine in 'Howard's Dining Room' or the local craic synonymous with our Ferrybank Lounge. State of the art leisure club and superior conference facilities. Banqueting for 500 pax. Enjoy golf, fishing, hovercrafting, quadracing which are all available locally. Sister hotel to the Springhill Court Kilkenny.

Member of Chara Hotel Group

B&B from € 75.00 to € 110.00

ROBERT MCCARTHY
GENERAL MANAGER

American Express
Diners
Mastercard
Visa

Seasonal offers please call

92 92

Open All Year

B&B rates are per person sharing per night incl. Breakfast

BRIDGE HOTEL

BRIDGE STREET,
ARKLOW,
CO. WICKLOW
TEL: 0402-31666 FAX: 0402-31666

HOTEL ★★ MAP 8 O 8

The Bridge Hotel is a family-run 15 bedroomed hotel situated at the bridge in Arklow beside the Avoca River and only 10 mins walk to the sea. Arklow has a strong seafaring heritage and is famous for its pottery. The town offers a great variety of holiday activities whether you swim, play golf, tennis, fish or walk. Arklow is an ideal base from which to see the beautiful scenery of Wicklow. Only 6.5km to Ballykissangel.

B&B from €40.00 to €45.00

JIM HOEY
PROPRIETOR

Mastercard
Visa

15 14

Closed 25 December

CLOGGA BAY HOTEL

CLOGGA,
ARKLOW,
CO. WICKLOW
TEL: 0402-39299 FAX: 0402-91538

HOTEL ★★ MAP 8 O 8

Family owned and managed establishment situated 3km south of Arklow Town. Set on a 2 acre garden in the country by the sea, approx 60km from Rosslare and Dublin. A central location for touring Wicklow and Wexford. All rooms en suite with colour T.V. and direct dial telephone. Local attractions include golf, fishing and swimming. Our restaurant offers good traditional food.

B&B from €40.00 to €45.00

FIOUNNUALA JAMESON
PROPRIETOR

American Express
Mastercard
Visa

10 10

Open All Year

GLENART CASTLE HOTEL

GLENART CASTLE,
ARKLOW,
CO. WICKLOW
TEL: 0402-31031 FAX: 0402-31032
EMAIL: glenart@eircom.net

HOTEL U MAP 8 O 8

The Hidden Castle of Glenart set amidst 63 acres of gardens and woodlands. Built circa 1750 by the Earls of Carysfort, situated in the heart of the Avoca Valley. Only an hour's drive from Dublin, via N11. Local attractions include fishing, shooting, hillwalking and horse riding. A short drive to Arklow and golf courses including Druid's Glen, Collattin, Woodenbridge and the Arklow Golf Course. Minutes away from the picturesque Ballykissangel (Avoca) Village.

B&B from €55.00 to €85.00

DESMOND NAIK
DIRECTOR

Mastercard
Visa

28 28

Open All Year

Room rates are per room per night

BALLYKNOCKEN COUNTRY HOUSE

GLENEALY,
ASHFORD,
CO. WICKLOW

TEL: 0404-44627 FAX: 0404-44696
EMAIL: cfulvio@ballyknocken.com
WEB: www.ballyknocken.com

GUESTHOUSE ★★★★ MAP 8 P 9

1850s romantic farmhouse, elegantly furnished with antiques. Charming bedrooms, some with iron beds and claw feet baths offer lovely views over gardens and forest. Relax by the Drawing Room's log fire before the splendid dinner using garden and local produce. Superb breakfasts. Near to Wicklow Mountains, Glendalough, Powerscourt. Excellent golf, e.g. Druid's Glen. Lovely walks on site. Dublin 29 miles. Frommers recommended. AA ♦♦♦♦. Gift vouchers available.

B&B from €45.00 to €49.50

CATHERINE FULVIO
PROPRIETOR

Mastercard
Visa

☺ Midweek specials from €128.00

🛏🛎☎🖥Ⓣ🅲❄🔍Ὗ🅟🆈
7   7

Open All Year

BEL-AIR HOTEL

ASHFORD,
CO. WICKLOW

TEL: 0404-40109 FAX: 0404-40188
EMAIL: belairhotel@eircom.net
WEB: www.holidaysbelair.com

HOTEL U MAP 8 P 9

Bel-Air Hotel is a family run hotel and equestrian centre, situated in the centre of 81 hectares of farm and parkland. Managed by the Murphy Freeman family since 1937. The lovely gardens have a breathtaking view to the sea. The traditional family atmosphere and rich history make the hotel a popular venue, a good restaurant, rooms en suite with tea making facilities, T.V. and hairdryers. Bel Air Holiday village adjacent to hotel.

Member of Equestrian Holidays Ireland

B&B from €51.00 to €60.00

FIDELMA FREEMAN
OWNER

American Express
Diners
Mastercard
Visa

🛏🛎☎🖥Ⓣ🅲❄Ὗ🅰alc
10   10

Closed 24 December - 11 January

CHESTER BEATTY INN

ASHFORD VILLAGE,
CO. WICKLOW

TEL: 0404-40206 FAX: 0404-49003
EMAIL: hotelchesterbeatty@eircom.net
WEB: www.hotelchesterbeatty.ie

HOTEL U MAP 8 P 9

The Chester Beatty Inn is in the village of Ashford on the main N11 road, 35 mins south of Dublin. Ideally situated for touring, golf (adjacent to Druids Glen and many other golf courses), fishing, hill walking and gardens (opposite Mount Usher Gardens, 15 mins from Powerscourt Gardens). Charming country inn style family run hotel comprising 12 luxury en suite rooms, award-winning restaurant, lounge and traditional Irish bar all with open log fires. Secure private car park.

B&B from €50.00 to €75.00

KITTY & PAUL CAPRANI

American Express
Diners
Mastercard
Visa

🏌

🛏🛎☎🖥Ⓣ🅲CM❄Ὗ♪🅿🆂
12   12

🅰alc

Closed 23 - 26 December

B&B rates are per person sharing per night incl. Breakfast

BROOKLODGE

MACREDDIN VILLAGE,
NEAR AUGHRIM,
CO. WICKLOW
TEL: 0402-36444 FAX: 0402-36580
EMAIL: brooklodge@macreddin.ie
WEB: www.brooklodge.com

HOTEL ★★★★ MAP 8 O 8

A stunning luxury hotel in a spectacular Wicklow valley, yet just one hour from south Dublin. Our restaurant, The Strawberry Tree, serves only free range, organic and wild foods in possibly Ireland's most dramatic dining rooms. Macreddin Village hosts Acton's Country Pub and Brewery, an organic bakery and smokehouse, a collection of food, wine and outdoor-wear shops and equestrian and clay pigeon shooting centres. 15 minutes from Glendalough, Ballykissangel and great golf courses.

B&B from €87.50 to €135.00

JOE KELLY & EVAN DOYLE
HOSTS

American Express
Diners
Mastercard
Visa

Midweek 2 nights B&B + 1 Dinner from €205.00pps

40   40

Open All Year

LAWLESS'S HOTEL

AUGHRIM,
CO. WICKLOW

TEL: 0402-36146 FAX: 0402-36384
EMAIL: reservations@lawlesshotel.com
WEB: www.lawlesshotel.com

HOTEL ★★★ MAP 8 O 8

Lawless's Hotel, established in 1787, is a charming family run hotel which has been tastefully renovated. The award-winning restaurant enjoys a well established reputation for fine cuisine. Approximately one hour from Dublin, nestling in the Wicklow Hills, there is a wide choice of excellent golf courses nearby as well as scenic hill-walking, pony trekking and trout fishing in the adjacent river. Other accommodation available in hotel grounds.

Member of Irish Country Hotels

B&B from €64.50 to €77.50

SEOIRSE & MAEVE O'TOOLE
PROPRIETORS

Diners
Mastercard
Visa

Midweek specials from €180.00

14   14

Closed 24 - 26 December

BEECHWOOD HOUSE

MANOR KILBRIDE,
BLESSINGTON,
CO. WICKLOW
TEL: 01-458 2802
EMAIL: amccann@beechwoodhouse.ie
WEB: www.beechwoodhouse.ie

GUESTHOUSE N MAP 8 N 10

A beautiful Country House set in 2 acres of mature gardens. Beechwood House is a house for all seasons, full of charm and a relaxed informal atmosphere with large bright guest rooms all en suite. Food is home cooked and vegetarian a speciality. Only 40 minutes from Dublin Airport and ferry terminals escape to an invigorating landscape of forests lakes and mountains. Centrally located to tour both Dublin City and Wicklow.

B&B from €35.00 to €70.00

BARRY EDWARDS & ADRIENNE
MCCANN

Mastercard
Visa

6   6

Closed 24 December - 08 January

Room rates are per room per night

TULFARRIS HOTEL & GOLF RESORT

BLESSINGTON LAKES,
CO. WICKLOW

TEL: 045-867600 FAX: 045-867565
EMAIL: info@tulfarris.com
WEB: www.tulfarris.com

HOTEL ★★★★ MAP 8 N 10

Tulfarris Hotel and Golf Resort is located on the Wicklow/Kildare border, near Blessington & within 50 minutes drive of Dublin City Centre & Airport. The 18th century Tulfarris Estate is nestled between the spectacular Wicklow Mountains & Blessington Lakes. It has 80 tastefully furnished en suite bedrooms, a courtyard bar and an excellent restaurant. Facilities include an indoor heated swimming pool, gym, sauna, steam room, sunbed, massage, tennis courts and a spectacular 18 hole Championship Golf Course.

B&B from € 68.00 to € 99.00

JIM & MAEVE HAYES
MANAGING DIRECTOR & PROP

American Express
Diners
Mastercard
Visa

☺ Weekend specials from €99.00

80 80

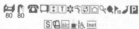

Open All Year

CROFTON BRAY HEAD INN

STRAND ROAD,
BRAY,
CO. WICKLOW
TEL: 01-286 7182 FAX: 01-286 7182

GUESTHOUSE ★★ MAP 8 P 10

This 130 year old building is situated on the seafront, under the Bray Head Mountain. A 10 minute walk away from an excellent commuter train to Dublin, but also ideally located for touring Wicklow - The Garden of Ireland. The Bray Head Inn has ample car-parking and is fully licensed. It has a lift, en suite bedrooms with TV and Telephone. Our very reasonable prices include full Irish Breakfast.

B&B from € 40.00 to € 45.00

ENA REGAN CUMMINS

Mastercard
Visa

30 30

Closed 02 October - 02 June

HEATHER HOUSE HOTEL

STRAND ROAD,
BRAY,
CO. WICKLOW
TEL: 01-268 8000 FAX: 01-286 4254
EMAIL: info@heatherhousehotel.com
WEB: www.heatherhousehotel.com

HOTEL P MAP 8 P 10

A Family run hotel with spectacular seaviews. Catering for the business or leisure guest, with well appointed en suite accommodation, as well as self catering apartments. The Martello Bar offers a superb carvery and bar food menu or dine in the Tower Bistro from our select menu and fine wines. Conference and banqueting facilities. Ideally located for touring Dublin City and County Wicklow. Located 5 minutes from all public transport and N11 Motorway.

B&B from € 50.00 to € 70.00

JOHN DUGGAN

American Express
Mastercard
Visa

44 44

Open All Year

B&B rates are per person sharing per night incl. Breakfast

ROYAL HOTEL AND LEISURE CENTRE

MAIN STREET,
BRAY,
CO. WICKLOW
TEL: 01-286 2935 FAX: 01-286 7373
EMAIL: royal@regencyhotels.com
WEB: www.regencyhotels.com

HOTEL ★★★   MAP 8 P 10

Located in the coastal resort of Bray, ideally positioned at the gateway to the garden county of Ireland and yet only 30 minutes DART journey from Dublin City Centre. Leisure facilities include a pool, sauna, steamroom, whirlpool spa and jacuzzi. Other facilities include a Massage and Beauty Clinic and creche. The hotel is established for conferences, weddings and corporate banquets. The Heritage Restaurant offers fine dining in luxurious surroundings and you can enjoy live musical entertainment most nights. 24 hour supervised car park.

B&B from €65.00 to €120.00

MAUREEN MCGETTIGAN-O'CONNOR
GENERAL MANAGER

Diners
Mastercard
Visa

☺ Weekend specials from €105.00

90 90

IRISH
HOTELS
FEDERATION

Open All Year

WESTBOURNE HOTEL

QUINSBORO ROAD,
BRAY,
CO. WICKLOW
TEL: 01-286 2362 FAX: 01-286 8530

HOTEL ★★   MAP 8 P 10

The Westbourne Hotel is ideally located on the north east coast of the 'Garden of Ireland' in the charming town of Bray. Only minutes from exceptional scenery, beaches and has fast access to Dublin via the DART. Newly refurbished bedrooms en suite, direct dial phone, TV and tea/coffee making facilities. Clancy's Traditional Irish Bar, craic agus ceol. Food served all day. Dusty's contemporary Style bar is recently refurbished and offers comfortable and stylish surroundings in a very relaxed atmosphere.

B&B from €50.00 to €55.00

SUSAN MC CARTHY
GENERAL MANAGER

Mastercard
Visa

13 13

IRISH
HOTELS
FEDERATION

Closed 25 - 26 December

WOODLAND COURT HOTEL

SOUTHERN CROSS,
BRAY,
CO. WICKLOW
TEL: 01-276 0258 FAX: 01-276 0298
EMAIL: info@woodlandscourthotel.com
WEB: www.woodlandscourthotel.com

HOTEL ★★★   MAP 8 P 10

Located just minutes from the N11 motorway and 12 miles from Dublin City Centre the Woodland Court Hotel has much to offer the tourist and business traveller. 65 well-appointed en suite rooms, state of the art conference/business centre and excellent meals in our restaurant. An ideal venue for touring Dublin City and County Wicklow. Special group and business rates available on request. A haven of relaxation.

Room Rate from €60.00 to €140.00

RUTH CONNOLLY
GENERAL MANAGER

American Express
Diners
Mastercard
Visa

☺ Weekend specials from €120.00pps

65 65

IRISH
HOTELS
FEDERATION

Open All Year

Room rates are per room per night

RATHSALLAGH HOUSE, GOLF AND COUNTRY CLUB

DUNLAVIN,
CO. WICKLOW

TEL: 045-403112 FAX: 045-403343
EMAIL: info@rathsallagh.com
WEB: www.rathsallagh.com

GUESTHOUSE ★★★★   MAP 8 N 9

Winner of the prestigious Country House of the Year Award 2000 and a member of Ireland's Blue Book, Rathsallagh is a large 4**** country house converted from Queen Anne stables in 1798. Rathsallagh, with its own 18 hole Championship Golf Course, is set in a peaceful oasis of 530 acres of rolling parkland with thousands of mature trees, lakes and streams. On the west side of the Wicklow Mountains close to Punchestown and The Curragh Racecourses, yet only 1 hour from Dublin Airport.

Member of Ireland's Blue Book

B&B from €125.00 to €145.00

THE O'FLYNN FAMILY
PROPRIETORS

American Express
Diners
Mastercard
Visa

Closed 02 January - 30 January

POWERSCOURT ARMS HOTEL

ENNISKERRY,
CO. WICKLOW

TEL: 01-282 8903 FAX: 01-286 4909

HOTEL ★   MAP 8 O 10

Powerscourt Arms Hotel owned by the McTernan Family. Snuggling in the foothills of the Wicklow Mountains the Powerscourt Arms is an ideal base for touring expeditions. It is an intimate family run hotel with 12 bedrooms furnished to include direct dial telephone, en suite bathrooms and multi channel TV, ample car parking facilities. The restaurant seats up to 45 people. Our lounge, with strong features of American white ash, serves bar food daily. The public bar also has its own atmosphere complete with an open fire.

B&B from €45.00 to €50.00

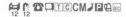

CHARLES MCTERNAN
GENERAL MANAGER

Mastercard
Visa

Closed 24 - 26 December

SUMMERHILL HOUSE HOTEL

ENNISKERRY,
CO. WICKLOW

TEL: 01-286 7928 FAX: 01-286 7929
EMAIL: info@summerhillhousehotel.com
WEB: www.summerhillhousehotel.com

HOTEL ★★★   MAP 8 O 10

This charming hotel is just a short walk to the quaint village of Enniskerry, and the famous Powerscourt Gardens. Located on the N11, 19km south of Dublin City & 15km to Dunlaoire Ferryport. 57 spacious bedrooms, private free car parking, traditional Irish breakfast, hill walking & nature trails, local golf courses, family rooms (2 adults and 3 children). Enjoy a rare blend of the Wicklow countryside close to Dublin City.

Member of Logis of Ireland

B&B from €40.00 to €85.00

EILEEN MURPHY
GENERAL MANAGER

American Express
Mastercard
Visa

Open All Year

B&B rates are per person sharing per night incl. Breakfast

GLENVIEW HOTEL

GLEN-O-THE-DOWNS,
DELGANY,
CO. WICKLOW
TEL: 01-287 3399 FAX: 01-287 7511
EMAIL: sales@glenviewhotel.com
WEB: www.glenviewhotel.com

HOTEL U   MAP 8 O 10

Only 30 minutes from Dublin City Centre, the AA/RAC 4 star Glenview Hotel & Leisure Club is the unique environment for business and pleasure. Facilities include 70 deluxe bedrooms, leisure centre with indoor pool, award-winning Woodlands Restaurant, Conservatory Bar, conference facilities for up to 200 pax. Recent developments include beauty treatment and therapy room, snooker room, childrens' playroom and woodland walks. Golf nearby.

B&B from €95.00 to €115.00

ANNE MARIE WHELAN
GENERAL MANAGER

American Express
Diners
Mastercard
Visa

Weekend specials from €160.00

70 70

Open All Year

DERRYBAWN MOUNTAIN LODGE

DERRYBAWN,
LARAGH, GLENDALOUGH,
CO. WICKLOW
TEL: 0404-45644 FAX: 0404-45645
EMAIL: derrybawnlodge@eircom.net
WEB: www.derrybawnlodge.com

GUESTHOUSE ★★★   MAP 8 O 9

Family-run guesthouse, situated on the slopes of Derrybawn Mountain. A walkers' paradise close by famous Wicklow Way. Tranquil setting, mountain views, all rooms bath & shower en suite. Spacious dining and lounge area to relax. Enjoy National Park, Glenmalure, historic Glendalough and Clara Vale. Members of local mountain rescue team. A warm welcome awaits you. Group dinners by request only.

Member of Premier Guesthouses

B&B from €40.00 to €45.00

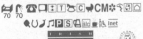

TERESA KAVANAGH
PROPRIETOR

American Express
Mastercard
Visa

8   8

Closed 24 - 27 December

Room rates are per room per night

GLENDALOUGH HOTEL

GLENDALOUGH,
CO. WICKLOW

TEL: 0404-45135 FAX: 0404-45142
EMAIL: info@glendaloughhotel.ie
WEB: www.glendaloughhotel.ie

HOTEL ★★★ MAP 8 O 9

The Glendalough Hotel, built in the early 1800s, is a family run hotel situated in the heart of Wicklow's most scenic valley and within the Glendalough National Park. The hotel has recently been extended offering 40 beautifully decorated en suite bedrooms with satellite TV and direct dial phone. The hotel's restaurant offers superb cuisine and wines in a tranquil environment overlooking the Glendasan River. The Tavern Bar serves good pub food and offers entertainment at weekends.

B&B from €65.00 to €85.00

PATRICK CASEY

American Express
Diners
Mastercard
Visa

Weekend specials from €130.00

40 40

Closed 06 January - 01 February

CHARLESLAND GOLF HOTEL & COUNTRY CLUB

CHARLESLAND,
GREYSTONES,
CO. WICKLOW

TEL: 01-287 8200 FAX: 01-287 0078
EMAIL: hotel@charlesland.com
WEB: www.charlesland.com

HOTEL ★★ MAP 8 P 10

Charlesland boasts 12 spacious en suite rooms. All rooms have remote control TV, DD phone and internet access, tea/coffee making facilities as well as spectacular views of the golf course and Irish sea. Food is our speciality and our menu is available all day. Ideal not only for the golfer but also for visitors touring the area. Located just off the N11 near Druids Glen, 20 miles from Dublin City, DART station nearby.

B&B from €45.00 to €60.00

PATRICK BRADSHAW
DIRECTOR OF GOLF

American Express
Mastercard
Visa

12 12

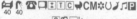

Open All Year

LA TOUCHE HOTEL

TRAFALGAR ROAD,
GREYSTONES,
CO. WICKLOW

TEL: 01-287 4401 FAX: 01-287 4504
EMAIL: enquiries@latouche.net
WEB: www.latouche.net

HOTEL ★★ MAP 8 P 10

Our hotel has a superb location overlooking the sea in the garden of Ireland. At our doorstep are Glendalough, Powerscourt and Mount Usher Gardens. All rooms are newly refurbished en suite, satellite TV and tea/coffee facilities. Our Captain's Lounge is the main meeting place for locals and visitors alike with a carvery and evening menu 7 days a week. The Waterfront Conference Centre caters for parties up to 500. Also available are Bennigans Fun Bar and Club Life Night Club.

B&B from €45.00 to €80.00

DECLAN RYAN
GENERAL MANAGER

American Express
Mastercard
Visa

29 29

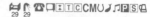

Open All Year

B&B rates are per person sharing per night incl. Breakfast

AVONBRAE GUESTHOUSE

RATHDRUM,
CO. WICKLOW

TEL: 0404-46198 FAX: 0404-46198
EMAIL: info@avonbrae.com
WEB: www.avonbrae.com

GUESTHOUSE ★★★ MAP 8 O 9

A small, long established, family run guesthouse, nestling in the Wicklow Hills. We pride ourselves in our good food and personal attention and extend a warm welcome to first time guests and to the many who return again and again. Horse riding, trekking, fishing and excellent golf available locally. We specialise in hill walking holidays and to relax - our own indoor heated pool and games room.

B&B from €35.00 to €35.00

PADDY GEOGHEGAN
PROPRIETOR

American Express
Mastercard
Visa

6 6

Closed 30 November - 28 February

HUNTER'S HOTEL

NEWRATH BRIDGE,
RATHNEW,
CO. WICKLOW

TEL: 0404-40106 FAX: 0404-40338
EMAIL: reception@hunters.ie
WEB: www.hunters.ie

HOTEL ★★★ MAP 8 P 9

One of Ireland's oldest coaching inns, its award winning gardens along River Vartry provide a haven from the world at large. Restaurant provides the very best of Irish food, fresh fish. Local amenities include golf, tennis, horseriding and fishing. Beautiful sandy beaches and sightseeing in the Garden of Ireland. Dublin 44.8km. Rosslare 115.2km. Off N11 at Rathnew or Ashford. Irish Country Houses and Restaurant Association. Refurbished 95-96. 1996 new Conference Room added.

Member of Ireland's Blue Book

B&B from €90.00 to €100.00

GELLETLIE FAMILY
PROPRIETORS

American Express
Mastercard
Visa

16 16

Closed 24 - 26 December

TINAKILLY COUNTRY HOUSE AND RESTAURANT

WICKLOW,
(RATHNEW),
CO. WICKLOW

TEL: 0404-69274 FAX: 0404-67806
EMAIL: reservations@tinakilly.ie
WEB: www.tinakilly.ie

HOTEL ★★★★ MAP 8 P 9

This Victorian mansion was built for Captain Halpin, who laid the world's telegraph cables. The bedrooms, some with 4 posters, are furnished in period style and most overlook the Irish Sea. Award winning cuisine is prepared from garden vegetables, local fish and Wicklow lamb. The family welcome ensures a relaxing, memorable stay. Available locally - golf, horse riding, Powerscourt, Mount Usher Gardens and Wicklow Mountains. Dublin 46km. Awarded RAC Gold Ribbon for Excellence. Blue Book member.

Member of Small Luxury Hotels

B&B from €102.00 to €125.00

JOSEPHINE & RAYMOND POWER
PROPRIETORS

American Express
Diners
Mastercard
Visa

51 51

Open All Year

Room rates are per room per night

GORMANSTOWN MANOR

FARM GUEST HOUSE,
NEAR WICKLOW TOWN (OFF N11),
CO. WICKLOW
TEL: 0404-69432 FAX: 0404-61832
EMAIL: gormanstownmanor@eircom.net
WEB: http://homepage.eircom.net/~gormanstownmanor

GUESTHOUSE ★★ MAP 8 P 9

A warm welcome awaits you at this charming family guesthouse. Bright spacious en-suite bedrooms. Peaceful relaxed atmosphere, spectacular surroundings. We have a golf driving range and an 18 hole golf pitch 'n' putt with a professional golf pro in attendance daily. Landscaped gardens, nature walks & superb personal services. Ideally located for golf and touring the Garden of Ireland. Breathtaking scenery, mountains, valleys, rivers, lakes & woodlands. Enjoy stunning sandy beaches of Brittas Bay, sailing, fishing, gardens, heritage, horseriding, polo, golf.

B&B from € 38.00 to € 57.00

MARGARET MURPHY
PROPRIETOR

Mastercard
Visa

:/

🛏🔥☎🖶Ⓣ🄲CM✳🎵P🅂
9 9

IRISH HOTELS FEDERATION

Open All Year

GRAND HOTEL

WICKLOW TOWN,
CO. WICKLOW

TEL: 0404-67337 FAX: 0404-69607
EMAIL: grandhotel@eircom.net
WEB: www.grandhotel.ie

HOTEL ★★★ MAP 8 P 9

This charming hotel is the perfect base for touring the beautiful Garden of Ireland. Situated in Wicklow Town, it is only a 40 minute drive from Dublin on the N11. Enjoy golf, fishing, hill walking, sandy beaches and sightseeing locally. 33 large, bright, comfortable bedrooms all en suite with direct dial telephone, multi channel TV and tea/coffee making facilities. Fine food served in the restaurant and bar all day. Lively lounge bar. Conference facilities.

B&B from € 52.00 to € 82.50

JOHN SULLIVAN
GENERAL MANAGER

Mastercard
Visa

:/🍴

☺ Midweek specials 3 nights B+B + 2 Dinners from €230.00

🛏🔥☎🖶🅱Ⓣ🄲↩CM🎵🎵🄿🄰
33 33

🆎♿

IRISH HOTELS FEDERATION

Closed 24 - 26 December

VALLEY HOTEL AND RESTAURANT

WOODENBRIDGE,
VALE OF AVOCA, ARKLOW,
CO. WICKLOW
TEL: 0402-35200 FAX: 0402-35542

HOTEL CR MAP 8 O 8

Quaint country family run hotel. Ideally located for touring County Wicklow. 1.5 miles from Ballykissangel. 1 hour to Dublin and Rosslare. Surrounded by woodlands and forest and gold miner stream running by hotel. Walking distance to Woodenbridge Golf Club. Our restaurant offers excellent food and our bars are lively with good atmosphere. Hill walking, fishing, beaches are all within minutes of the hotel. Falconry related activities, hawking and birds of prey holidays now available at the hotel.

B&B from € 40.00 to € 45.00

DOREEN O'DONNELL
PROPRIETOR

American Express
Diners
Mastercard
Visa

:/🎵

🛏🔥☎🖶Ⓣ🄲↩CM🔄∪🎵🄿🅂
10 10

♿🆎♿

IRISH HOTELS FEDERATION

Open All Year

B&B rates are per person sharing per night incl. Breakfast

WOODENBRIDGE HOTEL

VALE OF AVOCA,
ARKLOW,
CO. WICKLOW
TEL: 0402-35146 FAX: 0402-35573
EMAIL: wbhotel@iol.ie
WEB: www.woodenbridgehotel.com

HOTEL ★★★ MAP 8 0 8

Family owned and run with 23 en suite bedrooms, rooms with balconies overlooking scenic 18 hole Woodenbridge Golf Course. Dating from 1608, the hotel is the oldest in Ireland. Our restaurant and bar serve the very best of food. Winner of tourism menu awards for 1998/'99. Bar food served all day. Horse riding, fishing, golfing, fine beaches and walking are all available locally. Near Avoca, film location for Ballykissangel. Adequate car parking.

B&B from €57.00 to €77.00

ESTHER O'BRIEN & BILL O'BRIEN
PROPRIETORS

American Express
Mastercard
Visa

Closed 25 December

Room rates are per room per night

MIDLANDS/LAKELANDS
East Coast and Midlands

The East Coast and Midlands of Ireland offers a great diversity in scenery and a wealth of attractions to the visitor. Whether you are walking in the Wicklow Mountains or the Slieve Blooms, exploring the Shannon or the Cooley Peninsula or just relaxing on the sandy beaches,

this ancient Region has something for everybody. Catch the excitement of the Stradbally Steam Festival, the Wicklow Gardens Festival, Mullingar Bachelor's Festival and the Longford Summer Festival. In addition, there are many Summer Schools and other events, that take place throughout the Region.

MAJOR ATTRACTIONS

The Region is rich in archeological and historical sites of great interest, from the passage graves in the Boyne Valley, and the new Bru Na Boinne Visitor Centre, the early Christian settlements of Clonmacnoise and Glendalough to more recent wonders such as the Japanese Gardens at Tully; Wicklow Gaol, Wicklow Town; Avondale House in Rathdrum; Kilruddery House and Gardens, Bray; Russborough House in Blessington and Powerscourt Gardens and Waterfall, Enniskerry.

Other popular attractions include Newgrange Farm, Slane; Mosney; Crookstown Mill in Ballitore; Tullamore; Locke's Distillery, Kilbeggan; Athlone Castle Visitor Centre, Newtowncashel Heritage Centre and the designated Heritage towns of Athy, Kildare Town, Ardagh, Carlingford, Trim, Kells, Baltinglass, Abbeyleix and Tullamore; Heywood Gardens, Gash Gardens and Donaghmore Farm Museum in Co. Laois; Wineport Sailing Centre, Athlone; Holy Trinity Visitor Centre, Carlingford and the National Gardens Exhibition Centre, Kilquade.

In addition, Corlea Trackway Exhibition Centre, Kenagh; Ardagh Heritage Centre and the County Museum, Dundalk are also worth a visit as is the new Tullamore Dew Heritage Centre. Indeed there are many other interesting places to visit throughout the Region.

High quality golfing and equestrian facilities are widely available in the Region. Coarse, Game and Sea fishing is also available as is Cruising, Walking and other activities. There is a great variety of accommodation from the most luxurious of Hotels to the more modest family run unit and other types of accommodation, each in their own way offering superb service to the visitor.

Full details on all festivals and events, heritage and special interest activities from angling to walking in the East Coast and Midlands Region are available from the local Tourist Information Office or from East Coast and Midlands Tourism, Market House, Mullingar, Co. Westmeath.
Tel: (00 353) 044-48650
Fax: (00 353) 044-40413
E-mail: info@ecoast-midlandstourism.ie
Web site: www.ecoast-midlands.travel.ie

Newbridge Bealtaine Festival,
Newbridge, Co.Kildare
May

Budweiser Irish Derby Weekend, The Curragh,
Co. Kildare.
June

The Birr Vintage Week, Co. Offaly
August

Event details correct at time of going to press

HOTEL KILMORE

DUBLIN ROAD,
CAVAN TOWN

TEL: 049-433 2288 FAX: 049-433 2458
EMAIL: kilmore-sales@quinn-hotels.com
WEB: www.quinnhotels.com

HOTEL ★★★ MAP 11 L 14

The Hotel Kilmore is ideally located in the heart of Ireland's Lakeland District. Recently refurbished, the hotel offers 39 luxuriously appointed rooms. Renowned for fine cuisine, our AA Rosette Annalee Restaurant boasts a wide selection of dishes including local fish and game, complemented by an extensive wine list. Ideal venue for conferences and private functions. The Hotel Kilmore is the perfect base for a business visit or to enjoy the varied leisure pursuits in the area.

Member of Quinn Hotels

B&B from €70.00 to €85.00

PAUL HENRY
GENERAL MANAGER

American Express
Diners
Mastercard
Visa

39   39

Closed 24 - 26 December

CABRA CASTLE HOTEL

KINGSCOURT,
CO. CAVAN

TEL: 042-966 7030 FAX: 042-966 7039
EMAIL: sales@cabracastle.com
WEB: www.cabracastle.com

HOTEL ★★★★ MAP 11 M 14

Follow in the footsteps of Oliver Cromwell and James II, and treat yourself to a stay in a castle. Cabra Castle stands on 88 acres of gardens and parkland, with its own nine hole golf course. The bar and restaurant offer views over countryside, famous for its lakes and fishing, as well as Dun a Ri Forest Park. An ideal venue for that holiday, specialising in golfing and equestrian holidays. Member of: Manor House Hotels Tel: 01-295 8900.

Member of Manor House Hotels

B&B from €60.00 to €100.00

HOWARD CORSCADDEN
MANAGER

American Express
Mastercard
Visa

80   80

Closed 23 - 27 December

PARK HOTEL

VIRGINIA,
CO. CAVAN

TEL: 049-854 6100 FAX: 049-854 7203
EMAIL: virginiapark@eircom.net
WEB: www.bichotels.com

HOTEL ★★★ MAP 11 L 13

Beautifully restored hotel set in its own 100 acre historic estate. Located on the shores of Lough Ramor and nestled among some of the country's most beautifully landscaped gardens. Guests can avail of our 9 hole golf course, 15 miles of walking trails and excellent fishing locally. Dine in the beautiful surroundings of our AA award-winning restaurant. Our conference facilities can cater for up to 100 delegates.

B&B from €60.00 to €80.00

HOLLY HEENAN

American Express
Mastercard
Visa

Weekend specials from €130.00

26   26

Open All Year

RIVER FRONT HOTEL (THE)

MAIN STREET,
VIRGINIA,
CO. CAVAN

TEL: 049-854 7561 FAX: 049-854 7761
EMAIL: sharkeys@destination-ireland.com
WEB: www.destination-ireland.com/sharkeys

HOTEL ★★ MAP 11 L 13

Egon Ronay award-winning family run hotel, situated in the heart of Virginia, 80km from Dublin, on the main route to Donegal. It is furnished to the highest standards, direct dial phone, TV in all rooms. Enjoy a day's fishing or travelling around the lake region and return to relax in the comfort of our restaurant and sample some of the delights of our award-winning chef. It has both à la carte and dinner menus, carvery and extensive bar menu. Food served all day. 9 hole golf course 5 minutes walk.

B&B from €45.00 to €70.00

JIMMY MURRAY/ANTOINETTE MCQUAID
PROPRIETORS

Mastercard
Visa

13 13

Open All Year

TONLEGEE HOUSE AND RESTAURANT

ATHY,
CO. KILDARE

TEL: 0507-31473 FAX: 0507-31473
EMAIL: marjorie@tonlegeehouse.com
WEB: www.tonlegeehouse.com

GUESTHOUSE ★★★★ MAP 7 M 9

Tonlegee House is situated on its own grounds, just outside Athy and only an hour from the bustle of Dublin. Our guests' relaxation is assured in the tranquil comfort of this lovingly restored Georgian Country House and Restaurant. With its antique furnishings and open fires it is an ideal place to stay for either an activity filled or leisurely break. Recommended by the Bridgestone Guide's Best 100 Places to Stay in Ireland.

Member of Premier Guesthouses

B&B from €55.00 to €55.00

MARJORIE MOLLOY
PROPRIETOR

American Express
Mastercard
Visa

12 12

Closed 01 - 14 November

ARDENODE HOTEL

BALLYMORE EUSTACE,
CO. KILDARE

TEL: 045-864198 FAX: 045-864139
EMAIL: info@ardenodehotel.com
WEB: www.ardenodehotel.com

HOTEL U MAP 8 N 10

Situated on the borders of Counties Wicklow and Kildare and just 20km from Dublin City, this hotel is a perfect base for touring. The Ardenode is a family run country house hotel, set in 7 acres of scenic gardens where personal attention, a warm welcome and friendly service awaits you. Enjoy fine dining in our gourmet restaurant. Relax in the scenic Garden Lounge. Conference facilities and banqueting rooms available.

B&B from €65.00 to €65.00

BROWNE SISTERS
MANAGERS

American Express
Mastercard
Visa

17 17

Closed 24 - 26 December

KILKEA CASTLE

CASTLEDERMOT,
CO. KILDARE

TEL: 059-914 5156 FAX: 059-914 5187
EMAIL: kilkea@iol.ie
WEB: www.kilkeacastle.ie

HOTEL ★★★★ MAP 7 M 8

Kilkea Castle is the oldest inhabited Castle in Ireland. Built in 1180, offering the best in modern comfort while the charm and elegance of the past has been retained. The facilities include de luxe accommodation, a fine dining room, d'Lacy's Restaurant, restful bar/lounge area, full banqueting and conference facilities and full on site leisure centre with an indoor heated swimming pool, sauna, jacuzzi, steamroom and fully equipped gym. 18 hole golf course encircles the Castle.

B&B from € 110.00 to € 175.00

SHANE CASSIDY
GENERAL MANAGER

American Express
Diners
Mastercard
Visa

🏠 ☎ 📶 CM 🍴 ◻ Q U 18
36 36

P ♿ alc

IRISH
HOTELS
FEDERATION

Closed 23 - 27 December

STANDHOUSE HOTEL LEISURE & CONFERENCE CENTRE

CURRAGH RACECOURSE,
CURRAGH (THE),
CO. KILDARE

TEL: 045-436177 FAX: 045-436180
EMAIL: reservations@standhousehotel.com
WEB: www.standhousehotel.com

HOTEL U MAP 7 M 10

Standhouse Hotel has a tradition which dates back to 1700. Situated beside the Curragh Racecourse it has become synonymous with The Classics. The premises has been restored to its former elegance and offers the discerning guest a fine selection of quality restaurants, bars, leisure facilities, including 20 metre pool, state of the art gym, jacuzzi, steam room, sauna and plunge pool. Conference facilities cater for 2 to 500 delegates.

B&B from € 80.00 to € 130.00

PAT KENNY
GENERAL MANAGER

American Express
Diners
Mastercard
Visa

🏠 ☎ 📶 T C CM 🍴 ◻ U
63 63

🎵 P S ♿ alc

IRISH
HOTELS
FEDERATION

Closed 25 - 26 December

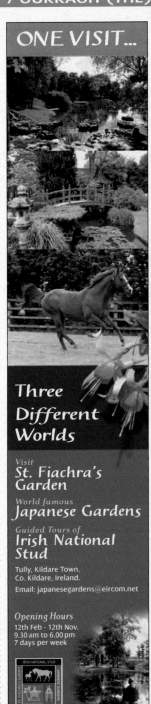
Room rates are per room per night

CURRAGH LODGE HOTEL

DUBLIN ROAD,
KILDARE TOWN,
CO. KILDARE

TEL: 045-522144 FAX: 045-521247

HOTEL ★★ MAP 7 M 10

The Curragh Lodge Hotel is situated in Kildare Town on the N7 from Dublin going south. Steeped in history, Kildare is a must for tourists not only for its heritage but for its other attractions such as the Japanese Gardens and the Irish National Stud and Horse Museum. The Curragh Lodge Hotel offers excellent accommodation, food, drink, service and entertainment. Minutes away from the classic Curragh Racecourse and midway between Belfast and Cork. It is an ideal stopover.

B&B from €51.00 to €65.00

RICHARD QUINN
MANAGER

Mastercard
Visa

🛉 👤 ☎ 🖵 T C CM ♪ 🎵 S 🔲 alc 🛏
21 21

IRISH
HOTELS
FEDERATION

Closed 25 Decemebr

AMBASSADOR HOTEL

KILL,
CO. KILDARE

TEL: 045-877064 FAX: 045-877515
EMAIL: ambassador-sales@quinn-hotels.com
WEB: www.quinnhotels.com

HOTEL ★★★ MAP 8 N 10

Situated just 20km from Dublin City, this 36 bedroomed hotel is ideally located for those travelling from the south or west. Our restaurants boast excellent cuisine and our bar provides music 4 nights per week. Local amenities include 3 race courses, The Curragh, Naas and Punchestown, four golf courses, Goffs Horse Sales, (just across the road) and plenty of horse riding. The Ambassador has something for everybody.

Member of Quinn Hotels

B&B from €57.50 to €80.00

RITA GLEESON
GENERAL MANAGER

American Express
Diners
Mastercard
Visa

😊 Weekend specials from €130.00

🛉 👤 ☎ 🖵 T C 🛒 CM ☀ ♨ ♪ 🎵 🔲
36 36

alc 🛏

IRISH
HOTELS
FEDERATION

Open All Year

LEIXLIP HOUSE HOTEL

CAPTAIN'S HILL,
LEIXLIP,
CO. KILDARE

TEL: 01-624 2268 FAX: 01-624 4177
EMAIL: info@leixliphouse.com
WEB: www.leixliphouse.com

HOTEL ★★★ MAP 8 N 11

A most elegant Georgian house hotel built in 1772. Leixlip House is a mere 20 mins drive from Dublin City centre. The hotel has been lovingly restored and offers the discerning guest the highest standards of comfort and hospitality. It can cater for conferences of up to 70 people and our banqueting facilities can comfortably accommodate 120 people. Our signature restaurant The Bradaun has been awarded several accolades and offers varied and interesting menus & wine lists.

Member of The Small Hotel Company

B&B from €70.00 to €100.00

CHRISTIAN SCHMELTER
GENERAL MANAGER

American Express
Diners
Mastercard
Visa

🛉 👤 ☎ 🖵 T C 🛒 CM ♨ 🎵 P 🔲 alc 🛏
19 19

Open All Year

GLENROYAL HOTEL, LEISURE CLUB & CONFERENCE CENTRE

STRAFFAN ROAD,
MAYNOOTH,
CO. KILDARE

TEL: 01-629 0909 FAX: 01-629 0919
EMAIL: info@glenroyal.ie
WEB: www.glenroyal.ie

HOTEL ★★★ MAP 8 N 11

A premier 3*** hotel offering the finest accommodation and leisure facilities. 20 mins from Dublin City Centre on the M4. We boast two 20m pools, a hydro spa, sauna, jacuzzi, steam room, gym and beauty salon. Nancy Spain's Bar serves good food and drink all day. The Lemongrass Restaurant is located on the 1st floor and serves Asian cuisine. We can facilitate conferences and meetings for numbers up to 550. The K Club and Carton Golf Club are within 5 miles of the hotel. For racing enthusiasts Punchestown & The Curragh are easily accessible.

B&B from €70.00 to €90.00

HELEN COURTNEY
GENERAL MANAGER

American Express
Diners
Mastercard
Visa

Weekend specials from €145.00

100 100

Closed 25 December

STRAFFAN COURT HOTEL

STRAFFAN ROAD,
MAYNOOTH,
CO. KILDARE

TEL: 01-628 5002 FAX: 01-628 9781
EMAIL: bookings@straffancourthotel.com
WEB: www.straffancourthotel.com

HOTEL ★★ MAP 8 N 11

The Straffan Court Hotel is a family owned and managed hotel situated in the heart of County Kildare. Ideally positioned close to the M4 and M50. 20 mins from the city centre. Our location is ideal for those interested in golf, racing and all equestrian activities. Only a 5 min drive from the prestigious K Club - an 18-hole championship golf course designed by Arnold Palmer and venue for the Ryder Cup in 2006. It is an ideal haven for the golf enthusiast. Many golf courses nearby.

B&B from €43.80 to €53.95

LINDA MC PHILLIPS

American Express
Diners
Mastercard
Visa

21 21

IRISH HOTELS FEDERATION

Closed 24 - 28 December

Room rates are per room per night

HAZEL HOTEL

DUBLIN ROAD,
MONASTEREVIN,
CO. KILDARE
TEL: 045-525373 FAX: 045-525810
EMAIL: sales@hazelhotel.com
WEB: www.hazelhotel.com

HOTEL ★★ MAP 7 N 10

The Hazel Hotel is a family run country hotel on the main Dublin/Cork/Limerick road (N7). All bedrooms have bath/shower, colour TV and international direct dial telephone. The hotel's restaurant has extensive à la carte and table d'hôte menus. Ample car parking. Entertainment is provided. Ideal base for going to the Curragh, Naas or Punchestown racecourses. Several golf courses close by. National Stud and Japanese Gardens only 7 miles from hotel. No service charge.

Member of Logis of Ireland

B&B from € 60.00 to € 70.00

MARGARET KELLY
PROPRIETOR

American Express
Diners
Mastercard
Visa

24 24

Inet FAX

IRISH
HOTELS
FEDERATION

Closed 25 - 26 December

HARBOUR HOTEL & RESTAURANT

LIMERICK ROAD,
NAAS,
CO. KILDARE
TEL: 045-879145 FAX: 045-874002

HOTEL ★★ MAP 8 N 10

Looking after the needs of our guests and providing quality service is a priorty in this family run hotel. All rooms have colour TV, direct dial telephone, hair dryer and teasmaid. We offer superb home cooked food, extensive à la carte and table d'hôte menus and excellent wine list. Relax and enjoy a drink in our comfortable lounge. Conveniently situated to Dublin City, ferry, airport, Punchestown, The Curragh and Mondello.

B&B from € 47.50 to € 65.00

MARY MONAGHAN
PROPRIETOR

American Express
Diners
Mastercard
Visa

10 10

IRISH
HOTELS
FEDERATION

Closed 24 - 29 December

KILLASHEE HOUSE HOTEL

KILLASHEE,
NAAS,
CO. KILDARE
TEL: 045-879277 FAX: 045-879266
EMAIL: reservations@killasheehouse.com
WEB: www.killasheehouse.com

HOTEL N MAP 8 N 10

Killashee House Hotel is ideally located on 80 acres of gardens, 20 minutes from Dublin and 1 mile from Naas. From its winding drive to its magnificent Bell Tower, this Victorian house blends the dignity of a major business hotel with the casual atmosphere of a fine country resort. Killashee House Hotel consists of 84 luxurious guest rooms, including executive suites, all traditionally appointed combining opulent luxury with perfect attention to detail. State of the art country club with superb leisure facilities.

B&B from € 110.00 to € 210.00

ODHRAN LAWLOR
GENERAL MANAGER

American Express
Mastercard
Visa

Weekend specials from €205.00

84 84

IRISH
HOTELS
FEDERATION

Closed 25 - 26 December

ANNAGH LODGE GUESTHOUSE

NAAS ROAD,
NEWBRIDGE,
CO. KILDARE

TEL: 045-433518 FAX: 045-433538
EMAIL: annaghlodge@eircom.net
WEB: www.annaghlodge.ie

GUESTHOUSE ★★★ MAP 7 M 10

AA♦♦♦♦. New purpose-built guesthouse in peaceful setting, ideally located beside all town amenities, including hotels, restaurants and leisure centres. Facilities include private parking and sauna. Annagh Lodge provides the highest standard of comfort in superior rooms with all modern conveniences combined with excellent service. Dublin and the airport are 30 mins drive. Curragh, Naas and Punchestown racecourses, 8 golf courses and fishing are a short drive. Access for wheelchairs.

Member of Best Guest

B&B from €40.00 to €65.00

DERNA WALLACE
PROPRIETOR

Mastercard
Visa

9 9 Inet

IRISH
HOTELS
FEDERATION

Closed 23 December - 02 January

EYRE POWELL HOTEL

MAIN STREET,
NEWBRIDGE,
CO. KILDARE

TEL: 045-438822 FAX: 045-438828
EMAIL: epowel@indigo.ie

HOTEL CR MAP 7 M 10

The Eyre Powell Hotel is a 33 bedroom hotel situated in the heart of Newbridge. Its rooms are well appointed and all en suite with DD phone, TV and trouser press. The Charlotte Room Restaurant can cater for up to 60 pax while a pre dinner drink can be enjoyed in Jacobs Well Bar. Conference facilities available for groups of 10 to 120 people.

B&B from €44.44 to €76.18

BRIDGET HAYDEN
MANAGER

American Express
Diners
Mastercard
Visa

33 33

IRISH
HOTELS
FEDERATION

Closed 24 - 27 December

GABLES GUESTHOUSE & LEISURE CENTRE

RYSTON,
NEWBRIDGE,
CO. KILDARE

TEL: 045-435330 FAX: 045-435355
EMAIL: gablesguesthse@ireland.com

GUESTHOUSE ★★★ MAP 7 M 10

Set on the banks of the Liffey, our family run guesthouse has 19 bedrooms with bath/shower, multi channel TV, direct dial telephone, hairdryer and teas maid. Our leisure centre includes a 14 metre indoor swimming pool, jacuzzi, steam room, sauna and fully equipped gymnasium. Horse racing, golfing and fishing are well catered for locally. A warm and friendly welcome awaits you at the Gables. Brochures available on request.

B&B from €38.00 to €57.00

RAY CRIBBIN
PROPRIETOR

Mastercard
Visa

19 19

Closed 23 December - 02 January

Room rates are per room per night

KEADEEN HOTEL

NEWBRIDGE,
CO. KILDARE

TEL: 045-431666 FAX: 045-434402
EMAIL: keadeen@iol.ie
WEB: www.keadeenhotel.kildare.ie

HOTEL ★★★★ MAP 7 M 10

Kildare's longest family run hotel, the Keadeen is ideally located on 10 acres of magnificent landscape gardens, just 35 minutes from Dublin off the M7. This charming 4**** hotel offers unrivalled standards of service and facilities with a variety of 77 luxurious spacious bedrooms, including suites and demi-suites, a superb indoor health and fitness complex and 18 metre ozone pool. An extensive range of conference / banqueting suites for up to 1000 delegates.

B&B from €87.00 to €154.00

ROSE O'LOUGHLIN
PROPRIETOR

American Express
Diners
Mastercard
Visa

☺ Weekend specials from €140.00

77 77

Closed 24 - 27 December

K CLUB

AT STRAFFAN,
CO. KILDARE

TEL: 01-601 7200 FAX: 01-601 7299
EMAIL: resortsales@kclub.ie
WEB: www.kclub.ie

HOTEL ★★★★★ MAP 8 N 11

Ireland's only AA 5 Red Star hotel, located 30 minutes from Dublin Airport, invites you to sample its pleasures. Leisure facilities include an 18 hole championship golf course designed by Arnold Palmer, home to the Smurfit European Open and venue for the Ryder Cup in 2006. In addition, both river and coarse fishing are available with full health & leisure club and sporting activities. Meeting and private dining facilities also available.

Member of Preferred Hotels & Resorts WW

Room Rate from €270.00 to €485.00

RAY CARROLL
CHIEF EXECUTIVE

American Express
Diners
Mastercard
Visa

79 79

Open All Year

ABBEYLEIX MANOR HOTEL

ABBEYLEIX,
CO. LAOIS

TEL: 0502-30111 FAX: 0502-30220
EMAIL: info@abbeyleixmanorhotel.com
WEB: www.abbeyleixmanorhotel.com

HOTEL ★★★ MAP 7 L 8

Already making a name for itself for its high standard of service, the recently opened Abbeyleix Manor Hotel with its fabulous bar and restaurant, is the perfect stop-off point halfway between Dublin and Cork on the N8. All the luxury bedrooms are en suite and food is available all day. Abbeyleix's friendly, rural atmosphere will revive the most jaded traveller and with golf, fishing and walking available locally, there is plenty to see and do.

B&B from €40.00 to €50.00

DONAL CRONIN
MANAGER

American Express
Diners
Mastercard
Visa

23 23

Closed 25 - 26 December

CASTLE ARMS HOTEL

THE SQUARE,
DURROW,
CO. LAOIS

TEL: 0502-36117 FAX: 0502-36566
EMAIL: castlearmshotel@hotmail.com

HOTEL ★ MAP 7 L 8

The Castle Arms Hotel is a family run hotel situated in the award winning picturesque village of Durrow. We are situated 1.5 hours from Dublin, two hours from Cork & three hours from Belfast. Our reputation is for good food, service & friendliness. Local amenities include fishing, Granstown Lake is described as being the best Coarse fishing lake in Europe. Trout can be fished from the local Rivers Erkina and Nore, horse trekking & many golf courses within easy reach. Brand Central designer outlet is 10 mins drive away. Ideal for a weekend away shopping.

B&B from € 42.50 to € 45.00

SEOSAMH MURPHY
GENERAL MANAGER

American Express
Mastercard
Visa

14 14

IRISH
HOTELS
FEDERATION

Open All Year

CASTLE DURROW

DURROW,
CO. LAOIS

TEL: 0502-36555 FAX: 0502-36559
EMAIL: info@castledurrow.com
WEB: www.castledurrow.com

HOTEL N MAP 7 L 8

Lord, Lady or Mistress?? Crisp linen, soft velvet, smokey leather and tall Georgian windows. Break away and enjoy the contemporary style and comfort that characterises Castle Durrow. Each room is individually fashioned and lavishly spacious, all with views of the estate and its restored gardens. Fine fusion dining, outdoor activities, conference and wedding facilities - only 90 minutes from Dublin on the main Cork Road (N8), Co. Laois. Escape to Castle Durrow ...... without leaving it all behind.

B&B from € 90.00 to € 130.00

SHELLY & PETER STOKES
OWNERS

American Express
Diners
Mastercard
Visa

24 24

IRISH
HOTELS
FEDERATION

Closed 01 - 15 January

HERITAGE - PORTLAOISE (THE)

PORTLAOISE,
CO. LAOIS

TEL: 0502-78588 FAX: 0502-78577
EMAIL: res@theheritagehotel.com
WEB: www.theheritagehotel.com

HOTEL N MAP 7 L 9

The Heritage - Portlaoise, is a new luxury hotel in the centre of Portlaoise Town. Direct rail & road access. Only 1 hour from Dublin City. Offering 110 opulent bedrooms, three bars, Nite Club, eight conference suites, two banqueting suites, two restaurants, Coffee Bean, health & fitness club with beauty spa. Secure parking for guests. A different kind of leisure & corporate experience. September 2003 - opening an 18 hole championship golf course designed by Seve Ballesteros.

B&B from € 75.00 to € 150.00

JERRY HEALY
GENERAL MANAGER

American Express
Diners
Mastercard
Visa

110 110

Closed 23 - 27 December

KILLESHIN HOTEL

PORTLAOISE,
CO. LAOIS

TEL: 0502-21663 FAX: 0502-21976
EMAIL: killeshinhotel@eircom.net

HOTEL ★★★ MAP 7 L 9

Centrally located just off the M7 approximately one and a half hours south of Dublin, you will find the ideal location for your weekend break. The Killeshin Hotel is the ideal stopover for the tourist or traveller. The location, cuisine and ambience together with our friendly relaxed style will ensure a memorable stay. Leisure centre which comprises 20 metre swimming pool, steam room, sauna, jacuzzi and state of the art gymnasium are now open.

B&B from €60.00 to €60.00

P.J. MC CANN
GROUP GENERAL MANAGER

American Express
Diners
Mastercard
Visa

44 44

Open All Year

RICHMOND INN GUESTHOUSE

CLONDRA,
CO. LONGFORD

TEL: 043-26126 FAX: 043-26126
EMAIL: therichmondinn@eircom.net

GUESTHOUSE U MAP 11 J 13

A family run guesthouse and pub in the picturesque village of Clondra. 9km from Longford Town. The Richmond Inn occupies a prime position in this pretty village, standing on the banks of the Royal Canal overlooking the harbour. Your hosts are Des & Frances McPartland who assure their patrons of a warm welcome and fine home cooking. All rooms are en suite with TV, direct dial phone, tea/coffee making facilities. Local amenities include fishing, horse riding, golf, walking and cycling.

B&B from €35.00 to €45.00

DES AND FRANCES MCPARTLAND
OWNERS

Mastercard
Visa

5 5

Open All Year

LONGFORD ARMS HOTEL

MAIN STREET,
LONGFORD

TEL: 043-46296 FAX: 043-46244
EMAIL: longfordarms@eircom.net
WEB: www.longfordarms.ie

HOTEL ★★★ MAP 11 J 13

Ideally located in the heart of the midlands, this comfortable hotel, newly renovated to exacting standards has a vibrant and relaxing atmosphere. The hotel boasts a state of the art conference centre, new health and leisure centre, excellent restaurant and award winning coffee shop where you can be assured of fine food, service and a warm welcome in relaxing convivial surroundings. Available locally: 18 hole golf course, angling, equestrian centre and watersports on the Shannon.

B&B from €65.00 to €80.00

SIOBHAN SMYTH
MANAGER

American Express
Diners
Mastercard
Visa

Weekend specials from €125.00

60 60

Closed 24 - 26 December

NUREMORE HOTEL & COUNTRY CLUB

**CARRICKMACROSS,
CO. MONAGHAN**

TEL: 042-966 1438 FAX: 042-966 1853
EMAIL: nuremore@eircom.net
WEB: www.nuremore-hotel.ie

HOTEL ★★★★   MAP 12 N 14

Set in tranquil and beautiful surroundings, amidst a championship 18-hole golf course, the Nuremore offers unrivalled standards of service and sporting, leisure and conference facilities. The Country Club boasts an 18m swimming pool, whirlpool, sauna, steam-room, gymnasium, tennis courts and a beauty treatment centre. There are a wide range of spacious rooms and demi-suites on offer and our award-winning restaurant serves superb cuisine in idyllic surroundings. 1.5 hours from Dublin.

B&B from €110.00 to €160.00

JULIE GILHOOLY
PROPRIETOR

American Express
Diners
Mastercard
Visa

69 69

Open All Year

GLENCARN HOTEL AND LEISURE CENTRE

**MONAGHAN ROAD,
CASTLEBLAYNEY,
CO. MONAGHAN**

TEL: 042-974 6666 FAX: 042-974 6521
EMAIL: reservations@theglencarnhotel.ie

HOTEL ★★★   MAP 11 M 15

Situated on the main Dublin route to the North West. This hotel has 27 bedrooms all en suite, with direct dial telephone, TV (family rooms available). Beside Lough Muckno Forest Park, great for fishing, water skiing, boating or a leisurely stroll. The Glencarn has established its name for quality food and efficient service. Music in the Temple Bar & night club. Our leisure centre boasts a sauna, jacuzzi, steam rooms, changing rooms, plunge pool, childrens pool, 21 meter swimming pool, gym, indoor bowling.

B&B from €57.00 to €75.00

PATRICK MCFADDEN
GENERAL MANAGER

American Express
Diners
Mastercard
Visa

Weekend specials from €135.00

27 27

Closed 24 - 26 December

FOUR SEASONS HOTEL & LEISURE CLUB

**COOLSHANNAGH,
MONAGHAN TOWN,
CO. MONAGHAN**

TEL: 047-81888 FAX: 047-83131
EMAIL: info@4seasonshotel.ie
WEB: www.4seasonshotel.ie

HOTEL ★★★   MAP 11 M 16

Elegance without extravagance!! Enjoy the excellent service, warmth and luxury of this family run hotel. Relax by the turf fire in the Still Bar or savour the food in the informal setting of the Range Restaurant. For an alternative option we offer fine dining in our new restaurant, Avenue. The rooms have all modern facilities and residents have unlimited use of our leisure facilities, 18m pool, jacuzzi, steamroom, sauna and gym. Also available massage and sunbed. Available locally: 18-hole golf course, angling, equestrian centre and water sports.

B&B from €65.00 to €100.00

FRANK MCKENNA
MANAGING DIRECTOR

American Express
Diners
Mastercard
Visa

Weekend specials from €150.00

44 44

Closed 25 - 26 December

Room rates are per room per night

HILLGROVE HOTEL

OLD ARMAGH ROAD,
MONAGHAN TOWN,
CO. MONAGHAN

TEL: 047-81288 FAX: 047-84951
EMAIL: hillgrove@quinn-hotels.com
WEB: www.quinnhotels.com

HOTEL U   MAP 11 M 16

This hotel combines comfort and genuine Irish hospitality, only 2 hours from Dublin, it offers 44 superbly appointed rooms, comfortable surroundings and a delightful restaurant. On the boundaries of the ecclesiastical capital of Ireland, the ancient seat of the Kings, the Hillgrove is perfectly situated for those who enjoy the rich tapestry of local history. There is a variety of activities offered by Monaghan, the most northerly town in the Lakeland Region.

Member of Quinn Hotels

B&B from €70.00 to €95.00

ROSS MEALIFF
GENERAL MANAGER

American Express
Diners
Mastercard
Visa

😊 Weekend specials from €143.00

44 44

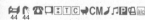

Closed 25 - 26 December

BROSNA LODGE HOTEL

BANAGHER-ON-THE-SHANNON,
CO. OFFALY

TEL: 0509-51350 FAX: 0509-51521
EMAIL: della@iolfree.ie
WEB: www.brosnalodge.com

HOTEL ★★   MAP 7 J 10

A family owned country hotel, close to the River Shannon, welcomes guests with superb hospitality and relaxed elegance. Mature gardens surround the hotel. With unique peat bogs, mountains, the Shannon and Clonmacnois, you will delight in this gentle little known part of Ireland. Fishing, golf, pony trekking, nature and historical tours arranged locally. Enjoy beautiful food in our restaurant, The Fields and drinks in Pat's Olde Bar. Courtesy of Choice Programme.

B&B from €35.00 to €35.00

PAT & DELLA HORAN
PROPRIETORS

American Express
Diners
Mastercard
Visa

😊 Weekend specials from €95.00

14 14

Closed 25 - 26 December

COUNTY ARMS HOTEL

RAILWAY ROAD,
BIRR,
CO. OFFALY

TEL: 0509-20791 FAX: 0509-21234
EMAIL: countyarmshotel@eircom.net
WEB: www.countyarmshotel.com

HOTEL ★★★   MAP 7 J 9

One of the finest examples of late Georgian architecture (C.1810), its well preserved interior features are outstanding. The atmosphere is warm, cosy & peaceful. Our hotel gardens and glasshouses provide fresh herbs, fruit and vegetables for our award winning menus. All our recently renovated bedrooms have private bathroom, telephone, colour TV & tea maker. 2 rooms adapted with facilities for disabled. Locally available golf, horseriding, fishing, tennis & heated indoor pool.

Member of MinOtel Ireland Hotel Group

B&B from €50.00 to €85.00

WILLIE & GENE LOUGHNANE
OWNERS

American Express
Diners
Mastercard
Visa

😊 Weekend specials from €140.00

24 24

Closed 25 December

Room rates are per room per night

MALTINGS GUESTHOUSE

CASTLE STREET,
BIRR,
CO. OFFALY
TEL: 0509-21345 FAX: 0509-22073
EMAIL: themaltingsbirr@eircom.net

GUESTHOUSE ★★★ MAP 7 J 9

Secluded on a picturesque riverside setting beside Birr Castle, in the centre of Ireland's finest Georgian town. Built circa 1810 to store malt, for Guinness, and converted in 1994 to a 13 bedroom guesthouse with full bar and restaurant. All bedrooms are comfortably furnished with bath/shower en suite, colour TV and phones.

B&B from €32.00 to €35.00

MAEVE GARRY
MANAGERESS

Mastercard
Visa

☺ Weekend specials from €85.00

13 13

Closed 24 - 27 December

MONEYGUYNEEN COUNTRY HOUSE

KINNITTY CASTLE DEMESNE,
KINNITY, BIRR,
CO. OFFALY
TEL: 0509-37337 FAX: 0509-37389
EMAIL: kinnittycastle@eircom.net
WEB: www.kinnittycastle.com

GUESTHOUSE P MAP 7 J 9

Truly a romantic secret hideaway, Moneyguyneen Country House is situated at the foothills of the Slieve Bloom Mountains. Nestled in the centre of 145 acres of lush rolling parkland, Moneyguyneen Country House possesses an ambience that has more in common with a private home filled with family and friends. Whether you are relaxing in the drawing room or feasting on the exquisite cuisine in our elegant dining room you are certain to be delighted.

B&B from €60.00 to €65.00

CON RYAN
PROPRIETOR

American Express
Mastercard
Visa

12 12

Open All Year

SPINNERS TOWN HOUSE

CASTLE ST,
BIRR,
CO. OFFALY
TEL: 0509-21673 FAX: 0509-21672
EMAIL: spinners@indigo.ie
WEB: www.spinners-townhouse.com

GUESTHOUSE ★★★ MAP 7 J 9

With an outlook over the majestic walls of Birr Castle, the townhouse offers a modern revival of Georgian architecture and style. An enclosed courtyard garden and 13 spacious stylish bedrooms, thoughtfully designed for comfort and relaxation offering an hospitable oasis for the weary traveller. En suite rooms, direct dial phone and tour guide on request, French/German spoken. Our Bistro is internationally renowned for food and wine...A complete hospitality package.

B&B from €32.50 to €45.00

LIAM F MALONEY
MANAGING DIRECTOR

American Express
Diners
Mastercard
Visa

13 13

Open All Year

Room rates are per room per night

MOORHILL HOUSE HOTEL

MOORHILL,
CLARA ROAD, TULLAMORE,
CO. OFFALY
TEL: 0506-21395 FAX: 0506-52424
EMAIL: info@moorhill.ie
WEB: www.moorhill.ie

HOTEL U   MAP 7 K 10

Moorhill is a unique experience in the best possible ways. Combining the classic quality of a Victorian country house with the informal ambience of a modern hotel. In Moorhill, we have placed particular emphasis on marrying the elegant surroundings and atmosphere of the hotel with a warm Irish welcome and friendly efficient service. Centrally located and ideal for a relaxing break from daily life or to conduct business at a quiet & efficient pace.

B&B from €45.00 to €60.00

DAVID AND ALAN DUFFY

American Express
Mastercard
Visa

10 10

Closed 24 - 26 December

SEA DEW GUESTHOUSE

CLONMINCH ROAD,
TULLAMORE,
CO. OFFALY
TEL: 0506-52054 FAX: 0506-52054

GUESTHOUSE ★★★   MAP 7 K 10

Set in a mature garden of trees, Sea Dew is a purpose built guesthouse, providing guests with a high standard of comfort, located only 5 minutes walk from the town centre. The conservatory breakfast room will give you a bright start to the day, where there is an excellent selection of fresh produce. All bedrooms are spacious with en suite facilities, TV and direct dial telephones. Golfing, fishing, horse riding and shooting are available nearby. Access for wheelchairs.

B&B from €40.00 to €40.00

CLAIRE & FRANK GILSENAN
PROPRIETORS

Mastercard
Visa

12 12

Closed 23 December - 02 January

TULLAMORE COURT HOTEL
CONFERENCE & LEISURE CENTRE

TULLAMORE,
CO. OFFALY

TEL: 0506-46666 FAX: 0506-46677
EMAIL: info@tullamorecourthotel.ie
WEB: www.tullamorecourthotel.ie

HOTEL U   MAP 7 K 10

The Tullamore Court Hotel, Conference and Leisure Centre has brought a new style and sophistication to the midlands since its opening in 1997. Its contemporary design, furnishing and warm bright colour scheme create an atmosphere of luxury, elegance and style. Situated on the outskirts of Tullamore, the hotel is within easy reach of all parts of Ireland making it the ideal central location for your conference or short break.

B&B from €120.00 to €140.00

JOE O'BRIEN
MANAGING DIRECTOR

American Express
Diners
Mastercard
Visa

Weekend specials from €140.00

72 72

Closed 24 - 26 December

CREGGAN COURT HOTEL

KILMARTIN N6 CENTRE,
N6 ROUNDABOUT, ATHLONE,
CO. WESTMEATH
TEL: 0902-77777 FAX: 0902-77111
EMAIL: info@creggancourt.com
WEB: www.creggancourt.com

HOTEL N   MAP 7 J 11

The Creggan Court Hotel located just off the N6 in Athlone, midway between Dublin & Galway. The ideal base to explore Clonmacnois, Ely O'Carroll country and the Shannon Basin, Athlone a golfer's paradise, surrounded by local championship golf courses including Glasson Golf Club. The Creggan Court Hotel offers spacious en suite family rooms, direct dial ISDN lines. Casual dining in our Granary Bar & Restaurant or a romantic dinner for two in our Lemon Tree Restaurant.

B&B from €35.00 to €55.00

PATRICIA FLYNN
GENERAL MANAGER

American Express
Diners
Mastercard
Visa

73 73

Inet FAX

Closed 25 - 27 December

GLASSON GOLF HOTEL AND COUNTRY CLUB

GLASSON,
ATHLONE,
CO. WESTMEATH
TEL: 090-648 5120 FAX: 090-648 5444
EMAIL: info@glassongolf.ie
WEB: www.glassongolf.ie

HOTEL N   MAP 11 J 11

Glasson Golf Hotel is a newly - registered hotel in the very heart of Ireland. Fitted to 4*** standard, the spacious rooms provide magnificent views over Lough Ree or the golf course, in a relaxing environment. The hotel is suited to both the discerning golfer and those looking for peace and relaxation in beautiful surroundings. Designed by Christy O' Connor Junior, the golf course has established a deserved international reputation as one of Ireland's premier inland courses. "Play and Stay"!!.

B&B from €85.00 to €110.00

GARETH JONES & FIDELMA REID
GENERAL MANAGER/OPERATIONS

American Express
Diners
Mastercard
Visa

☺ Sunday-Thursday 1 B&B, 1 round of golf, 1 Dinner from €150.00 pps

29 29

ald & Inet FAX

IRISH
HOTELS
FEDERATION

Open All Year

Room rates are per room per night

HODSON BAY HOTEL

ATHLONE,
CO. WESTMEATH

TEL: 0902-80500 FAX: 0902-80520
EMAIL: info@hodsonbayhotel.com
WEB: www.hodsonbayhotel.com

HOTEL ★★★ MAP 11 J 11

Located on the lakeshore of Lough Ree, commanding breathtaking views of the neighbouring golf club and surrounding countryside. Offering sandy beaches and a modern marina with cruiser berthing, summer season daily lake cruise. The purpose built conference centre, leisure complex and award-winning bar and two rosette AA fish restaurant combine to make the hotel one of the finest in Ireland. It also boasts a full Beauty Salon with massage and beauty treatments. Exit Athlone bypass, take the N61 Roscommon Road.

B&B from €55.00 to €108.00

TONY MANLEY
GENERAL MANAGER

American Express
Diners
Mastercard
Visa

Weekend specials from €125.00

133 133

Open All Year

ROYAL HOEY HOTEL

ATHLONE,
CO. WESTMEATH

TEL: 0902-72924 FAX: 0902-75194
EMAIL: royalhotel@oceanfree.net

HOTEL ★★ MAP 11 J 11

The Royal Hoey hotel offers comfort and cuisine. Today, the Royal is a modern hotel with all the services and comforts associated with today's travellers' needs. There are 38 luxuriously appointed bedrooms, colour TV, telephone, passenger lift to all floors, secure car parking, fully licensed bar and function room. Excellent restaurant. Fast food coffee dock. Restful lounge space, where you can relax and enjoy a slower pace of life.

B&B from €55.00 to €66.00

MARY HOEY
PROPRIETOR

American Express
Diners
Mastercard
Visa

38 38

Closed 25 - 27 December

SHAMROCK LODGE HOTEL AND CONFERENCE CENTRE

CLONOWN ROAD,
ATHLONE,
CO. WESTMEATH

TEL: 0902-92601 FAX: 0902-92737
EMAIL: info@shamrocklodgehotel.ie
WEB: www.shamrocklodgehotel.ie

HOTEL U MAP 11 J 11

Extensive landscaped gardens form a tranquil setting for this elegant manor style country house. The hotel is situated in the heart of Ireland, just 5 minutes walk from Athlone Town centre, making it the ideal location for conferences or as a touring base for the rest of Ireland. Our superbly appointed en suite bedrooms are equipped with all modern facilities while still retaining their old world charm.

B&B from €55.00 to €75.00

PADDY McCAUL
PROPRIETOR

American Express
Diners
Mastercard
Visa

Midweek special 3 nights B&B & 2 Dinners from €190.00

27 27

Closed 24 - 26 December

WINEPORT LODGE

GLASSON,
ATHLONE,
CO. WESTMEATH
TEL: 0902-85466 FAX: 0902-85471
EMAIL: lodge@wineport.ie
WEB: www.wineport.ie

HOTEL P MAP 11 J 11

Wineport Lodge is stunningly located on the edge of Ireland's peaceful inland waterways. Housed in a modern cedar-clad structure, it is the perfect place to dine and stay, in the heart of Ireland. If you're looking for a convenient hideaway to relax, unwind and enjoy a little piece of heaven, then Wineport Lodge is the ideal place to drop in and revive your jaded soul.

Member of Ireland's Blue Book

Room Rate from € 175.00 to €275.00

JANE ENGLISH & RAY BYRNE

American Express
Diners
Mastercard
Visa

Midweek specials from €295.00

10 10   Inet

Closed 24 - 26 December

AUSTIN FRIAR HOTEL

AUSTIN FRIARS STREET,
MULLINGAR,
CO. WESTMEATH
TEL: 044-45777 FAX: 044-45880
EMAIL: reception@austin-friar.com
WEB: www.austin-friar.com

HOTEL U MAP 11 L 12

Offering warm hospitality in the best of Irish tradition, the Austin Friar Hotel provides a range of modern facilities and a dedicated professional and friendly service. Unique in its structural design, the hotel was built in an elliptical shape and features a central atrium. All rooms are en suite with interiors of warm natural colour and soft furnishing giving a modern, sophisticated appearance. Austins, the Californian-style restaurant, is the ideal place to enjoy good food.

B&B from €45.00 to €80.00

MARGARET HARDMAN
GENERAL MANAGER

American Express
Diners
Mastercard
Visa

19 19

IRISH
HOTELS
FEDERATION

Closed 24 - 26 December

Room rates are per room per night

BLOOMFIELD HOUSE HOTEL & LEISURE CLUB

BELVEDERE, TULLAMORE ROAD,
MULLINGAR,
CO. WESTMEATH
TEL: 044-40894 FAX: 044-43767
EMAIL: reservations@bloomfieldhouse.com
WEB: www.bloomfieldhouse.com

HOTEL ★★★ MAP 11 L 12

Situated 2 miles south of Mullingar on the shores of Lough Ennell, Bloomfield House is the perfect place to unwind and relax. Only 1 hour from Dublin, the hotel can boast 65 en suite rooms, a lake-view bar and restaurant and a full leisure centre including massage, aromatherapy and beauty therapies. It is adjacent to Mullingar Golf Club and Belvedere House & Gardens and a full range of activities can be arranged, from equestrian to fishing. Email: sales@bloomfieldhouse.com for further details.

B&B from €80.00 to €120.00

SEAMUS LAFFAN
GENERAL MANAGER

American Express
Diners
Mastercard
Visa

Weekend specials from €190.00

65 65

Closed 24 - 26 December

CROOKEDWOOD HOUSE

CROOKEDWOOD,
MULLINGAR,
CO. WESTMEATH
TEL: 044-72165 FAX: 044-72166
EMAIL: info@crookedwoodhouse.com
WEB: www.crookedwoodhouse.com

GUESTHOUSE ★★★★ MAP 11 L 12

White wash Cellar Restaurant with bar overlooking Lough Derraverragh. Noel specialises in using the best of local ingredients such as lamb, beef & game in season. Marie Bardon takes care of front of house and will assist in making the right choices from the menu and wine list. 8 luxurious modern style en suite bedrooms.

B&B from €70.00 to €82.50

NOEL KENNY
PROPRIETOR

American Express
Diners
Mastercard
Visa

Special Offer - Sunday lunch free with Fri + Sat dinner B&B

8 8

Closed 24 - 26 December

GREVILLE ARMS HOTEL

MULLINGAR,
CO. WESTMEATH
TEL: 044-48563 FAX: 044-48052
EMAIL: grevillearmshotel@eircom.net
WEB: www.grevillearms.com

HOTEL ★★★ MAP 11 L 12

In the heart of Mullingar town, the Greville Arms is a home from home where customers and their comfort is our main concern. Bedrooms all en suite with colour TV and DD phone. The Greville Restaurant is renowned for its cuisine and fine wines. No visit to Mullingar would be complete without a visit to our Ulysses Bar with its life-sized wax figure of James Joyce and other memorabilia.

B&B from €55.00 to €70.00

JOHN COCHRANE
GENERAL MANAGER

American Express
Diners
Mastercard
Visa

Weekend specials from €130.00

39 39

Closed 25 December

MULLINGAR PARK HOTEL

MARLINSTOWN,
MULLINGAR,
CO. WESTMEATH
TEL: 044-44446 FAX: 044-35937
EMAIL: info@mullingarparkhotel.com
WEB: www.mullingarparkhotel.com

UNDER CONSTRUCTION - OPENING MARCH 2003

HOTEL P MAP 11 L 12

This stylish new hotel has been designed to a superior 4**** standard. 95 luxurious bedrooms equipped to international standards. Leisure facilities include 18 metre swimming pool, whirlpool, sauna, steam - room, gymnasium and beauty treatment rooms. 40 km from Dublin and is accessible off the N4, Dublin \ Sligo \ Castlebar Road. Extensive conference and banqueting facilities available. Enjoy golf, fishing, equestrian activities and visit Belvedere House and Gardens locally.

B&B from €80.00 to €100.00

SEÁN & JOESPHINE HUGHES
PROPRIETORS

American Express
Diners
Mastercard
Visa

☺ Weekend specials from €180.00 pps

95 95

Open All Year

AN TINTAIN GUESTHOUSE

MAIN STREET,
MULTYFARNHAM,
CO. WESTMEATH
TEL: 044-71411 FAX: 044-71434
EMAIL: antintain@ireland.com
WEB: www.antintain.info

GUESTHOUSE ★★★ MAP 11 K 12

Situated in a picturesque riverside setting with listed forge, in the quaint village of Multyfarnham. Behind the old world frontage lies a modern, luxurious, purpose built 3*** guesthouse and restaurant, furnished to the highest standards, complete with TV, direct dial phone and hairdryer, all rooms en suite. Enjoy a relaxing drink and candlelit dining in our renowned fully licensed restaurant. Located in the heart of the country we are an ideal base for touring.

Member of Premier Guesthouses

B&B from €35.00 to €40.00

JACK & CAROLINE SLEATOR

American Express
Mastercard
Visa

8 8

Closed 23 - 29 December

Room rates are per room per night

SOUTH EAST
The Sunny South East- Coast & County

There is no better place on earth - convenient, full of interest and with that special appeal - than the Sunny South East of Ireland. Enjoy it at any time, especially in the 'Secret Season', when its many interest points and charms will be revealed at their most relaxed best. Many daytime attractions – of the more than 60 - are open and welcoming year round. Discover for yourself that elusive yet tangible difference that has made our visitor numbers grow by twenty two percent - second only to Dublin – as compared with an average of just six percent for the other five regions.

The South East is one of the best-loved holiday regions even among Irish people. It combines the tranquil elegance of historic old towns and villages with the classic splendour of mediaeval Kilkenny, Viking Wexford and regal Waterford, the Crystal City and regional capital.

The enchanting coastline offers a necklace of small, intimate, fishing villages, interspaced by safe, sandy beaches. Their charm, especially when coupled with our mild climate, all conspire to give substance to the region's age old title - The Sunny South East.

Inland, the deep and ancient river valleys of the Blackwater, Barrow, Nore, Slaney and Suir rivers still retain the dim echo of invaders and traders, merchants and early missionaries that helped shape this fascinating land.

Our five great rivers, again rich in fish and wild life, have carved a patchwork of fertile valleys and plains through Carlow, Kilkenny, South Tipperary, Waterford and Wexford as they meander their majestic, unhurried way to the Celtic Sea.

There is so much to do in the South East. Our greatest activity, Golf - lauded by even Tiger Woods - is to be enjoyed on more than 30 courses, both links and parkland. Equestrian fans and racegoers, greyhound followers and anglers will each enjoy, in their own way, the wide-open

spaces that beckon everywhere. Walkers and cyclists appreciate the wide range – and varied lengths – of waymarked ways. The well signposted touring routes for motorist appeal to a growing band of devotees.

Call into any of our tourist offices at Carlow, Kilkenny, Wexford or Rosslare and pick up a wide range of literature to help you plan and secure the best possible pleasure from your visit.

If you have not yet explored the South East take time to enjoy it this year. You will find a special welcome awaits you. For all details contact: South East Tourism, 41 The Quay, Waterford Tel 051 875823 • Fax 051 877388 Email infor@southeasttourism.ie Visit our website: www.southeastireland.com

Carlsberg Kilkenny Roots Festival, Kilkenny.
May

Waterford Spraoi & International Rhythm Festival, Co. Waterford.
August

Kilkenny Arts Festival
August

Wexford Opera Festival,
October / November

Event details correct at time of going to press

BALLYVERGAL HOUSE

DUBLIN ROAD,
CARLOW

TEL: 059-914 3634 FAX: 059-914 0386
EMAIL: ballyvergal@indigo.ie
WEB: www.ballyvergal.com

GUESTHOUSE ★★★ MAP 7 M 8

A large family run guesthouse conveniently located just outside Carlow Town on the Dublin Road (N9), adjacent to Carlow's 18 hole championship golf course. We offer our guests en suite rooms with TV, direct dial phone and hairdryer, a large residents' lounge and extensive private car parking. Most importantly you are assured of a warm friendly welcome. We are ideally located for golf (Carlow, Mount Wolseley, Kilkea Castle, Mount Juliet), angling, shooting, horseriding and pitch & putt.

B&B from € 30.00 to € 37.00

CON & ITA MARTIN
PROPRIETORS

American Express
Mastercard
Visa

10 10 🚗🏠📞🖥️T/A C ✿⚲∪PS

Closed 22 - 31 December

BARROWVILLE TOWN HOUSE

KILKENNY ROAD,
CARLOW TOWN,
CO. CARLOW

TEL: 059-914 3324 FAX: 059-914 1953

WEB: www.barrowvillehouse.com

GUESTHOUSE ★★★ MAP 7 M 8

A period listed residence in own grounds, 3 minutes walk to town centre. Well appointed rooms with all facilities. Antique furnishing. Traditional or buffet breakfast served in conservatory overlooking the gardens. Ideal location for golf, at Carlow, Kilkea, Mt Wolseley, touring SE, Glendalough, Kilkenny, Waterford and visiting various gardens. Recommended by AA RAC ♦♦♦♦♦, Bridgestone 100 Best, Jameson Guide. Guesthouse of the year 2000 and other good guide books. German spoken. Multilingual web site.

Member of Premier Guesthouses of Ireland

B&B from € 35.00 to € 37.50

RANDAL & MARIE DEMPSEY
PROPRIETORS

American Express
Mastercard
Visa

7 7 🚗🏠📞🖥️T✿PS

Open All Year

CARLOW GUESTHOUSE

GREEN LANE,
DUBLIN ROAD,
CARLOW

TEL: 059-913 6033 FAX: 059-913 6034
EMAIL: carlowguesthouse@eircom.net
WEB: www.carlowguesthouse.com

GUESTHOUSE ★★★ MAP 7 M 8

Located 5 minutes walk north of town centre (N9), with off street private car park, our 9 guest rooms soon to be 13 are all en suite & equipped with tea/coffee facilities, TV, radio, telephone, hairdryer, trouser press, complimentary mineral water & toiletries. A premier Guesthouse of Ireland member we carry an AA ♦♦♦♦ recommendation. An ideal base for touring the southeast, only a short drive from Japanese Gardens, Wicklow Mountains, Kilkenny Castle, Waterford Glass, Rock of Cashel & numerous championship golf courses & race tracks.

Member of Premier Guesthouses of Ireland

B&B from € 35.00 to € 70.00

GER MCCORMACK

Mastercard
Visa

😊 Midweek specials from €95.00
(Jan-May Oct-Nov)

9 9 🚗🏠📞🖥️T CM✿∪PS

Open All Year

COSMO BROWN @ THE RITZ

TULLOW STREET,
CARLOW TOWN,
CO. CARLOW
TEL: 0503-41384 FAX: 0503-41398
EMAIL: info@cosmobrown.com
WEB: www.cosmobrown.com

HOTEL P MAP 7 M 8

Located on Carlow's principal social and shopping street, Cosmo Brown @ the Ritz offers our visitors comprehensive hospitality. Fabulous food served daily in either of our stylish, contemporary and truly comfortable bars. Live Jazz or Lounge Music can be enjoyed after an evening meal Upstairs at Cosmo Brown, and concluding with our 19 luxurious en suite bedrooms, each carrying through the simple contemporary style of the hotel and fitted with wide-screen TV.

B&B from €45.00 to €52.00

JOANNE BUCKLEY
MARKETING MANAGER

American Express
Diners
Mastercard
Visa

☺ Midweek specials from €135.00 pps

🛏️📞🖥️©CM♫🖨️aid♿Inet
19 19

Open All Year

DOLMEN HOTEL AND RIVER COURT LODGES

KILKENNY ROAD,
CARLOW
TEL: 0503-42002 FAX: 0503-42375
EMAIL: reservations@dolmenhotel.ie
WEB: www.dolmenhotel.ie

HOTEL ★★★ MAP 7 M 8

Nestled along the scenic banks of the River Barrow and set in 20 acres of landscaped beauty is the Dolmen Hotel, 1.5km from Carlow. Fishing, golf, shooting and horseriding are just some of the sporting facilities surrounding the hotel. With 52 beautifully appointed rooms including 3 luxury suites with en suite, TV, direct dial phone, trouser press and hairdryer. Our 1 bedroomed lodges are ideal for the sporting enthusiast. One of the largest conference and banqueting facilities in the South East.

B&B from €39.00 to €80.00

PÁDRAIG BLIGHE
GENERAL MANAGER

American Express
Diners
Mastercard
Visa

♫🍸

🛏️📞🖥️T©✂CM❄️♿🚲P🅿️🅱️
52 52

aid🚲Inet

Closed 25 December

SEVEN OAKS HOTEL

ATHY ROAD,
CARLOW
TEL: 059-913 1308 FAX: 059-913 2155
EMAIL: sevenoak@eircom.net
WEB: www.sevenoakshotel.com

HOTEL ★★★ MAP 7 M 8

Ideally located just 3 mins walk to Carlow town centre also bus/train station. We specialise in the best of Irish foods in our Tudor Bar carvery and intimate T.D. Molloy's Restaurant. Individually designed rooms, combining a selection of executive suites. Rooms are accessible by lift. Fully equipped conference facilities, with professional and friendly staff make the Seven Oaks Hotel an ideal venue for all such occasions whether large or small. Work out in our fully equipped Greekbank Health and Leisure Club with 20m Swimming Pool, Gym, Sauna & Steam Room.

B&B from €57.50 to €80.00

MICHAEL MURPHY
MANAGING DIRECTOR

American Express
Diners
Mastercard
Visa

♫🍸

☺   Special offers apply

🛏️📞🖥️T©✂CM❄️🚲📷♫
60 60

P🅱️aid🚲♿

Closed 25 - 27 December

B&B rates are per person sharing per night incl. Breakfast

LORD BAGENAL INN

MAIN STREET,
LEIGHLINBRIDGE,
CO. CARLOW
TEL: 059-972 1668 FAX: 059-972 2629
EMAIL: info@lordbagenal.com
WEB: www.lordbagenal.com

HOTEL ★★★ MAP 7 M 8

Situated in the heritage village of Leighlinbridge along the River Barrow, with private marina and gardens, we are ideally located to explore the South East. Our en suite bedrooms are luxuriously furnished to the highest standards. Award winning restaurant reputed for fine food and excellent wines. Locals and visitors frequent our bar where carvery lunch and bar food are served daily. Children always welcome. Weddings, conferences, banquets catered for. Gold Medal Entente Florale Floral Pride.

B&B from €55.00 to €80.00

JAMES & MARY KEHOE

American Express
Diners
Mastercard
Visa

⌂ ⌂ ☎ ◻ ☕ ⌨ CMCS✲∪♪♬P
12 12
🏠 a|c ⛶ ⅋ Inet FAX

Closed 25 December

MOUNT WOLSELEY HOTEL, GOLF AND COUNTRY CLUB

TULLOW,
CO. CARLOW
TEL: 0503-51674 FAX: 0503-52123
EMAIL: wolseley@iol.ie
WEB: www.mountwolseley.ie

HOTEL ★★★ MAP 8 N 8

In a world of its own located 1 hours drive from Dublin, Mount Wolseley which is steeped in history but today is renowned as a luxury 40 roomed hotel, set in opulent surroundings & offering panoramic views of the 18 hole championship golf course. Offering the perfect & idyllic location for your wedding, function, business meeting or short break featuring bars, lounges, restaurant & carvery. The hotel itself contains full conference & leisure facilities which include a 20m swimming pool, sauna, steam room, jacuzzi, beauty salon, sunbeds & snooker room.

B&B from €75.00 to €95.00

STEPHEN ANDERSON
HOTEL MANAGER

American Express
Mastercard
Visa

∖♪

⌂ ⌂ ☎ ◻ ✚ ⌂ ◻ ☕ CM✲🛉🔲◻✎
40 40
∪🔞♪♬P🏠 a|c ⛶ ⅋

I R I S H
HOTELS
FEDERATION

Closed 25 December

through the waters of time

With soaring mountains, verdant river valleys and rich rolling countryside, Co. Carlow in Ireland's Sunny South-East, offers the perfect backdrop for golf, trekking, angling, horse riding, canoeing and quading. Take a trip and discover mystical pre-christian monuments, ancient ecclesiastical sites, grand country houses and gardens and picturesque award winning villages.

For all your tourism needs contact CARLOW TOURISM
36 Dublin Street, Carlow.

Phone: +353 (0)503 30411
Email: info@carlowtourism.com
Website: www.carlowtourism.com

Room rates are per room per night

WATERSIDE

THE QUAY,
GRAIGUENAMANAGH,
CO. KILKENNY

TEL: 0503-24246 FAX: 0503-24733
EMAIL: info@waterside.iol.ie
WEB: www.watersideguesthouse.com

GUESTHOUSE ★★★ MAP 7 M 7

A beautifully restored 19th century cornstore with feature wooden beams and imposing granite exterior. Riverside location, all rooms have a view of the River Barrow. Excellent base for boating, fishing, hillwalking. 16km from Mount Juliet for golf. Nearby 13th century Duiske Abbey. 27km from historical Kilkenny. Superb restaurant features continental cuisine & international flavour wine list. Relaxed & friendly approach. Perfect for small groups. Guided hillwalking for groups.

B&B from €39.00 to €55.00

BRIAN & BRIGID ROBERTS
MANAGERS

American Express
Mastercard
Visa

😊 Weekend specials from €110.00

🛏️📞📺TC✈️⛵S🅿️aid
10 10

IRISH
HOTELS
FEDERATION

Open All Year

BAMBRICKS TROYSGATE HOUSE

KILKENNY CITY,
KILKENNY

TEL: 056-51000 FAX: 056-51200
EMAIL: troysgate@eircom.net

GUESTHOUSE U MAP 7 L 7

Troysgate House, formerly the Jailhouse of the old walled-in medieval City of Kilkenny. Conveniently located in the heart of the city. 17 en suite rooms. Angling, swimming, horse riding nearby. Kilkenny Golf Course 1km away. It is an historic and charming old world inn which has retained its character while serving the needs of the modern world. Troysgate House incorporates Bambrick's renowned traditional pub which truly has an atmosphere all of its own.

B&B from €32.00 to €60.00

PAT LYNCH
MANAGER

Mastercard
Visa

🍴🦅

🛏️📞📺TC✈️CMU🎵🎶🎯
17 17
S🅿️aid FAX

IRISH
HOTELS
FEDERATION

Open All Year

BERKELEY HOUSE

5 LOWER PATRICK STREET,
KILKENNY

TEL: 056-64848 FAX: 056-64829
EMAIL: berkeleyhouse@eircom.net

GUESTHOUSE ★★★ MAP 7 L 7

A warm and genuine welcome awaits you here at this charming owner operated period residence, uniquely situated in the very heart of medieval Kilkenny City. Berkeley House boasts ample private car parking, 9 spacious & tastefully decorated rooms, all en suite with multi channel TV, direct dial phone & tea/coffee facilities. We pride ourselves with a dedicated and professional team and ensure that every effort will be made to make your stay with us a most enjoyable one.

B&B from €45.00 to €55.00

DECLAN CURTIS
MANAGER

Mastercard
Visa

🛏️📞📺TC✈️U🅿️
9 9

IRISH
HOTELS
FEDERATION

Closed 23 - 28 December

B&B rates are per person sharing per night incl. Breakfast

BRANNIGANS GLENDINE INN

CASTLECOMER ROAD,
KILKENNY

TEL: 056-772 1069 FAX: 056-777 0714
EMAIL: branigan@iol.ie
WEB: http://kilkennyaccommodation.com

GUESTHOUSE ★★   MAP 7 L 7

The Glendine Inn has been a licensed tavern for over 200 years. It consists of 7 bedrooms (all en suite), a residents' lounge and dining room on 1st floor. Downstairs there are lounge and public bars serving snack or bar lunches. We are ideally located for golf (course 200m away), the railway station and the historic city of Kilkenny are only 1.5km away. We assure you of a friendly welcome.

B&B from €30.00 to €48.00

MICHAEL BRANNIGAN
PROPRIETOR

American Express
Diners
Mastercard
Visa

7 7

IRISH HOTELS FEDERATION

Open All Year

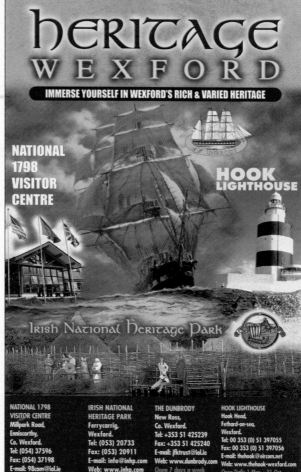

HERITAGE
WEXFORD
IMMERSE YOURSELF IN WEXFORD'S RICH & VARIED HERITAGE

NATIONAL 1798 VISITOR CENTRE

HOOK LIGHTHOUSE

Irish National Heritage Park

NATIONAL 1798 VISITOR CENTRE
Millpark Road,
Enniscorthy,
Co. Wexford.
Tel: (054) 37596
Fax: (054) 37198
E-mail: 98com@iol.ie
Web: www.1798centre.com
Adults £4
Families £12
Group Rates on application
We are situated just off the N11 and N30, only 5 minutes from Enniscorthy town centre. Ample parking.

IRISH NATIONAL HERITAGE PARK
Ferrycarrig,
Wexford.
Tel: (053) 20733
Fax: (053) 20911
E-mail: info@inhp.com
Web: www.inhp.com
Open 7 days
9.30am - 6.30pm
Last Admission 5pm
Facilities also include restaurant, craft and gift shop, mullet language audio visual and guided tours.

THE DUNBRODY
New Ross,
Co. Wexford.
Tel: +353 51 425239
Fax: +353 51 425240
E-mail: jfktrust@iol.ie
Web: www.dunbrody.com
Open 7 days a week
9.00am - 6.00pm
April to September

HOOK LIGHTHOUSE
Hook Head,
Fethard-on-sea,
Wexford.
Tel: 00 353 (0) 51 397055
Fax: 00 353 (0) 51 397056
E-mail: thehook@eircom.net
Web: www.thehook-wexford.com
Open Daily 1 Mar. - 31 Oct.
9.30am - 5pm.
Last Guided tour 5.00pm.
Late opening during high season
Contact the centre for details of opening hours, Nov. - Feb.
Visit Duncannon Fort (Jun. - Sept.)

NATIONAL 1798 VISITOR CENTRE The award winning centre tells the story of the 1798 Rebellion. Discover and explore the world of Rebels and Redcoats and experience a fascinating insight into the birth of modern democracy in Ireland. The weather-independent Centre tells the story through film, sound, interactive computers and colourful storyboards culminating in a spectacular four screen reenactmet of the Battle of Vinegar Hill. After your tour, relax in our bright, airy tea room or browse in the craft shop.

IRISH NATIONAL HERITAGE PARK Stroll through the park with it's homesteads, places of ritual and burial modes. Your sences come alive with sights and sounds stretching back almost nine thousand years.

DUNBRODY Visit Ireland's unique emigrant ship. The Dunbrody is a full scale reconstruction of a 19th century Famine ship, an authentic replica of the Three Masted Barque built in Quebec in 1845 for the Graves family of New Ross.

HOOK LIGHTHOUSE Visit one of the Oldest Operational Lighthouses in the World. "By hooke or by Crooke" you will be enthralled. Guided tours of the lighthouse, Multi-lingual Literature, Café, Craft Shop, Car and Coach Parking.

Room rates are per room per night

BUTLER HOUSE

PATRICK STREET,
KILKENNY

TEL: 056-776 5707 FAX: 056-776 5626
EMAIL: res@butler.ie
WEB: www.butler.ie

GUESTHOUSE ★★★ MAP 7 L 7

Sweeping staircases, magnificent plastered ceilings & marble fireplaces are all features of this 16th Century Dower House of Kilkenny Castle. The house is a combination of contemporary furnishings and period elegance. The larger superior rooms have graceful bow windows with lovely views of the walled Georgian garden and Kilkenny Castle. These rooms offer peace and tranquillity to the weary traveller, with the added advantage of being in the heart of the city. Conference facilities. AA ◆◆◆◆.

B&B from €62.50 to €105.00

GABRIELLE HICKEY
MANAGER (ACTING)

American Express
Diners
Mastercard
Visa

:/ ♪↑

☺ Midweek specials from €135.00

⌂♪☎⊡T C ♥CM✲∪♪P♥≛
13 13

inet

IRISH HOTELS FEDERATION

Closed 24 - 29 December

CLUB HOUSE HOTEL

PATRICK STREET,
KILKENNY

TEL: 056-772 1994 FAX: 056-777 1920
EMAIL: clubhse@iol.ie
WEB: www.clubhousehotel.com

HOTEL ★★ MAP 7 L 7

Situated uniquely in a cultural & artistic centre & against the background of Kilkenny's medieval city, the magnificent 18th century Club House Hotel maintains a 200 year old tradition of effortless comfort, hospitality and efficiency. En suite rooms are decorated in both modern & period style with complimentary beverages, TV, hairdryer & phone. Food is locally sourced, cooked and presented to highest standards. Victors Bar old world charm and luxury. Live music Saturday nights traditional Irish song & dance Tuesday nights July & August.

Member of MinOtel Ireland Hotel Group

B&B from €48.95 to €99.00

JAMES P. BRENNAN
MANAGING DIRECTOR

American Express
Diners
Mastercard
Visa

:/

☺ Weekend specials from €125.00

⌂♪☎⊡T C ♥CM∪♪P S Ⓖalc
28 28

IRISH HOTELS FEDERATION

Closed 24 - 27 December

FANAD HOUSE

CASTLE ROAD,
KILKENNY

TEL: 056-776 4126 FAX: 056-775 6001
EMAIL: fanadhouse@hotmail.com
WEB: www.fanadhouse.com

GUESTHOUSE N MAP 7 L 7

Overlooking Kilkenny Castle Park, Fanad House is a five minute walk from the city centre. The newly built guesthouse offers all en suite rooms with complimentary beverages, multi-channel TV, hairdryer and direct dial phone. Extensive breakfast menu available. Private and secure parking provided. An ideal base for exploring the medieval city. We are adjacent to Kilkenny Tennis Club. Owner operated is your guarantee for an enjoyable stay.

B&B from €45.00 to €70.00

PAT WALLACE
PROPRIETOR

Mastercard
Visa

⌂♪☎⊡C ♥CM✲∪♪P≛ FAX
8 8

IRISH HOTELS FEDERATION

Open All Year

B&B rates are per person sharing per night incl. Breakfast

HOTEL KILKENNY

COLLEGE ROAD,
KILKENNY

TEL: 056-776 2000 FAX: 056-776 5984
EMAIL: kilkenny@griffingroup.ie
WEB: www.griffingroup.ie

HOTEL ★★★ MAP 7 L 7

Hotel Kilkenny is situated in picturesque landscaped gardens, less than 10 minutes walk from medieval Kilkenny City. Facilities include 103 completely refurbished rooms, the wonderful Broom's Bistro, relaxing Rosehill Bar and the superb 5 star Active Health + Fitness Club with 20m pool and spa area, excellent gymnasium, beauty treatment rooms and hairdressing salon. Excellent conference facilities available for 4-400 delegates. Why resort to less?

B&B from €65.00 to €140.00

RICHARD BUTLER
GENERAL MANAGER

American Express
Diners
Mastercard
Visa

103 103

Open All Year

KILFORD ARMS

JOHN STREET,
KILKENNY

TEL: 056-61018 FAX: 056-61128
EMAIL: kilfordarms@indigo.ie
WEB: www.travel-ireland.com/irl/kilford.htm

GUESTHOUSE U MAP 7 L 7

Enviably located, just minutes walk from city centre and railway station, the Kilford Arms offers a personal service and great range of facilities. The White Oak Restaurant serves fresh local produce in comfortable surroundings. PV's traditional bar has entertainment nightly, with food served daily. O'Faoláin's Bar is Kilkenny's most vibrant bar, with 3 levels of stunning architecture, DJ's and late bar nightly. Welcome to the Kilford Arms.

B&B from €45.00 to €95.00

PIUS PHELAN
OWNER

Mastercard
Visa

Midweek specials from €100.00

50 50

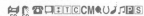

Open All Year

KILKENNY HIBERNIAN HOTEL

1 ORMONDE STREET,
KILKENNY CITY,
KILKENNY

TEL: 056-777 1888 FAX: 056-777 1877
EMAIL: info@hibernian.iol.ie
WEB: www.kilkennyhibernianhotel.com

HOTEL U MAP 7 L 7

Kilkenny's finest boutique hotel. Nestled in the Shadow of Kilkenny Castle, the Kilkenny Hibernian Hotel is a national treasure. The overall result is one of atmosphere, elegance and comfort, combined with a service that is hospitable, friendly and above all professional. Offering 46 luxury bedrooms, incorporating Junior Suites and Penthouses, the Classic Hibernian Bar, the City's leading Contemporary Bar - Morrisons & one of the regions leading restaurants - Jacobs Cottage. With secure off street parking, ideal for the smaller incentive meeting. Owner operated.

Member of Best Loved Hotels

B&B from €97.50 to €140.00

DAVID LAWLOR
GENERAL MANAGER/DIRECTOR

American Express
Diners
Mastercard
Visa

46 46

Inet FAX

Closed 24 - 26 December

Room rates are per room per night

KILKENNY HOUSE

FRESHFORD ROAD,
KILKENNY

TEL: 056-777 0711 FAX: 056-777 0698
EMAIL: kilkennyhouse@eircom.net

GUESTHOUSE ★★★ MAP 7 L 7

Situated 1km from the city on the northside's R693 near St. Lukes Hospital. A long established Georgian style house purpose built for guests. Set in 2 acres of mature gardens with secure private car parking. All rooms are en suite with power shower, TV, hairdryer, DD phone, pine furniture, oak floors, tea/coffee facilities. Traditional and buffet breakfast served in the conservatory overlooking the gardens. Owner operated, guarantees Kilkennys best value accommodation.

B&B from €27.50 to €37.50

MICHELENE AND TED DORE
PROPRIETORS

Mastercard
Visa

10 10

Closed 21 - 28 December

KILKENNY ORMONDE HOTEL

ORMONDE STREET,
KILKENNY

TEL: 056-23900 FAX: 056-23977
EMAIL: info@kilkennyormonde.com
WEB: www.kilkennyormonde.com

HOTEL ★★★★ MAP 7 L 7

The new Kilkenny Ormonde Hotel, Bord Failte 4**** accredited, is designed to compliment its famous sister hotel, the Aghadoe Heights in Killarney, bringing the same level of service and excellence to Kilkenny City. The Kilkenny Ormonde is centrally located just off High Street and is adjacent to a secure 24 hour car park. With 118 large superior rooms, a conference centre with 10 meeting rooms and extensive leisure club, the Kilkenny Ormonde is ideal for both the leisure and corporate traveller.

B&B from €62.50 to €127.50

PATRICK CURRAN
GENERAL MANAGER/DIRECTOR

American Express
Diners
Mastercard
Visa

118 118

Closed 24 - 26 December

KILKENNY RIVER COURT

THE BRIDGE,
JOHN STREET,
KILKENNY

TEL: 056-772 3388 FAX: 056-772 3389
EMAIL: reservations@kilrivercourt.com
WEB: www.kilrivercourt.com

HOTEL ★★★★ MAP 7 L 7

Award winning RAC/AA 4**** hotel, leisure club and conference centre. City centre location, stunning views of Kilkenny Castle and the River Nore. Ideal as a conference venue or simply sheer relaxation. Leisure facilities, which include swimming pool, sauna, geyser pool, jacuzzi, fully equipped gymnasium and beauty salon. Bridge House - dedicated conference and business centre. Limited free carparking. Within easy access of Dublin, Waterford and Cork.

B&B from €70.00 to €190.00

PETER WILSON
GENERAL MANAGER

American Express
Diners
Mastercard
Visa

90 90

Closed 25 - 27 December

B&B rates are per person sharing per night incl. Breakfast

LACKEN HOUSE

DUBLIN ROAD,
KILKENNY

TEL: 056-776 1085 FAX: 056-776 2435
EMAIL: info@lackenhouse.ie
WEB: www.lackenhouse.ie

GUESTHOUSE ★★★ MAP 7 L 7

Stay at Lacken House and enjoy high quality accommodation, superb food and a friendly welcome. We are a family run guest house, situated in Kilkenny City, where you can enjoy exploring the medieval city. Superior & standard bedrooms available, all bedrooms are en suite with colour TV and tea/coffee facilities. Private car parking available for all residents. Our house features the home cooking of our award winning chefs, where fresh food is cooked to perfection. Full bar service is also available.

B&B from €45.00 to €95.00

JACKIE & TREVOR TONER
OWNERS

American Express
Mastercard
Visa

☺ View our website for special offers

🛏🛌☎📠T🅣C CM✳⚓♪P🅢🄐alc ☕♿
10 10

IRISH HOTELS FEDERATION

Closed 24 - 27 December

LANGTON HOUSE HOTEL

69 JOHN STREET,
KILKENNY

TEL: 056-776 5133 FAX: 056-776 3693
EMAIL: langtons@oceanfree.net
WEB: www.langtons.ie

HOTEL ★★★ MAP 7 L 7

Langton's Kilkenny, award-winning bar and restaurant; it has won National Pub of the Year 4 times. Now open, a wonderful new hotel extension with a 'five star' finish and the same standards of excellence that have made Langton's famous. Complete with executive, penthouse and art deco rooms the new Langton's Hotel completes the award-winning picture.

B&B from €50.00 to €95.00

PAUL MORRISSEY
MANAGER

American Express
Diners
Mastercard
Visa

🛏🛌☎📠T🅣C⚓CM✳♪P🄐alc ☕
30 30

IRISH HOTELS FEDERATION

Closed 25 December

LAURELS

COLLEGE ROAD,
KILKENNY

TEL: 056-61501 FAX: 056-71334
EMAIL: laurels@eircom.net
WEB: www.thelaurelskilkenny.com

GUESTHOUSE N MAP 7 L 7

Purpose built townhouse 6-10 minutes walk from city centre and castle. Private car parking. All rooms en-suite (some with whirlpool baths & super king sized beds). TV, Hairdryer, Tea/Coffee in all rooms. Some of the comments in Visitors Book: "Absolutely Wonderful", "Best B&B we had in Ireland", "First class & recommendable", "What more could one ask for, and a whirlpool bath too", "Wonderful".

B&B from €35.00 to €65.00

BRIAN AND BETTY McHENRY

Mastercard
Visa

🛏🛌☎📠T🅣C⚓CM✳⚓♪P🅢☕
9 9

♿ Inet FAX

IRISH HOTELS FEDERATION

Open All Year

Room rates are per room per night

METROPOLE HOTEL

HIGH STREET,
KILKENNY

TEL: 056-63778 FAX: 056-70232
EMAIL: metropolekilkenny@holidayhomes.com
WEB: www.metropolekilkenny.com

HOTEL ★ MAP 7 L 7

The Metropole Hotel is situated in the heart of Kilkenny City. Occupies a dominant position in Kilkenny's main shopping area (High Street). Within walking distance of all the city's medieval buildings e.g. Kilkenny Castle, Roth House and St. Canice's Cathedral. All bedrooms are en suite with multi channel TV, direct dial telephone and tea/coffee facilities. Live entertainment. Bord Failte approved.

B&B from €30.00 to €65.00

ROBERT DELANEY
PROPRIETOR

Mastercard
Visa

12 12

IRISH HOTELS FEDERATION

Open All Year

NEWPARK HOTEL

CASTLECOMER ROAD,
KILKENNY

TEL: 056-776 0500 FAX: 056-776 0555
EMAIL: info@newparkhotel.com
WEB: www.newparkhotel.com

HOTEL ★★★ MAP 7 L 7

The recently refurbished Newpark Hotel (3***, AA***), set in 40 acres of parkland in Ireland's Medieval city. 111 bedrooms en suite with TV, hairdryer, phone and tea/coffee making facilities. The executive leisure centre includes a 52ft. pool, sauna, jacuzzi, steam room and gym. Gullivers Restaurant specialises in fine dining. The "Scott Dove Bar and Bistro" serves carvery lunch and a superb evening bar menu, with live entertainment most nights. State of the art conference and banqueting facilities.

Member of Best Western Hotels

B&B from €70.00 to €120.00

DAVID O'SULLIVAN
GENERAL MANAGER

American Express
Diners
Mastercard
Visa

Weekend specials from €200.00

111 111

IRISH HOTELS FEDERATION

Open All Year

O'MALLEYS GUESTHOUSE

ORMONDE ROAD,
KILKENNY CITY

TEL: 056-777 1003 FAX: 056-776 2680
EMAIL: o'malleys@eircom.net

GUESTHOUSE ★★ MAP 7 L 7

Situated on the Ormonde Road in Kilkenny City. The house itself is in a quiet courtyard with private parking. A modern building, tastefully decorated and spotlessly clean, with en suite, multi-channel TV, direct dial phone and tea/coffee making facilities. One minutes walk from pubs, restaurants, shopping and all major tourist attractions. Welcoming and friendly. A real home from home.

B&B from €30.00 to €60.00

CAROLINE & EIMER CROGHAN
MANAGERS

American Express
Mastercard
Visa

8 8

Closed 24 - 26 December

B&B rates are per person sharing per night incl. Breakfast

SAN ANTONIO

CASTLECOMER ROAD,
KILKENNY

TEL: 056-71834 FAX: 056-56393
EMAIL: sanantonio@eircom.net
WEB: www.sanantonio.kilkenny.20m.com

GUESTHOUSE N MAP 7 L 7

San Antonio is a family run guesthouse. Just a 10 minute walk to Kilkenny City Centre. All our rooms are en suite with tea/coffee making facilities, multi channel TV, hairdryers and telephones. Private car parking available for all residents. Ideally located to explore the Medieval City and south east area. You are assured a warm and friendly welcome.

B&B from €30.00 to €45.00

MARIE ROCHE
OWNER

Mastercard
Visa

8   8

Open All Year

SPRINGHILL COURT HOTEL

WATERFORD ROAD,
KILKENNY

TEL: 056-772 1122 FAX: 056-776 1600
EMAIL: springhillcourt@eircom.net
WEB: www.springhillcourt.com

HOTEL ★★★ MAP 7 L 7

The Springhill Court Hotel is situated only minutes from Kilkenny's vibrant and lively city centre. Now totally refurbished and offering 86 spacious en suite bedrooms, a dedicated conference centre, superb restaurant and a relaxed and friendly 'themed' Paddock Bar. From summer 2003 full leisure facilities will be available including 20m pool, sauna, jacuzzi & gym. Ideal base for touring the South East. Car parking available. Sister Hotel: The Arklow Bay Conference & Leisure Hotel, Wicklow.

Member of Chara Hotel Group

B&B from €55.00 to €99.00

JOHN HICKEY
GENERAL MANAGER

American Express
Diners
Mastercard
Visa

Weekend specials from €130.00

86   86

Open All Year

ZUNI RESTAURANT & TOWNHOUSE

26 PATRICK STREET,
KILKENNY

TEL: 056-772 3999 FAX: 056-775 6400
EMAIL: info@zuni.ie
WEB: www.zuni.ie

HOTEL U MAP 7 L 7

Zuni is a small, contemporary family run hotel and restaurant. We are located at 26 Patrick Street, Kilkenny City Centre. Ideally located for all Kilkenny's historic sights, great shopping, wonderful restaurants, bars and night clubs. Our restaurant at Zuni offers an unforgettable dining experience with excellent food prepared by our award winning chefs. Flawless friendly service in a relaxed atmosphere.

B&B from €45.00 to €80.00

PAULA BYRNE & SANDRA MCDONALD
HOSTS

American Express
Mastercard
Visa

Midweek specials from €115.00 pps
(2B&B 1D)

13   13

Closed 23 - 27 December

Room rates are per room per night

CARROLLS HOTEL

KNOCKTOPHER,
CO. KILKENNY

TEL: 056-68082 FAX: 056-68290
EMAIL: info@carrollshotel.com
WEB: www.carrollshotel.com

HOTEL ★★ MAP 7 L 6

Situated on the N10 between Kilkenny and Waterford. Enjoy the excellent service, warmth and luxury of our newly opened family-run hotel. All rooms are en suite with TV and direct dial phone. Our Sionnach Síoc Restaurant has an excellent reputation for good food. The hotel provides live music 2 nights a week. Golfing, karting, fishing, horse riding and shooting are available nearby.

B&B from €40.00 to €95.00

WILLIAM CARROLL
PROPRIETOR

American Express
Diners
Mastercard
Visa

10 10

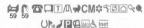

Closed 24 - 26 December

RISING SUN

MULLINAVAT,
VIA WATERFORD,
CO. KILKENNY

TEL: 051-898173 FAX: 051-898435
EMAIL: info@therisingsun.ie
WEB: www.therisingsun.ie

GUESTHOUSE ★★★ MAP 4 L 6

A family run guesthouse, 12.8km from Waterford City on the main Waterford - Dublin Road. It has 10 luxurious bedrooms all en suite with D/D telephone and TV. The Rising Sun Guesthouse is an ideal base for sports enthusiasts, surrounded by some beautiful golf courses within 15-30 minutes drive. The old world charm of stone and timberwork sets the tone of comfort and relaxation in the bar and lounge. Traditional home cooked lunches and bar food served daily. Full à la carte menu and wine list.

B&B from €40.00 to €60.00

CLAIRE PHELAN
MANAGER

American Express
Mastercard
Visa

10 10

Closed 24 - 28 December

MOUNT JULIET CONRAD

THOMASTOWN,
CO. KILKENNY

TEL: 056-73000 FAX: 056-73019
EMAIL: mountjulietinfo@conradhotels.com
WEB: www.conradhotels.com

HOTEL ★★★★ MAP 7 L 6

Celebrating 12 years as one of the most prestigious resorts in Europe, 2001 saw the opening of the Sybaritic new Spa at Mount Juliet Conrad. Guests are also invited to enjoy fishing, clay shooting, archery and horse riding on this magnificent 1500 acre estate. Guests can choose between the elegance of the newly refurbished, Mount Juliet House, the Club Rooms at the Hunters Yard or the 2 bedroom Rose Gardens Lodges. Mount Juliet also boasts an 18-hole golf course which hosted the American Express World Golf Championship in September 2002.

Member of Conrad Group of Hotels

Room Rate from €190.00 to €550.00

ANDREW PHELAN
GENERAL MANAGER

American Express
Diners
Mastercard
Visa

59 59

Open All Year

B&B rates are per person sharing per night incl. Breakfast

CAHIR HOUSE HOTEL

THE SQUARE,
CAHIR,
CO. TIPPERARY
TEL: 052-42727 FAX: 052-42727
EMAIL: cahirhousehotel@eircom.net

HOTEL ★★★ MAP 3 J 6

At the crossroads to the South where the N8 meets N24. We enjoy a town centre location. Visit the Rock of Cashel, Cahir Castle, Swiss Cottage, Mitchelstown Caves, or enjoy drives to the Galtee and Comeragh Mountains or Lismore Castle. Enjoy excellent fishing on the River Suir. 8 golf courses to be played locally. Serving carvery lunch daily. Visit O'Briens, bar food served daily till late. Our Butlers Pantry Restaurant offers quality local cuisine table d'hôte and à la carte menus available. All bedrooms finished to a very high standard all en suite.

B&B from €35.00 to €70.00

LIAM DUFFY M.I.H.C.I.

American Express
Mastercard
Visa

Weekend specials from €100.00

40 40

Closed 24 - 26 December

KILCORAN LODGE HOTEL

CAHIR,
CO. TIPPERARY

TEL: 052-41288 FAX: 052-41994
EMAIL: kilcoran@eircom.net
WEB: www.tipp.ie/kilcoran.htm

HOTEL ★★★ MAP 3 J 6

Kilcoran, a former hunting lodge set in spacious grounds overlooking beautiful countryside. An ideal holiday base located equal distance (15 min drive) between Tipperary, Cashel, Clonmel and Mitchelstown and 45 mins drive from Cork, Kilkenny and Limerick on the main Cork-Dublin road. The hotel has the charm of bygone days yet all the modern facilities of a 3 star hotel. Guests have free access to Shapes Leisure Centre with indoor pool etc. Golf, hillwalking, fishing, etc. locally.

B&B from €55.00 to €65.00

JACQUELINE MULLEN
MANAGING DIRECTOR

American Express
Diners
Mastercard
Visa

Midweek specials €135.00

23 23

Open All Year

CARRAIG

MAIN STREET,
CARRICK-ON-SUIR,
CO. TIPPERARY
TEL: 051-641455 FAX: 051-641604
EMAIL: info@carraighotel.com
WEB: www.carraighotel.com

HOTEL ★★★ MAP 3 K 5

Now under new ownership, The Carraig has been recently renovated to the highest standards. 14 en suite rooms with DD telephone, TV and tea/coffee making facilities. Carvery lunch served daily 12.30 - 2.30pm Weavers Restaurant open nightly 6-9.30pm serving the best in local produce. Weekend entertainment including Soda Club on Friday, Saturday and Sunday night. An ideal base from which to play the South East golf circuit due to several courses within half an hours drive.

B&B from €50.00 to €57.00

PAT POWER

American Express
Diners
Mastercard
Visa

14 14

Closed 24 - 26 December

AULBER HOUSE

DEERPARK,
CASHEL,
CO. TIPPERARY
TEL: 062-63713 FAX: 062-63715
EMAIL: beralley@eircom.net
WEB: www.aulberhouse.com

GUESTHOUSE ★★★ MAP 3 J 6

Aulber House - newly built luxury guesthouse. Ideally located on the outskirts of the historic town of Cashel. Home away from home. Perfect base for touring the South. Beautiful views of the Rock of Cashel and Hoare Abbey from some rooms and lobby. All rooms are spacious with en suite, power showers, direct dial phones, TV, hairdryers and computer modems. Non smoking bedrooms and dining room. Golf and angling facilities available locally.

B&B from € 40.00 to € 60.00

BERNICE & SEÁN ALLEY

Mastercard
Visa

12 12

Closed 24 - 28 December

BAILEYS OF CASHEL

MAIN STREET,
CASHEL,
CO. TIPPERARY
TEL: 062-61937 FAX: 062-63957
EMAIL: info@baileys-ireland.com
WEB: www.baileys-ireland.com

GUESTHOUSE ★★★ MAP 3 J 6

Baileys is a beautifully restored listed Georgian House ideally situated right in the town centre with private parking available. With en suite bedrooms individually and tastefully decorated, Baileys is perfect for an overnight stop or a relaxing weekend stay. The fully licenced Cellar Restaurant, with its open fire and cosy atmosphere, is a wonderful place to enjoy excellent food and wine with friendly and attentive service. AA rated 4 ◆◆◆◆

B&B from € 40.00 to € 45.00

PHIL DELANEY
MANAGER

American Express
Diners
Mastercard
Visa

8 8

Closed 24 - 28 December

CASHEL PALACE HOTEL

MAIN STREET,
CASHEL,
CO. TIPPERARY
TEL: 062-62707 FAX: 062-61521
EMAIL: reception@cashel-palace.ie
WEB: www.cashel-palace.ie

HOTEL ★★★★ MAP 3 J 6

Built in 1730 as an Archbishop's Palace, the Cashel Palace has been restored as a hotel, complemented by tranquil walled gardens and a private walk to the famous Rock of Cashel. Our 23 bedrooms are all en suite with TV, phone, trouser press. Our Bishop's Buttery Restaurant is open for lunch and dinner, while the Guinness Bar is open for light snacks daily, both offering modern Irish cuisine at affordable prices. Sunday lunch served in our Palace Suite.

B&B from € 92.50 to € 175.00

SUSAN & PATRICK MURPHY
PROPRIETORS

American Express
Diners
Mastercard
Visa

23 23

Closed 12 - 25 January

B&B rates are per person sharing per night incl. Breakfast

DUNDRUM HOUSE HOTEL

DUNDRUM,
CASHEL,
CO. TIPPERARY
TEL: 062-71116 FAX: 062-71366
EMAIL: dundrumh@iol.ie
WEB: www.dundrumhousehotel.com

HOTEL ★★★ MAP 3 I 7

A Haven of peace and tranquillity, the hotel is surrounded by the manicured fairways of its own 18 hole championship course designed by Philip Walton. The Country Club features the Venue Clubhouse Bar/Restaurant, state of the art Health & Leisure centre with 20m deck level indoor pool, gym, jacuzzi, sauna. Beauty treatments by appointment. Elegant guest bedroom with antiques, and penthouse suites. Rossmore Restaurant is renowned for fine foods and wines.

Member of Manor House Hotels

B&B from €75.00 to €119.00

AUSTIN & MARY CROWE
PROPRIETORS

American Express
Diners
Mastercard
Visa

Midweek specials from €155.00

86 86

Closed 24 - 26 December

LEGENDS TOWNHOUSE & RESTAURANT

THE KILN,
CASHEL,
CO. TIPPERARY
TEL: 062-61292
EMAIL: info@legendsguesthouse.com
WEB: www.legendsguesthouse.com

GUESTHOUSE ★★★ MAP 3 I 5

Legends Townhouse and Restaurant, graded AA ♦♦♦♦ is uniquely situated at the foot of the Rock of Cashel. Awarded Bridgestone 100 Best Places To Stay & 100 Best Restaurants In Ireland. A warm welcome, friendly & attentive service will help you unwind & relax. Enjoy excellent cuisine in our own restaurant, fine wines & a good night's rest before waking to an extensive breakfast selection served in the shadow of 'The Rock'. An ideal base for touring Waterford, Kilkenny, Cork & Limerick. Local amenities: 18 hole golf, pony trekking, guided walks, craft centres.

B&B from €32.00 to €64.00

ROSEMARY & MICHAEL O'NEILL

Mastercard
Visa

Weekend specials from €105.00

7 7

Closed 16 February - 11 March

BRIGHTON HOUSE

1 BRIGHTON PLACE,
CLONMEL,
CO. TIPPERARY
TEL: 052-23665 FAX: 052-25210
EMAIL: brighton@iol.ie
WEB: www.tipp.ie/brighton.htm

GUESTHOUSE ★★ MAP 3 K 5

Family run 3 storey Georgian guest house, with a hotel ambience and antique furnishings. Clonmel Town centre - the largest inland town in Ireland bridging Rosslare Harbour (132km) with Killarney (160km) and the South West. Host to Fleadh Cheoil na hEireann 1993/94. Visit Rock of Cashel, Mitchelstown Caves, Cahir Castle etc. Golf, fishing and pony trekking arranged locally. All rooms direct dial phones, TV, radio, hairdryer and tea/coffee making facilities.

B&B from €35.00 to €50.00

BERNIE MORRIS
PROPRIETOR

Mastercard
Visa

6 5

Open All Year

Room rates are per room per night

CLONMEL ARMS HOTEL

CLONMEL,
CO. TIPPERARY

TEL: 052-21233 FAX: 052-21526
EMAIL: theclonmelarms@eircom.net
WEB: www.tipp.ie/clonmellarms.htm

HOTEL ★★★ MAP 3 K 5

In the heart of Clonmel, it is the perfect base for golfers and touring the South East. Perfectly located in the town centre, this elegant hotel has a perfect combination of old world character, superb cuisine and friendly attentive service. We are pleased to arrange for you, golf on Tipperarys premier courses. The Paddock Bar serves carvery lunch daily and a superb evening bar menu. Live entertainment every weekend. Private parking.

B&B from €57.00 to €100.00

NEILUS MCDONNELL
MANAGER

American Express
Diners
Mastercard
Visa

30 30

Closed 25 December

FENNESSY'S HOTEL

GLADSTONE STREET,
CLONMEL,
CO. TIPPERARY

TEL: 052-23680 FAX: 052-23783
EMAIL: info@fennessyshotel.com
WEB: www.fennessyshotel.com

HOTEL ★★ MAP 3 K 5

Long established hotel. This beautiful Georgian building is newly restored and refurbished. Right in the centre of Clonmel, it is easily located opposite the town's main church. All bedrooms have direct dial phone, en suite, TV, hair dryer, tea/coffee facilities, some have jacuzzi. Family run hotel. Elegant ambience throughout. Golf, hillwalking, historical sites, pony trekking all available locally. Private fishing arranged. Swimming pool and fitness centre nearby. After your visit, you will wish to return.

B&B from €35.00 to €50.00

RICHARD AND ESTHER FENNESSY
PROPRIETORS

American Express
Mastercard
Visa

10 10

Open All Year

HOTEL MINELLA & LEISURE CENTRE

CLONMEL,
CO. TIPPERARY

TEL: 052-22388 FAX: 052-24381
EMAIL: frontdesk@hotelminella.ie
WEB: www.hotelminella.ie

HOTEL ★★★ MAP 3 K 5

Country house hotel set in landscaped grounds along the River Suir. Hotel Minella prides itself in its exceptional service & hospitality. Rooms throughout are elegantly furnished, 5 suites with jacuzzis, 3 with 4-poster beds & private steam rooms. The Award Winning Leisure Centre is a favourite with its guests: 20 meter pool, Gym, Outdoor Canadian Hot Tub, Steam Room, Massage & Therapy Rooms. Tennis court. AA Rosette Restaurant. Conference room for 500. Family owned. An ideal venue for touring the South East.

B&B from €80.00 to €120.00

ELIZABETH NALLEN
MANAGING DIRECTOR

American Express
Diners
Mastercard
Visa

Weekend specials from €165.00

70 70

Closed 23 - 29 December

B&B rates are per person sharing per night incl. Breakfast

MULCAHYS

**47 GLADSTONE STREET,
CLONMEL,
CO. TIPPERARY**

TEL: 052-25054 FAX: 052-24544
EMAIL: mulcahys@eircom.net
WEB: www.mulcahys.ie

GUESTHOUSE ★★ MAP 3 K 5

Mulcahys is run by the Higgins family. Our bedrooms are tastefully designed, all en suite with tea/coffee making facilities, multi channel TV and hairdryer. The carvery opens for lunch from 12pm and our "East Lane" menu is served from 6pm which includes lobsters and oysters from our fish tank. "Dance the night away" at our award winning nightclub "Dannos". Some of Ireland's best golf courses are within easy reach of Clonmel and the River Suir has been described as an "anglers paradise".

B&B from €40.00 to €100.00

ROS DONAGHUE

American Express
Mastercard
Visa

10 10

Closed 24 December - 02 January

RECTORY HOUSE HOTEL

**DUNDRUM,
CO. TIPPERARY**

TEL: 062-71266 FAX: 062-71115
EMAIL: rectoryh@iol.ie
WEB: www.rectoryhousehotel.com

HOTEL ★★★ MAP 3 I 7

Charming country house hotel, set in it's own secluded tree lined gardens. Comfort and tranquility are offered to our guests in tastefully decorated rooms en suite. Friendly and attentive service, our candlelit restaurant and conservatory offers modern and classic cuisine, old and new world wines. The ideal country retreat to unwind and relax, ideally located for golfing, fishing, ramblers, horse racing, GAA sports.

B&B from €47.50 to €60.00

GERARD ALDWELL
GENERAL MANAGER

Mastercard
Visa

Winter weekend specials from €100.00

10 10

Open All Year

AHERLOW HOUSE HOTEL

**GLEN OF AHERLOW,
CO. TIPPERARY**

TEL: 062-56153 FAX: 062-56212
EMAIL: aherlow@iol.ie
WEB: www.aherlowhouse.ie

HOTEL ★★★ MAP 3 I 6

Aherlow House Hotel and 4**** de luxe holiday homes. The Hotel & Lodges are set in the middle of a coniferous forest just 4 miles from Tipperary Town. Originally a hunting lodge now converted into an exquisitely furnished hotel. Aherlow House welcomes you to its peaceful atmosphere, enhanced by a fine reputation for hospitality, excellent cuisine and good wines. Overlooks the Glen of Aherlow and has beautiful views of the Galtee Mountains. Activities can be arranged.

B&B from €62.00 to €82.00

FRANCES FOGARTY
MANAGER

American Express
Diners
Mastercard
Visa

30 30

Open All Year

Room rates are per room per night

GLEN HOTEL

GLEN OF AHERLOW,
CO. TIPPERARY

TEL: 062-56146 FAX: 062-56152

HOTEL ★★ MAP 3 I 6

The Glen Hotel set in the shadows of the majestic Galtee Mountains, amidst the splendour of the Aherlow Valley is just 5 miles from Tipperary Town. To relax, dream, reminisce or plan - this is the ideal haven. Our bedrooms are all en suite and have been recently tastefully redecorated. This family operated hotel has built up a fine reputation for excellent cuisine and offers friendly and efficient service. Hill walking, horse riding, fishing and golf.

B&B from €40.00 to €59.00

MARGOT AND JAMES COUGHLAN
PROPRIETORS

American Express
Diners
Mastercard
Visa

Weekend specials from €110.00

23 23

Open All Year

HORSE AND JOCKEY INN

HORSE AND JOCKEY,
(NEAR CASHEL),
CO. TIPPERARY

TEL: 0504-44192 FAX: 0504-44747
EMAIL: horseandjockeyinn@eircom.net
WEB: www.horseandjockeyinn.com

HOTEL ★★★ MAP 7 J 7

The Horse and Jockey Inn, located at the heartland of County Tipperary, midway between Cork and Dublin on the N8 holds great association with people from sporting, cultural and political walks of life. Our modern refurbishment includes spacious lounge and bar facilities, a high quality restaurant, de luxe accommodation and a modern conference centre. Experience the atmosphere that's steeped in tradition and share with us the real Ireland, in the comfort of our new inn.

B&B from €70.00 to €70.00

TOM EGAN
PROPRIETOR

American Express
Diners
Mastercard
Visa

29 29

Inet FAX

Open All Year

ARDAGH HOUSE

KILLENAULE,
CO. TIPPERARY

TEL: 052-56224 FAX: 052-56224
EMAIL: ahouse@iol.ie

GUESTHOUSE ★ MAP 3 K 7

Fully licensed family guesthouse, piano lounge bar, residents' lounge, rooms en suite, home cooking. Set in the shadow of romantic Slievenamon, in the area of the Derrynaflan Chalice, the famous Coolmore Stud, in the heart of the Golden Vale. Near Holycross Abbey, Cashel and Kilkenny. Central for hunting, fishing, shooting, golf, horse riding and less strenuous walks through the hills of Killenaule. Finally, just one hour from the sea.

B&B from €30.00 to €34.00

MICHAEL & MARY McCORMACK
MANAGERS

American Express
Mastercard
Visa

6 6

Closed 25 December

B&B rates are per person sharing per night incl. Breakfast

ACH NA SHEEN GUESTHOUSE

CLONMEL ROAD,
TIPPERARY TOWN,
CO. TIPPERARY
TEL: 062-51298 FAX: 062-80467
EMAIL: gernoonan@eircom.net

GUESTHOUSE ★★ MAP 316

Family run guesthouse, 5 minutes from the town centre with a spacious sunlounge and diningroom overlooking gardens and the beautiful Galtee Mountains. Our 10 rooms, 8 are en suite, are all equipped with TV and tea/coffee making facilities. Ach-na-Sheen is adjacent to the picturesque Glen of Aherlow where fishing and hill walking can be arranged. Golf can be enjoyed at any number of nearby championship courses. G & S Noonan offer you the utmost in Irish hospitality.

B&B from € 33.00 to € 40.00

GER & SYLVIA NOONAN
PROPRIETORS

Mastercard

Visa

10 8

Closed 18 December - 01 March

BALLYGLASS COUNTRY HOUSE

GLEN OF AHERLOW ROAD,
BALLYGLASS,
TIPPERARY TOWN
TEL: 062-52104 FAX: 062-52229
EMAIL: info@ballyglasshouse.com
WEB: www.ballyglasshouse.com

HOTEL U MAP 316

Ballyglass Country House is an 18th Century country residence set in it's own grounds on the outskirts of Tipperary and just 2km from the beautiful Glen of Aherlow. Here at this family run hotel you can enjoy the best of local produce in our "Colonel's Restaurant" and relax in front of a real coal fire in our "Forge Bar". Ballyglass Country House is perfectly situated for touring Munster. Golfing, fishing, hillwalking & horseriding are all available locally.

B&B from € 40.00 to € 45.00

JOAN AND BILL BYRNE
PROPRIETORS

American Express

Mastercard

Visa

Weekend specials from €90.00

10 10

Closed 24 - 25 December

ROYAL HOTEL

BRIDGE STREET,
TIPPERARY TOWN,
CO. TIPPERARY
TEL: 062-33244 FAX: 062-33596
EMAIL: royalht@iol.ie
WEB: www.royalhoteltipperary.com

HOTEL ★★ MAP 316

Situated in Tipperary Town, a familiar meeting place serving excellent food from 8am to 10pm daily, using finest quality local produce, tastefully decorated rooms with all amenities. Just a few minutes from Tipperary Race Course, 3 outstanding golf clubs (special arrangements & packages available to the hotel for Tipperary, Dundrum & Ballykisteen clubs). Sport & Leisure Complex 3 mins from the hotel. The Excell Theatre within a short walking distance. So if its business or pleasure, a warm welcome awaits you.

B&B from € 50.00 to € 70.00

KAREN BYRNES & EOIN O'SULLIVAN
HOSTS

American Express

Diners

Mastercard

Visa

16 16

Open All Year

Room rates are per room per night

NEWTOWN FARM GUESTHOUSE

GRANGE,
ARDMORE, VIA YOUGHAL,
CO. WATERFORD
TEL: 024-94143 FAX: 024-94054
EMAIL: newtownfarm@eircom.net
WEB: www.newtownfarm.com

GUESTHOUSE ★★★ MAP 3 K 3

Family-run farm guesthouse in scenic location, surrounded by its own farmlands with dairying as the main enterprise, with views of the Atlantic Ocean, hills and cliff walks. All bedrooms en suite with tea/coffee making facilities, TV, DD phone and hairdryer. Grange is 6 minutes from the beach and Ardmore Round Tower and Cathedral, built in the 12th century, raises its heights to 97 feet. 2 hours drive from Port of Rosslare. Signposted on N25 turn left at Flemings Pub, 200m.

Member of Premier Guesthouses

B&B from €33.00 to €36.00

TERESA O'CONNOR
PROPRIETOR

Mastercard

Visa

☺ Midweek specials from €95.00

7   7

Closed 31 November - 31 January

ROUND TOWER HOTEL

COLLEGE ROAD,
ARDMORE,
CO. WATERFORD
TEL: 024-94494 FAX: 024-94254
EMAIL: rth@eircom.net

HOTEL U MAP 3 K 3

Situated within walking distance of Ardmore's award-winning beach, the Round Tower Hotel offers 12 well appointed en suite bedrooms. Fresh local produce feature prominently on both the bar and restaurant menus. The ancient monastic settlement of St. Declan & the Round Tower are situated behind the hotel. Ardmore also boasts some world famous cliff walks and breathtaking scenery. Ardmore is 21kms from Dungarvan & a 2 hour drive from the port of Rosslare on the Primary N25 route.

B&B from €45.00 to €50.00

AIDAN QUIRKE
PROPRIETOR

Mastercard

Visa

12   12

Closed 21 - 28 December

HANORAS COTTAGE

NIRE VALLEY,
BALLYMACARBRY,
CO. WATERFORD
TEL: 052-36134 FAX: 052-36540
EMAIL: hanorascottage@eircom.net
WEB: www.hanorascottage.com

GUESTHOUSE ★★★★ MAP 3 K 5

A haven of peace and tranquillity in the Comeragh Mountains, Hanoras Cottage has everything for discerning guests. Relax in the sheer bliss of an adult only house with the soothing sounds of the Nire River running by. Spacious rooms with jacuzzi tubs. Superior rooms for that special occasion! Enjoy excellent cuisine from our Ballymaloe school chefs who cater for all diets. AA & RAC ◆◆◆◆◆ awards. Walking, golf, horse-riding and just relaxing! National award winners, Breakfast of the Year 2002.

B&B from €75.00 to €125.00

THE WALL FAMILY
PROPRIETORS

Mastercard

Visa

10   10

Closed 20 - 28 December

B&B rates are per person sharing per night incl. Breakfast

RICHMOND HOUSE

CAPPOQUIN,
CO. WATERFORD

TEL: 058-54278 FAX: 058-54988
EMAIL: info@richmondhouse.net
WEB: www.richmond.house.net

GUESTHOUSE ★★★★ MAP 3 J 4

Delightful 18th century Georgian Countryhouse and fully licenced award winning restaurant set in private grounds. Relax in total peace and tranquillity in front of log fires. Each room is a perfect blend of Georgian splendour combined with all modern comforts for the discerning guest. AA ♦♦♦♦♦. Recommended in the Bridgestone Guides; 100 Best Places to Stay, 100 Best Restaurants in Ireland and all leading guides. Ideal location for a short break.

B&B from €65.00 to €108.00

PAUL & CLAIRE DEEVY
PROPRIETORS

American Express
Diners
Mastercard
Visa

Closed 23 December - 20 January

THREE RIVERS GUEST HOUSE

CHEEKPOINT,
CO. WATERFORD

TEL: 051-382520 FAX: 051-382542
EMAIL: mail@threerivers.ie
WEB: www.threerivers.ie

GUESTHOUSE ★★★ MAP 4 M 5

AA Selected ♦♦♦ guesthouse overlooking scenic Waterford Estuary. Situated on the outskirts of the historic village, Cheekpoint, with its award winning pubs and seafood restaurants. Sample the delights of breakfast in our Estuary View dining room or relax over coffee in our spacious lounge. Ideal base for touring the sunny South East, close to Waterford, Dunmore East, Tramore and 2km from Faithlegg Golf Course. All rooms en suite with direct dial phone.

Member of Premier Guesthouses

B&B from €34.00 to €45.00

TIM & AINE HAIER

American Express
Mastercard
Visa

Midweek specials from €96.00

Closed 20 December - 7 January

Room rates are per room per night

BARNAWEE BRIDGE GUESTHOUSE

KILMINION,
DUNGARVAN,
CO. WATERFORD
TEL: 058-42074

GUESTHOUSE ★★★ MAP 3 K 4

Our newly built guesthouse with fabulous sea and mountain views near all local amenities including three 18 hole golf courses, indoor swimming, sea angling, tennis, fishing and bird watching. Also various country side walks. Food & drinks available locally, also a kitchenette for tea/coffee and snacks available for all our customers. All rooms are very spacious with en suite and color T.V. The making for a very enjoyable stay. Mobile number: 087 2620269.

B&B from €35.00 to €50.00

MICHELLE DWANE/GARY TREEN
PROPRIETORS

Mastercard

Visa

☺ Midweek specials from €95.00

CLONEA STRAND HOTEL, GOLF & LEISURE

CLONEA,
DUNGARVAN,
CO. WATERFORD
TEL: 058-45555 FAX: 058-42880
EMAIL: info@clonea.com
WEB: www.clonea.com

HOTEL ★★★ MAP 3 K 4

Clonea Strand Hotel overlooking Clonea Beach. Family run by John and Ann McGrath. All rooms en suite with tea/coffee making facilities, hairdryer and colour TV. Indoor leisure centre with heated pool, jacuzzi, sauna, Turkish bath, gymnasium and ten pin bowling alley. Situated close by is our 18 hole golf course bordering on the Atlantic Ocean with a scenic background of Dungarvan Bay and Comeragh Mountains. Our Bay Restaurant specialises in locally caught seafood.

B&B from €45.00 to €95.00

MARK KNOWLES
GEN.MGR.GROUP/MARKETING

American Express

Diners

Mastercard

Visa

58 58

IRISH
HOTELS
FEDERATION

Open All Year

LAWLORS HOTEL

BRIDGE STREET,
DUNGARVAN,
CO. WATERFORD
TEL: 058-41122 FAX: 058-41000
EMAIL: lawlorshotel@cablesurf.com
WEB: www.lawlors-hotel.ie

HOTEL ★★★ MAP 3 K 4

Lawlors Hotel is family run with 89 bedrooms, all en suite with tea/coffee making facilities, TV and direct dial phone. Lawlors is the ideal choice for your stay in the beautiful West Waterford countryside. Conferences, Weddings, Parties, Seminars are especially catered for. Good food is a speciality at Lawlors and the friendly atmosphere of Dungarvan Town is brought to life in the Old Worlde bar surroundings.

B&B from €46.00 to €75.00

MICHAEL BURKE
PROPRIETOR

American Express
Diners
Mastercard
Visa

Weekend specials from €160.00

89 89

S aid

IRISH HOTELS FEDERATION

Closed 25 December

PARK HOTEL

DUNGARVAN,
CO. WATERFORD
TEL: 058-42899 FAX: 058-42969
EMAIL: photel@indigo.ie
WEB: www.flynnhotels.com

HOTEL ★★★ MAP 3 K 4

Overlooking the Colligan River Estuary, owned and run by the Flynn Family, whose experience in the hotel business is your best guarantee of an enjoyable and memorable stay. The hotel's spacious and comfortable bedrooms have been furnished with flair and imagination. All have private bathroom, direct dial telephone, 16 channel satellite TV. The hotel's leisure centre has a 20m swimming pool, sauna, steam room & gym.

B&B from €52.00 to €66.00

PIERCE FLYNN
MANAGER

American Express
Diners
Mastercard
Visa

29 29

aid

IRISH HOTELS FEDERATION

Closed 24 - 28 December

POWERSFIELD HOUSE

BALLINAMUCK,
DUNGARVAN,
CO. WATERFORD
TEL: 058-45594 FAX: 058-45550
EMAIL: powersfieldhouse@cablesurf.com
WEB: www.powersfield.com

GUESTHOUSE ★★★ MAP 3 K 4

Powersfield House is situated just outside Dungarvan on the R672. Ideally located for the three 18-hole Golf Courses and beautiful beaches. The bedrooms are individually decorated using antique furniture, crisp linens and fresh flowers. Dinner is served on Thursday, Friday and Saturday nights in our restaurant. Advance booking advised. Wine and beer license. AA ♦♦♦♦♦, Bridgestone 100 Best Restaurants, 100 Best Places to Stay in Ireland.

Member of Premier Guesthouses

B&B from €45.00 to €60.00

EUNICE & EDMUND POWER

American Express
Mastercard
Visa

6 6

aid Inet

IRISH HOTELS FEDERATION

Open All Year

Room rates are per room per night

SEAVIEW

WINDGAP,
N25/YOUGHAL ROAD, DUNGARVAN,
CO. WATERFORD
TEL: 058-41583 FAX: 058-41679
EMAIL: faheyn@gofree.indigo.ie
WEB: www.amireland.com/seaview/

GUESTHOUSE ★★★ MAP 3 K 4

Want your vacation to never stop being a vacation? Enjoy breakfast overlooking the sea? Play one of Dungarvans three 18 hole golf courses or take a bus tour of the area and let someone else do the driving. How about dinner, entertained by traditional Irish musicians, at the nearby Marine Bar? Make every ounce of your vacation count. Try Seaview on N25 5km west of Dungarvan. Fax and e-mail facilities available. Continental and Full Irish breakfast served. Laundry service available.

B&B from €35.00 to €35.00

NORA & MARTIN & MEALLA FAHEY

Mastercard
Visa

8 8

Open All Year

BEACH GUEST HOUSE

1 LOWER VILLAGE,
DUNMORE EAST,
CO. WATERFORD
TEL: 051-383316 FAX: 051-383319
EMAIL: beachouse@eircom.net
WEB: www.vizor.ie/beachouse

GUESTHOUSE N MAP 4 M 5

Newly built in a superb location overlooking Dunmore East Strand. The Beach Guest House provides luxury accommodation, stunning sea views and private parking. A central base from which to explore charming hidden coves, superb cliff walks and neat rows of pretty thatched cottages in this picturesque village 10 miles from Waterford, in the centre of Dunmore with excellent restaurants and sporting amenities nearby including 4 championship golf courses within 10 miles.

B&B from €30.00 to €50.00

BREDA BATTLES
HOST

Mastercard
Visa

7 7

Closed 01 November - 28 February

HAVEN HOTEL

DUNMORE EAST,
CO. WATERFORD
TEL: 051-383150 FAX: 051-383488
EMAIL: info@thehavenhotel.com
WEB: www.thehavenhotel.com

HOTEL ★★ MAP 4 M 5

The Haven Hotel is family owned and managed. Situated in Dunmore East, one of Ireland's most beautiful seaside resorts. The restaurant is renowned for its first class food and specialises in prime rib beef, steaks and locally caught seafood. The Haven is an ideal location for day trips to the many surrounding golf clubs. Children are also made especially welcome with our motto being - the children of today are the customers of tomorrow.

B&B from €55.00 to €65.00

JEAN & JOHN KELLY
MANAGERS/OWNERS

Mastercard
Visa

24 24

Closed 30 October - 03 March

B&B rates are per person sharing per night incl. Breakfast

OCEAN HOTEL

DUNMORE EAST,
CO. WATERFORD

TEL: 051-383136 FAX: 051-383576
EMAIL: oceanhotel@ireland.com

HOTEL ★★ MAP 4 M 5

The Ocean Hotel 15 minutes drive from Waterford City, is situated in one of Ireland's most picturesque villages. The Jewel of the sunny South East. We offer you the personal attention & service only a family run hotel can provide. Our extensive à la carte menu is available in both dining room and bar with a strong emphasis on seafood dishes. Our menu is reasonably priced. Golf packages arranged. Our new Alfred D Snow Bar is air conditioned with décor depicting a nautical theme. Entertainment in the bar most nights during the summer and Saturday nights all year around.

B&B from €45.00 to €60.00

BRENDAN GALLAGHER
PROPRIETOR

American Express
Diners
Mastercard
Visa

12 12

Closed 25 December

FAITHLEGG HOUSE HOTEL

FAITHLEGG,
CO. WATERFORD

TEL: 051-382000 FAX: 051-382010
EMAIL: reservations@fhh.ie
WEB: www.faithlegg.com

HOTEL U MAP 4 M 5

A Tower Group Hotel - Faithlegg House Hotel is located on the already renowned 18-hole championship golf course, overlooking the Estuary of the River Suir. This elegantly restored Country House Hotel incorporates 82 bedrooms, including 14 master rooms in the original house; a unique fitness, health and beauty club featuring a 17m pool; plus comprehensive meeting, conference and event management facilities. RAC ◆◆◆◆ recommended.

Member of Tower Hotel Group

B&B from €90.00 to €167.50

MADGE BARRY
GENERAL MANAGER

American Express
Diners
Mastercard
Visa

☺ Weekend specials from €215.00

82 82

Closed 22 - 26 December

LISMORE HOTEL

MAIN STREET,
LISMORE,
CO. WATERFORD

TEL: 058-54555 FAX: 058-53068
EMAIL: lismorehotel@eircom.net

HOTEL ★★ MAP 3 J 4

Situated in the heart of historical Lismore, on the Munster Blackwater River, this newly refurbished hotel is the ideal location for a relaxing break. Take a walk back through time and enjoy Lismore with its majestic castle and gardens, historical cathedral and peaceful river walks. Horse riding, fishing and golf are all available locally. Our warm and friendly staff await your arrival and we look forward to serving you in our award winning restaurant.

B&B from €40.00 to €65.00

SEÁN READ
MANAGER

Mastercard
Visa

20 20

Closed 25 December

Room rates are per room per night

GRAND HOTEL

TRAMORE,
CO. WATERFORD

TEL: 051-381414 FAX: 051-386428
EMAIL: thegrandhotel@eircom.net
WEB: www.grand-hotel.ie

HOTEL ★★★ MAP 4 L 5

The Grand Hotel is owned and managed by the Treacy family, and has been refurbished to combine luxury with elegance of a bygone age and to maintain the tradition of efficient service in a warm hospitable atmosphere. Al 83 bedrooms have TV, DD phone, tea/coffee making facilities. Award wining Doneraile Restaurant with panoramic views of Tramore Bay. Plus two bars serving bar food daily & entertainment nightly in high season. A child friendly hotel. New Duffys Bar since May 2002

B&B from €48.00 to €70.00

TOM & ANNA TREACY
PROPRIETORS

American Express
Diners
Mastercard
Visa

83 83

Open All Year

MAJESTIC HOTEL

TRAMORE,
CO. WATERFORD

TEL: 051-381761 FAX: 051-381766
EMAIL: info@majestic-hotel.ie
WEB: www.majestic-hotel.ie

HOTEL ★★★ MAP 4 L 5

A warm welcome awaits you at the family owned and managed Majestic Hotel, overlooking Tramore Bay and its famous 3 miles of sandy beach. Only 10km from Waterford City. All 60 bedrooms are en suite with TV, phone, hairdryer & tea/coffee facilities. Full leisure facilities available to guests at Splashworld Health and Fitness Club near hotel. Special golf packages on South East sunshine circuit. Les Routiers Gold Key Award 1999.

Member of Les Routiers Ireland

B&B from €45.00 to €65.00

ANNETTE & DANNY DEVINE
PROPRIETORS

American Express
Mastercard
Visa

☺ Weekend specials from €102.00

60 60

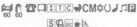

Open All Year

O'SHEA'S HOTEL

STRAND STREET,
TRAMORE,
CO. WATERFORD

TEL: 051-381246 FAX: 051-390144
EMAIL: info@osheas-hotel.com
WEB: www.osheas-hotel.com

HOTEL ★★★ MAP 4 L 5

O'Shea's is an intimate family run hotel, genuinely warm and welcoming to all, situated beside Tramore's safe sandy beach. Just minutes from "Splashworld Health & Fitness Club" (special discount for guests). All our rooms are en suite with TV, phone, tea/coffee making facilities. Superb restaurant, award winning bar food, entertainment most nights. We specialise in golfing holidays - choice of excellent courses in the South East. We look forward to meeting you.

B&B from €45.00 to €70.00

NOREEN & JOE O'SHEA
PROPRIETORS

American Express
Diners
Mastercard
Visa

☺ Weekend specials from €110.00

30 30

Closed 22 - 31 December

B&B rates are per person sharing per night incl. Breakfast

SANDS HOTEL (THE)

STRAND ROAD,
TRAMORE,
CO. WATERFORD

TEL: 051-381355 FAX: 051-393869

HOTEL N   MAP 4 L 5

The Sands Hotel, newly refurbished
and extended. All rooms en suite with
TV, direct dial telephone, tea/coffee
facilities. Situated in the heart of
Tramore's tourist area, a minute's
walk from the beach and
Splashworld. A choice of 6 bars with
entertainment, to suit all ages,
including late night bar. Carvery
lunches, evening grill menu, full bar
food menu. Friendly atmosphere and
homely welcome.

B&B from €45.00 to €64.00

MARY BROPHY
GENERAL MANAGER

Mastercard

Visa

20 20

alc ▣ ♿

ARD RÍ HOTEL

FERRYBANK,
WATERFORD

TEL: 051-832111 FAX: 051-832863
EMAIL: reservations@ardri.org
WEB: www.mceniff-hotels.com

HOTEL ★★★   MAP 4 L 5

Friendly, cosy hotel with fantastic
leisure facilities, on 10 acres of
parkland, overlooking Waterford City
and The River Suir. Enjoy
unforgettable family holidays with our
famous Applejacks Kiddies Club or
indulge your taste buds with a meal
prepared by our Executive Chef
Norbert Thul. Situated on the main
Rosslare road, the hotel is ideally
located for fascinating day trips -
Waterford Crystal, Reginald's Tower,
The Dunbrody Famine Ship plus lots
more. Callsave: 1850 615 615.

Member of McEniff Hotels

B&B from €99.00 to €132.00

MICHAEL LENNON
MANAGER

American Express
Diners
Mastercard
Visa

98 98

ARLINGTON LODGE
COUNTRY HOUSE HOTEL

JOHN'S HILL,
WATERFORD

TEL: 051-878584 FAX: 051-878127
EMAIL: info@arlingtonlodge.com
WEB: www.arlingtonlodge.com

HOTEL N   MAP 4 L 5

Newly opened, the former Bishop's
House has been lovingly restored to
provide all the amenities of a luxury 4
star standard country house hotel.
Each deluxe bedroom has a unique
style, whilst the elegance of the
Robert Paul Restaurant perfectly
reflects the superb quality of the finest
cuisine. For a short break, a
memorable wedding, special
occasion or intimate retreat for a
business meeting, Arlington Lodge is
the perfect venue, "an oasis" in
Waterford City.

B&B from €75.00 to €125.00

MAURICE KELLER
MANAGER/PROPRIETOR

American Express
Mastercard
Visa

☺   Special offers available

20 20

Room rates are per room per night

BELFRY HOTEL

CONDUIT LANE,
WATERFORD

TEL: 051-844800 FAX: 051-844814
EMAIL: info@belfryhotel.ie
WEB: www.belfryhotel.ie

HOTEL ★★★ MAP 4 L 5

This new, family-run city centre hotel is a wonderful blend of modern and traditional design, creating a warm and welcoming atmosphere. With 49 luxurious bedrooms, the delightful Riada's Restaurant and stylish Chapter House Bar, we offer our guests comfort, excellent food and relaxation combined with professional service and friendly hospitality. Superb range of golf courses and local amenities nearby. Golf packages available.

B&B from €50.00 to €90.00

SHARON REID
GENERAL MANAGER

American Express
Mastercard
Visa

☺ Special offers available throughout the year

49 49

Inet

IRISH HOTELS FEDERATION

Closed 24 - 26 December

BRIDGE HOTEL

NO 1 THE QUAY,
WATERFORD

TEL: 051-877222 FAX: 051-877229
EMAIL: info@bridgehotelwaterford.com
WEB: www.bridgehotelwaterford.com

HOTEL ★★★ MAP 4 L 5

Whether your stay in Waterford's Viking City is one of business or pleasure, you will quickly find that the Bridge Hotel, situated in the heart of this vibrant and exciting city, is exactly where you will want to stay. This 100 en suite bedroom hotel offers the finest traditions of quality & service expected from a modern 3*** hotel. Our restaurants specialise in local seafood & succulent steaks. Relax & enjoy a drink in our Timbertoes Bar. 2 minutes walk from bus & rail stations. Entertainment 5 nights a week.

Member of MinOtel Ireland Hotel Group

B&B from €50.00 to €89.00

BRIDGET & JIM TREACY
PROPRIETORS

American Express
Diners
Mastercard
Visa

☺ Weekend specials from €135.00

100 100

Inet

IRISH HOTELS FEDERATION

Closed 24 - 26 December

COACH HOUSE

BUTLERSTOWN CASTLE,
BUTLERSTOWN, CORK ROAD,
WATERFORD

TEL: 051-384656 FAX: 051-384751
EMAIL: coachhse@iol.ie
WEB: www.iol.ie/~coachhse

GUESTHOUSE ★★★ MAP 4 L 5

Surround yourself with comfort in this elegantly restored 19th century house. Situated 3 miles from Waterford City (Waterford Crystal 5 mins away) in an historic, tranquil, romantic setting (13th century castle in grounds). All rooms en suite. Private sauna available. 5 golf courses within 6 miles radius. Excellent pubs, restaurants nearby. 3*** Irish Tourist Board, AA ◆◆◆◆, Michelin recommended, Best Magazine's No.1 in Ireland. 'Crackling log fires and personal attention'.

B&B from €37.50 to €47.50

DES O'KEEFFE
PROPRIETOR

American Express
Diners
Mastercard
Visa

7 7

IRISH HOTELS FEDERATION

Closed 20 December - 20 January

B&B rates are per person sharing per night incl. Breakfast

DIAMOND HILL COUNTRY HOUSE

**SLIEVERUE,
WATERFORD**

TEL: 051-832855 FAX: 051-832254
EMAIL: diamondhill29@hotmail.com
WEB: www.diamondhillhouse.com

GUESTHOUSE ★★★ MAP 4 L 5

Situated 2km from Waterford City off the Rosslare Waterford Road N25. Convenient to ferrys. A long established guesthouse of considerable charm and friendliness, set in its own national award winning gardens. The house has been extensively refurbished incorporating family heirlooms and antiques resulting in a countryside oasis, a haven of luxury and tranquillity, yet only mins from the bustling city of Waterford. Recommended by Frommers, Foders, Michelin, AA ◆◆◆◆. Member of Premier Guesthouses.

Member of Premier Guesthouses

B&B from €32.00 to €40.00

MARJORIE SMITH LEHANE
OWNER

Mastercard

Visa

18 18

Closed 25 - 26 December

DOOLEY'S HOTEL

**THE QUAY,
WATERFORD**

TEL: 051-873531 FAX: 051-870262
EMAIL: hotel@dooleys-hotel.ie
WEB: www.dooleys-hotel.ie

HOTEL ★★★ MAP 4 L 5

The waters of the River Suir swirl past the door of this renowned hotel, which is situated on The Quay in Waterford. With its high level of comfort and good service Dooley's is an ideal choice for a centrally located hotel, close to all amenities, culture and business centres. This family run hotel caters for the corporate/leisure traveller. The hotel has a purpose-built conference centre with full facilities - The Rita Nolan Conference and Banqueting Suite. Enjoy the style and comfort of our New Ship Restaurant and Dry Dock Bar.

Member of Holiday Ireland Hotels

B&B from €51.00 to €96.00

JUNE DARRER
PROPRIETOR/MANAGER

American Express

Diners

Mastercard

Visa

113 113

Inet

Closed 25 - 27 December

FORTE TRAVELODGE

**CORK ROAD (N25),
WATERFORD**

TEL: 1800-709709 FAX: 051-358890

WEB: www.travelodge.co.uk

HOTEL U MAP 4 L O5

Situated on the N25 primary route from Rosslare Harbour to Cork, 1 mile from Waterford City and minutes from the Waterford Crystal Factory, this superb hotel offers comfortable yet affordable accommodation. Each room can sleep up to 3 adults, a child under 12 years and a baby in a cot. Price is fixed per room regardless of the number of occupants. Each room is en suite and has colour TV. Sited next to Little Chef Restaurant. Freephone from UK: 0800 850 950.

Room Rate from €69.00 to €79.00

TRACEY O'CONNOR
MANAGER

American Express

Diners

Mastercard

Visa

32 32

Open All Year

Room rates are per room per night

GRANVILLE HOTEL

MEAGHER QUAY,
WATERFORD

TEL: 051-305555 FAX: 051-305566
EMAIL: stay@granville-hotel.ie
WEB: www.granville-hotel.ie

HOTEL ★★★ MAP 4 L 5

One of Waterford's most prestigious city centre hotels, RAC**** overlooking the River Suir. This family run hotel is one of Ireland's oldest with significant historical connections. Justly proud of the Granville's heritage, owners Liam and Ann Cusack today vigorously pursue the Granville's long tradition of hospitality, friendliness and comfort. It has been elegantly refurbished, retaining its old world Georgian character. Award winning Bianconi Restaurant, Thomas Francis Meagher Bar.

Member of Best Western Hotels

B&B from €70.00 to €100.00

LIAM AND ANN CUSACK
MANAGERS/PROPRIETORS

American Express
Diners
Mastercard
Visa

Weekend specials from €125.00

98 98

Inet

IRISH HOTELS FEDERATION

Closed 25 - 27 December

IVORY'S HOTEL

TRAMORE ROAD,
WATERFORD

TEL: 051-358888 FAX: 051-358899
EMAIL: info@ivoryshotel.ie
WEB: www.ivoryshotel.ie

HOTEL ★★★ MAP 4 L 5

A friendly, family-run hotel, Ivory's Hotel is Waterford's best value. Ideally located adjacent to Waterford Crystal Factory & city centre. Each en suite room combines the convenience of direct dial phone, multi-channel TV with welcoming tea/coffee making facilities, in comfortable surroundings. The hotel boasts Una's Signature Restaurant, emphasising the best fresh local produce. Unwind in McGinty's Pub Carvery & allow us to arrange golf, fishing. Secure car park and children's playground. Groups, families & small dogs welcome.

B&B from €50.00 to €90.00

DECLAN & NATALIE IVORY
MANAGING PROPRIETORS

American Express
Diners
Mastercard
Visa

Weekend specials from €123.00

40 40

Open All Year

O'GRADY'S RESTAURANT & GUESTHOUSE

CORK ROAD,
WATERFORD

TEL: 051-378851 FAX: 051-374062
EMAIL: info@ogradyshotel.com
WEB: www.ogradys.ie

GUESTHOUSE U MAP 4 L 5

O'Gradys Restaurant and Guesthouse is ideally located on the main Cork Road (N25), adjacent to the Waterford Crystal factory and city centre. Family-run by Euro Toque chef Cornelius and his wife Sue; they offer the excellent combination of reasonably priced accommodation and a superb licensed Michelin recommended restaurant which specialises in fresh local seafood. Private off street parking. 4 championship golf courses nearby. Tennis, horseriding and fishing. French and Gaelic spoken.

B&B from €40.00 to €45.00

CORNELIUS AND SUE
PROPRIETORS

American Express
Diners
Mastercard
Visa

9 9

Inet

IRISH HOTELS FEDERATION

Closed 23 December - 05 January

B&B rates are per person sharing per night incl. Breakfast

QUALITY HOTEL WATERFORD

CANADA STREET,
THE QUAYS,
WATERFORD

TEL: 051-856600 FAX: 051-856605
EMAIL: marinagm@gofree.indigo.ie
WEB: www.choicehotelsireland.ie

HOTEL U MAP 4 L 5

The Quality Hotel is ideally located on the banks of the River Suir just minutes walk from the bustling city centre. Featuring generously appointed en suite guestrooms and executive suites, the hotel is your ideal base for touring the South East. Relax by the river in Lannigans Restaurant & Bar and enjoy our international menus. Complimentary secure car park. Conference facilities for up to 50 delegates.

Member of Choice Hotels Ireland

B&B from €50.00 to €100.00

DECLAN MEAGHER
GENERAL MANAGER

American Express
Diners
Mastercard
Visa

Weekend specials from €149.00

81 81

Closed 22 December - 05 January

RHU GLEN COUNTRY CLUB HOTEL

LUFFANY,
SLIEVERUE,
WATERFORD

TEL: 051-832242 FAX: 051-832242
EMAIL: info@rhuglennhotel.com
WEB: www.rhuglennhotel.com

HOTEL ★★ MAP 4 L 5

Built within its own grounds with parking for cars, coaches, etc., the hotel is family run. Situated on the N25 Rosslare to Waterford Road, convenient to ferries, it offers a superb location whether your pleasure be golfing, fishing, or simply exploring the South East. All rooms are en suite with direct dial phone and multi-channel TV. The restaurant is renowned for its service of fine food. Relax and enjoy our lounge bars and ballroom with live entertainment provided by Ireland's top artistes.

B&B from €40.00 to €55.00

LIAM MOONEY
PROPRIETOR

American Express
Diners
Mastercard
Visa

Weekend specials from €100.00

19 19

Closed 24 - 25 December

RICE GUESTHOUSE
O'DRISCOLL'S BAR

35 & 36 BARRACK STREET,
WATERFORD

TEL: 051-371606 FAX: 051-357013
EMAIL: info@riceguesthouse.com
WEB: www.riceguesthouse.com

GUESTHOUSE U MAP 4 L 5

Waterford's premier city centre guesthouse, located 2 minutes from Waterford's city square shopping centre and Waterford Crystal Gallery, offers our customers hotel accommodation at guesthouse prices. Purpose built in 1997 all rooms en suite with cable TV, direct dial phones & tea/coffee facilities. O'Driscoll's Bar offers ceol & craic with live music 5 nights a week, bar food and the finest Irish hospitality. Tee times arranged for golfers. Midweek and weekend break specials available.

Member of Premier Guesthouses

B&B from €45.00 to €60.00

JOHN & OLIVE O'DRISCOLL

Mastercard
Visa

20 20

Closed 23 - 27 December

Room rates are per room per night

ST. ALBANS GUESTHOUSE

CORK ROAD,
WATERFORD

TEL: 051-358171 FAX: 051-358171
EMAIL: stalbansbandb@yahoo.com
WEB: www.hotelbnb.com

GUESTHOUSE ★★ MAP 4 L 5

St. Albans is a well established family run guesthouse. Ideally located minutes walk from Waterford City Centre and Waterford Crystal. Our very spacious superbly appointed rooms are all en suite with multi-channel TV, tea/coffee facilities and hairdryer. Secure parking at rear of premises. 4 championship golf courses in vicinity. Horse riding 3km. Tennis courts, swimming pool 2 minutes. Several local beaches and breathtaking scenery. Bus and train station a short distance. Freephone: U.K.: 0800 912 3910 USA: 0877 207 3910

B&B from €33.00 to €45.00

TOM & HELEN MULLALLY
PROPRIETORS

Mastercard
Visa

8 8

Closed 18 - 28 December

TOWER HOTEL & LEISURE CENTRE

THE MALL,
WATERFORD

TEL: 051-875801 FAX: 051-870129
EMAIL: reservations@thw.ie
WEB: www.towerhotelwaterford.com

HOTEL ★★★ MAP 4 L 5

A Tower Group Hotel - with its riverside location in the heart of Waterford City and 140 guest bedrooms with every modern amenity, the Tower Hotel is the largest hotel in the South East region and the flagship hotel of the Tower Group. Facilities include: Two new restaurants - traditional Carvery and continental style Bistro; Riverside Bar; Leisure & Fitness centre with 20m pool and private guest car park.

Member of Tower Hotel Group

B&B from €63.00 to €99.00

PAUL MCDAID
GENERAL MANAGER

American Express
Diners
Mastercard
Visa

Weekend specials from €115.00

140 140

Closed 24 - 28 December

WATERFORD CASTLE HOTEL & GOLF CLUB

THE ISLAND,
BALLINAKILL,
WATERFORD

TEL: 051-878203 FAX: 051-879316
EMAIL: info@waterfordcastle.com
WEB: www.waterfordcastle.com

HOTEL U MAP 4 L 5

Waterford Castle Hotel & Golf Club is uniquely situated on a 310 acre island overlooking the estuary of the River Suir, 3 miles from Waterford City. Access to the island is by a chain linked car ferry. Highest standards of comfort, tastefully furnished with antiques and open fireplaces. The 15th century Castle combines gracious living of an elegant past with every modern comfort, service and convenience. Own 18 hole championship golf course, set in a peaceful oasis of beautiful parkland with nature plantations.

Room Rate from €190.00 to €440.00

GILLIAN BUTLER
GENERAL MANAGER

American Express
Diners
Mastercard
Visa

Specials from €310.00

19 19

Open All Year

B&B rates are per person sharing per night incl. Breakfast

WOODLANDS HOTEL

**DUNMORE ROAD,
WATERFORD**

**TEL: 051-304574 FAX: 051-304575
EMAIL: woodhl@iol.ie
WEB: www.woodlandshotel.ie**

HOTEL ★★★ MAP 4 L 5

This contemporary hotel offers spacious bedrooms, 20m pool and full leisure and dining facilities. Our aim is to exceed your expectations and make Woodlands the most memorable hotel you have visited. We hope to achieve this by personal attention and value for money. "Chamber of Commerce and Vodafone Customer Excellence Award, March 2002".

B&B from €50.00 to €85.00

DEREK ANDREWS

American Express
Diners
Mastercard
Visa

Weekend specials from €120.00

46 46

Open All Year

DUNBRODY COUNTRY HOUSE HOTEL & RESTAURANT

**ARTHURSTOWN,
CO. WEXFORD**

**TEL: 051-389600 FAX: 051-389601
EMAIL: info@dunbrodyhouse.com
WEB: www.dunbrodyhouse.com**

HOTEL ★★★★ MAP 4 M 5

Dunbrody Country House Hotel & Cookery School is regarded as one of Ireland's top country retreats. Offering unrivalled cuisine with a wonderfully relaxed ambience, guests return again and again. Members of both Small Luxury Hotels of the World and Ireland's Blue Book. Dunbrody is also recommended by numerous guides and is the recipient of many awards.

Member of Ireland's Blue Book

B&B from €112.50 to €192.50

KEVIN & CATHERINE DUNDON
OWNERS

American Express
Diners
Mastercard
Visa

Midweek specials from €225.00

20 20

Closed 22 - 27 December

BAYVIEW HOTEL

**COURTOWN HARBOUR,
GOREY,
CO. WEXFORD**

**TEL: 055-25307 FAX: 055-25576
EMAIL: bayview@iol.ie
WEB: www.bayview.ie**

HOTEL ★★ MAP 8 O 7

The Bayview is owned and run by the McGarry Family. The hotel is overlooking the marina at Courtown Harbour. It is renowned for its good food and friendly atmosphere. All rooms are en suite with TV, video channel and direct dial telephone. Self catering apartments in hotel. Courtown's 18 hole golf course 2km. It is an ideal setting for weddings and parties. Nearby is the Courtown superb indoor 25m pool.

B&B from €60.00 to €70.00

BRIAN MCGARRY
MANAGER

American Express
Mastercard
Visa

Midweek specials from €165.00

13 13

Closed 01 November - 01 March

Room rates are per room per night

COURTOWN HOTEL

COURTOWN HARBOUR,
GOREY,
CO. WEXFORD
TEL: 055-25210 FAX: 055-25304

WEB: www.courtownhotel.com

HOTEL ★★ MAP 8 0 7

The family run Courtown Hotel & Leisure Centre is renowned for its friendly atmosphere and excellent cuisine. Featuring the AA - award winning "Bradley's" Restaurant and a selection of lounge bars. All rooms are en suite with T.V. and direct dial telephone. Residents enjoy complimentary use of our leisure facilities which include an indoor heated swimming pool, sauna, jacuzzi & steam room. Weddings and parties a speciality.

B&B from €35.00 to €70.00

SANDRA MELIA
PROPRIETOR

American Express
Diners
Mastercard
Visa

☺ Weekend specials from €110.00

22 22

Closed 10 November - 13 February

HARBOUR HOUSE GUESTHOUSE

COURTOWN HARBOUR,
COURTOWN, GOREY,
CO. WEXFORD
TEL: 055-25117 FAX: 055-25117
EMAIL: stay@harbourhouseguesthouse.com
WEB: www.harbourhouseguesthouse.com

GUESTHOUSE ★★ MAP 8 0 7

Harbour House just off the main Rosslare/Dublin N11 route and only 6km from Gorey is ideally located in the renowned seaside resort of Courtown Harbour. Harbour House is the ideal base for both business and holiday travellers and is central to all amenities and only three minutes from Courtown's sandy beaches. All rooms are en suite. Private car park. Come and enjoy Courtown's new 25m swimming pool. 2 kiddies pools and a 65m water slide all set within 63 acres of woodland with beautiful river walks.

B&B from €35.00 to €37.50

DONAL & MARGARET O'GORMAN
PROPRIETORS

American Express
Diners
Mastercard
Visa

13 13

Closed 31 October - 10 April

HOTEL CURRACLOE

CURRACLOE,
CO. WEXFORD

TEL: 053-37308 FAX: 053-37587
EMAIL: hotelcurracloe@eircom.net
WEB: www.hotelcurracloe.com

HOTEL ★★ MAP 4 0 6

Hotel Curracloe is ideally situated, only five miles from Wexford Town, minutes from Blue/Green Flag beaches and central to golfing, angling, bird-watching, hill walking and horse riding amenities. Our 29 rooms are en suite with modern facilities and our award-winning Blake Restaurant and Tavern Pub serve the best of home produce. The Brent Banqueting Room will cater for every special occasion. Our friendly staff will ensure that Hotel Curracloe is the perfect base for your leisure time in the sunny South East.

B&B from €40.00 to €50.00

JOHN & MARGARET HANRAHAN
OWNERS

Mastercard
Visa

29 29

Open All Year

B&B rates are per person sharing per night incl. Breakfast

LEMONGROVE HOUSE

BLACKSTOOPS,
ENNISCORTHY,
CO. WEXFORD
TEL: 054-36115 FAX: 054-36115
EMAIL: lemongrovehouse@iolfree.ie

GUESTHOUSE ★★★ MAP 4 N 6

Spacious luxury home 1km north of Enniscorthy just off roundabout on Dublin/Rosslare Road (N11). Lemongrove House is set in mature gardens with private parking. All rooms en suite with direct dial phone, TV, hairdryer and tea/coffee making facilities. Recommended by Guide du Routard, AA and other leading guides. Within walking distance of a choice of restaurants, pubs and new pool and leisure centre. Locally we have beaches, golf, horseriding, walking and quad track.

B&B from €30.00 to €38.00

COLM & ANN MCGIBNEY
OWNERS

Mastercard

Visa

☺ Midweek specials from €90.00

6 6

Closed 20 - 29 December

MURPHY - FLOODS HOTEL

MARKET SQUARE,
ENNISCORTHY,
CO. WEXFORD
TEL: 054-33413 FAX: 054-33413
EMAIL: mfhotel@indigo.ie
WEB: www.murphyfloods.com

HOTEL ★★ MAP 4 N 6

Overlooking Market Square of historic 6th century Enniscorthy Town on Slaney salmon river. Package rates for golf breaks, midweek and weekends. Elegant restaurant, in Georgian style, presents menus of quality and variety. Room service, excellent bar food, packed lunches available, cots provided, night porter service. Central for touring lovely Slaney Valley and sunny South East. Rosslare Ferry 43km, Waterford 56km, Dublin 120km, Shannon 240km. 1km from National 1798 Centre.

B&B from €35.00 to €45.00

MICHAEL J WALL
PROPRIETOR

American Express

Diners

Mastercard

Visa

☺ Weekend specials from €91.00

19 19

Closed 24 - 28 December

PINES COUNTRY HOUSE HOTEL

CAMOLIN,
ENNISCORTHY,
CO. WEXFORD
TEL: 054-83600 FAX: 054-83588
EMAIL: thepines@eircom.net
WEB: www.pinescountryhousehotel.com

HOTEL ★★ MAP 4 N 6

This delightful family run hotel with award-winning Resturant serving European and real Indian food. Top class accommodation, state of the art gym, sauna steam, plunge pool, pony trekking, hill walking, birdwatching. Nearby Courtown and Curracloe beaches, historic ferns, heritage park, quad trekking, fishing, music and on-site Bouncy Castle/ slide, horseriding.

Member of Which Hotels

B&B from €30.00 to €65.00

FRANK MURHILL
DIRECTOR MANAGER

Mastercard

Visa

☺ Weekend specials from €115.00

11 11

Open All Year

Room rates are per room per night

RIVERSIDE PARK HOTEL

THE PROMENADE,
ENNISCORTHY,
CO. WEXFORD
TEL: 054-37800 FAX: 054-37900
EMAIL: info@riversdaleparkhotel.com
WEB: www.riversideparkhotel.com

HOTEL ★★★ MAP 4 N 6

Nestling along the scenic banks of the River Slaney the Riverside Park Hotel is an ideal base for touring the treasures of the sunny South East. With a choice of two superb restaurants the Mooring and Alamo, Tex-Mex at its best, and a luxurious bar with spectacular views, a memorable evening is guaranteed. Only 30 minutes from Rosslare and 1 hour from Dublin. The hotel has 60 bedrooms, all tastefully decorated with emphasis on luxury and relaxation.

B&B from €63.00 to €86.50

JIM MAHER
GENERAL MANAGER

American Express
Diners
Mastercard
Visa

Weekend specials from €170.00

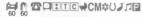

60 60

Alc Inet FAX

IRISH HOTELS FEDERATION

Closed 24 - 26 December

TREACY'S HOTEL

TEMPLESHANNON,
ENNISCORTHY,
CO. WEXFORD
TEL: 054-37798 FAX: 054-37733
EMAIL: info@treacyshotel.com
WEB: www.treacyshotel.com

HOTEL ★★★ MAP 4 N 6

Situated in the heart of beautiful Enniscorthy, Treacy's Hotel is in the ideal location for both excitement and relaxation. Whether it's sport, music, fine dining or a memorable night life you desire, you need look no further. A world of choice is available to discerning diners; options include our outstanding hotel restaurant, our oriental style Thai Restaurant or our award-winning Temple Bar. Follow up a tantalising experience with a true taste of Irish entertainment in our Temple Bar and Benedicts superpub. "One of the South East's best loved hotels".

B&B from €55.00 to €95.00

ANTON & YVONNE TREACY

American Express
Diners
Mastercard
Visa

48 48

Alc Inet

IRISH HOTELS FEDERATION

Closed 24 - 26 December

HORSE AND HOUND INN

BALLINABOOLA,
FOULKSMILLS,
CO. WEXFORD
TEL: 051-428323 FAX: 051-428471
EMAIL: info@horseandhound.net

GUESTHOUSE ★★★ MAP 4 N 5

The Horse and Hound Inn, Ballinaboola, Co. Wexford is owned and run by the Murphy Family. Situated six miles from New Ross on the N25 from Rosslare. It is a convenient venue for a meal and a rest. Best Irish produce is used in preparing specialities of fish and beef dishes. There are twelve bedrooms should you wish to stay. Catering for all needs - from private parties, weddings to conferences.

B&B from €45.00 to €45.00

CHRISTY MURPHY

Mastercard
Visa

12 12

Alc

Open All Year

B&B rates are per person sharing per night incl. Breakfast

ASHDOWN PARK HOTEL CONFERENCE & LEISURE CENTRE

COACH ROAD,
GOREY,
CO. WEXFORD
TEL: 055-80500 FAX: 055-80777
EMAIL: info@ashdownparkhotel.com
WEB: www.ashdownparkhotel.com

HOTEL N MAP 8 O 7

A stylish new hotel and leisure centre, built to 4**** standards. 60 bedrooms, 6 of which are executive suites, offer all modern conveniences. Enjoy a drink in the Ivy Bar or Coach Bar, followed by dinner in the Rowan Tree Restaurant. State of the art leisure club sports an 18m pool, childrens' pool, sauna, steamroom, jacuzzi, gym and solarium. Centrally located close to Dublin and Rosslare, Ashdown Park is ideally located for touring Counties Wicklow and Wexford.

B&B from €65.00 to €95.00

LIAM MORAN
GENERAL MANAGER

American Express
Mastercard
Visa

60 60 Weekend specials from €150.00

Closed 24 - 26 December

MARLFIELD HOUSE HOTEL

GOREY,
CO. WEXFORD
TEL: 055-21124 FAX: 055-21572
EMAIL: info@marlfieldhouse.ie
WEB: www.marlfieldhouse.com

HOTEL ★★★★ MAP 8 O 7

This Regency period house is set amidst 36 acres of grounds and is filled with beautiful antiques. The Bowe family opened its doors to guests in 1978 and has gained an outstanding reputation since. The kitchen garden provides the produce for its award-winning conservatory dining room. Member of Relais et Châteaux and Ireland's Blue Book, AA Red Star and RAC Gold Ribbon Hotel.

Member of Relais & Châteaux

B&B from €118.00 to €128.00

MARY BOWE
PROPRIETOR

American Express
Diners
Mastercard
Visa

20 20

Closed 15 December - 25 January

HOTEL SALTEES

KILMORE QUAY,
CO. WEXFORD
TEL: 053-29601 FAX: 053-29602

HOTEL ★★ MAP 4 N 5

Hotel Saltees is situated in the picturesque fishing village of Kilmore Quay. Renowned for its thatched cottages and maritime flavour, it is located just 22km from Wexford Town and 19km from the international port of Rosslare. Offering excellent value accommodation, with all rooms en suite, TV, telephone and all well designed to cater for families. The Coningbeg Seafood Restaurant specialises in serving the freshest seafood. Shore and deep-sea fishing available locally.

B&B from €38.00 to €47.00

TOMMY AND NED BYRNE
PROPRIETORS

American Express
Mastercard
Visa

Weekend specials from €108.00

10 10

Open All Year

Room rates are per room per night

QUAY HOUSE

KILMORE QUAY,
CO. WEXFORD

TEL: 053-29988 FAX: 053-29808
EMAIL: quayplaice@eircom.net
WEB: www.quayhouseguesthouse.com

GUESTHOUSE ★★★ MAP 4 N 5

3*** Guesthouse. AA Selected ♦♦♦. Quay House is located in the centre of Kilmore Quay; famous for its thatched cottages, marina, sea angling, nature trails and walks along the Wexford Coast. Quay House offers you a stay that will bring you back again and again. Good food and wine served in our restaurant Quay Plaice. All inclusive mini breaks available excluding July & August. Private car park to rear.

B&B from €30.00 to €38.00

SIOBHAN MCDONNELL
PROPRIETOR

Mastercard
Visa

Closed 25 December

CLARION BRANDON HOUSE HOTEL, HEALTH CLUB & SPA

NEW ROSS,
CO. WEXFORD

TEL: 051-421703 FAX: 051-421567
EMAIL: brandonhouse@eircom.net
WEB: www.brandonhousehotel.ie

HOTEL ★★★ MAP 4 M 6

A de luxe country manor house set in landscaped grounds with panoramic views overlooking the River Barrow. Dine in the Gallery Restaurant or relax in the Library Bar. All rooms are elegantly furnished. Luxurious health & leisure club with 20m pool, sauna, steam room, jacuzzi, fully equipped gym, kiddies pool, hydrotherapy grotto and thalasso treatment room. Nearby golf, angling, beaches, horseriding & gardens. An ideal base for touring the sunny South East. Creche available.

Member of Choice Hotels Ireland

B&B from €63.00 to €80.00

GRACE MCPHILLIPS
GENERAL MANAGER

American Express
Diners
Mastercard
Visa

☺ Weekend specials from €138.00

Closed 24 - 26 December

CREACON LODGE HOTEL

CREACON,
NEW ROSS,
CO. WEXFORD

TEL: 051-421897 FAX: 051-422560
EMAIL: info@creaconlodge.com
WEB: www.creaconlodge.com

HOTEL ★★★ MAP 4 M 6

Set amidst the peace and tranquillity of the countryside. 45 minutes drive from Rosslare, 2 hours from Dublin and only a short scenic drive to the Hook Peninsula and JFK Park. Relax and enjoy our beautiful gardens, comfy sofas and log fires and sample the delights of our award winning restaurant and bar. All bedrooms are en suite with DD phone, colour TV. Local amenities include golf, angling, horse-riding, water sports and sandy beaches. The Dunbrody Famine Ship is not to be missed.

B&B from €45.00 to €75.00

JOSEPHINE FLOOD

Mastercard
Visa

☺ Weekend specials from €120.00

Closed 22 - 28 December

B&B rates are per person sharing per night incl. Breakfast

CEDAR LODGE HOTEL & RESTAURANT

CARRIGBYRNE,
NEWBAWN, (NEAR NEW ROSS),
CO. WEXFORD
TEL: 051-428386 FAX: 051-428222
EMAIL: cedarlodge@eircom.net
WEB: www.prideofeirehotels.com

HOTEL ★★★ MAP 4 N 6

Charming 3*** country hotel located in a picturesque setting, 30 minutes drive from Rosslare Port on the N25 New Ross Road. All bedrooms en suite with direct dial phone and TV. The restaurant, which concentrates on freshly prepared produce, is noted for its good food. Recommended by Michelin, Good Hotel Guide, RAC. Forest walks nearby. Golf, horse riding, JF Kennedy Park, county museum, heritage park and sandy beaches within easy driving distance. The Cedar Lodge is a de luxe hotel - a cut above the rest.

B&B from € 100.00 to € 100.00

TOM MARTIN
PROPRIETOR

American Express
Diners
Mastercard
Visa

28 28

HOTELS
FEDERATION

Closed 20 December - 01 February

CHURCHTOWN HOUSE

TAGOAT,
ROSSLARE,
CO. WEXFORD
TEL: 053-32555 FAX: 053-32577
EMAIL: info@churchtownhouse.com
WEB: www.churchtownhouse.com

GUESTHOUSE ★★★★ MAP 4 0 5

AA Guesthouse of the Year 1998, and RAC Little Gem 2001. Churchtown is a period house c.1703 where peace and tranquillity together with country house hospitality combine with modern comforts to make it 'A SPECIAL PLACE TO STAY'. A rural setting in mature gardens, 0.5 miles off the N25 and 5 mins from Rosslare Ferryport/Strand. Explore Wexford's 'Land of Living History', gardens, golf, beaches, birdwatching, fishing and riding. Evening meals served Tues-Sat. Please pre-book.

B&B from € 55.00 to € 75.00

AUSTIN AND PATRICIA CODY
OWNERS

American Express
Mastercard
Visa

14 14

HOTELS
FEDERATION

Closed 30 November - 01 March

CROSBIE CEDARS HOTEL

ROSSLARE,
CO. WEXFORD

TEL: 053-32124 FAX: 053-32243
EMAIL: info@crosbiecedars.iol.ie
WEB: www.crosbiecedarshotel.com

HOTEL ★★★ MAP 4 0 5

In Rosslare resort, only 3 minutes from the beach, and 5 minutes from Rosslare Golf Course, Crosbie Cedars Hotel provides a warm welcome with traditional hospitality. All rooms en suite TV, radio, direct dial telephone, hairdryer & tea/coffee facilities. Restaurant menus of excellent quality & variety. Extensive bar menu. Entertainment weekends and nightly July & August. Available nearby tennis, watersports, childrens' playground, crazy golf. 15 minutes to ferry.

B&B from € 42.00 to € 68.00

LIZ SINNOTT
GENERAL MANAGER

American Express
Diners
Mastercard
Visa

34 34

HOTELS
FEDERATION

Closed 24 - 26 December

Room rates are per room per night

DANBY LODGE HOTEL

ROSSLARE ROAD,
KILLINICK, ROSSLARE,
CO. WEXFORD
TEL: 053-58191 FAX: 053-58191
EMAIL: danby@eircom.net

HOTEL U   MAP 4 0 5

Nestling in the heart of South County Wexford, Danby Lodge Hotel has rightfully earned for itself a reputation for excellence in cuisine and accommodation. Once the home of the painter Francis Danby, 1793-1861, this hotel bears all the hallmarks of a charming country residence. Conveniently located on main Rosslare to Wexford Road (N25). Danby Lodge Hotel offers the visitor a quiet country getaway yet just minutes drive from the port of Rosslare and the town of Wexford. RAC and AA recommended.

B&B from €42.00 to €66.00

RAYMOND PARLE
OWNER

American Express
Diners
Mastercard
Visa

Midweek specials available

24 24

Closed 22 - 30 December

KELLY'S RESORT HOTEL

ROSSLARE,
CO. WEXFORD

TEL: 053-32114 FAX: 053-32222
EMAIL: kellyhot@iol.ie
WEB: www.kellys.ie

HOTEL ★★★★   MAP 4 0 5

Since 1895 the Kelly Family have created a truly fine resort hotel. Good food, wine and nightly entertainment are very much part of the tradition. Amenities include tennis, squash, snooker, bowls, croquet and an excellent choice of local golf courses. Pamper yourself and relax in our Health & Beauty Centre. 7-day break (July/August): 5-day midweek & 2-day weekend (Spring/Autumn). Special Activity Midweeks in Spring & Autumn - wine tasting, cooking demonstrations, gardening, painting, etc.

B&B from €77.00 to €110.00

WILLIAM J KELLY
MANAGER/DIRECTOR

American Express
Mastercard
Visa

Autumn & Spring Offers, 5 days full board from €550.00pps + 10% s.c

99 99

Closed 08 December - 21 February

CORAL GABLES

TAGOAT,
ROSSLARE HARBOUR,
CO. WEXFORD
TEL: 053-31213 FAX: 053-31414
EMAIL: coralgables@eircom.net
WEB: www.coralgablesguesthouse.com

GUESTHOUSE ★★   MAP 4 0 5

Coral Gables is situated on a hilltop in quiet secluded surroundings overlooking the Wexford/Rosslare N25, just 3km from the ferry. Good food and friendly atmosphere provides the perfect stopover for visitors arriving and departing through Rosslare Port or for golfing, fishing, horseriding or relaxing on our safe sandy beaches. Our guesthouse has 15 en suite rooms with direct dial phone, tea/coffee facilities, hairdryer, TV, central heating, private car parking. TV lounge.

B&B from €30.00 to €45.00

SARAH & PAUL HASLAM
PROPRIETORS

Mastercard
Visa

15 15

Open All Year

B&B rates are per person sharing per night incl. Breakfast

EURO LODGE

ROSSLARE HARBOUR,
CO. WEXFORD

TEL: 053-33118 FAX: 053-33120
EMAIL: eurolodge@eircom.net
WEB: www.euro-lodge.com

GUESTHOUSE ★★★ MAP 405

Euro Lodge offers luxury accommodation, conveniently located only 600m from Rosslare Ferryport. All our rooms have bathroom en suite with colour TV, phone, tea/coffee facilities. Twin and family rooms available. An ideal location to stay while touring the South East. Close to all amenities. With two 18 hole golf courses, sandy beaches, fishing, horse riding and leisure centre nearby. Ample private car parking. Ideal for coach parties.

Room Rate from €63.00 to €70.00

HELEN SINNOTT
MANAGER

Mastercard
Visa

38 38

Closed 01 November - 31 March

FERRYPORT HOUSE

ROSSLARE HARBOUR,
CO. WEXFORD

TEL: 053-33933 FAX: 053-33033
EMAIL: thh@iol.ie
WEB: www.tuskarhousehotel.com

GUESTHOUSE ★★★ MAP 405

A new luxury guesthouse conveniently located close to Rosslare Ferryport (400m). The last guesthouse when leaving Ireland and the first on your return. It has 17 en suite bedrooms with direct dial phone, colour TV, central heating, tea/coffee making facilities, hairdryer and private car parking. Local amenities include golf, fishing, horse riding and safe sandy beaches.

B&B from €25.00 to €55.00

BILLY & PATRICA ROCHE
PROPRIETORS

Mastercard
Visa

17 17

Open All Year

HOTEL ROSSLARE

ROSSLARE HARBOUR,
CO. WEXFORD

TEL: 053-33110 FAX: 053-33386
EMAIL: info@hotelrosslare.ie
WEB: www.hotelrosslare.ie

HOTEL ★★★ MAP 405

Hotel Rosslare, the longest established hotel in Rosslare Harbour, enjoys spectacular views over the harbour and Europort. Enjoy a meal in the Anchorage Bistro overlooking the bay or spend some time in the historic Portholes Bar. Relax in our en suite rooms, most with sea views, direct dial phone, satellite TV and tea/coffee making facilities. Superbly located, we are only a short drive from 6 golf courses, magnificent beaches, angling, horse riding and Wexford Town.

B&B from €45.00 to €65.00

JAMES KELLY
GENERAL MANAGER

American Express
Diners
Mastercard
Visa

25 25

alc

Closed 24 - 25 December

Room rates are per room per night

ROSSLARE GREAT SOUTHERN HOTEL

**ROSSLARE HARBOUR,
CO. WEXFORD**

TEL: 053-33233 FAX: 053-33543
EMAIL: res@rosslare-gsh.com
WEB: www.gshotels.com

HOTEL ★★★ MAP 405

In Rosslare, a favourite resort, the Great Southern Hotel provides a warm welcome with traditional hospitality. The hotel is beautifully situated on a clifftop overlooking Rosslare Harbour. All rooms are en suite with TV, radio, hairdryer and tea/coffee facilities. Enjoy the leisure centre with indoor swimming pool, jacuzzi, steam room, the comfortable lounges and excellent food of the Mariner's Restaurant. Central reservations Tel: 01-214 4800 or UTELL.

Room Rate from €80.00 to €150.00

**ROISIN BUCKLEY
GENERAL MANAGER**

American Express
Diners
Mastercard
Visa

☺ Weekend specials from €130.00

100 100

Closed 02 January - 02 February

TUSKAR HOUSE HOTEL

**ROSSLARE HARBOUR,
CO. WEXFORD**

TEL: 053-33363 FAX: 053-33033
EMAIL: thh@iol.ie
WEB: www.tuskarhousehotel.com

HOTEL ★★★ MAP 405

Family run hotel enjoying panoramic views of Rosslare Bay, just 219m from ferry and train terminals. Most have en suite bedrooms with telephone, TV, central heating and some with balconies. Dinner served nightly until 11pm and Sunday lunch 12.30 to 2.30, with local seafood a speciality, Chinese menu is also available. Regular entertainment in the lively Punters Bar. Local amenities include: golf, fishing, horse riding and safe beaches. Michelin recommended.

B&B from €40.00 to €60.00

**ORLA ROCHE
GENERAL MANAGER**

American Express
Diners
Mastercard
Visa

☺ Weekend specials from €110.00

30 29

Closed 25 - 26 December

FAYTHE GUEST HOUSE

**THE FAYTHE,
SWAN VIEW,
WEXFORD**

TEL: 053-22249 FAX: 053-21680
EMAIL: faythhse@iol.ie
WEB: www.faytheguesthouse.com

GUESTHOUSE ★★★ MAP 406

Family run guesthouse in quiet part of town centre, is built on the grounds of a former castle of which one wall remains today. All rooms refurbished recently, some overlook our gardens and Wexford Harbour. Due to all improvements we are now graded to 3***. All rooms have bathroom en suite, colour TV, direct dial phone, clock radio and tea/coffee making facilities. Rosslare Ferry Port is only 15 minutes drive (early breakfast on request). We also have a large private car park.

B&B from €26.00 to €40.00

**DAMIAN AND SIOBHAN LYNCH
PROPRIETORS**

Mastercard
Visa

10 10

Closed 24 - 30 December

B&B rates are per person sharing per night incl. Breakfast

FERRYCARRIG HOTEL

FERRYCARRIG BRIDGE,
WEXFORD

TEL: 053-20999 FAX: 053-20982
EMAIL: ferrycarrig@griffingroup.ie
WEB: www.griffingroup.ie

HOTEL ★★★★ MAP 4 N 6

Ferrycarrig Hotel boasts one of the most inspiring locations of any hotel in Ireland, with sweeping views across the River Slaney Estuary. Facilities include 103 bedrooms and suites, two award winning waterfront restaurants - including Tides Gourmet Restaurant, the new contemporary style Drydock bar, an excellent conference centre and the superb 5***** Active Health and Fitness club with 20m pool and spa area. The hotel is part owner of St. Helen's Bay Golf Course.

B&B from € 65.00 to € 140.00

MARK BROWNE
GENERAL MANAGER

American Express
Diners
Mastercard
Visa

103 103

♪♫PS🛗 Inet

Open All Year

Room rates are per room per night

RIVERBANK HOUSE HOTEL

THE BRIDGE,
WEXFORD

TEL: 053-23611 FAX: 053-23342
EMAIL: river@indigo.ie
WEB: www.riverbankhousehotel.com

HOTEL ★★★ MAP 4 O 6

The Riverbank House Hotel commands magnificent views of the old Viking town, the River Slaney and the miles of golden beach surrounding Wexford. The hotel boasts an excellent à la carte menu, delicious bar food together with an exciting wine list. Benefiting from its own private car park, the hotel offers easy access to five of the best golf courses in the South East, sea angling sites & shooting - ensuring that whatever your stay, business or leisure, it will be most enjoyable.

B&B from € 45.00 to € 77.00

COLM CAMPBELL
GENERAL MANAGER

American Express
Diners
Mastercard
Visa

24 24

🍴A/C🚿

Closed 25 December

SAINT GEORGE

GEORGE STREET,
WEXFORD

TEL: 053-43474 FAX: 053-24814
EMAIL: stgeorge@eircom.net

GUESTHOUSE ★★ MAP 4 O 6

You are sure of a warm welcome here at the Saint George, a family-run guesthouse in the centre of Wexford Town, the heart of the sunny South East. We are close to all amenities and provide a private lock-up car park. All our bedrooms have bathroom en suite. They are equipped with direct dial phone, colour TV, hairdryer, tea/coffee making facilities. All rooms are non smoking, but there is a smoking lounge available. Only 15 minutes drive from Rosslare Ferry Port. Early breakfast on request.

B&B from € 30.00 to € 35.00

KAYME SCALLAN
PROPRIETOR

Mastercard
Visa

9 9

Closed 01 December - 01 February

TALBOT HOTEL CONFERENCE AND LEISURE CENTRE

TRINITY STREET,
WEXFORD

TEL: 053-22566 FAX: 053-23377
EMAIL: sales@talbothotel.ie
WEB: www.talbothotel.ie

HOTEL ★★★ MAP 4 0 6

Located in the heart of Wexford Town is the Talbot Hotel Conference & Leisure Centre. Our Quay Leisure Centre offers extensive leisure facilities for the fitness enthusiast and for those who just want pure pampering. Award winning Slaney Restaurant offers fresh Wexford fayre and an extensive wine list. Evening entertainment in the Trinity Bar at weekends. Bedrooms are fully equipped with direct dial phone, satellite TV and are tastefully decorated for your comfort and relaxation.

Member of Select Hotels of Ireland

B&B from €70.00 to €80.00

JAMES O'BRIEN
GENERAL MANAGER

American Express
Diners
Mastercard
Visa

Weekend specials from €165.00

99 99 CMCS

Inet

IRISH HOTELS FEDERATION

Closed 24 - 26 December

WESTGATE HOUSE

WESTGATE,
WEXFORD

TEL: 053-22167 FAX: 053-22167
EMAIL: westgate@wexmail.com
WEB: www.wexford-online.com/westgate

GUESTHOUSE ★★ MAP 4 0 6

Westgate House stands in a charming, traditional area across the road from the famed Selskar Abbey and Westgate Castle. It is an historic house, formerly Westgate Hotel in 1812. It has been refurbished in period style with taste and elegance, with beautifully furnished bedrooms which create a sense of ease and timelessness. Matching this, it offers full modern amenities. Situated in the exciting town centre with superb shops, pubs and restaurants. A secure lock-up car park is provided.

B&B from €33.00 to €35.00

M & D ALLEN
OWNERS

Mastercard
Visa

10 10

IRISH HOTELS FEDERATION

Open All Year

WHITES HOTEL

GEORGE STREET,
WEXFORD

TEL: 053-22311 FAX: 053-45000
EMAIL: info@whiteshotel.iol.ie
WEB: www.whiteshotel.ie

HOTEL ★★★ MAP 4 0 6

Est. 1779, this charming 3*** hotel is centrally located in the historic and picturesque town of Wexford. The hotel's facilities include a health & fitness club, Harpers superb brasserie restaurant offering the finest local and international dishes for lunch & dinner and the immensely popular Harpers Bar, where carvery lunches and bar food is served daily and which is open late Thurs-Sun. The hotel is 5 mins walk from the bus and train station and only 20 mins drive from Rosslare Europort.

Member of Best Western Hotels

B&B from €53.00 to €67.50

MICHAEL CONNOLLY
GENERAL MANAGER

American Express
Diners
Mastercard
Visa

Midweek specials 3 Dinners B&B
from €115.00

82 82 CM

alc

IRISH HOTELS FEDERATION

Open All Year

B&B rates are per person sharing per night incl. Breakfast

WHITFORD HOUSE HOTEL

NEW LINE ROAD,
WEXFORD

TEL: 053-43444 FAX: 053-46399
EMAIL: whitford@indigo.ie
WEB: www.whitford.ie

HOTEL ★★★ MAP 4 N 5

One of the leading family run tourist establishments in the South East. Footprints award winning restaurant receives constant accolades for excellence, presentation and value. Seafood a speciality. Standard and superior de luxe accommodation. Entertainment at weekends. Unwind in our indoor swimming pool, leisure centre opening June 2003. For younger members we boast a children's playground. Locally there is golf, fishing, horse riding and excellent beaches. AA, RAC and Michelin recommended.

B&B from €60.00 to €80.00

THE WHITTY FAMILY

American Express
Mastercard
Visa

Weekend specials from €130.00
Jan, Feb, March, Nov, Dec.

36 36

Closed 23 December - 03 January

Room rates are per room per night

SOUTH WEST
The spectacular South West

Located in the south-west corner of Ireland, the Cork and Kerry region offers its visitors a great diversity of scenery, culture and leisure activities. Cork and Kerry claim some of the most varied and spectacular scenery in the country.

The Queenstown Story, Cobh, Co. Cork

Natural attractions abound, from the West Cork coast, the Beara and Dingle peninsulas and the Ring of Kerry to the Lakes of Killarney and the Bandon, Lee and Blackwater valleys.

With its remarkable charm, bumpy bridges, hilly streets and distinctive continental air the city of Cork will not fail, like the rest of the Region, to captivate and welcome all visitors, young and old. Cobh, situated on the southern short of the Great Island, lies in one of the world's largest natural harbours. The Queenstown Story in Cobh tells the story of emigration and the history of sail and steam in Cork Harbour. Cobh was the last port of call for the ill-fated Titanic.

The coast road from Kinsale to Skibbereen passes through many attractive villages and towns giving breath-taking views of the south west coastline. Kinsale, a town which has retained its old world charm and character is firmly established as one of Ireland's leading gourmet centres. Passing onto Clonakilty, Ireland's 1999 national Tidy Towns winners, one of Cork's many picturesque and colourful towns.There are many amenities in the area, with places of interest to visit, sporting and leisure activities and festivals.

The unspoilt coastal and inland waters of Cork and Kerry offer numerous water sports, from fishing to sailing, diving and windsurfing.

The Ring of Kerry is a journey through some of the country's most outstanding scenery. It is not only one of great natural beauty - it is enhanced by the influence of both ancient folklore and local traditions. With its three famous lakes and great mountain ranges Killarney has been the inspiration of poets and painters over many centuries. A spectacular attraction is the Skellig Experience Centre at Valentia Island which imaginatively tells the story of the history of the Skelligs.

The Dingle Peninsula has some of the most intersting antiquities, historic sites and varied scenery in the whole country. Dingle, the most westerly town in Europe is an excellent centre for the visitor. It still retains much of its old-world atmosphere with its many shops and restaurants.

For further information contact:
Cork Kerry Tourism, Aras Failte,
Grand Parade, Cork.
Tel. (021) 4255100. Fax. (021) 4255199
email: info@corkkerrytourism.ie
web: www.corkkerry.ie

Killarney Tourist Office, Beech Road,
Killarney, Co. Kerry.
Tel. (064) 31633. Fax (064) 34506.

The Skellig Experience Visitor
Centre, Valentia Island, Co. Kerry

SEA VIEW GUEST HOUSE

CLUIN VILLAGE,
ALLIHIES, BEARA,
CO. CORK
TEL: 027-73004 FAX: 027-73211
EMAIL: seaviewg@iol.ie
WEB: www.seaviewallihies.com

GUESTHOUSE ★★★ MAP 1 C 2

Sea View Guest House is a family run concern in the remote and unspoilt Beara Peninsula. All bedrooms are en suite with TV and telephone. Situated in the village of Allihies, it is within walking distance of a beach, playground and tennis court. The nearby hills afford excellent opportunities for walking, offering breathtaking views. Traditional Irish music and a friendly welcome can be found in the village pubs.

Member of Premier Guesthouses

B&B from € 30.00 to € 40.00

JOHN AND MARY O'SULLIVAN
PROPRIETORS

Mastercard
Visa

10 10

Closed 31 October - 01 March

BAYVIEW HOTEL

BALLYCOTTON,
CO. CORK
TEL: 021-464 6746 FAX: 021-464 6075
EMAIL: info@bayviewhotel.net
WEB: www.bayviewhotel.net

HOTEL ★★★★ MAP 3 J 3

The Bayview Hotel is a luxury 35 bedroom hotel, magnificently situated overlooking Ballycotton Bay and fishing harbour. Private gardens with steps lead to the sea and bathing spot. The Capricho Restaurant produces innovative Irish cuisine and was awarded 2 rosettes by the AA. There are 6 superb golf courses in the area with sea angling, heritage centres and many other activities available. GDS Access Code: UI Toll Free 1-800-44-UTELL.

Member of Manor House Hotels

B&B from € 89.00 to € 107.00

STEPHEN BELTON
GENERAL MANAGER

American Express
Diners
Mastercard
Visa

35 35

Closed 28 October - 17 April

SPANISH POINT SEAFOOD RESTAURANT & GUEST HOUSE

BALLYCOTTON,
CO. CORK
TEL: 021-464 6177 FAX: 021-464 6179
EMAIL: spanishp@indigo.ie

GUESTHOUSE ★★★ MAP 3 J 3

Spanish Point Seafood Restaurant & Guest accommodation is situated on a cliff face overlooking Ballycotton Bay. The conservatory restaurant specialises in seafood which is caught from our own trawler. Mary Tattan, Chef/Owner, trained at Ballymaloe Cookery School. We have recently built on a new lounge and sun deck for our residents and guests to enjoy. Local cliff walk and beaches to be enjoyed.

B&B from € 40.00 to € 40.00

MARY TATTAN
CHEF/OWNER

Diners
Mastercard
Visa

5 5

Closed 21 - 26 December

Room rates are per room per night

BALLYLICKEY MANOR HOUSE AND RESTAURANT

BALLYLICKEY,
BANTRY BAY,
CO. CORK
TEL: 027-50071 FAX: 027-50124
EMAIL: ballymh@eircom.net
WEB: www.ballylickeymanorhouse.com

GUESTHOUSE ★★★★ MAP 2 E 2

Overlooking beautiful Bantry Bay in 4 hectares of parkland and ornamental gardens, bordered by the Ouvane River, Ballylickey, a 17th century manor house together with cottages around the swimming pool, offers both standard rooms, luxury suites and apartments. An outdoor heated swimming pool, private fishing, 2 golf courses (3 and 8km) and riding nearby. Ballylickey is a member of the Irish Country House and Restaurant Association and of Relais and Châteaux International.

Member of Ireland's Blue Book

B&B from € 102.00 to €171.00

MR AND MRS GRAVES
OWNERS

American Express
Diners
Mastercard
Visa

🚪🛏 ☎📺T C☀🏊⚓U🅿🏠abc
11   11

Closed 15 November - 15 March

SEA VIEW HOUSE HOTEL

BALLYLICKEY,
BANTRY,
CO. CORK
TEL: 027-50073 FAX: 027-51555
EMAIL: info@seaviewhousehotel.com
WEB: www.seaviewhousehotel.com

HOTEL ★★★★ MAP 2 E 2

Delightful country house hotel and restaurant, set back in extensive grounds on main Bantry/Glengarriff Road. All bedrooms en suite, D.D. telephone and colour TV. Ideal for touring West Cork & Kerry. Two golf courses nearby. Recommended Egon Ronay, Good Hotel Guide etc. For the restaurant, AA Rosettes & Bord Failte Awards of Excellence. Seafood a speciality. Member of Manor House Hotels. A wing of new superior rooms was added in Winter 2000 and also a conservatory to the dining room. Special midweek & weekend rates on request, subject to availability.

Member of Manor House Hotels

B&B from € 70.00 to €90.00

KATHLEEN O'SULLIVAN
PROPRIETOR

American Express
Diners
Mastercard
Visa

☺ Special offers on request

🚪🛏 ☎📺C⚓U🅿🏠abc
25   25

Closed 15 November - 15 March

ABBEY HOTEL

BALLYVOURNEY,
CO. CORK
TEL: 026-45324 FAX: 026-45449
EMAIL: abbeyhotel@eircom.net
WEB: www.theabbeyhotel.net

HOTEL U MAP 2 F 3

Family run hotel nestles in the valley of the Sullane River among the Cork and Kerry Mountains on the N22. It combines a friendly atmosphere and excellent catering. An ideal base for touring Kerry and Cork. A wide range of activities is available to you at the hotel including fishing, mountaineering, nature walks and golfing. 39 bedrooms with private facilities, direct dial phone & colour TV. Within 20 minutes drive are two 18 hole golf courses and trout fishing on the Sullane River.

B&B from €35.00 to €50.00

CORNELIUS CREEDON
PROPRIETOR

American Express
Diners
Mastercard
Visa

🚪🛏 ☎📺T C♥CM☀U🎵🅿
39   39
S🏊abc⚓

Closed 23 December - 01 January

B&B rates are per person sharing per night incl. Breakfast

BALTIMORE BAY GUEST HOUSE

THE WATERFRONT,
BALTIMORE,
CO. CORK

TEL: 028-20600 FAX: 028-20495
EMAIL: baltimorebay@youenjacob.com
WEB: www.youenjacob.com

GUESTHOUSE ★★★ MAP 2 E 1

Baltimore Bay Guest House is a superbly appointed new guesthouse with 8 spacious bedrooms. 5 bedrooms have a magnificent view of the sea. Two restaurants are attached to the guesthouse, La Jolie Brise budget restaurant, Egon Ronay listed, and Chez Youen, Egon Ronay Best Irish Fish Restaurant of the Year in 1994 and listed as one of the best places to stay in Ireland. Sawday Guide. Guide du Routard. Youen & Mary Jacob and sons, Proprietors. Sailing facilities.

B&B from €40.00 to €60.00

YOUEN & MARY JACOB
OWNER-MANAGERS

American Express
Mastercard
Visa

🏨🛏️📺T©CMU♩S♿♿
 8 8

Open All Year

Room rates are per room per night

BALTIMORE HARBOUR HOTEL & LEISURE CENTRE

BALTIMORE,
CO. CORK

TEL: 028-20361 FAX: 028-20466
EMAIL: info@bhrhotel.ie
WEB: www.bhrhotel.ie

HOTEL ★★★ MAP 2 E 1

The hotel is situated overlooking the Harbour & Islands in the charming coastal village of Baltimore. It is the ideal haven from which to explore the beauty and wonders of West Cork and the sea and to enjoy the many varied activities available locally, including sailing, golfing, angling, diving, horse-riding, walking, cycling and of course the Islands. We are especially suited for families and offer children's entertainment during peak season. Enjoy our superb indoor leisure centre. Newly refurbished bedrooms.

B&B from €55.00 to €85.00

ANTHONY PALMER
GENERAL MANAGER

American Express
Diners
Mastercard
Visa

😊 Weekend specials from €115.00

🏨🛏️📺T©CM❄♿🏊🛶♿
64 64
♩🎵PS♿♿

Closed 01 January - 10 January

CASEY'S OF BALTIMORE

BALTIMORE,
CO. CORK

TEL: 028-20197 FAX: 028-20509
EMAIL: caseys@eircom.net
WEB: www.caseysofbaltimore.com

HOTEL ★★★ MAP 2 E 1

A warm welcome awaits you at Casey's of Baltimore. Situated at the entrance to Baltimore with its lovely views overlooking the bay, this superb family run hotel is the perfect place to spend some time. All rooms feature en suite bathrooms, satellite TV, tea/coffee facility, direct dial phone, hairdryer and trouser press. The traditional pub and restaurant feature natural stone and wood décor, a spectacular view, extensive menu - seafood is our speciality. Activities can be arranged.

Member of Irish Country Hotels

B&B from €64.50 to €77.50

ANN & MICHAEL CASEY
OWNERS

American Express
Diners
Mastercard
Visa

☺ Midweek specials from €138.00

14 14

aic Inet

IRISH HOTELS FEDERATION

Closed 10 - 17 October

MUNSTER ARMS HOTEL

OLIVER PLUNKETT STREET,
BANDON,
CO. CORK

TEL: 023-41562 FAX: 023-41562
EMAIL: info@munsterarmshotel.com
WEB: www.munsterarmshotel.com

HOTEL U MAP 2 G 2

Set at the gateway to West Cork, 30 high quality en suite bedrooms with tea/coffee facilities, direct dial telephone, remote control T.V. radio and hairdryer. Set in beautiful scenic West Cork accessible by the N71 route from Cork City. Renowned for its homely atmosphere and superb quality. Ideal touring base and easily accessible to Kinsale, Cork City, Blarney, Killarney and West Cork. Relax and be pampered! Guests of the Munster Arms Hotel may use the leisure facilities at the local Bandon Leisure Centre for a nominal fee payable direct to the leisure centre.

B&B from €42.50 to €50.00

JOHN COLLINS/DON O'SULLIVAN

American Express
Diners
Mastercard
Visa

30 30

IRISH HOTELS FEDERATION

Closed 25 - 26 December

ATLANTA HOUSE

MAIN STREET,
BANTRY,
CO. CORK

TEL: 027-50237 FAX: 027-50237
EMAIL: atlantaguesthouse@eircom.net
WEB: www.atlantaguesthouse.com

GUESTHOUSE ★★★ MAP 2 E 2

Atlanta House is a long established family run guesthouse situated in the centre of Bantry. It is an ideal base from which to tour West Cork and Kerry if you are walking, cycling or driving. Golf, fishing and horseriding are all close by. Rooms are en suite with TV, D.D phone & tea/coffee making facilities. Private parking available for motorbikes. We assure you of a warm welcome and we look forward to seeing you in Bantry.

B&B from €27.00 to €30.00

RONNIE & ESTHER O'DRISCOLL
OWNERS

American Express
Mastercard
Visa

10 10

IRISH HOTELS FEDERATION

Closed 20 - 31 December

B&B rates are per person sharing per night incl. Breakfast

BANTRY BAY HOTEL

WOLFE TONE SQUARE,
BANTRY,
CO. CORK
TEL: 027-50062 FAX: 027-50261
EMAIL: bantrybay@eircom.net
WEB: www.bantrybayhotel.com

HOTEL ★★ MAP 2 E 2

The Bantry Bay has been operated by the O'Callaghan family for over 50 years in the centre of historic Bantry. Extensively renovated since 1995, the premises consists of a choice of family, tourist and commercial accommodation. All rooms are en suite with TV, DD phone, teamaker and hairdryer. They are complemented by our beautiful maritime theme bar and restaurant. Carvery in operation daily. Guests assured of a hearty O'Callaghan welcome.

B&B from €46.09 to €48.88

VIVIAN O'CALLAGHAN SNR/JNR
PROPRIETOR/MANAGER

American Express
Diners
Mastercard
Visa

14 14

I R I S H
HOTELS
FEDERATION

Closed 24 - 27 December

VICKERY'S INN

NEW STREET,
BANTRY,
CO. CORK
TEL: 027-50006 FAX: 027-50006
EMAIL: vickerys_inn@westcork.com
WEB: www.westcork.com/vickerys-inn

GUESTHOUSE ★★ MAP 2 E 2

Originally a coaching inn established 1850. All bedrooms en suite with TV, telephones, tea/coffee making facilities. Extensive menus available. Guide du Routard recommended. Ideally situated to explore the scenic West Cork/Kerry region. Golf, horseriding, river, lake and seafishing close by. Internet access available.

B&B from €33.00 to €40.00

HAZEL VICKERY
PROPRIETOR

American Express
Diners
Mastercard
Visa

13 13

I R I S H
HOTELS
FEDERATION

Closed 23 - 30 December

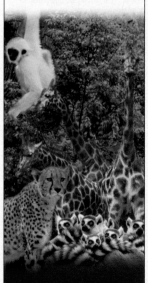
Room rates are per room per night

WESTLODGE HOTEL

BANTRY,
CO. CORK

TEL: 027-50360 FAX: 027-50438
EMAIL: reservations@westlodgehotel.ie
WEB: www.westlodgehotel.ie

HOTEL ★★★ MAP 2 E 2

3*** hotel beautifully situated in the scenic surroundings of Bantry Bay. Super health and leisure centre including indoor heated swimming pool, children's pool, toddlers pool, sauna, steam room, jacuzzi, gym, aerobics, squash. Outdoor amenities include tennis, pitch & putt, wooden walks. The Westlodge specialise in family holidays with organised activities during June, July & August. A warm and friendly welcome awaits you at the Westlodge. Self-catering cottages available.

Member of Holiday Ireland Hotels

B&B from €60.00 to €80.00

EILEEN M O'SHEA FIHCI
GENERAL MANAGER

American Express
Diners
Mastercard
Visa

☺ Weekend specials from €120.00

90 90

Closed 23 - 28 December

ASHLEE LODGE

TOWER,
BLARNEY,
CO. CORK

TEL: 021-438 5346 FAX: 021-438 5726
EMAIL: info@ashleelodge.com
WEB: www.ashleelodge.com

GUESTHOUSE ★★★★ MAP 2 H 3

Welcome to a guesthouse who simply puts you first. Located just outside Blarney on R617, Ashlee Lodge offers luxurious bedrooms, all individually decorated with a golf theme. All rooms have large en suite bathroms, air conditioning, king size beds, wide screen TV/CD units, DD telephone, modem access, trouser press and safe. Our suites boast whirlpool baths and lounge areas. Relax in our sauna and Canadian hot tub. Gourmet breakfasts and secure car parking.

Member of Best Loved Hotels of the World

B&B from €38.00 to €82.00

ANNE & JOHN O'LEARY
PROPRIETORS

American Express
Diners
Mastercard
Visa

☺ Midweek specials from €100.00

10 10

Inet FAX

Open All Year

BLARNEY CASTLE HOTEL

BLARNEY,
CO. CORK

TEL: 021-438 5116 FAX: 021-438 5542
EMAIL: info@blarneycastlehotel.com
WEB: www.blarneycastlehotel.com

HOTEL ★★★ MAP 2 H 3

Established in 1837, still run by the Forrest family. Picturesque inn on a peaceful village green, 5 miles from Cork City. Tastefully appointed spacious bedrooms. Unspoilt traditional bar. Restaurant specialising in finest local produce. Killarney, Kenmare, Kinsale, Cobh, West Cork, Waterford and numerous golf courses all an easy drive. Immediately to the left the magnificent grounds of Blarney Castle guarding that famous stone, to the right, Blarney Woollen Mills. Private car park for hotel guests. Quality entertainment nightly in village.

B&B from €50.00 to €65.00

IAN FORREST
MANAGER

American Express
Diners
Mastercard
Visa

☺ Weekend specials from €125.00

13 13

alc Inet

Closed 25 - 26 December

B&B rates are per person sharing per night incl. Breakfast

Room rates are per room per night

CO. CORK
BLARNEY / CARRIGALINE

SUNSET RIDGE HOTEL

KILLEENS,
BLARNEY,
CO. CORK

TEL: 021-438 5271 FAX: 021-438 5565
EMAIL: sunsetridge@holidayhound.com
WEB: www.holidayhound.com/sunsetridge

HOTEL ★   MAP 2 H 3

Situated on main Cork/Limerick road, Cork City 4.8km / Blarney Village 3.2km. All rooms en suite, TV, direct dial phone. Fully licensed bar, complimentary entertainment Wed/Sat/Sun, bar food available. Our restaurant offers a selection of lunch, dinner and à la carte menus daily. Local amenities include horse riding, golf and fishing. A scenic nature trail walk links our hotel with Blarney Village. Special rates for group bookings. Bus tours catered for.

B&B from €42.00 to €60.00

DENIS CRONIN
MANAGER

American Express
Diners
Mastercard
Visa

28 28

Closed 25 - 26 December

WATERLOO INN

WATERLOO,
BLARNEY,
CO. CORK

TEL: 021-438 5113 FAX: 021-438 2829
EMAIL: waterlooinn@eircom.net
WEB: www.blarneybandb.com

GUESTHOUSE ★★   MAP 2 H 3

Enjoy a holiday in an old country inn located just 1.5 miles from Blarney Castle and 6 miles from Cork City. Set in a peaceful location this riverside inn offers comfortable rooms with tea/coffee making facilities. Relax in our conservatory, have a drink in the bar or walk up to the old round tower of Waterloo. All leisure activities nearby (golf, horse riding etc). This is an ideal centre to tour the South of Ireland. Secure parking available.

B&B from €28.00 to €32.00

PATRICIA DORAN/MARY DUGGAN
PROPRIETORS

Mastercard
Visa

6 4

Closed 15 November - 15 February

CARRIGALINE COURT HOTEL & LEISURE CENTRE

CARRIGALINE,
CO. CORK

TEL: 021-485 2100 FAX: 021-437 1103
EMAIL: carrigcourt@eircom.net
WEB: www.carrigcourt.com

HOTEL U MAP 3 H 3

Luxury RAC 4**** hotel, located just minutes from city centre, airport and ferry terminal. Spacious bedrooms with satellite TV, tea/coffee facilities, ISDN line and all modern comforts as standard. Superb restaurant and traditional Irish bar. Exquisite leisure centre incl. 20m pool, sauna, jacuzzi, steamroom and gym. Golf arranged at Cork's best courses. Local activities include sailing, angling, horse riding and a host of other activities in this beautiful area.

B&B from €85.00 to €100.00

JOHN O'FLYNN
GENERAL MANAGER

American Express
Diners
Mastercard
Visa

☺ Weekend specials from €140.00

52 52

Closed 25 December

194 SOUTH WEST   B&B rates are per person sharing per night incl. Breakfast

FERNHILL GOLF & COUNTRY CLUB

FERNHILL,
CARRIGALINE,
CO. CORK

TEL: 021-437 2226 FAX: 021-437 1011
EMAIL: fernhill@iol.ie
WEB: www.fernhillgolfhotel.com

GUESTHOUSE ★★★ MAP 3 H 3

Fernhill Golf & Country Club is the ideal venue for your relaxing holiday; 18 hole golf course (free to residents), indoor swimming pool, sauna and a tennis court. Fishing and horse riding nearby. 10 mins from Cork City and Airport, 5 mins from Ringaskiddy Ferries, 30 mins from Kinsale. All rooms en suite, TV, direct dial phone, tea/coffee making facilities, full bar and restaurant all day in clubhouse. Music at weekends.

B&B from €45.00 to €75.00

MICHAEL BOWES
OWNER

American Express
Diners
Mastercard
Visa

18 18

Closed 20 December - 06 January

GLENWOOD HOUSE

BALLINREA ROAD,
CARRIGALINE,
CORK

TEL: 021-437 3878 FAX: 021-437 3878
EMAIL: glenwoodhouse@eircom.net
WEB: www.glenwoodhotel.com

GUESTHOUSE ★★★★ MAP 3 H 3

Glenwood House is a purpose built, self contained Guesthouse, designed with all guest requirements in mind. The rooms are large and spacious, offering similar facilities to those of quality hotels, firm orthopaedic beds, heated towel rails, complimentary beverages, trouser press, satelite TV, power shower and many more. Located close to Ringaskiddy Ferry Port (5mins), Cork City (7mins), Kinsale (15mins), Crosshaven (5mins), Airport (5mins). We offer secure car parking, and have facilities to look after disabled guests. All accommodation is of hotel quality.

Member of Premier Guesthouses

B&B from €40.00 to €55.00

ADRIAN SHEEDY
PROPRIETOR

Mastercard
Visa

10 10

Inet FAX

Closed 17 December - 05 January

Room rates are per room per night

CASTLE (THE)

CASTLETOWNSHEND,
CO. CORK

TEL: 028-36100 FAX: 028-36166
EMAIL: castle_townshend@hotmail.com
WEB: www.castle-townshend.com

GUESTHOUSE ★ MAP 2 F 1

18th century Townshend family home overlooking Castlehaven Harbour. Set in own grounds at water's edge with access to small beach and woods. Most bedrooms en suite on second floor with excellent sea views. Panelled hall/sitting room with TV and open fire. Breakfast in elegant dining room. Mary Ann's Restaurant close by. Ideal for touring Cork and Kerry. Also self catering apartments and cottages. For illustrated brochure please apply.

B&B from €40.00 to €70.00

MRS COCHRANE-TOWNSHEND

Mastercard
Visa

Closed 15 December - 15 January

DEERPARK HOTEL

LIMERICK ROAD,
CHARLEVILLE,
CO. CORK

TEL: 063-81581 FAX: 063-81581
EMAIL: info@deerparkhotel.com
WEB: www.charleville.com

HOTEL ★★ MAP 2 G 5

The Deerpark Hotel is the ideal centre for your stay in North Cork, South Limerick, South Tipperary area. Convenient to Blarney, Cork, Adare, Shannon and the Glen of Aherlow. Horse riding, bicycle hire, fishing, pitch & putt, special green fees at one of Munster's finest inland 27 hole courses (18 & 9) are all available locally to our guests. Extensive à la carte menu throughout the day. Site on 9 acres with mature gardens. The Sheehan Family welcome you to the Deerpark Hotel.

Room Rate from €65.00 to €80.00

ROSARIO & MARK SHEEHAN
PROPRIETORS

Mastercard
Visa

Open All Year

DUNMORE HOUSE HOTEL

MUCKROSS,
CLONAKILTY,
CO. CORK

TEL: 023-33352 FAX: 023-34686
EMAIL: dunmorehousehotel@eircom.net
WEB: www.dunmorehousehotel.com

HOTEL ★★★ MAP 2 G 2

Situated on the South West coast of Ireland, Dunmore House Hotel is family owned. Rooms are beautifully decorated, all with spectacular views of the Atlantic Ocean. Sample a true taste of West Cork with our home-cooked local produce and seafood. Private foreshore available for sea angling. Green fees at the on-site golf club are free to residents. Wheelchair access throughout hotel. Interesting collection of local and modern Irish art.

Member of Green Book of Ireland

B&B from €65.00 to €70.00

DERRY & MARY O'DONOVAN
PROPRIETORS

American Express
Diners
Mastercard
Visa

Closed 19 February - 06 March

B&B rates are per person sharing per night incl. Breakfast

EMMET HOTEL

EMMET SQUARE,
CLONAKILTY,
CO. CORK
TEL: 023-33394 FAX: 023-35058
EMAIL: emmethotel@eircom.net
WEB: www.emmethotel.com

HOTEL U MAP 2G2

Ideally located in a Georgian square within two minutes walk of the main street and a five minute drive to beautiful beaches. The Emmet offers old fashioned courtesy with a very friendly ambience. Our restaurant, O'Keeffes of Clonakility is acclaimed as one of the best in West Cork, using local organic produce with the emphasis on fresh seafood, booking is advisable. Leisure centre, golf, riding and angling available locally. New patio garden, serving food and drink daily during the summer months. Also, barbeque facilities for parties up to 40 max.

B&B from € 40.00 to € 65.00

TONY & MARIE O'KEEFFE
MANAGERS

American Express
Diners
Mastercard
Visa

🖐️👜☎️⛴️T⃣C⃣🛏️CM❄️☋♪P⃣🖐️
20 20
S⃣🅰alc 🍴

Closed 24 - 26 December

FERNHILL HOUSE HOTEL

CLONAKILTY,
CO. CORK
TEL: 023-33258 FAX: 023-34003
EMAIL: info@fernhillhousehotel.com
WEB: www.fernhillhousehotel.com

HOTEL ★★ MAP 2G2

Fernhill House is a family run old Georgian style hotel located on picturesque grounds 0.8km from Clonakilty. All bedrooms en suite with tea/coffee making facilities, phone, TV and hairdryer. Conference and function facilities available, Par 3 golf 18 hole Pitch & Putt course. Our hotel offers an intimate homely atmosphere, excellent food and a comfortable bar. Holiday with us and enjoy scenic West Cork from centrally situated Fernhill House Hotel.

B&B from € 50.00 to € 55.00

MICHAEL & TERESA O'NEILL
PROPRIETORS

American Express
Diners
Mastercard
Visa

🖐️👜☎️⛴️T⃣C⃣🛏️CM❄️☋P⃣S⃣🖐️
11 11
alc ♿

IRISH
HOTELS
FEDERATION

Closed 23 December - 01 January

Clonakilty ...
Seeing is Believing

Discover Our Clonakilty
Your ideal holiday destination, activity centre and West Cork touring base.

Famous for Music

10 Miles of Sandy Beaches

National Tidy Towns and World Environmental Gold Medal Winners

For Further Information:
Please Contact:
Clonakilty and District Chamber of Tourism

"In existence to care for you"

Tel: 00 353 23 35047
E-mail: tourism@clonakilty.ie
Website: www.clonakilty.ie

Room rates are per room per night

LODGE & SPA AT INCHYDONEY ISLAND

CLONAKILTY,
CO. CORK

TEL: 023-33143 FAX: 023-35229
EMAIL: reservations@inchydoneyisland.com
WEB: www.inchydoneyisland.com

HOTEL ★★★★   MAP 2 G 2

Situated on the idyllic island of Inchydoney, between two EU blue flag beaches, the hotel offers de luxe rooms, a fully equipped thalassotherapy (seawater) spa, restaurant, Dunes Pub and function and meeting facilities. Within a short distance guests can enjoy sailing, golf at the Old Head of Kinsale, riding and deep sea fishing. The style of cooking in the Gulfstream Restaurant reflects the wide availability of fresh seafoods and organically grown vegetables.

B&B from €143.00 to €170.50

MICHAEL KNOX-JOHNSTON

American Express
Diners
Mastercard
Visa

67 67

Open All Year

O'DONOVAN'S HOTEL

PEARSE STREET,
CLONAKILTY,
WEST CORK

TEL: 023-33250 FAX: 023-33250
EMAIL: odhotel@iol.ie
WEB: www.odonovanshotel.com

HOTEL ★★   MAP 2 G 2

Charles Stewart Parnell, Marconi and Gen. Michael Collins found time to stop here. This fifth generation, family run hotel is located in the heart of Clonakilty Town. Abounding in history, the old world charm has been retained whilst still providing the guest with facilities such as bath/shower en suite, TV etc. Our restaurant provides snacks and full meals and is open to non-residents. Ideal for conferences, private functions, meetings etc., with lock up car park.

B&B from €50.00 to €60.00

O'DONOVAN FAMILY
PROPRIETORS

American Express
Mastercard
Visa

26 26

Closed 25 - 29 December

QUALITY HOTEL AND LEISURE CENTRE

CLONAKILTY,
CO. CORK

TEL: 023-36400 FAX: 023-35404
EMAIL: qualityhotel@eircom.net
WEB: www.qualityhotelclon.com

HOTEL ★★★   MAP 2 G 2

Clonakilty is a thriving and busy attractive town with a wealth of musical and artistic cultural activities. This unique hotel complex which opened in July 1999, offers the following excellent facilities, 81 en suite bedrooms, 12 two-bedroom suites, 5 executive holiday homes, Lannigans Restaurant, Oscars Bar with regular entertainment, an award winning leisure centre and a three screen multiplex cinema complete the complex. The ideal destination for your breakaway.

Member of Choice Hotels Ireland

B&B from €38.00 to €90.00

DAVID HENRY
GENERAL MANAGER

American Express
Diners
Mastercard
Visa

Weekend specials from €108.00

81 81

Closed 24 - 27 December

B&B rates are per person sharing per night incl. Breakfast

RANDLES CLONAKILTY HOTEL

WOLFE TONE STREET,
CLONAKILTY,
WEST CORK
TEL: 023-34749 FAX: 023-35035
EMAIL: clonakilty@randleshotels.com

HOTEL N MAP 2 G 2

Nestled in the beauty and tranquillity of glorious West Cork stands the all new Randles Clonakilty Hotel. When you walk through the doors of the hotel you will understand what makes the Randles Group of hotels synonymous with high standards. Maxwell Irwins Bar with its wood-panelling interior has been designed to accommodate for fine wining and dining. Newly opened in this hotel, is our leisure centre. Conference room 20-25 persons.

B&B from €45.00 to €95.00

PATRICIA SHANAHAN
GENERAL MANAGER

Mastercard
Visa

Weekend specials from €120.00

30 30

Closed 21 - 27 December

COMMODORE HOTEL

COBH,
CO. CORK
TEL: 021-481 1277 FAX: 021-481 1672
EMAIL: commodorehotel@eircom.net

HOTEL ★★ MAP 3 1 3

The Commodore Hotel, owned by the O'Shea family for 30 years overlooks Cork Harbour. 25 minutes from city centre. Facilities: indoor pool, snooker, entertainment, roof garden. Available locally free golf and pitch & putt. Ideal for visiting Fota Wildlife Park, Fota Golf Course, Blarney etc, The Jameson and Queenstown Heritage Centres. All 42 rooms have full facilities, 21 overlook Cork Harbour (supplement applies). Ringaskiddy Ferryport 15 mins via river car ferry.

Member of Logis of Ireland

B&B from €49.00 to €95.00

PATRICK O'SHEA
GENERAL MANAGER

American Express
Diners
Mastercard
Visa

Weekend specials from €120.00

42 42

IRISH
HOTELS
FEDERATION

Closed 24 - 27 December

Titanic Trail
Cobh, Co. Cork

Explore Cobh's Fascinating history and the towns' direct links with Titanic! The original Titanic Trail guided walking tour takes place every day all year.

Leaving at **11am daily** from the Commodore Hotel this famous tour is educational, interesting and fun. Cost is €7.50 which includes a complimentary glass of Guinness in Jack Doyle's Bar. Duration is approximately 75 minutes.

Afternoon Trails can also be arranged. Groups welcome. Hotel presentations also arranged.

Contact: Michael Martin
Author and Creator Titanic Trail

Tel: + 353 (21) 4815211
Mobile: +353 (87) 276 7218
Email: info@titanic-trail.com
URL www.titanic-trail.com

Room rates are per room per night

WATERSEDGE HOTEL

YACHT CLUB QUAY,
COBH,
CO. CORK

TEL: 021-481 5566 FAX: 021-481 2011
EMAIL: watersedge@eircom.net
WEB: www.watersedgehotel.ie

HOTEL ★★★ MAP 3 I 3

Situated on the waterfront overlooking Cork Harbour. All rooms en suite with satellite TV, tea making facilities, direct dial phone, modem, hairdryer, trouser press. Our restaurant, Jacobs Ladder, is renowned for its seafood, steaks, ambience and friendly staff. Local activities and sightseeing include Cobh Heritage Centre (next door), Cathedral, Titanic Trail, Fota Wildlife Park, Fota House & Garden's, golf, sailing, angling, tennis, horseriding. Ideal touring base for Cork City, Kinsale & Blarney.

B&B from €50.00 to €100.00

MARGARET & MIKE WHELAN
PROPRIETORS

American Express
Diners
Mastercard
Visa

19 19

Closed 23 - 28 December

AIRPORT LODGE

FARMERS CROSS, KINSALE ROAD,
CORK AIRPORT,
CO. CORK

TEL: 021-431 6920 FAX: 021-432 3013
EMAIL: airlodge@indigo.ie
WEB: www.corkairportlodge.com

GUESTHOUSE U MAP 2 H 3

Located at the gates of Cork Airport, 15 minutes drive from Ringaskiddy Ferryport and adjacent to all major roads around Cork City, we are ideal as a first/last night stop. Cork City is only 8km away, Kinsale 30km. We have extensive free car parking and provide a welcome break before you continue your journey.

Room Rate from €45.00 to €90.00

MARY & MAURICE BERGIN
PROPRIETORS

Mastercard
Visa

5   5

Closed 24 - 29 December

GREAT SOUTHERN HOTEL

CORK AIRPORT,
CO. CORK

TEL: 021-494 7500 FAX: 021-494 7501
EMAIL: res@corkairport-gsh.com
WEB: www.gshotels.com

HOTEL N MAP 2 H 3

The Great Southern Hotel Cork Airport is a stylish contemporary hotel conveniently located within walking distance of the terminal at Cork Airport. With a wide range of meeting rooms, a business centre and a leisure centre with gymnasium, steam room and jacuzzi, it is the perfect base for business meetings or for first or last night stays. Bookable worldwide through Utell International or Central Reservations: 01-214 4800.

Room Rate from €90.00 to €150.00

PAT CUSSEN
GENERAL MANAGER

American Express
Diners
Mastercard
Visa

81 81

Inet FAX

Closed 24 - 26 December

B&B rates are per person sharing per night incl. Breakfast

ACHILL HOUSE

WESTERN ROAD,
CORK CITY

TEL: 021-427 9447 FAX: 021-427 9447
EMAIL: info@achillhouse.com
WEB: www.achillhouse.com

GUESTHOUSE ★★★ MAP 2 H 3

Stay in luxury, comfort and style at Achill House. This elegant period house is ideally located in the heart of Cork City and opposite UCC. All rooms have deluxe ensuite bathrooms with optional jacuzzi. An extensive breakfast menu caters for all tastes, from hearty Irish breakfasts to lighter options. Achill House is convenient to ferry, airport and bus termini, the perfect base for exploring Cork and Kerry. A warm and relaxed atmosphere awaits you whether on business or pleasure.

B&B from €35.00 to €45.00

HELENA MCSWEENEY
PROPRIETOR

Mastercard
Visa

☺ Sunday 10% Discount

6 6

Inet

IRISH
HOTELS
FEDERATION

Open All Year

ACORN HOUSE

14 ST. PATRICK'S HILL,
CORK

TEL: 021-450 2474 FAX: 021-450 2474
EMAIL: info@acornhouse-cork.com
WEB: www.acornhouse-cork.com

GUESTHOUSE ★★★ MAP 2 H 3

Acorn House is a refurbished listed Georgian house of architectural merit dating back to 1810. It is a 3 minute walk to St. Patrick Street, Cork City's principal thoroughfare with theatres and excellent choice of restaurants. 5 minutes walk to bus and rail stations, 15 minutes drive to airport and car ferry. Rooms en suite with TV, phone and tea/coffee facilities.
Recommended by Michelin, Stilwell and the Lonely Planet.

B&B from €32.00 to €55.00

JACKIE BOLES
PROPRIETOR

Mastercard
Visa

9 9

IRISH
HOTELS
FEDERATION

Closed 22 December - 16 January

FOTA HOUSE & GARDENS

"Enjoy Cork's Newest Visitor Attraction"

Fota House is Ireland's finest example of Regency period architecture, with magnificent neo classical interiors. Surrounded by parkland, Fota House boasts superb gardens and a world-renowned arboretum.

Why not enjoy a visit to Fota House and Gardens, where a friendly welcome awaits.

Facilities at Fota House & Gardens include self-guided tours, a gift/craft shop and our tearoom celebrated for its "authentic country house fare".
Also available for Corporate Hire

DIRECTIONS

Located 8 miles east of Cork City, just off the main Cork – Waterford Road, (N25). Take the exit for Cobh and follow directions for Fota Estate. The entrance to Fota House is shared with Fota Wildlife Park. Access is also available by train. Car parking available on site.

OPEN DAILY-7 DAYS
Admission Charge Applies

CARRIGTWOHILL, CO. CORK
Tel: 00 353 21 4815543
Fax: 00 353 21 4815541
Email: info@fotahouse.com
Web: www.fotahouse.com

Room rates are per room per night

AMBASSADOR HOTEL

MILITARY HILL,
ST. LUKES,
CORK

TEL: 021-455 1996 FAX: 021-455 1997
EMAIL: info@ambassadorhotel.ie
WEB: www.ambassadorhotel.ie

HOTEL U MAP 2 H 3

Located on a hilltop, the Ambassador Hotel commands spectacular views over Cork City and Harbour. 60 spacious bedrooms luxuriously decorated to the highest standards. A gourmet award-winning "Season's Restaurant", Cocktail Bar, Embassy Bar, Conference Centre and Banqueting facilities, all combine to ensure a memorable stay. Additional conference suites, bedrooms, sauna and gym opening 2003.

Member of Best Western Hotels

B&B from €45.00 to €90.00

DUDLEY FITZELL

American Express
Diners
Mastercard
Visa

☺ Weekend specials from €124.00

60 60

Closed 24 - 26 December

ANTOINE HOUSE

WESTERN ROAD,
CORK

TEL: 021-427 3494 FAX: 021-427 3092
EMAIL: info@antoinehouse.com
WEB: www.antoinehouse.com

GUESTHOUSE ★★ MAP 2 H 3

Located at gateway to West Cork and Kerry for business or pleasure. An ideal base from which to explore, less than one mile from city centre and in close proximity to airport, train, ferry, Blarney and Fota. All rooms en suite with direct dial phones, Satellite TV, hairdryer, tea/coffee facilities. Private lock up car park at rear, golf, shooting, fishing, horse-riding, flying can be arranged. Children welcome. Frommers recommended and AA listed.

B&B from €30.00 to €50.00

KEVIN CROSS
PROPRIETOR

American Express
Diners
Mastercard
Visa

10 10

Closed 26 - 28 December

ASHLEY HOTEL

COBURG STREET,
CORK CITY

TEL: 021-450 1518 FAX: 021-450 1178
EMAIL: ashleyhotel@eircom.net
WEB: www.ashleyhotel.com

HOTEL U MAP 2 H 3

The Ashley Hotel is family-owned, run by Anita Coughlan and her enthusiastic staff, with all the benefits of a city centre location to shops and other attractions. It is the perfect place to relax and have fun. The Ashley has plenty to offer you with a secure lock-up car park, 27 rooms with bathroom en suite, tea/coffee making facilities and direct dial phone with a lively bar and restaurant.

B&B from €48.00 to €60.00

ANITA COUGHLAN

American Express
Diners
Mastercard
Visa

27 27

Closed 24 December - 01 January

B&B rates are per person sharing per night incl. Breakfast

BLARNEY STONE

WESTERN ROAD,
CORK CITY

TEL: 021-427 0083 FAX: 021-427 0471
EMAIL: bsgh@eircom.net
WEB: www.blarneystoneguesthouse.com

GUESTHOUSE ★★★ MAP 2 H 3

This newly refurbished Victorian residence has character and charm and offers you luxurious accommodation in the heart of the city. Situated opposite University College and within close proximity to a selection of restaurants, bars and entertainment places. Also ideally located for ferry, airport, train and bus. All rooms are tastefully decorated to the highest standard with de luxe en suite optional jacuzzi, TV, DD phone, tea/coffee making facilities. A warm and friendly atmosphere awaits you.

B&B from € 32.00 to € 65.00

ANGELA HARTNETT
PROPRIETOR

Mastercard
Visa

🛏 🦮 ☎ 🖳 T C CM❖ 🗘 P S 🔌 Inet
8 8

Open All Year

BRAZIER'S WESTPOINT HOUSE

WESTERN ROAD,
(OPP. UCC),
CORK

TEL: 021-427 5526 FAX: 021-425 1955
EMAIL: info@braziersguesthouse.com
WEB: www.braziersguesthouse.com

GUESTHOUSE ★★★ MAP 2 H 3

A warm welcome and friendly service awaits you at the family run Brazier's Westpoint House which is located less than 10 minutes walk from Cork City centre and opposite University College Cork. Tastefully decorated, all rooms are en suite with colour TV, direct dial phone, hairdryers, tea/coffee facilities and we have a private lock-up carpark at the rear. An ideal base to visit Cork and tour the beautiful South West. AA approved.

B&B from € 32.00 to € 50.00

JOY BRAZIER
PROPRIETOR

American Express
Mastercard
Visa

🛏 🦮 ☎ 🖳 C ➜ CM❖ P 🔌
8 8

IRISH
HOTELS
FEDERATION

Closed 23 December - 06 January

Cork Vision Centre

Cork Vision Centre
@ St. Peters
Aisling Chorcai
North Main Street
Cork
Tel: (021) 427 9925
Fax: (021) 427 9987
Email: visioncentre@eircom.net
www.corkvisioncentre.com

Learn more before you explore!
Tour Corks Model City
City Scope, Restoration Cork
Cork on Film
Photo-Cork, a visual taste of Cork
Our City, Touch Screen Tourist
information.

Visiting Exhibitions
Open Tuesday-Saturday
10am-5pm
Admission Free

Room rates are per room per night

BROOKFIELD HOTEL

BROOKFIELD HOLIDAY VILLAGE,
COLLEGE ROAD,
CORK

TEL: 021-480 4700 FAX: 021-480 4793

HOTEL ★★★ MAP 2 H 3

Brookfield Hotel, College Road is just 1 mile from Cork City Centre. Set on 10 acres of rolling parkland, it is truly a rural setting. *24 bright, modern bedrooms. *Family rooms. *Interconnecting rooms. *Enjoy our leisure and fitness centre which incorporates 25m indoor pool. Kiddies pool, water slide, saunas, steam room, spa jacuzzi, outdoor hot tub, massage, gym, sunbeds, outdoor tennis courts.

B&B from €52.00 to €106.00

MIRIAM RYAN
RESERVATIONS MANAGER

American Express
Mastercard
Visa

24 24

Closed 23 December - 02 January

COMFORT INN & SUITES CORK

MORRISON'S QUAY,
CORK

TEL: 021-427 5858 FAX: 021-427 5833
EMAIL: morisons@iol.ie
WEB: www.choicehotelscork.com

HOTEL ★★★ MAP 2 H 3

Comfort Inn & Suites Cork is situated in the heart of the business and shopping district. Less than a 5 minute walk from Patrick Street, Cork's vibrant main thoroughfare. This contemporary styled hotel meets all accommodation requirements for the individual traveller as well as for the family holiday. An excellent base to explore the City and Co. Cork.

Member of Choice Hotels Ireland

B&B from €65.00 to €110.00

ROSE O' DONOVAN
GENERAL MANAGER

American Express
Diners
Mastercard
Visa

Weekend specials from €138.00

56 56

Closed 24 - 27 December

COMMONS INN

NEW MALLOW ROAD,
CORK

TEL: 021-421 0300 FAX: 021-421 0333
EMAIL: info@commonsinn.com
WEB: www.commonsinn.com

HOTEL ★★★ MAP 3 H 3

Close to Cork City, on the main Cork to Blarney road, this family run hotel contains the popular Commons Bar, Baileys Restaurant and the Roebuck Room function centre. All rooms contain two queen sized beds and are priced per room. Enjoy carvery lunch in the bar or dinner in one of Cork's best restaurants. Whether you're in Cork on business or for pleasure we are at your service.

Room Rate from €65.00 to €90.00

ASHLEY O'NEILL
ACCOMMODATION MANAGER

American Express
Diners
Mastercard
Visa

40 40

FAX

Closed 24 - 27 December

B&B rates are per person sharing per night incl. Breakfast

CRAWFORD GUESTHOUSE

WESTERN ROAD,
CORK

TEL: 021-427 9000 FAX: 021-427 9927
EMAIL: info@crawfordguesthouse.com
WEB: www.crawfordguesthouse.com

GUESTHOUSE ★★★ MAP 3 H 3

One of Cork's finest guesthouses offering bed & breakfast in a contemporary setting. All the bedrooms provide comfort and luxury with oak-wood furniture and orthopaedic 6ft king size beds. De luxe en suites include jacuzzi baths and power showers. Fax/modem points in all rooms. Located directly across from University College Cork. 10 min. walk city centre. Private lock up car park. AA ◆◆◆◆ & RAC ◆◆◆◆ and Sparkling Diamond award 2003.

B&B from €40.00 to €65.00

CECILIA O'LEARY
MANAGER

American Express
Mastercard
Visa

🛏 ☎ ▯ T C CMP ☐ Inet FAX
12 12

IRISH HOTELS FEDERATION

Closed 23 - 27 December

D'ARCYS

7 SIDNEY PLACE,
WELLINGTON ROAD,
CORK

TEL: 021-450 4658 FAX: 021-450 2791
EMAIL: accommodation@darcysguesthouse.com
WEB: www.darcysguesthouse.com

GUESTHOUSE ★ MAP 2 H 3

Not until you enter 7 Sidney Place do you realise what a large building it is. High ceilings and large spacious rooms. The front rooms have views over the city. Rooms are uncluttered, calm, cool places, very peaceful in the centre of the city. Children are welcome. Breakfast is not to be missed. Try freshly squeezed fruit juices, smoked salmon and scrambled eggs and home made preserves. 48 hour cancellation policy.

B&B from €40.00 to €45.00

CLARE D'ARCY
PROPRIETOR

American Express
Diners
Mastercard
Visa

🛏 ☎ C ☐
6   2

IRISH HOTELS FEDERATION

Closed 23 - 27 December

CORK CITY *GAOL*

Step back in time to see what 19th & early 20th Century life was like in Cork - inside & outside prison walls! Amazingly lifelike figures, furnished cells, sound effects and fascinating exhibitions.

OPEN 7 DAYS
Throughout the year.
At same location the
RADIO MUSEUM

Sunday's Well, Cork City
Tel: 021-430 50 22
Email: corkgaol@indigo.ie
www.corkcitygaol.com

Room rates are per room per night

DOUGHCLOYNE HOTEL

DOUGHCLOYNE,
CORK CITY

TEL: 021-431 2535 FAX: 021-431 6086
EMAIL: dough1@iol.ie

HOTEL ★★★ MAP 2 H 3

The Doughcloyne Hotel is situated 2 miles from the city centre, close to the University Hospital in Wilton and Cork Airport, South Link N28 exit Doughcloyne Sarsfields Road roundabout. Our restaurant presents bonne cuisine with friendly service. The lounge bar is noted for its lunch-time barfood and live music at the weekends. Guests have complimentary use of Brookfield Leisure Centre with a 25m swimming pool located near by.

B&B from €45.00 to €55.00

JEAN CASSIDY/ANNE FERNANDEZ
RESERVATIONS

American Express
Diners
Mastercard
Visa

Weekend specials from €89.00

50 50

Closed 24 December - 02 January

EAGLE LODGE GUEST HOUSE

1 WILLOWBROOK,
WESTERN ROAD,
CORK

TEL: 021-427 7380 FAX: 021-427 6432
EMAIL: eaglelodgecork@eircom.net
WEB: www.eaglelodge.net

GUESTHOUSE ★★★ MAP 2 H 3

Eagle Lodge is a 10 minute walk from city centre and close to bus and train stations. All rooms en suite with TV, tea/coffee making facilities, hair dryer and ironing facilities. An ideal base from which to tour West Cork and Kerry. Situated opposite University College. Eagle Lodge is within a short walk of many traditional Irish pubs and a variety of restaurants to suit all tastes.

B&B from €35.00 to €50.00

NORA MURRAY
PROPRIETOR

American Express
Diners
Mastercard
Visa

3 nights B&B from €99.00 p.p.s.

7 7

Open All Year

FAIRY LAWN GUESTHOUSE

WESTERN ROAD,
CORK

TEL: 021-454 3444 FAX: 021-454 4337
EMAIL: fairylawn@holidayhound.com
WEB: www.holidayhound.com/fairylawn.htm

GUESTHOUSE ★★★ MAP 3 H 3

Newly restored & beautifully extended, this luxury guesthouse, with open fires, is tastefully decorated throughout. Bedrooms provide comfort with orthopaedic 6 ft beds(optional), satellite TV. DD phones, hairdryers & hospitality trays. Deluxe en suites with power showers. This family-run guesthouse, where a warm welcome awaits you & breakfast is not to be missed. Opposite UCC. Close to City Centre, ample private parking to the front. AA ♦♦♦♦. RAC ♦♦♦♦ & Sparkling Diamond Award 2001 & 2002. Ideal touring base for South of Ireland.

B&B from €39.00 to €59.00

TONY & JOAN MCGRATH
PROPRIETORS

Mastercard
Visa

14 14

Open All Year

B&B rates are per person sharing per night incl. Breakfast

FORTE TRAVELODGE

BLACKASH,
KINSALE ROAD,
CORK
TEL: 1800-709709 FAX: 021-431 0723

WEB: www.travelodge.co.uk

HOTEL U   MAP 3 H 3

Situated a couple of miles from Cork City Centre, minutes from the Airport and on the direct routes to/from the car ferry, beautiful Kinsale and West Cork, this superb modern hotel offers comfortable yet affordable accommodation. Each room is large enough to sleep up to three adults, a child under 12 and a baby in a cot. Excellent range of facilities from en suite bathroom to colour TV. Sited next to Little Chef Restaurant. Freephone from UK 0800 850 950.

Room Rate from €69.00 to €79.00

DEBBIE O'CONNOR
MANAGER

American Express
Diners
Mastercard
Visa

🛏🛋📺T CM✳🅿🚗🖨aid📠📶 Inet
60   60

Open All Year

GARNISH HOUSE

WESTERN ROAD,
CORK
TEL: 021-427 5111 FAX: 021-427 3872
EMAIL: garnish@iol.ie
WEB: www.garnish.ie

GUESTHOUSE ★★★   MAP 3 H 3

RAC 4◆◆◆◆ and AA 4◆◆◆◆. A stay in Garnish House is a memorable one. The personal atmosphere and attention instantly make you pleasantly at home. Luxury rooms some with jacuzzi baths offer comfort, are unique and charming. Being welcomed with genuine Irish hospitality - cup of tea and an array of delicacies as featured on National TV. 24hr reception, Opposite U.C.C. Awards: Sparkling Diamond, Warm Welcome 1-100 best places to stay. 4**** standard suites and studio accommodation available.

B&B from €40.00 to €66.00

JOHANNA LUCEY
MANAGERESS

American Express
Diners
Mastercard
Visa

🛏🛋☎📺T C🚗CM🅿🖨 Inet
14   14

IRISH
HOTELS
FEDERATION

Open All Year

GRESHAM METROPOLE

MACCURTAIN STREET,
CORK
TEL: 021-450 8122 FAX: 021-450 6450
EMAIL: info@gresham-metropolehotel.com
WEB: www.gresham-hotels.com

HOTEL ★★★   MAP 3 H 3

Located in the heart of Cork, The Gresham Metropole has been stylishly refurbished to the highest standards. 11 bright, airy, meeting rooms with butler service. The superb leisure centre includes three pool areas, a whirlpool spa, sauna, steam room, aerobics studio and gym. Dining in the Riverview Restaurant, with light snacks and beverages in the Waterside café. The Met Bar is popular with guests and locals alike. Complimentary car parking for guests.

B&B from €95.00 to €175.00

JOE KEARNEY
GENERAL MANAGER

American Express
Diners
Mastercard
Visa

🍴🥂
Weekend specials from €140.00

😊

🛏🛋☎📺🖥T C🚗CM🕯🖨📷🛎♨
🎵🅿🖴aid📠 Inet

IRISH
HOTELS
FEDERATION

Open All Year

HAYFIELD MANOR HOTEL

PERROTT AVENUE,
COLLEGE ROAD,
CORK

TEL: 021-484 5900 FAX: 021-431 6839
EMAIL: enquiries@hayfieldmanor.ie
WEB: www.hayfieldmanor.ie

HOTEL ★★★★★ MAP 2 H 3

Tucked away in its own oasis of calm just a mile from the heart of Cork City Ireland's second largest city, Hayfield Manor is one of Ireland's most elegantly decorated hotels. The superb accommodation is renowned for its antique furniture, authentic fabric designs and marble bathrooms. Enjoy the private leisure centre and unwind with a relaxing massage or treatment. The Manor Room award winning cuisine is a treat, or you can relax in the cosy bar (try the oysters and Guinness). AA 4 Red Star. RAC Gold Ribbon.

Member of Small Luxury Hotels of the World

B&B from €109.00 to €190.00

MARGARET NAUGHTON
GENERAL MANAGER

American Express
Diners
Mastercard
Visa

Weekend specials from €310.00pps

87 87

Open All Year

HOTEL ISAACS

48 MAC CURTAIN STREET,
CORK

TEL: 021-450 0011 FAX: 021-450 6355
EMAIL: cork@isaacs.ie
WEB: www.isaacs.ie

HOTEL ★★★ MAP 3 H 3

A homely city centre hotel set in its own courtyard garden and Greene's Restaurant even overlooks a waterfall! Our comfortable en suite rooms with an Irish literary theme have phone, TV, tea/coffee making facilities and hairdryers. New superior room facilities include air conditioning, mini-bar and ISDN access. We are 5-10 minutes from all amenities (commercial or leisure) including bus and train stations with nearby limited free carparking. Hotel Isaacs Cork is simply an oasis within Cork City Centre.

B&B from €47.50 to €100.00

PAULA LYNCH
GENERAL MANAGER

American Express
Mastercard
Visa

Weekend specials from €130.00

36 36

Closed 24 - 27 December

IMPERIAL HOTEL

SOUTH MALL,
CORK

TEL: 021-427 4040 FAX: 021-427 5375
EMAIL: reservations@imperialhotelcork.ie
WEB: www.flynnhotels.com

HOTEL ★★★ MAP 3 H 3

Located in the heart of Cork City, the Imperial Hotel is a short walk away from numerous shops, restaurants, pubs and all other local attractions. All 90 en suite bedrooms are tastefully decorated with restful warm colours such as browns and golds. The bedrooms have all the modern conveniences a discerning guest requires. In addition to Clouds Restaurant, the Imperial Hotel has an authentic french-style brasserie and a lively well known bar. The Imperial Hotel is reowned with locals and guests alike.

B&B from €58.00 to €92.00

JOHN FLYNN
PROPRIETOR

American Express
Diners
Mastercard
Visa

90 90

Closed 24 - 27 December

B&B rates are per person sharing per night incl. Breakfast

JOHN BARLEYCORN HOTEL

RIVERSTOWN,
GLANMIRE,
CORK

TEL: 021-482 1499 FAX: 021-482 1221
EMAIL: johnbarleycorn@eircom.net

HOTEL ★★ MAP 3 H 3

This fine 18th century residence retains all the atmosphere and charm of a rustic coach stop. Nestling in its own grounds of river and trees, just a short 6km jaunt from Cork City, just off the R639 (alternative Cork/Dublin Road). Ideal base for trips to Blarney, Kinsale, Fota and Cobh Heritage Centre. We welcome all guests with enthusiasm and attention.

B&B from €45.00 to €55.00

OLIVIA LOFTUS
MANAGERESS

American Express
Diners
Mastercard
Visa

17   17

Closed 24 - 26 December

JURYS CORK HOTEL

WESTERN ROAD,
CORK

TEL: 021-427 6622 FAX: 021-427 4477
EMAIL: cork@jurysdoyle.com
WEB: www.jurysdoyle.com

HOTEL ★★★★ MAP 2 H 3

Quite simply the finest hotel in Cork with a genteel southern charisma all of its own. Set on the banks of the Lee in the heart of the city, smart shopping and prime business districts are within a few minutes walk. Top-class international facilities are complemented by the warmth and friendliness for which "Corkonians" are noted.

B&B from €65.00 to €131.00

FERGAL SOMERS
GENERAL MANAGER

American Express
Diners
Mastercard
Visa

185 185

Closed 24 - 26 December

JURYS INN CORK

ANDERSON'S QUAY,
CORK

TEL: 021-427 6444 FAX: 021-427 6144
EMAIL: jurysinncork@jurysdoyle.com
WEB: www.jurysdoyle.com

HOTEL ★★★ MAP 2 H 3

Jurys Inn Cork enjoys a superb location right in the heart of Cork City, overlooking the River Lee. Vibrant business and shopping districts and a host of restaurants, bars, museums and galleries are literally within a few minutes walk. An excellent base to explore city or the very stunning Co. Cork countryside.

Room Rate from €78.00 to €128.00

JULIEANN BRENNAN
GENERAL MANAGER

American Express
Diners
Mastercard
Visa

133 133

Closed 24 - 27 December

Room rates are per room per night

KILLARNEY GUEST HOUSE

WESTERN ROAD,
(OPP. UCC),
CORK

TEL: 021-427 0290 FAX: 021-427 1010
EMAIL: killarneyhouse@iol.ie
WEB: www.killarneyguesthouse.com

GUESTHOUSE ★★★ MAP 2 H 3

This charming guesthouse is renowned for its unique blend of comfort, style and hospitality. Its sumptuous breakfast menu includes a buffet table laden with fresh produce and home baking. All rooms are en suite with optional jacuzzi bath. A close walk to the city centre and opposite the University College Cork. Large lock up car park for your security. AA acclaimed and RAC 4 ◆◆◆◆ Award 2002.

B&B from €45.00 to €65.00

MARGARET O'LEARY
MANAGERESS

American Express
Mastercard
Visa

🛏🦢☎🖵Ⓣ©CMP♨
19 19

IRISH
HOTELS
FEDERATION

Closed 23 - 26 December

KINGSLEY HOTEL

VICTORIA CROSS,
CORK

TEL: 021-480 0500 FAX: 021-480 0527
EMAIL: resv@kingsleyhotel.com
WEB: www.kingsleyhotel.com

HOTEL U   MAP 2 H 3

This de luxe hotel is nestled on the River Lee, located only minutes from Cork's Airport. State of the art facilities, an elegant atmosphere and tranquil surroundings. The Sabrona Lounge and Library with open fires are havens of tranquillity. Otters Brasserie is a creative dining experience. Poachers Bar is a distinctly different hotel bar. For business clients a customised business centre and conference facilities. The Kingsley Club allows guests unwind at leisure.

Member of Concorde International

B&B from €90.00 to €155.00

MICHAEL ROCHE
GENERAL MANAGER

American Express
Diners
Mastercard
Visa

 Weekend specials from €160.00

🛏🦢☎🖵⚡Ⓣ©♥CM❄🔍🏠U
69 69
🅿🄹🛏🚗🆔 Inet FAX

IRISH
HOTELS
FEDERATION

Open All Year

LANCASTER LODGE

WESTERN ROAD,
CORK

TEL: 021-425 1125 FAX: 021-425 1126
EMAIL: info@lancasterlodge.com
WEB: www.lancasterlodge.com

GUESTHOUSE ★★★★ MAP 2 H 3

Lancaster Lodge is a purpose-built 39 roomed en suite guesthouse including luxury suites with jacuzzi baths. Located alongside Jurys Hotel and only five minutes from the city centre, the guesthouse provides free private parking, 24-hour reception, an extensive breakfast menu, spacious rooms including wheelchair facilities and lift to each floor. For comfort and convenience Lancaster Lodge awaits you.

B&B from €48.00 to €80.00

SUSAN LEAHY
MANAGERESS

American Express
Diners
Mastercard
Visa

🛏🦢☎🖵⚡Ⓣ©♥UPS Inet
39 39

IRISH
HOTELS
FEDERATION

Closed 23 - 25 December

B&B rates are per person sharing per night incl. Breakfast

LOTAMORE HOUSE

TIVOLI,
CORK

TEL: 021-482 2344 FAX: 021-482 2219
EMAIL: lotamore@iol.ie
WEB: www.lotamorehouse.com

GUESTHOUSE ★★★★ MAP 3 H 3

A beautiful house with 20 en suite rooms, 4**** and all the amenities of a hotel. 9 mins drive from the city centre but having a quiet location surrounded by 4 acres. Cobh Heritage Centre, Fota Island, many golf courses. Blarney, Kinsale within easy reach. Situated 3 mins from the Lee Tunnel. Ideally situated for travelling to the airport, ferry terminals, West Cork, Killarney and the Ring of Kerry.

B&B from € 45.00 to € 52.00

MAIREAD HARTY
PROPRIETOR/MANAGER

American Express
Mastercard
Visa

☺ 2 Nights B&B €100.00

Closed 20 December - 07 January

LOUGH MAHON HOUSE

TIVOLI,
CORK

TEL: 021-450 2142 FAX: 021-450 1804
EMAIL: info@loughmahon.com
WEB: www.loughmahon.com

GUESTHOUSE ★★★ MAP 3 H 3

Family run comfortable Georgian house with private parking. Convenient to city centre, bus and rail station. En suite bedrooms are decorated to a high standard with every comfort for our guests. TV, direct dial phone, tea/coffee maker, hair dryer, trouser press and ironing facilities available. Near to Fota Wildlife Park, Cobh Heritage Centre, golf clubs and fishing. Ideal base for trips to Blarney Castle, Kinsale and Killarney. 2 mins Lee Tunnel.

Member of Premier Guesthouses

B&B from € 35.00 to € 44.50

MARGOT MEAGHER
PROPRIETOR

American Express
Mastercard
Visa

Closed 23 - 28 December

MARYBOROUGH HOUSE HOTEL

MARYBOROUGH HILL,
DOUGLAS,
CORK

TEL: 021-436 5555 FAX: 021-436 5662
EMAIL: maryboro@indigo.ie
WEB: www.maryborough.com

HOTEL ★★★★ MAP 3 H 3

Distinctive, delightful and different. Maryborough is set on 24 acres of listed gardens and woodland, located only 10 minutes from Cork City. This charming 18th century house with its creatively designed extension features exquisite conference, banqueting and leisure facilities. 79 spacious rooms, some with balconies overlooking the magnificent gardens and orchards. Zing's Restaurant, in contemporary relaxed design is an exciting mix of modern flavours and styles. 4 mins from Lee Tunnel. Wheelchair friendly.

B&B from € 80.00 to € 115.00

JUSTIN MCCARTHY
GENERAL MANAGER

American Express
Diners
Mastercard
Visa

Weekend specials from €152.00

Closed 24 - 26 December

Room rates are per room per night

QUALITY HOTEL CORK

JOHN REDMOND STREET,
CORK

TEL: 021-455 1793 FAX: 021-455 1665
EMAIL: qualshan@indigo.ie
WEB: www.choicehotelscork.com

UNDER REFURBISHMENT - RE-OPENING MAY 2003

HOTEL U   MAP 2 H 3

Quality Hotel Cork is situated in the shadow of the famous Shandon Bells. Less than a 5 minute walk from Patrick Street, Cork's vibrant main thoroughfare, this modern hotel combines its rich heritage with all the conveniences expected by today's corporate and leisure guests. Lannigans Restaurant and leisure centre opening early 2003. Limited car parking available. A superb venue for conferences and meetings.

Member of Choice Hotels Ireland

B&B from €45.00 to €85.00

SHANE MCSHORTALL
GENERAL MANAGER

American Express
Diners
Mastercard
Visa

Weekend specials from €138.00

64 64

Closed 24 - 27 December

REDCLYFFE GUEST HOUSE

WESTERN ROAD,
CORK

TEL: 021-427 3220 FAX: 021-427 8382
EMAIL: redclyffe@eircom.net
WEB: www.redclyffe.com

GUESTHOUSE U   MAP 2 H 3

Redclyffe is a charming Victorian red brick guesthouse, family run and decorated to the highest standard. Opposite University, museum, consultants clinic and Jury's hotel. 13 luxurious bedrooms, all en suite with direct dial phone, satellite TV, hairdryer & tea/coffee making facilities. 10 minutes walk to city centre, No 8 bus at door. Easy drive to airport & car ferry. AA approved. Spacious car park front & rear. Be assured of a warm welcome. Additional e-mail: info@redclyffe.com

B&B from €30.00 to €35.00

MICHAEL & MAURA SHEEHAN
PROPRIETORS

American Express
Diners
Mastercard
Visa

13 13

Open All Year

ROCHESTOWN PARK HOTEL

ROCHESTOWN ROAD,
DOUGLAS,
CORK

TEL: 021-489 0800 FAX: 021-489 2178
EMAIL: info@rochestownpark.com
WEB: www.rochestownpark.com

HOTEL ★★★★   MAP 3 H 3

The Rochestown Park Hotel is a manor style hotel set in mature gardens. Facilities include an award winning leisure centre and Ireland's Premier Thalasso Therapy Centre. A large proportion of our 160 bedrooms are air-conditioned and overlook our gardens and Mahon Golf Club. We cater for weekend breaks, conferences, meetings, as well as groups, families and weddings.

B&B from €62.00 to €93.00

LIAM LALLY
GENERAL MANAGER

American Express
Diners
Mastercard
Visa

160 160

Closed 24 - 26 December

B&B rates are per person sharing per night incl. Breakfast

ROSERIE VILLA GUEST HOUSE

MARDYKE WALK,
OFF WESTERN ROAD,
CORK

TEL: 021-427 2958 FAX: 021-427 4087
EMAIL: info@roserievilla.com
WEB: www.roserievilla.com

GUESTHOUSE ★★★ MAP 2 H 3

Roserie Villa is a 10 minute walk from city centre and close to bus and train stations. 16 en suite bedrooms with direct dial telephone, TV, tea/coffee making facilities, hairdryer and ironing facilities. An ideal base for the busy executive or holiday maker to explore the south west. Airport and ferry 15 minutes drive. Golf, tennis, cricket, fishing nearby and just minutes from university college.

B&B from €45.00 to €50.00

PADDY MURPHY
PROPRIETOR

American Express
Mastercard
Visa

🛏️📶☎️💻CPS⚙️
16 16

Open All Year

SAINT KILDA GUESTHOUSE

WESTERN ROAD,
CORK

TEL: 021-427 3095 FAX: 021-427 5015
EMAIL: gerald@stkildas.com
WEB: www.stkildas.com

GUESTHOUSE ★★★ MAP 2 H 3

Exclusive overnight accommodation just 10 minutes walk to city centre. Directly opposite university with long-established tennis and cricket clubs at rear. Magnificent swimming and leisure centre nearby. Killarney 1 hour, Kinsale 30 minutes, airport and Blarney Castle 20 minutes. Recommended by Frommers, Stilwells and Lonely Planet guides. A short pleasant drive to numerous golf courses including Old Head of Kinsale, Fota Island, Lee Valley and Monkstown.

B&B from €30.00 to €40.00

GERALD COLLINS
PROPRIETOR

Mastercard
Visa

🛏️📶☎️⬜TCPS⚙️
20 20

Closed 22 December - 07 January

SEVEN NORTH MALL

7 NORTH MALL,
CORK

TEL: 021-439 7191 FAX: 021-430 0811
EMAIL: sevennorthmall@eircom.net

GUESTHOUSE ★★★★ MAP 2 H 3

Comfortable 240 year old listed house on tree lined mall, facing south, overlooking River Lee. Adjacent to all sites including theatres, art galleries, Shandon, the University and some of Ireland's best restaurants. Individually decorated en suite bedrooms include direct dial telephone, cable TV, trouser press and hair dryer. Small conference room, private car park and accommodation for disabled guests. Children over 12 welcome. ITB Graded 4★★★★.

B&B from €45.00 to €60.00

ANGELA HEGARTY
PROPRIETOR

Mastercard
Visa

⛳

🛏️📶☎️⬜✳️P
7 7

IRISH
HOTELS
FEDERATION

Closed 21 December - 06 January

Room rates are per room per night

SILVERSPRINGS MORAN HOTEL

TIVOLI,
CORK

TEL: 021-450 7533 FAX: 021-450 7641
EMAIL: silversprings@morangroup.ie
WEB: www.silverspringshotel.ie

HOTEL ★★★★ MAP 3 H 3

4★★★★ hotel set in sylvan terraced grounds overlooking the River Lee. 109 bedrooms including 5 deluxe suites all with cable TV, trouser press and tea/coffee facilities. Centrally located only 5 minutes from the city centre and 7 miles from Cork International Airport. Excellent base for touring Cork's many visitor attractions. Onsite facilities include a choice of two restaurants where guests can enjoy an array of Irish and International cuisine. Lively weekend entertainment in Thadys Bar. Full leisure facilities available incl. 25m pool. Free parking. A Moran hotel.

B&B from € 55.00 to € 100.00

TOM & SHEILA MORAN
PROPRIETORS

American Express
Diners
Mastercard
Visa

109 109

Closed 25 - 26 December

VICTORIA HOTEL

PATRICK STREET,
COOK STREET,
CORK

TEL: 021-427 8788 FAX: 021-427 8790
EMAIL: info@thevictoriahotel.com
WEB: www.thevictoriahotel.com

HOTEL ★★ MAP 3 H 3

The Victoria Hotel is situated in Cork City Centre. All rooms have bath & shower, direct dial phone, TV and hair dryer. Family suites available. Built in 1810, it was frequented by European Royalty and was home to some of our own great political leaders, including Charles Stewart Parnell who made his major speeches from its upper balcony. James Joyce recounts his stay in one of his novels.

Member of MinOtel Hotel Group

B&B from € 40.00 to € 90.00

KING FAMILY

American Express
Mastercard
Visa

29 29

Closed 24 - 26 December

VIENNA WOODS HOTEL

GLANMIRE,
CORK

TEL: 021-482 1146 FAX: 021-482 1120
EMAIL: vienna@iol.ie
WEB: www.viennawoodshotel.com

HOTEL ★★★ MAP 3 H 3

Enjoy our unique 50 bedroom luxury hotel, formerly an 18th century mansion home. Superb location & setting on 20 acres of mature woodland yet only minutes from Cork City. Award winning cuisine with the option of casual dining in the Conservatory or an extensive menu in The Blue Room. "Golfers Paradise" conveniently close to a choice of Cork's leading courses (booked exclusively by the world media coverage for Murphy's Irish Open).

B&B from € 55.00 to € 100.00

JOHN & DARINA GATELY
PROPRIETORS

American Express
Diners
Mastercard
Visa

50 50

Closed 24 - 26 December

B&B rates are per person sharing per night incl. Breakfast

WHISPERING PINES HOTEL

CROSSHAVEN,
CO. CORK

TEL: 021-483 1843 FAX: 021-483 1679
EMAIL: reservations@whisperingpineshotel.com
WEB: www.whisperingpineshotel.com

HOTEL ★★ MAP 3 I 3

Whispering Pines, personally run by the Twomey Family is a charming hotel sheltered by surrounding woodland & overlooking the Owenabue River. In this idyllic setting one can enjoy good company, quality homecooked food & a host of amenities to ensure your stay is a restful & memorable experience. All rooms with direct dial phone, tea/coffee facilities & TV. Our 3 angling boats fish daily from April-Oct. Ideal base for touring Cork/Kerry Region. Cork Airport 12kms & Cork City 19km. AA approved.

B&B from €35.00 to €55.00

NORMA TWOMEY
PROPRIETOR

American Express
Diners
Mastercard
Visa

🦐 🏠 ☎ 🖵 T C ➔ C M ❋ U J P S 🔲
15   15

HOTELS
FEDERATION

Closed 01 December - 31 January

GLANWORTH MILL COUNTRY INN

GLANWORTH (NEAR FERMOY),
CO. CORK

TEL: 025-38555 FAX: 025-38560
EMAIL: glanworth@iol.ie
WEB: www.glanworthmill.com

GUESTHOUSE ★★★★ MAP 3 I 4

A water mill, a Norman castle, a river, an ancient bridge, gorgeous rooms, a gourmet restaurant, tea rooms, library, craft shop, courtyard garden, leisure garden and river walk... you'll find it here at Glanworth Mill. Unwind in this 1790 water mill with its sense of history & love of literature. There is a wealth of activities nearby - fishing, horse-riding, golf, hill walking, historic trails, houses & gardens to visit. Hidden Gem Award 2000. AA guest accommodation for Ireland 2001/2002. All in the lush Blackwater Valley of North Cork. Open weekends November - April.

B&B from €59.00 to €69.00

EMELYN HEAPS & LYNNE GLASSCOE

American Express
Diners
Mastercard
Visa

☺   Check for specials

🦐 🏠 ☎ T C C M ❋ U J P 🔲 alc ▪
10   10

HOTELS
FEDERATION

Closed 01 November - 30 April

CASEY'S HOTEL

THE VILLAGE,
GLENGARRIFF,
CO. CORK

TEL: 027-63010 FAX: 027-63072
EMAIL: caseyshotel@yahoo.com

HOTEL ★★ MAP 1 D 2

Casey's Hotel has been run by the same family since 1884. Recently refurbished to cater for the expectations of the modern traveller. All rooms en suite with direct dial phones and TV. The hotel offers personal, friendly service with old fashioned courtesy, private car park and gardens. Casey's Hotel is the perfect base for day trips to Barley Cove, Gougane Barra, Killarney and the Ring of Kerry. Come and discover the unspoilt beauty of the Beara Peninsula. Hill walking tours arranged.

B&B from €37.00 to €50.00

DONAL & EILEEN DEASY
OWNERS

American Express
Diners
Mastercard
Visa

🦐 🏠 ☎ 🖵 T C ❋ P S 🔲 alc ▪
19   19

HOTELS
FEDERATION

Closed 20 December - 10 March

Room rates are per room per night

GLENGARRIFF ECCLES HOTEL

GLENGARRIFF,
CO. CORK

TEL: 027-63003 FAX: 027-63319
EMAIL: eccleshotel@iol.ie
WEB: www.eccleshotel.com

HOTEL ★★★ MAP 2 D 2

Located opposite Garnish Island, in beautiful Bantry Bay. The Glengarriff Eccles Hotel is one of the oldest established hotels in Ireland (1745). Now fully restored this family run hotel boasts 66 en suite bedrooms, many with panoramic views, restaurant and bar. New banqueting area completed 2002. Ideally situated to explore the beauty of the Beara peninsula. Golf (3 courses within 20 km), fishing, hillwalking, all nearby. 17km from Bantry.

B&B from € 45.00 to € 75.00

THOS O'BRIEN
GENERAL MANAGER

American Express
Mastercard
Visa

66 66

Closed 23 - 28 December

GOUGANE BARRA HOTEL

GOUGANE BARRA,
BALLINGEARY,
CO. CORK

TEL: 026-47069 FAX: 026-47226
EMAIL: gouganebarrahotel@eircom.net
WEB: www.gouganebarra.com

HOTEL ★★ MAP 2 E 3

Situated on its own grounds overlooking Gougane Barra Lake, the source of the River Lee. Most bedrooms enjoy fine views of the lake, glens and hills beyond. Ideally situated for touring the beauty spots of Cork and Kerry, 72km west of Cork City and Airport. A walk along the banks of the Lee through the forest park which covers 162 hectares, will take you through varied scenery of mystic beauty. We are members of Irish Country Hotels. GDS Access Code UI Toll Free: 1-800-44-Utell.

Member of Irish Country Hotels

B&B from € 57.00 to € 68.00

BREDA & CHRISTOPHER LUCEY

American Express
Diners
Mastercard
Visa

28 28

Closed 15 October - 19 April

INNISHANNON HOUSE HOTEL

INNISHANNON,
CO. CORK

TEL: 021-477 5121 FAX: 021-477 5609
EMAIL: info@innishannon-hotel.ie
WEB: www.innishannon-hotel.ie

HOTEL ★★★ MAP 2 G 2

The most romantic hotel in Ireland built in 1720 in the Petit Chateau style on the banks of the river Bandon, close to Kinsale. All rooms en suite with TV, DD phone, radio, etc. Award winning restaurant (AA**, RAC, Egon Ronay) serving fresh fish and lobster. Superb wine cellar, stunning views, boating and free salmon and trout fishing from the grounds. Horse-riding and golf nearby. GDS code: UI Toll Free 1-800-44 UTELL.

B&B from € 100.00 to € 120.00

BREDA KEANE
GENERAL MANAGER

American Express
Diners
Mastercard
Visa

13 13

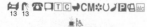

Closed 23 - 27 December

B&B rates are per person sharing per night incl. Breakfast

DUHALLOW PARK HOTEL

KANTURK,
CO. CORK

TEL: 029-56042 FAX: 029-56152
EMAIL: info@duhallowpark.ie
WEB: www.duhallowpark.ie

HOTEL N   MAP CODE

Duhallow Park Hotel, 18th century manor house, a superbly appointed, comfortable hotel situated in the upper Blackwater Valley of North Cork. Duhallow Park has been extended and refurbished recently. It occupies a majestic elevated site, affording panoramic views over river valleys and mountainside. All rooms are en suite fitted and equipped to modern day standards along with restaurant, bar and ballroom facilities.

B&B from €45.00 to €55.00

DENISE LENNON
OPERATIONS MANAGER

American Express
Mastercard
Visa

☺ Weekend specials from €100.00pps

35 35

Closed 24 - 26 December

ACTONS HOTEL

PIER ROAD,
KINSALE,
CO. CORK

TEL: 021-477 2135 FAX: 021-477 2231
EMAIL: info@actonshotelkinsale.com
WEB: www.actonshotelkinsale.com

HOTEL ★★★   MAP 2 H 2

Located in landscaped gardens overlooking Kinsale's beautiful harbour. Renowned for its cuisine and friendly atmosphere, Actons also features an award-winning restaurant (Kinsale Good Food Circle Member), Bar/Bistro and new Health & Fitness Club. Located in the historic town of Kinsale with restaurants, pubs, cafés, art & craft shops etc. Activities nearby: golfing, fishing, sailing, walking, historical sites.

B&B from €70.00 to €130.00

JACK WALSH
GENERAL MANAGER

American Express
Diners
Mastercard
Visa

☺ Midweek 3 B&B + 2 D
from €250.00

76 76

Closed 05 - 31 January

BLUE HAVEN HOTEL RESTAURANT

3 PEARSE STREET,
KINSALE,
CO. CORK

TEL: 021-477 2209 FAX: 021-477 4268
EMAIL: bluehaven@iol.ie
WEB: www.bluehavenkinsale.com

HOTEL ★★★   MAP 2 H 3

Situated on the site of the old fish market in the centre of Kinsale, Ireland's famous Blue Haven Hotel offers it's guests the highest standards in gracious comfort, superb award winning cuisine and the warmest hospitality. Each of our seventeen bedrooms is individually furnished with a loving touch to ensure your stay will be unique. Enjoy a meal in our gourmet restaurant, which has an excellent reputation both locally & internationally. "Hotel of the year winner".

B&B from €70.00 to €90.00

DAPHNE GREENE
OWNER/MANAGER

American Express
Diners
Mastercard
Visa

17 17

Open All Year

Room rates are per room per night

TEL: 021-4// ___ 477 4944
EMAIL: captquarters___com.net
WEB: www.captains-kinsale.com

HARBOUR LODGE

SCILLY,
KINSALE,
CO. CORK

TEL: 021-477 2376 FAX: 021-477 2675
EMAIL: relax@harbourlodge.com
WEB: www.harbourlodge.com

JIM EDWARDS

MARKET QUAY,
KINSALE,
CO. CORK

TEL: 021-477 2541 FAX: 021-477 3228
EMAIL: liam@jimedwardskinsale.com
WEB: www.jimedwardskinsale.com

GUESTHOUSE ★★★ MAP 2 H 2

This Georgian period townhouse is situated close to the yacht club marina and in easy walking distance of all restaurants and town centre amenities. It offers quality accommodation in a maritime ambience. The spacious and tranquil lounge overlooks the harbour. The wheelchair accessible groundfloor rooms (1 twin / 1 single, sharing shower / toilet) are also very convenient for the elderly. TV, direct dial phone, tea/coffee making facilities, hairdryer in all rooms. German and French spoken.

GUESTHOUSE ★★★★ MAP 2 H 2

Harbour Lodge has been refurbished and upgraded to make it one of the finest guesthouses on the coast. Comfort, personal service, charm and sophistication in a relaxed ambience complement the spacious rooms and huge beds with fine linen. The sweeping view of Kinsale Bay, the spectacular Orangerie and terrace is quite unique. The private parking is our competitions envy. Staff and management are here for our guests 24 hours.

GUESTHOUSE ★★ MAP 2 H 2

All rooms are tastefully decorated with en suite with TV, tea/coffee facilities, telephone. Situated in the heart of the town means easy access to all the lively bars and entertainment of the town. The guest house boasts an excellent seafood restaurant (fully licenced) which is a member of the Kinsale Good Food Circle and ensures a gourmet breakfast.

B&B from €33.00 to €45.00

B&B from €66.00 to €99.00

B&B from €35.00 to €40.00

BERNY & CAPT. RUDI TEICHMANN
CO-OWNERS

Mastercard
Visa

RAOUL DE GENDRE
PROPRIETOR

American Express
Diners
Mastercard
Visa

JIM EDWARDS

American Express
Mastercard
Visa

2 nights B&B + 1 Dinner from
€169.00

6 4

9 9

7 7

IRISH
HOTELS
FEDERATION

IRISH
HOTELS
FEDERATION

Closed 26 January - 13 March

Open All Year

Open All Year

B&B rates are per person sharing per night incl. Breakfast

KIERANS FOLKHOUSE INN

GUARDWELL,
KINSALE,
CO. CORK
TEL: 021-477 2382 FAX: 021-477 4085
EMAIL: folkhse@indigo.ie

GUESTHOUSE ★★★ MAP 2 H 2

A charming 250 year old, award winning Country Inn, managed by Denis and Geraldine Kieran for the past 15 years, awarded the Irish "Inn of the Year". 27 en suite rooms, the Backroom Niteclub and live entertainment centre and the Spanish themed "Cordoba" Bar which was awarded the "Dining Pub of the Year 2000" & features live music nightly. Shrimps Seafood Bistro is one of the newest members of the Kinsale Good Food Circle. It's an attractive restaurant featuring a unique stained glass wall & contemporary paintings, including works by artist Geraldine.

Member of Logis of Ireland

B&B from €40.00 to €55.00

GERALDINE & DENIS KIERAN
OWNERS

American Express
Mastercard
Visa

27 27

Closed 25 December

KILCAW HOUSE

KINSALE,
SITUATED ON R600,
CO. CORK
TEL: 021-477 4155 FAX: 021-477 4755
EMAIL: info@kilcawhouse.com
WEB: www.kilcawhouse.com

GUESTHOUSE ★★★ MAP 2 H 2

A family run guesthouse on the outskirts of Kinsale with safe off the road parking and wonderful country views. It is built with a traditional flair yet is modern and luxurious. The bedrooms are spacious, furnished in antique pine, en suite with TV, phone and tea/coffee making facilities. Just a 20 minute drive from Airport and Ferry. An ideal base for touring Blarney, Cobh and Old Head of Kinsale.

B&B from €28.00 to €38.00

HENRY & CHRISTINA MITCHELL
OWNERS

American Express
Mastercard
Visa

7 7

Open All Year

LONG QUAY HOUSE

LONG QUAY,
KINSALE,
CO. CORK
TEL: 021-477 3201 FAX: 021-477 4563
EMAIL: longquayhouse@eircom.net

GUESTHOUSE ★★★ MAP 2 H 2

Long Quay House is a Georgian residence which typifies its era with rooms of splendid dimensions, furnished to afford the greatest possible guest comfort. Bedrooms are en suite (majority with bath), TV, direct dial phone, tea making facilities and hair dryer. Located centrally overlooking inner harbour, yacht marina and within walking distance of all Kinsale's gourmet restaurants and many tourist attractions. Sea angling trips by local skippers arranged. AA recognised establishment ◆◆◆◆.

B&B from €31.75 to €55.00

JIM & PETER DEASY
HOSTS

Mastercard
Visa

7 7

Closed 15 November - 27 December

Room rates are per room per night

OLD BANK HOUSE

11 PEARSE STREET,
NEXT TO POST OFFICE, KINSALE,
CO. CORK
TEL: 021-477 4075 FAX: 021-477 4296
EMAIL: oldbank@indigo.ie
WEB: www.oldbankhousekinsale.com

GUESTHOUSE ★★★★ MAP 2 H 2

The Old Bank House is a Georgian residence of great character & charm providing luxurious accommodation in the historic harbour town of Kinsale. Each bedroom has super King or Twin beds, antique furniture and original art, whilst bathrooms are beautifully appointed with tub and shower, top quality toiletries and Egyptian cotton towels and bathrobes. Gourmet breakfast by award winning Master Chef Michael Riese. Golf friendly and tee times arranged. Voted one of the "Top 100 Places to Stay in Ireland" every year since 1990. RAC ◆◆◆◆ AA ◆◆◆◆.

B&B from €85.00 to €130.00

MICHAEL & MARIE RIESE
PROPRIETORS
American Express
Mastercard
Visa

Closed 23 - 26 December

QUAYSIDE HOUSE

PIER ROAD,
KINSALE,
CO. CORK
TEL: 021-477 2188 FAX: 021-477 2664
EMAIL: quaysidehouse@eircom.net
WEB: www.euroka.com/quayside

GUESTHOUSE ★★★ MAP 2 H 2

A family run guesthouse ideally located in a picturesque setting overlooking the Kinsale Harbour adjacent to town centre, yachting marina and all amenities. All bedrooms are en suite with direct dial telephone, TV and tea/coffee making facilities. Kinsale's famous gourmet restaurants are all within walking distance and Kinsale's golf club is just a five minute drive. Sea angling trips can be arranged.

B&B from €25.00 to €50.00

MARY COTTER
Mastercard
Visa

Open All Year

TIERNEY'S GUEST HOUSE

MAIN STREET,
KINSALE,
CO. CORK
TEL: 021-477 2205 FAX: 021-477 4363
EMAIL: mtierney@indigo.ie
WEB: www.tierneys-kinsale.com

GUESTHOUSE ★★ MAP 2 H 2

Tierney's Guest House. A well established guest house perfectly situated in the heart of magnificent award-winning Kinsale. Our guest house offers all amenities, TV, en suite, hair dryers, tea/coffee on request. Tastefully decorated and a warm welcome guaranteed. Stay in Tierney's and be in the centre of Kinsale and enjoy the Gourmet Restaurants, various bars & music lounges, breathtaking scenery, water sports, golf, etc.

B&B from €33.00 to €36.00

MAUREEN TIERNEY
OWNER
American Express
Mastercard
Visa

Closed 23 - 27 December

B&B rates are per person sharing per night incl. Breakfast

TRIDENT HOTEL

WORLD'S END,
KINSALE,
CO. CORK

TEL: 021-477 2301 FAX: 021-477 4173

EMAIL: info@tridenthotel.com
WEB: www.tridenthotel.com

HOTEL ★★★ MAP 2 H 2

The hotel enjoys a superb waterfront location. All rooms are en suite, many with sea views. Award-winning Savannah Waterfront Restaurant is a member of the 'Good Food Circle', the popular Wharf Tavern provides bar food daily & weekend entertainment in summer. Leisure facilities include sauna, gym, steam room & jacuzzi. Conference & Banqueting facilities for large & small groups. Golf, sailing, fishing, tours & cruises available locally. Private parking & wheelchair access.

B&B from €55.00 to €120.00

HAL MCELROY
MANAGING DIRECTOR

American Express
Mastercard
Visa

58 58

Closed 24 - 27 December

WHITE HOUSE

PEARSE ST. & THE GLEN,
KINSALE,
CO. CORK

TEL: 021-477 2125 FAX: 021-477 2045

EMAIL: whitehse@indigo.ie
WEB: www.whitehouse-kinsale.ie

GUESTHOUSE ★★★ MAP 2 H 2

The White House epitomises Kinsale hospitality with 3*** accommodation, Chelsea's Bistro, Le Restaurant D'Antibes and a thoroughly modern bar where all the old values of guest satisfaction, comfort and value for money prevail. We have welcomed both visitors and locals since the 1850s and from its earliest days it has enjoyed a reputation for fine food, drinks of good cheer and indulgent service. Today we pride ourselves on enhancing that tradition. A member of Kinsale's Good Food Circle.

Member of Premier Guesthouses

B&B from €45.00 to €76.00

MICHAEL & ROSE FRAWLEY
PROPRIETORS

American Express
Diners
Mastercard
Visa

 Weekend specials from €125.00

10 10

Closed 24 - 25 December

WHITE LADY HOTEL

LOWER O'CONNELL ST,
KINSALE,
CO. CORK

TEL: 021-477 2737 FAX: 021-477 4641

EMAIL: wlady@indigo.ie

HOTEL ★★ MAP 2 H 2

Looking after your needs and making you feel at home is the priority in this 10 bedroom hotel. All rooms have en suite facilities, TV and direct dial phone. Our restaurant provides you with a very varied and reasonably priced menu, while it also offers a selection of fresh seafood. Our on-site nite club ensures a lively atmosphere at weekends. Golf, horse riding and sea angling trips can be arranged at your request.

B&B from €50.00 to €70.00

ANTHONY COLLINS/ROMAN MINIHANE
OWNERS

American Express
Mastercard
Visa

10 10

Closed 24 - 26 December

Room rates are per room per night

CASTLE HOTEL & LEISURE CENTRE

MAIN STREET,
MACROOM,
CO. CORK
TEL: 026-41074 FAX: 026-41505
EMAIL: castlehotel@eircom.net
WEB: www.castlehotel.ie

HOTEL ★★★ MAP 2 F3

Experience an intimate welcome to the spectacular south west from the Buckley family, proprietors for fifty years. Our exciting new €5 million development includes new superior bedrooms, award-winning "B's" Restaurant, spacious Dan Buckleys Bar, Next Door Café, extensive foyer and reception area and the Ardilaun Conference and Banqueting Centre. Relax in our superb health and leisure centre or enjoy reduced green fees on Macroom's 18 hole golf course and free pitch & putt.

Member of Irish Country Hotels

B&B from €64.50 to €77.50

DON & GERARD BUCKLEY
PROPRIETORS

American Express
Diners
Mastercard
Visa

3 B&B, 2 dinners, 2 golf from €190.00

60 60

Closed 24 - 28 December

COOLCOWER HOUSE

COOLCOWER,
MACROOM,
CO. CORK
TEL: 026-41695 FAX: 026-42119
EMAIL: coolcowe@gofree.indigo.ie

GUESTHOUSE ★★ MAP 2 F3

Coolcower House is a large country residence on picturesque grounds. The house is ideally located within easy driving distance of all the tourist attractions in the Cork-Kerry region including Killarney, Kenmare, Kinsale, Blarney and Bantry. Located on the river's edge for coarse fishing and boating. Also outdoor tennis court. Restaurant offers the best of home produce on its à la carte and dinner menus. Fully licensed bar. TVs and Tea/Coffee making facilities, also direct dial telephones and hairdryers in all bedrooms.

B&B from €32.00 to €35.00

EVELYN CASEY

Mastercard
Visa

Midweek specials from €85.00

12 12

Closed 14 December - 06 March

VICTORIA HOTEL

THE SQUARE,
MACROOM,
CO. CORK
TEL: 026-41082 FAX: 026-42148
EMAIL: hotelvictoria@eircom.net
WEB: www.thevictoria-hotel.com

HOTEL ★★ MAP 2 F3

Situated in the centre of Macroom Town, the Victoria is a small friendly hotel, family owned and managed. An ideal base for your visit to the beautiful Lee Valley or the scenic south west. Local amenities include fishing, local 18 hole golf course, hiking, walking and horse riding. All our rooms are en suite with telephone, TV and tea/coffee facilities. À la carte and full dinner menu available. Bar meals served all day.

B&B from €40.00 to €75.00

ENDA LINEHAN
MANAGERESS

American Express
Mastercard
Visa

Midweek nightly special rate from €35.00

15 15

alc FAX

Closed 25 December

B&B rates are per person sharing per night incl. Breakfast

CORTIGAN HOUSE

GOLF COURSE ROAD,
MALLOW,
CO. CORK
TEL: 022-22770 FAX: 022-22732
EMAIL: info@cortiganhouse.com
WEB: www.cortiganhouse.com

GUESTHOUSE ★★★ MAP 2 G 4

A warm welcome awaits you at our 18th century home, overlooking Mallow Castle & River Blackwater, renowned for salmon & trout angling. Just a 25 minute drive from Cork City & Blarney. Cortigan House is ideally based for touring Kinsale, Killarney and South West. We are adjacent to Mallow Golf Club and within easy drive of ten other courses. 5 min walk to excellent restaurants, traditional pubs and genealogy centre. Recommended by Le Guide du Routard. AA selected ◆◆◆◆.

B&B from €32.50 to €40.00

LIONEL & SHEILA BUCKLEY
PROPRIETORS

American Express
Mastercard
Visa

9 9

Closed 01 December - 01 February

HIBERNIAN HOTEL AND LEISURE CENTRE

MAIN STREET,
MALLOW,
CO. CORK
TEL: 022-21588 FAX: 022-22632
EMAIL: info@hibhotel.com
WEB: www.hibhotel.com

HOTEL ★★★ MAP 2 G 4

The Hibernian Hotel is a family owned hotel located at the heart of the Munster region, within easy access of Cork, Killarney and Blarney. The hotel has a beautiful Tudor style frontage and the interior is also tastefully decorated and the open fires create a very homely atmosphere. All rooms are en suite, fitted and equipped to modern-day standards. A choice of two bars provides excellent variety. Leisure facilities available from 1st January 2003.

B&B from €40.00 to €63.00

CATHERINE GYVES
GENERAL MANAGER

American Express
Diners
Mastercard
Visa

53 53

Closed 25 - 26 December

MALLOW PARK HOTEL

MALLOW,
CO. CORK

TEL: 022-21527 FAX: 022-51222
EMAIL: info@mallowparkhotel.com
WEB: www.mallowparkhotel.com

HOTEL ★★ MAP 2 G 4

The Mallow Park Hotel, situated in the centre of Mallow, is decorated to the highest standard with a warm and welcoming foyer lounge, Carvery, bistro and An Sibín traditional bar which provides the best of music entertainment every weekend, plus a hotel owned private car park. The Ballroom provides a great location for weddings, anniversaries and birthday parties. Conferences, fishing, walking or golf tours catered for. Mallow is an ideal location for touring the South West, Cork & the Ring of Kerry.

B&B from €45.00 to €60.00

TOM CURRAN
GENERAL MANAGER

American Express
Mastercard
Visa

20 20

Closed 25 December

Room rates are per room per night

SPRINGFORT HALL HOTEL

MALLOW,
CO. CORK

TEL: 022-21278 FAX: 022-21557
EMAIL: stay@springfort-hall.com
WEB: www.springfort-hall.com

HOTEL ★★★ MAP 2 G 4

Springfort Hall 18th century Georgian manor house, owned by the Walsh Family. Highly recommended restaurant, fully licensed bar, bedrooms en suite, colour TV and direct outside dial. 6km from Mallow off the Limerick Road, N20. Ideal for touring the South West, Blarney, Killarney, Ring of Kerry. Local amenities, 18-hole golf course, horse riding, angling on River Blackwater. Gulliver Central Reservations.

B&B from €51.00 to €76.00

WALSH FAMILY
PROPRIETORS

American Express
Diners
Mastercard
Visa

Midweek specials from €171.00

49   49

BARNABROW COUNTRY HOUSE

CLOYNE,
MIDLETON,
EAST CORK

TEL: 021-465 2534 FAX: 021-465 2534
EMAIL: barnabrow@eircom.net
WEB: www.barnabrowhouse.com

GUESTHOUSE ★★★ MAP 3 I 3

17th century family-run country house set in 35 acres of parkland adjacent to the historic village of Cloyne (580AD). The house has been extensively refurbished to offer a perfect blend of old world charm & new world comfort. Trinity Rooms, our new restaurant, provides a unique venue for that special celebration. This is the perfect setting to relax and soak up an atmosphere of peaceful unhurried living with log fires and candlelit dinners. Nearby: Ballymaloe & Stephen Pearse Pottery.

B&B from €50.00 to €75.00

GERALDINE O'BRIEN
PROPRIETOR

Diners
Mastercard
Visa

19   19

MIDLETON PARK HOTEL & SPA

OLD CORK ROAD,
MIDLETON,
CO. CORK

TEL: 021-463 5100 FAX: 021-463 5101
EMAIL: resv@midletonpark.com
WEB: www.midletonpark.com

HOTEL U MAP 3 I 3

The recently refurbished Midleton Park Hotel & Spa - ideal for business or pleasure is located in Midleton Town on the N25, 10 miles east of Cork City. Convenient to the industrial and commercial centres of the region and close to championship golf courses, Jameson Heritage Centre, Fota Wildlife Park and the Titanic Trail. Luxury guest rooms and award-winning restaurant. Our health club and wellness centre is dedicated to providing you with a wide range of alternative treatments and therapies designed to revitalise the body and mind.

B&B from €65.00 to €100.00

ANTHONY SAVAGE
RESIDENT MANAGER

American Express
Diners
Mastercard
Visa

80   80

B&B rates are per person sharing per night incl. Breakfast

FIR GROVE HOTEL

CAHIR HILL,
MITCHELSTOWN,
CO. CORK
TEL: 025-24111 FAX: 025-84541

HOTEL R   MAP 3 I 5

The Fir Grove Hotel is a modern hotel, set in its own grounds beneath the Galtee Mountains. Situated on the main Cork/Dublin Road, we are central to most of Munster's large towns and cities. We have a restaurant that serves good local food with a friendly service. All bedrooms are en suite with central heating and TV. Local facilities include golf, fishing, hill walks and pony trekking.

B&B from €37.50 to €45.00

PAT & BRENDA TANGNEY
PROPRIETORS

American Express
Diners
Mastercard
Visa

15 15

Closed 24 - 26 December

CELTIC ROSS HOTEL CONFERENCE & LEISURE CENTRE

ROSSCARBERY,
WEST CORK

TEL: 023-48722 FAX: 023-48723
EMAIL: info@celticrosshotel.com
WEB: www.celticrosshotel.com

HOTEL ★★★   MAP 2 F 1

Nestled in Rosscarbery Bay, the Celtic Ross Hotel is a place for those who want more than just a hotel. It is distinguished by its tower, which hosts a 5,000 year old 40ft tall bog yew. Facilities include 67 guest rooms, many overlooking the bay, Druids Restaurant, Library Bar and Tower, Old Forge Pub & Eaterie with regular entertainment. Full leisure centre including heated pool, bubble pool, baby pool, steam room, sauna and fully equipped gym.
Reservations: 1850-272737.
Email: reservations@celticross.com.
Special offers available.

B&B from €65.00 to €100.00

NOLLAIG HURLEY
GENERAL MANAGER

American Express
Diners
Mastercard
Visa

67 67

Closed 12 January - 13 February

COLLA HOUSE HOTEL

COLLA,
SCHULL,
CO. CORK
TEL: 028-28105 FAX: 028-28497
EMAIL: collahousehotels@eircom.net
WEB: www.cork-guide.ie

HOTEL ★   MAP 2 D 1

An attractive family run hotel situated in a magnificent position overlooking the sea, with panoramic views of the Atlantic Ocean, Cape Clear and Carbery's Hundred Isles. It is surrounded by its own pitch & putt course running direct to the sea. Colla House also has its own horse-riding school on its grounds. All bedrooms en suite with direct dial telephone and TV. Local amenities include 18 hole golf course, deep sea angling and boat trips to islands.

B&B from €35.00 to €60.00

MARTIN O'DONOVAN
PROPRIETOR

American Express
Diners
Mastercard
Visa

10 10

Open All Year

Room rates are per room per night

CORTHNA-LODGE GUESTHOUSE

AIRHILL,
SCHULL,
CO. CORK
TEL: 028-28517 FAX: 028-28032
EMAIL: info@corthna-lodge.net
WEB: www.corthna-lodge.net

GUESTHOUSE ★★★ MAP 1 D 1

A charming newly refurbished guesthouse within walking distance of the lovely Schull Village. Ideal base for all activities such as golfing, sailing, cycling, trekking etc. Boat trips to Cape Clear and Sherkin Island with their sandy beaches. Our large garden is the ideal place to relax. All bedrooms are en suite with TV. Free use of our gym and putting green. We take Mastercard and VISA.

B&B from €40.00 to €65.00

MARTIN & ANDREA MUELLER

Mastercard
Visa

Closed 15 October - 31 March

EAST END HOTEL

EAST END,
SCHULL,
CO. CORK
TEL: 028-28101 FAX: 028-27889
EMAIL: eastendhotel@eircom.net
WEB: www.eastendhotel.com

HOTEL ★★ MAP 2 D 1

A family run hotel overlooking Schull Harbour and within walking distance of the numerous amenities in this cosmopolitan village. The hotel's kitchen uses fresh produce and provides quality food all day. TV and DD phone in all rooms. Dine al fresco in our patio garden. We especially welcome families with young children.

Member of Irish Family Hotels

B&B from €34.90 to €48.90

VAL DUFFY
MANAGER

American Express
Diners
Mastercard
Visa

Closed 23 - 27 December

BALLYMALOE HOUSE

SHANAGARRY,
MIDLETON,
CO. CORK
TEL: 021-465 2531 FAX: 021-465 2021
EMAIL: res@ballymaloe.ie
WEB: www.ballymaloe.ie

GUESTHOUSE ★★★★ MAP 3 I 3

A large country house on a 400 acre farm near the coast, owned and run by the Allen family. Home and locally grown produce is served in the award winning restaurant. Small golf course, tennis court, outdoor pool, woodlands, gardens and pleasant walks are on the premises, also a craft and kitchen shop. The Ballymaloe Cookery School is nearby. Sea and river fishing can be arranged. Approx. 6 miles south of the N25 highway. Turn off outside Midleton or at Castlemartyr. Two miles beyond Cloyne on the Ballycotton road. See map no 3.

Member of Ireland's Blue Book

B&B from €95.00 to €140.00

MYRTLE ALLEN
PROPRIETOR

American Express
Diners
Mastercard
Visa

Closed 22 - 27 December

B&B rates are per person sharing per night incl. Breakfast

GARRYVOE HOTEL

SHANAGARRY,
MIDLETON,
CO. CORK

TEL: 021-464 6718 FAX: 021-464 6824
EMAIL: garryvoehotel@eircom.net
WEB: www.bayviewhotel.net

HOTEL ★★ MAP 3 J 3

The coastal location overlooking 5 miles of one of Ireland's finest beaches is the ideal holiday destination. The celebrated restaurant offers the very best of cuisine with fresh seafood a speciality. Activities include tennis, 6 golf courses in the area, Irish heritage centres, Fota Wildlife Park and many more. The Garryvoe Hotel will introduce an additional 36 bedrooms, conference rooms and leisure facilities during the summer of 2003.

Member of Irish Country Hotels

B&B from €57.00 to €68.00

STEPHEN BELTON
GENERAL MANAGER

American Express
Diners
Mastercard
Visa

🏠🎵📞🖥️T❄️🔍👤P🅿️Ⓐlc
19 19

Closed 25 - 26 December

ELDON HOTEL

BRIDGE STREET,
SKIBBEREEN,
WEST CORK

TEL: 028-22000 FAX: 028-22191
EMAIL: welcome@eldon-hotel.ie
WEB: www.eldon-hotel.com

HOTEL U MAP 2 E 1

Our aim is to provide the best of the simple things in life, good food, good drink and good company. Michael Collins found these when he visited the Eldon in the 1920s, our guests say they still find them today! Extracts of Collins' love letters to Kitty Kiernan and photos of his visits to the Eldon can be found in our new Porch Bar.

B&B from €45.00 to €85.00

ARTHUR LITTLE/LYDIA O'FARRELL
MANAGERS

American Express
Mastercard
Visa

🏠🎵📞🖥️T C♥CM❄️👤JP📄S
19 19

Ⓐlc 🖥️Inet

Closed 23 - 30 December

Room rates are per room per night

WEST CORK HOTEL

ILEN STREET,
SKIBBEREEN,
CO. CORK

TEL: 028-21277 FAX: 028-22333
EMAIL: info@westcorkhotel.com
WEB: www.westcorkhotel.com

HOTEL ★★★ MAP 2 E 1

The West Cork Hotel offers one of the warmest welcomes you will find in Ireland, and combines old-fashioned courtesy with the comfort of tastefully decorated and well-equipped accommodation. Guests can enjoy the friendly bar atmosphere or dine in the elegant restaurant. However long your stay the West Cork Hotel is the perfect base from which to discover and explore the glorious surroundings and activities available in West Cork.

B&B from €50.50 to €80.00

JOHN MURPHY
GENERAL MANAGER

American Express
Diners
Mastercard
Visa

☺ Midweek specials from €207.00

30 30

IRISH HOTELS FEDERATION

Closed 22 - 27 December

AHERNE'S TOWNHOUSE & SEAFOOD RESTAURANT

163 NORTH MAIN STREET,
YOUGHAL,
CO. CORK

TEL: 024-92424 FAX: 024-93633
EMAIL: ahernes@eircom.net
WEB: www.ahernes.com

GUESTHOUSE ★★★★ MAP 3 J 3

Open turf fires and the warmest of welcomes await you in this family run hotel in the historic walled port of Youghal. Our rooms exude comfort and luxury, stylishly furnished with antiques and paintings. Our restaurant and bar food menus specialise in the freshest of locally landed seafood. Youghal is on the N25, 35 mins from Cork Airport and is a golfer's paradise. There are 18 golf courses within 1 hours drive. Find us in Ireland's Blue Book and other leading guides. Old Head of Kinsale 50 mins drive.

Member of Ireland's Blue Book

B&B from €70.00 to €105.00

THE FITZGIBBON FAMILY

American Express
Diners
Mastercard
Visa

13 13

IRISH HOTELS FEDERATION

Closed 24 - 30 December

DEVONSHIRE ARMS HOTEL & RESTAURANT

PEARSE SQUARE,
YOUGHAL,
CO. CORK

TEL: 024-92827 FAX: 024-92900
EMAIL: devonshirearms@eircom.net

HOTEL ★★ MAP 3 J 3

Luxurious old world family run hotel. Centrally located in the town of Youghal with Blue Flag Beach, 18 hole golf course, riding and historical walking tours. All bedrooms individually decorated, TV, direct dial telephone, hair dryer and valet cleaning unit service. Our restaurant (AA2 Rosettes) offers fresh seafood and a wide range of dishes to suit all tastes, also à la carte bar menu. Half an hour from Cork, two hour drive from Rosslare N25.

B&B from €50.00 to €55.00

STEPHEN & HELEN O'SULLIVAN
PROPRIETORS

American Express
Diners
Mastercard
Visa

10 10

IRISH HOTELS FEDERATION

Closed 24 - 31 December

B&B rates are per person sharing per night incl. Breakfast

WALTER RALEIGH HOTEL

O'BRIEN PLACE,
YOUGHAL,
CO. CORK

TEL: 024-92011 FAX: 024-93560
EMAIL: info@walterraleigh.com
WEB: www.walterraleigh.com

HOTEL ★★ MAP 3 J 3

This historic and charming hotel is ideally located on the N25, in the seaside town of Youghal. It overlooks both the Blackwater Estuary and Youghal's five miles of "Blue Flag" beaches. The hotel is the ideal location for a quick break, with sea and fresh water angling outside our door and five renowned golf courses within fifteen minutes. For business, the hotel has a purpose built conference room with full facilities - The Blackwater Suite.

B&B from € 45.00 to € 100.00

JOHN MURRAY
GENERAL MANAGER

American Express
Diners
Mastercard
Visa

38 38

Áalc

IRISH
HOTELS
FEDERATION

Open All Year

BALLINSKELLIGS INN

BALLINSKELLIGS,
CO. KERRY

TEL: 066-947 9104 FAX: 066-947 9491
EMAIL: marie@ballinskelligsinn.com
WEB: www.ballinskelligsinn.com

GUESTHOUSE P MAP 1 B 3

Seaside accommodation in new en suite rooms with a great pub, restaurant and deli/shop on site. Directly on sandy beach, just off the Ring of Kerry, breathtaking mountain and sea views, family rooms, golf at Waterville, traditional music, boat trips to the Skellig Islands, walking, cycling, horse riding, angling, ancient ruins, art gallery all nearby. Come relax and experience the magic and wonder of real Ireland.

B&B from € 25.00 to € 32.00

MARIE SALUK
OWNER

Mastercard
Visa

14 14

Áalc Inet

IRISH
HOTELS
FEDERATION

Open All Year

19TH LODGE

GOLF-LINKS,
BALLYBUNION,
CO. KERRY

TEL: 068-27592 FAX: 068-27830
EMAIL: the19thlodge@eircom.net
WEB: www.ballybuniongolflodge.com

UNDER CONSTRUCTION - OPENING MAY 2003

GUESTHOUSE P MAP 5 D 6

Ballybunion's 19th Lodge is a golfer's paradise. Aptly named for its enviable location, directly opposite Ballybunion's famous links. Good five iron to first tee. Purpose built to suit our golfing clientele. With stunning views of the course from bedrooms. Enjoy your breakfast in our dining room overlooking the course, while you watch others tee-off. Breakfast menu available from 6 am. Golf storage and drying room and green-fee concessions for our guests.

B&B from € 45.00 to € 80.00

MARY & JAMES BEASLEY
OWNERS

Mastercard
Visa

12 12

Open All Year

Room rates are per room per night

CASHEN COURSE HOUSE

GOLF LINKS ROAD,
BALLYBUNION,
CO. KERRY
TEL: 068-27351 FAX: 068-28934
EMAIL: golfstay@eircom.net
WEB: www.playballybunion.com

GUESTHOUSE N MAP 5 D 6

Welcome to our new luxury guesthouse overlooking Ballybunion's famous golf courses with panoramic views of golf links, Cashen River & countryside. After a day's golf, relax in our spacious well appointed bedrooms & enjoy a jacuzzi bath in a luxurious bathroom. Air-con, DD telephone, computer access, trouser press, iron/ironing board in each bedroom. Small groups welcome for conference/golfing breaks. Ample parking for buses & cars. 2 mins drive to clubhouse. Will re-open in winter for groups by prior arrangement.

B&B from €50.00 to €90.00

DEIRDRE O'BRIEN
OWNER/MANAGER

American Express
Mastercard
Visa

Midweek specials from €140.00

9 9

Closed 01 December - 01 March

CLIFF HOUSE HOTEL

CLIFF ROAD,
BALLYBUNION,
CO. KERRY
TEL: 068-27777 FAX: 068-27783
EMAIL: cliffhousehotel@eircom.net

HOTEL ★★★ MAP 5 D 5

Overlooking Ballybunion's sandy beaches, the modern 3*** Cliff House Hotel, with 45 deluxe guest bedrooms, is a golfer's paradise. The region boasts 7 championship golf courses. Ballybunion's famous links are no more than a four-iron away, while Tralee, Killarney, Lahinch and Waterville Golf Clubs are all within easy reach. Every aspect of your golfing vacation is catered for - concession green fees are available at Ballybunion and tee times can be reserved for you.

B&B from €45.00 to €200.00

KEVIN O'CALLAGHAN
DIRECTOR

American Express
Diners
Mastercard
Visa

45 45

Closed 01 November - 17 March

EAGLE LODGE

BALLYBUNION,
CO. KERRY

TEL: 068-27224

GUESTHOUSE U MAP 5 D 6

Owner managed, delightful guesthouse situated in town centre. All bedrooms with bathrooms and central heating throughout. A beautiful lounge and private car park for guests. Local amenities include two championship golf courses, sea fishing, tennis, pitch and putt, swimming and boating. Extra value reduced green fees at Ballybunion Golf Club. Cliff walks and surfing also available.

B&B from €35.00 to €50.00

MILDRED GLEASURE

8 8

Open All Year

B&B rates are per person sharing per night incl. Breakfast

HARTY COSTELLO TOWN HOUSE

MAIN STREET,
BALLYBUNION,
CO. KERRY
TEL: 068-27129 FAX: 068-27489
EMAIL: hartycostello@eircom.net
WEB: www.hartycostello.com

GUESTHOUSE ★★★★ MAP 5 D 6

8 luxury bedrooms en suite, in a townhouse style, all modern conveniences. Elegant dining with traditional high standards of fresh food and wine in our Seafood Restaurant and Bar. Table d'hôte and extensive à la carte menus available. Local amenities, two championship golf links, cliff walks, hot seaweed baths, fishing, four golden beaches and bird watching. Ideal base for golfers or touring and horse riding.

B&B from €55.00 to €80.00

DAVNET & JACKIE HOURIGAN
OWNERS

American Express
Mastercard
Visa

☺ Weekend specials from €108.00

🛏📶☎📺🍴♨🚲🅰🈁📶
8 8

Closed 30 October - 01 April

IRAGH TI CONNOR

MAIN STREET,
BALLYBUNION,
CO. KERRY
TEL: 068-27112 FAX: 068-27787
EMAIL: iraghticonnor@eircom.net
WEB: www.golfballybunion.com

GUESTHOUSE P MAP 5 D 6

Iragh Ti Connor is a 19thc luxury country house recently completely restored. It contains 14 spacious bedrooms & 3 mini-suites, all filled with antique furniture, power showers, DD phone, satellite TV. Same day laundry facilities. The restaurant speciality is lobster straight from the sea tank. Full bar facilities offering guests a choice of mingling with the locals or relaxing by the fireside in the private drawing room. Tee times can be reserved on request. The ideal base for golfers with easy access to Lahinch, Doonbeg, Tralee, Waterville & Dooks Golf Club.

B&B from €95.00 to €120.00

JOAN & JOHN O'CONNOR
PROPRIETORS

American Express
Mastercard
Visa

🛏📶☎📺🇹CM♣🅿📶🈁📶🍴♿
17 17

Closed 23 - 26 December

Room rates are per room per night

MANOR INN	SOUTHERN HOTEL	TEACH DE BROC
DOON ROAD, BALLYBUNION, CO. KERRY	SANDHILL ROAD, BALLYBUNION, CO. KERRY	LINK ROAD, BALLYBUNION, CO. KERRY
TEL: 068-27577 FAX: 068-27757	TEL: 068-27022 FAX: 068-27085	TEL: 068-27581 FAX: 068-27919
EMAIL: drao@eircom.net WEB: www.ballybunion-manorinn.com	EMAIL: southotel@eircom.net WEB: www.southotel.com	EMAIL: teachdebroc@eircom.net WEB: www.ballybuniongolf.com

GUESTHOUSE ★★★ MAP 5 D 6

HOTEL U MAP 5 D 6

GUESTHOUSE ★★★★ MAP 5 D 6

The purpose built Manor Inn offers luxury accommodation overlooking the Atlantic at the mouth of the River Shannon. 1km from town centre, 2kms from world famous Ballybunion Golf Club. Bedrooms all en suite, TV, alarm radio, DD phone, computer port in bedroom, hairdryer, tea/coffee facilities and central heating. Antique bedroom furniture a feature. Private car parking. Local amenities: two 18 hole links courses, concession green fees available, seaweed bath, sea angling, pony trekking, surfing, swimming, cliff walking and Shannon Ferry.

The Southern Hotel overlooks Ballybunion's spacious beaches and 9th hole of Ballybunion Golf Course. Residents qualify for a special reduction in green fees from October to May. All rooms have, in addition to standard facilities, elegant designer furniture and many have stunning sea views. The hotel is family owned and its size allows a level of personal attention not often possible in larger hotels.

Tea to tee in 2 minutes is a reality when you stay at the golfers' haven of Teach De Broc, located directly opposite entrance gates to Ballybunion Golf Club. Enjoy the personal attention that this 4**** country house has to offer, with full breakfast served from dawn to facilitate early tee times to a glass of wine in our residents lounge with fellow golfers in the evening. Your hosts Aoife & Seamus will ensure that your stay at this golfers' haven is memorable. Limited Tee Times available for the old course through Teach De Broc.

B&B from €30.00 to €58.00

B&B from €40.00 to €60.00

B&B from €50.00 to €80.00

THE MANAGEMENT	CON McCARTHY MANAGER	SEAMUS AND AOIFE BROCK OWNERS
American Express Mastercard Visa	Mastercard Visa	Mastercard Visa

🛏️🔥☎️🖥️T🅲☀️∪🥂P♿Inet
9 9

🛏️🔥☎️🖥️T☀️CM🏌️🍷S🅿️
15 15

🛏️🔥☎️🖥️T☀️∪P🥂♿Inet
10 10

IRISH HOTELS FEDERATION

IRISH HOTELS FEDERATION

Closed 15 November - 14 March	Open All Year	Closed 15 December - 15 March

B&B rates are per person sharing per night incl. Breakfast

DERRYNANE HOTEL

CAHERDANIEL,
RING OF KERRY,
CO. KERRY

TEL: 066-947 5136 FAX: 066-947 5160
EMAIL: info@derrynane.com
WEB: www.derrynane.com

HOTEL ★★★ MAP 1 C 2

Amidst the most spectacular scenery in Ireland, halfway round the famous Ring of Kerry (on the N70) lies the Derrynane 3*** Hotel with 70 en suite bedrooms. Facilities include 15m outdoor heated pool, steamroom, sauna, gym and tennis court. We are surrounded by beautiful beaches and hills, lovely walks and Derrynane House and National Park. Deep sea angling, lake fishing, golf, horseriding, seasports, boat trips to Skellig Rock all within a short distance. Newly published hotel walking guide to the area.

Member of Best Western Hotels

B&B from €60.00 to €80.00

MARY O'CONNOR
MANAGER/DIRECTOR

American Express
Diners
Mastercard
Visa

☺ Midweek specials from €150.00

70 70

Closed 15 October - 15 April

SCARRIFF INN

CAHERDANIEL,
CO. KERRY

TEL: 066-947 5132 FAX: 066-947 5425
EMAIL: scarriff1@aol.com
WEB: www.caherdaniel.net

GUESTHOUSE ★★ MAP 1 C 3

This family-run guesthouse overlooks the best view in Ireland, with majestic views of Derrynane, Kenmare and Bantry Bay, situated halfway round the Ring of Kerry. All our rooms have sea views. Dine in our seafood restaurant and enjoy outstanding cuisine as recommended by Sir Andrew Lloyd Webber or relax in our Vista Bar and enjoy scenery and ambience. The area is varied in activities, the Kerry Way, several beautiful beaches within walking distance. Day trips to Skellig Rocks.

B&B from €28.95 to €38.95

KATIE O'CARROLL
PROPRIETOR

American Express
Mastercard
Visa

6 6

Closed 29 October - 15 March

BARNAGH BRIDGE COUNTRY GUEST HOUSE

CAMP,
TRALEE,
CO. KERRY

TEL: 066-713 0145 FAX: 066-713 0299
EMAIL: bbguest@eircom.net
WEB: www.barnaghbridge.com

GUESTHOUSE ★★★ MAP 1 C 5

A welcoming haven, Barnagh Bridge nestles between mountains and sea on the Dingle Peninsula. Our unique guesthouse is set in landscaped grounds with conservatory and dining room overlooking Tralee Bay. Family run with superb breakfasts including home baking and morning special. Ideal location for touring Dingle Peninsula and Ring of Kerry. Local golfing and walking. AA, RAC ◆◆◆◆, Frommers and other guides listed. Leave N86 at Camp, follow Conor Pass Road R560 for 1 mile.

Member of Premier Guesthouses

B&B from €20.00 to €40.00

HEATHER WILLIAMS
HOST

American Express
Mastercard
Visa

5 5

Closed 01 November - 31 March

Room rates are per room per night

ARD-NA-SIDHE

CARAGH LAKE,
KILLORGLIN,
CO. KERRY

TEL: 066-976 9105 FAX: 066-976 9282
EMAIL: sales@kih.liebherr.com
WEB: www.iol.ie/khl

HOTEL ★★★★ MAP 1 D 4

20 bedroom 4**** de luxe Victorian mansion delightfully located in its own park on Caragh Lake. Highest standards of comfort. Tastefully furnished with antiques and open fireplaces. Luxurious lounges and restaurant. Free boating, fishing and facilities of sister hotels - Hotel Europe and Hotel Dunloe Castle - available to guests. 10 major golf courses nearby. Special green fees. Central Reservations Tel: 064-31900 Fax: 064-32118.

B&B from €95.00 to €130.00

KATHLEEN DOWLING

American Express
Diners
Mastercard
Visa

20   20

Closed 01 October - 30 April

CARAGH LODGE

CARAGH LAKE,
CO. KERRY

TEL: 066-976 9115 FAX: 066-976 9316
EMAIL: caraghl@iol.ie
WEB: www.caraghlodge.com

GUESTHOUSE ★★★★ MAP 1 D 4

A Victorian fishing lodge standing in 7.5 acres of parkland containing many rare and subtropical trees and shrubs. Winner of the National Garden Award. The gardens sweep down to Caragh Lake, ideal for trout fishing. The lounges and dining room are very comfortably furnished and overlook the gardens and lake. Excellent cuisine includes local lamb and wild salmon. Golf and beaches within 5 minutes.

Member of Ireland's Blue Book

B&B from €90.00 to €163.00

MARY GAUNT
OWNER

American Express
Diners
Mastercard
Visa

15   15

Closed 12 October - 25 April

CARRIG HOUSE

CARAGH LAKE,
KILLORGLIN,
CO. KERRY

TEL: 066-976 9100 FAX: 066-976 9166
EMAIL: info@carrighouse.com
WEB: www.carrighouse.com

GUESTHOUSE ★★★★ MAP 1 D 4

Charming Victorian Manor on acres of woodlands and gardens (935 plant species) running down to the lake shore. Furnished in period style with antique furniture. Central to 12 superb golf courses, fishing, shooting, hillwalking or just lazing by the fireside with a good book. Critically acclaimed restaurant (open to non residents). Ideal for touring the Ring of Kerry, Dingle and Killarney. "Carrig is a lakeside dreamland with a stunning restaurant." (M Leland, Irish Examiner).

B&B from €62.00 to €95.00

FRANK & MARY SLATTERY
HOSTS/PROPRIETORS

Diners
Mastercard
Visa

16   16

Closed 01 December - 01 March

B&B rates are per person sharing per night incl. Breakfast

CRUTCH'S HILLVILLE HOUSE HOTEL

CONOR PASS ROAD, CASTLEGREGORY,
DINGLE PENINSULA,
CO. KERRY
TEL: 066-713 8118 FAX: 066-713 8159
EMAIL: macshome@iol.ie

HOTEL ★★ MAP 1 C 5

Unwind in this delightful country house owned and managed by Ron & Sandra MacDonell situated near Fermoyle Beach on Kerry's scenic Dingle Peninsula. The Fermoyle Room Restaurant offers traditional home cooking using fresh local produce & special diets are catered for upon request. The hotel offers friendly country house atmosphere, generously sized warm bedrooms - some with four poster beds, sea views, a cosy bar and open fires. Crutch's Hillville is located at Kilcummin junction, 4km west of Stradbally on the Conor Pass Road.

Member of Irish Country Hotels

B&B from € 40.00 to € 65.00

RON & SANDRA
PROPRIETORS

American Express
Diners
Mastercard
Visa

😊 3 B&B and 3 Dinners €225.00

19 19

🏠🛏️☎️ⓉⒸ♨️ⒸⓂ❄️⛵♿Ⓟ🐾Ⓢ
🅰️alc♿ Inet FAX

Open All Year

O'CONNOR'S GUESTHOUSE

CLOGHANE,
DINGLE PENINSULA,
CO. KERRY
TEL: 066-713 8113 FAX: 066-713 8270
EMAIL: oconnorsguesthouse@eircom.net
WEB: www.cloghane.com

GUESTHOUSE ★★ MAP 1 B 5

A long established, spacious country home with spectacular views of sea and mountains, overlooking Brandon Bay and within easy reach of Dingle on the Dingle Way. Private car park, guest lounge, open fire, home cooked meals, pub and a warm welcome are just some of the things awaiting our guests.

B&B from € 28.00 to € 35.00

MICHEAL & ELIZABETH O'DOWD
OWNERS

Mastercard
Visa

😊 Week partial board from €295.00

9 9

🏠🛏️ⓉⒶⒸ♨️ⒸⓂ❄️⛵♿ⓅⓈ🅰️alc♿

TRISH
HOTELS
FEDERATION

Closed 01 November - 28 February

Room rates are per room per night

ALPINE HOUSE

MAIL ROAD,
DINGLE,
CO. KERRY

TEL: 066-915 1250 FAX: 066-915 1966

EMAIL: alpinedingle@eircom.net
WEB: www.alpineguesthouse.com

GUESTHOUSE ★★★ MAP 1 B 4

Superb guesthouse run by the O'Shea Family. AA ♦♦♦♦ and RAC ♦♦♦♦ highly acclaimed. Elegant en suite bedrooms with TV, direct dial phone, hairdryers, central heating and tea/coffee facilities. Spacious dining room with choice of breakfast. Delightful guest lounge. 2 minutes walk to town centre, restaurants, harbour and bus stop. Local amenities include Slea Head Drive and Blasket Islands, also pony trekking, angling and boat trips to Fungi the dolphin.

B&B from € 28.00 to € 42.00

PAUL O'SHEA
MANAGER

American Express
Mastercard
Visa

10   10

Open All Year

BAMBURY'S GUEST HOUSE

MAIL ROAD,
DINGLE,
CO. KERRY

TEL: 066-915 1244 FAX: 066-915 1786

EMAIL: info@bamburysguesthouse.com
WEB: www.bamburysguesthouse.com

GUESTHOUSE ★★★ MAP 1 B 4

AA selected ♦♦♦♦, new house, excellent location, 2 minutes walk to town centre. Offering peaceful accommodation in spacious, double, twin or triple rooms all en suite with direct dial telephone and satellite TV. Attractive guest lounge to relax in. Private car parking, choice of breakfast in spacious dining room. Local attractions, Dingle Peninsula, horse riding, angling and golf on local 18 hole golf links. Reduced green fees can be arranged. Listed in all leading guides.

B&B from € 35.00 to € 50.00

BERNIE BAMBURY
PROPRIETOR

Mastercard
Visa

12   12

Open All Year

BARR NA SRAIDE INN

UPPER MAIN STREET,
DINGLE,
CO. KERRY

TEL: 066-915 1331 FAX: 066-915 1446

EMAIL: barrnasraide@eircom.net
WEB: http://homepage.eircom.net/~barrnasraide/

GUESTHOUSE ★★★ MAP 1 B 4

Family run bar/guesthouse. Located in the town centre. The Barr na Sraide Inn has been recently refurbished to a very high standard. An extensive menu awaits our guests for breakfast. End each day with a relaxing drink in our comfortable bar amongst the locals. Private enclosed car park. Ideal base for your stay in the South West. Golf, fishing, sailing, cycling, horse riding and trips to Fungi the dolphin available nearby.

B&B from € 40.00 to € 55.00

PATRICIA GEANEY

Mastercard
Visa

22   22

Closed 15 - 26 December

B&B rates are per person sharing per night incl. Breakfast

BOLAND'S GUESTHOUSE

GOAT STREET,
DINGLE,
CO. KERRY
TEL: 066-915 1426
EMAIL: bolanddingle@eircom.net
WEB: http://homepage.eircom.net/~bolanddingle

GUESTHOUSE ★★ MAP 1 B 4

A warm welcome awaits you in our family run guesthouse. Situated in Dingle Town with panoramic views of Dingle Bay. All our rooms are en suite with direct dial phones, TV, hairdryers, tea/coffee making facilities. Full breakfast menu in our conservatory dining room. Relax and enjoy the magnificent views of Dingle Bay from our guest lounge.

B&B from €26.00 to €40.00

BREDA BOLAND
OWNER

Mastercard
Visa

🛏️📶☎️🖥️TC⚓🚶🎵🛎️
7 7

Closed 16 December - 31 January

CAPTAINS HOUSE

THE MALL,
DINGLE,
CO. KERRY
TEL: 066-915 1531 FAX: 066-915 1079
EMAIL: captigh@eircom.net
WEB: http://homepage.eircom.net/~captigh/

GUESTHOUSE ★★★ MAP 1 B 4

A welcome awaits you at the Captains House situated in Dingle Town. Approached by foot bridge over the Mall Stream and through award-winning gardens, our three star family run guest house is tastefully furnished with items collected on the Captain's voyages. All rooms are en suite with direct dial telephones and TV. A breakfast menu featuring home made bread and preserves is served in the conservatory overlooking the garden.

B&B from €40.00 to €45.00

MARY & JIM MILHENCH
PROPRIETORS

American Express
Diners
Mastercard
Visa

🛏️📶☎️T❄️🚶🎵🛎️
8 8

Closed 01 December - 16 March

CLEEVAUN COUNTRY HOUSE

LADYS CROSS,
MILLTOWN, DINGLE,
CO. KERRY
TEL: 066-915 1108 FAX: 066-915 2228
EMAIL: cleevaun@iol.ie
WEB: www.cleevaun.com

GUESTHOUSE ★★★ MAP 1 B 4

Cleevaun AA/RAC ◆◆◆◆. Galtee regional breakfast winner. Cleevaun is set in landscaped gardens, beautifully perched overlooking Dingle Bay. All rooms with private bathrooms, satelite TV, DD phones, hairdryer, tea/coffee facilities. Relax & enjoy the magnificent views of Dingle Bay from our lounge or breakfast room while you choose from our award-winning breakfast menu. Cleevaun is often described as an oasis of peace & tranquillity. Recommend by Karen Browne's, AA / RAC etc. Local amenities 18 hole golf links, angling, pony trekking.

B&B from €36.00 to €46.00

CHARLOTTE CLUSKEY
HOST

Mastercard
Visa

🛏️📶☎️❄️🚶PS🛎️
8 8

Closed 15 November - 15 March

Room rates are per room per night

COASTLINE GUESTHOUSE

THE WOOD,
DINGLE,
CO. KERRY

TEL: 066-915 2494 FAX: 066-915 2493

EMAIL: coastlinedingle@eircom.net
WEB: www.coastlinedingle.com

GUESTHOUSE ★★★ MAP 1 B 4

Beautiful new guesthouse on the water's edge of Dingle Bay. All rooms are en suite with direct dial phone, TV, hairdryer, tea/coffee making facilities and many have panoramic views of the harbour. Ground floor rooms available. Enjoy our excellent breakfast and relax in our sitting room in the evening and watch the fishing fleet return with their catch. Private car park. 5 minutes walk to town centre. Ideal base to enjoy all Dingle has to offer - excellent restaurants and pubs.

B&B from €30.00 to €40.00

VIVIENNE O'SHEA
PROPRIETOR

Mastercard
Visa

🏨🛏️☎️🖥️T❄️🅿️🅂🔌
6   6

Closed 18 November - 31 January

DINGLE BENNERS HOTEL

MAIN STREET,
DINGLE,
CO. KERRY

TEL: 066-915 1638 FAX: 066-915 1412

EMAIL: info@dinglebenners.com
WEB: www.dinglebenners.com

HOTEL ★★★ MAP 1 B 4

Located in the heart of Dingle Town, the hotel is favoured for its old world charm and style. Luxuriously appointed bedrooms provide an intimate cosy atmosphere complemented with authentic Irish antique furnishings. Mrs Benners Bar & Lounges will captivate you on arrival, have a warm friendly welcome and will fill you with a sense of yesteryear. Special weekend and midweek packages available.

Member of Manor House Hotels

B&B from €89.00 to €107.00

PHILIP F. GAVIN
DIRECTOR

American Express
Diners
Mastercard
Visa

✔️

🏨🛏️☎️🖥️📺T🅲🚗CMU🅿️🅂🔌
52   52
♿

Closed 25 - 26 December

DINGLE SKELLIG HOTEL

DINGLE,
CO. KERRY

TEL: 066-915 0200 FAX: 066-915 1501

EMAIL: reservations@dingleskellig.com
WEB: www.dingleskellig.com

HOTEL ★★★★ MAP 1 B 4

Renowned hotel situated on the beautiful harbour of Dingle Bay. Luxurious leisure club & pool; jacuzzi, geyser pool, childrens' pool, steamroom, gymnasium. Ki-massage, reflexology & aromatherapy. Fungi Kids Club & Creche on weekends & holidays. Excellent cuisine specialising in locally caught seafood. Established conference & banqueting centre with stunning views for up to 250 people. Reduced green fees & guaranteed tee times (incl. weekends) at Ceann Sibeal. Health & Beauty Centre opening April 2003.

B&B from €60.00 to €120.00

PHILIP F.GAVIN
GENERAL MANAGER/ DIRECTOR

American Express
Diners
Mastercard
Visa

✔️🏌️🎾

😊 Weekend specials from €140.00

🏨🛏️☎️🖥️T🅰️🚲🅲🚗CMCS❄️
112 112
🎣📷🎵🅿️🅂🔌abc

Closed 21 - 27 December

B&B rates are per person sharing per night incl. Breakfast

DOYLES SEAFOOD BAR & TOWN HOUSE

JOHN STREET,
DINGLE,
CO. KERRY

TEL: 066-915 1174 FAX: 066-915 1816
EMAIL: cdoyles@iol.ie
WEB: www.doylesofdingle.com

GUESTHOUSE ★★★★ MAP 1 B 4

The Townhouse has the most delightful rooms in Dingle. 8 spacious rooms with full bathrooms all have recently been refurbished in a most comfortable style. Satellite TV, phone, trouser press/iron, tea/coffee facilities. The world renowned Restaurant has an old range, sugan chairs. Natural stone & wood combination gives Doyles a cosy country atmosphere. The menu consists only of fresh food and is chosen on a daily basis from the fish landed on Dingle boats. AA◆◆◆◆ RAC◆◆◆◆ Les Routiers "Restaurant of the Year" 2002.

Member of Ireland's Blue Book

B&B from €61.00 to €77.00

SEÁN CLUSKEY
HOST

Diners
Mastercard
Visa

8 8

IRISH
HOTELS
FEDERATION

Closed 15 November - 14 February

EMLAGH HOUSE

DINGLE,
CO. KERRY

TEL: 066-915 2345 FAX: 066-915 2369
EMAIL: info@emlaghhouse.com
WEB: www.emlaghhouse.com

GUESTHOUSE ★★★★ MAP 1 B 4

Welcome to Emlagh House, Georgian style family-run home, overlooking Dingle Harbour. Here you will certainly relax in our calm & gracious surroundings. Spacious rooms are individually decorated on the theme of native Irish wild flowers. Rooms have large en suites, separate shower/bath, DD phone, TV & video, radio/CD, ironing board/trouser press & PC outlets. A short stroll will bring you to the heart of Dingle Town to sample its delights. Golf & sea fishing nearby. AA ◆◆◆◆◆, Bridgestone Top 100, RAC ◆◆◆◆◆, RAC Sparkling Diamond Award & Warm Welcome.

B&B from €90.00 to €120.00

GRAINNE & MARION KAVANAGH

Mastercard
Visa

11 11

IRISH
HOTELS
FEDERATION

Closed 06 January - 28 February

GORMANS CLIFFTOP HOUSE AND RESTAURANT

GLAISE BHEAG, BALLYDAVID,
DINGLE PENINSULA, TRALEE,
CO. KERRY

TEL: 066-915 5162 FAX: 066-915 5003
EMAIL: gormans@eircom.net
WEB: www.gormans-clifftophouse.com

GUESTHOUSE ★★★★ MAP 1 B 5

A welcoming cliff top refuge on the western edge of the Dingle Peninsula. All rooms pay homage to the landscape, offering breathtaking views of the Ocean and Mountains. Our emphasis is on comfort, mini suites boasting king size beds and jacuzzi baths. Downstairs guests can gather around the fire to read or chat, dine handsomely in our fully licensed restaurant. AA ◆◆◆◆◆ premier select. Les Routiers "Hidden Gem Ireland" 2001. Georgina Campbell 'Guesthouse of the Year' 2002 (Jameson Guide) - Les Routiers 'Hotel of the Year 2001'.

Member of Best Loved Hotels of The World

B&B from €50.00 to €75.00

VINCENT AND SILE O'GORMAIN
PROPRIETORS

Mastercard
Visa

Week partial board from €525.00

9 9

IRISH
HOTELS
FEDERATION

Closed 10 January - 01 March

Room rates are per room per night

GREENMOUNT HOUSE

UPPER JOHN STREET,
DINGLE,
CO. KERRY
TEL: 066-915 1414 FAX: 066-915 1974
EMAIL: mary@greenmounthouse.com
WEB: www.greenmounthouse.com

GUESTHOUSE ★★★★ MAP 1 B 4

Greenmount House is the proud recipient of the 1997 RAC Guest House of the Year for Ireland. A charming 4★★★★ country house yet centrally located. Spacious lounges to relax in and take advantage of its magnificent scenic location overlooking Dingle Town & Harbour. Each bedroom has private bathroom TV/radio & direct dial phone. Award winning buffet breakfasts served in conservatory with commanding views of Dingle. Luxurious, peaceful retreat. Recognised by all leading guides.

B&B from €37.50 to €65.00

JOHN & MARY CURRAN
OWNERS

Mastercard
Visa

9   9

Closed 10 - 27 December

HEATON'S GUESTHOUSE

THE WOOD,
DINGLE,
CO. KERRY
TEL: 066-915 2288 FAX: 066-915 2324
EMAIL: heatons@iol.ie
WEB: www.heatonsdingle.com

GUESTHOUSE ★★★★ MAP 1 B 4

Superb 4★★★★ family run guesthouse situated on the shore of Dingle Bay with spectacular views, 5 minutes walk from the town. All rooms are en suite (pressure shower and bath), with TV, DD phone and tea/coffee welcome tray. Breakfast is our speciality. Luxury junior suites and de luxe rooms recently opened (rates available on request). Local amenities include golf, sailing, fishing, surfing, cycling, walking, horse riding and the renowned gourmet restaurants.

B&B from €38.00 to €59.00

NUALA & CAMERON HEATON
PROPRIETORS

Mastercard
Visa

16   16

Closed 07 January - 01 February

HILLGROVE INN

SPA ROAD,
DINGLE,
CO. KERRY
TEL: 066-915 1131 FAX: 066-915 1441
EMAIL: hillgrovedingle@eircom.net
WEB: www.hillgrovedingle.com

GUESTHOUSE P MAP 1 B 4

The Hillgrove is family owned and managed. Located 5 minutes walk from Dingle's main street. Our rooms are all en suite, with DD phone, TV and tea/coffee making facilities. Our private lounge is the ideal place to relax with full bar facilities available. The Hillgrove offers a perfect combination of professional service with cheerful and helpful staff. We will ensure that your stay is the highlight of your visit to our beautiful town.

B&B from €35.00 to €70.00

SANDRA KENNEDY

American Express
Diners
Mastercard
Visa

12   12

Closed 01 October - 01 May

B&B rates are per person sharing per night incl. Breakfast

MILLTOWN HOUSE

DINGLE,
CO. KERRY

TEL: 066-915 1372 FAX: 066-915 1095
EMAIL: milltown@indigo.ie
WEB: http://indigo.ie/~milltown/

GUESTHOUSE ★★★★ MAP 1 B 4

Award-winning family run Milltown House is ideally located overlooking Dingle Bay and Town from our private gardens. All rooms which retain the character of the 130 year old house are en suite, have tea/coffee making facilities, direct dial phone, TV, trouser press, hairdryer and safety deposit box. The house was home to Robert Mitchum during the making of David Lean's epic movie "Ryans Daughter". Assistance in planning your day. One of the most scenic and quiet locations in the town area, less than 15 minutes walk or 2 minutes drive!

B&B from €50.00 to €70.00

TARA KERRY

American Express
Mastercard
Visa

10 10

Closed 07 October - 12 March

OLD PIER

AN FHEOTHANACH,
BALLYDAVID, DINGLE,
CO. KERRY

TEL: 066-915 5242
EMAIL: info@oldpier.com
WEB: www.oldpier.com

GUESTHOUSE ★★★ MAP 1 B 4

Situated in the heart of the West Kerry Gaeltacht on the Dingle Peninsula overlooking beautiful Smerwick Harbour and the Atlantic Ocean. This family run establishment offers 3*** accommodation with beautiful sea and mountain vistas. The Old Pier Restaurant offers a broad range of locally caught seafood, prime steak and meat dishes. Adjacent activities include 18 hole golf course, deep sea angling, mountain walking and archaeology sites. A warm welcome awaits you.

B&B from €30.00 to €50.00

JACQUI & PÁDRAIG O CONNOR

Mastercard
Visa

☺ Discount for stays of 2 nights

6 6

Open All Year

PAX HOUSE

UPPER JOHN STREET,
DINGLE,
CO. KERRY

TEL: 066-915 1518 FAX: 066-915 2461
EMAIL: paxhouse@iol.ie
WEB: www.pax-house.com

GUESTHOUSE ★★★★ MAP 1 B 4

Pax House has undeniably one of the most spectacular views in the Peninsula. Quotes from our guest book "Peace Perfect Peace" and "A little bit of heaven". 1km from Dingle Town. Bedrooms incl. suites (rates on request) are beautifully appointed & all include a refrigerator. Breakfast is a major event with local meats, cheese & fish. Homemade breads & preserves. We offer guests charm, tranquillity and unequalled hospitality. Enjoy a drink on the balcony whilst watching the activity in the bay. Voted amongst top ten places to stay in Ireland. AA ◆◆◆◆◆.

Member of Premier Guesthouses

B&B from €45.00 to €60.00

RON & JOAN BROSNAN WRIGHT OWNERS

Mastercard
Visa

12 12

Closed 01 December - 01 March

Room rates are per room per night

SMERWICK HARBOUR HOTEL

**BALLYFERRITER,
DINGLE,
CO. KERRY**

TEL: 066-915 6470 FAX: 066-915 6473
EMAIL: info@smerwickhotel.com
WEB: www.smerwickhotel.com

HOTEL ★★★ MAP 1 B 5

Smerwick Harbour Hotel & Seafood Restaurant with its old world bar, is located a short distance from Dingle Town. Our local 18 hole golf course is on your doorstep, 4km away, reduced green fees for guests. All rooms en suite (family rooms also). Spacious lounge. Enjoy excellent cuisine in our seafood restaurant, specialising in local seafood and char grilled steaks. Quality barfood also available. Old world ambience, as featured on our web site. The best sandy beaches in Ireland nearby. New elevator installed. Groups & weddings catered for.

B&B from €40.00 to €76.00

FIONNBAR WALSH
MANAGER

American Express
Mastercard
Visa

Weekend specials from €95.00

Open All Year

TOWERS HOTEL

**GLENBEIGH,
CO. KERRY**

TEL: 066-976 8212 FAX: 066-976 8260
EMAIL: towershotel@eircom.net
WEB: www.towershotel.com

HOTEL ★★★ MAP 1 C 4

The family run Towers Hotel, on the Ring of Kerry, is an ideal place to relax and enjoy the splendours of Kerry. The hotel is a short distance from sandy beaches and dramatic mountains. Paradise for golfers, walkers, fishermen and anyone interested in the Kerry landscape. The Towers internationally known restaurant is renowned for its excellent seafood and distinguished atmosphere. Its traditional pub provides a chance to mingle with the people of Glenbeigh in a real Kerry atmosphere.

Member of Irish Country Hotels

B&B from €56.00 to €75.00

DOLORES SWEENEY
PROPRIETOR

American Express
Mastercard
Visa

Weekend specials from €120.00

Closed 01 November - 01 April

GLENCAR HOUSE HOTEL

**GLENCAR,
CO. KERRY**

TEL: 066-976 0102 FAX: 066-976 0167
EMAIL: info@glencarhouse.com
WEB: www.glencarhouse.com

HOTEL ★★ MAP 1 C 4

The Glencar House Hotel, built by the Marquise of Lansdowne in 1670, lies framed by the McGillycuddy Reeks and Carrantuohill, a spectacular location on the Caragh River & 2km from the lake. Salmon & trout fishing is available at the fishery & boats are for hire on three lakes. Local golf courses include Dooks, Beaufort, Waterville and Killarney. Declared an area of Special Conservation in 1997, it is the perfect place to experience tranquillity. Catering to special retreats in health & wellness, weddings & corporate functions with emphasis on organic cuisine.

Member of Great Fishing Houses of Ireland

B&B from €50.00 to €70.00

NANCY & DERMOT O'CARROLL

American Express
Mastercard
Visa

Week partial board from €495.00

Closed 16 October - 23 February

B&B rates are per person sharing per night incl. Breakfast

ASHBERRY LODGE

SNEEM ROAD,
N70, KENMARE,
CO. KERRY
TEL: 064-42720
EMAIL: ashberry@iolfree.ie
WEB: www.ashberrylodge.com

GUESTHOUSE ★★★ MAP 1 D 3

Welcome to our new family-run guesthouse which offers friendly comfortable accommodation with spacious en suite bedrooms, with views of the Caha Mountains, central heating, excellent showers, colour TV, direct dial phones and a breakfast menu. We are situated on the Ring of Kerry Road, N70, which is within a short walking distance to the town centre. It is an ideal homebase to tour the Ring of Beara, Ring of Kerry, Gap of Dunloe, Healy's Pass, and much more! Also available are two 18 hole golf courses.

B&B from €27.50 to €35.00

FRANCIE & REGINA MURPHY

Mastercard
Visa

🛏️♪📞🖥️©➰CM❄♒🅿️🅢▪
8 8

I R I S H
HOTELS
F E D E R A T I O N

Open All Year

BRASS LANTERN

OLD RAILWAY ROAD,
KENMARE,
CO. KERRY
TEL: 064-42600 FAX: 064-41311
EMAIL: thebrasslantern@eircom.net
WEB: www.kenmare-insight.com/brasslantern

GUESTHOUSE ★★★ MAP 1 D 3

We are ideally located on a quiet residential road 2 minutes walk from Kenmare centre. The house has been designed to ensure our guests enjoy a comfortable and peaceful stay. Spacious bedrooms with en suite facilities, telephone and TV. Ground floor rooms perfect for anyone who has difficulty with stairs. Tea and coffee available throughout the day. Relax in front of a glowing fire with a book from our library. Plan activities with the help of our guide books, maps and local knowledge.

B&B from €25.00 to €45.00

COLETTE JONES
MANAGER

Mastercard
Visa

🛏️♪📞🖥️©➰🅿️🅢 inet
6 6

I R I S H
HOTELS
F E D E R A T I O N

Closed 02 January - 10 March

DAVITTS

HENRY STREET,
KENMARE,
CO. KERRY
TEL: 064-42741 FAX: 064-42756
EMAIL: davittskenmare@eircom.net
WEB: www.davitts-kenmare.com

GUESTHOUSE ★★★ MAP 1 D 3

If you are looking for luxury accommodation in the heart of Kenmare, then Davitt's is the guesthouse for you. Bar/bistro, restaurant downstairs serving excellent food throughout the year. Family run premises that offers everything for a perfect holiday under one roof. All our luxury bedrooms are en suite with satellite TV, DD phones (pc compatible) and hairdryers. The rooms are sited at the back of the building guaranteeing a restful night in spacious, beautifully decorated rooms.

B&B from €38.00 to €45.00

DONAL & MARY CREMIN
PROPRIETORS

American Express
Mastercard
Visa

⛳

🛏️♪📞🖥️Ⓣ©CM♫🎵🅿️🄰🄸🄲 inet
11 11

Closed 24 - 27 December

FOLEYS SHAMROCK

HENRY STREET,
KENMARE,
CO. KERRY
TEL: 064-42162 FAX: 064-41799
EMAIL: foleyest@iol.ie
WEB: www.foleyskenmare.com

GUESTHOUSE ★★★ MAP 1 D 3

Foleys is situated in Kenmare, Kerry Heritage Town, ten very comfortable centrally heated en suite rooms with colour TV, phone & tea making facilities. Our chef owned restaurant & pub bistro serves Irish & international cuisine. Traditional sessions in the pub. Foleys is within walking distance of Kenmare's 18 hole golf course, horse riding & fishing trips can be arranged. One of Ireland's Best - Fodors. Also recognised by Routard & Michelin.

B&B from €30.00 to €55.00

MARGARET FOLEY
OWNER/MANAGER

Mastercard
Visa

Weekend specials from €89.00

10 10

Open All Year

KENMARE BAY HOTEL

KENMARE,
CO. KERRY
TEL: 064-41300 FAX: 064-41541
EMAIL: kenmare@leehotels.ie
WEB: www.leehotels.ie

HOTEL ★★★ MAP 1 D 3

At the Kenmare Bay we offer you the opportunity to get away from it all. Surrounded by the magic of the Kerry Mountains and with the mystical Ring of Beara on your doorstop your complete enjoyment is assured. Our executive head chef P.J. Ryan will satisfy your every need. The beautiful town of Kenmare offers you quality shopping, great pubs and some of Ireland's finest restaurants - some 30 to choose from.

Member of Lee Hotel Group

B&B from €40.00 to €65.00

TERRY O'DOHERTY
GENERAL MANAGER

Diners
Mastercard
Visa

weekend specials from €119.00

136 136

Closed 12 November - 13 March

B&B rates are per person sharing per night incl. Breakfast

LODGE (THE)

KILLOWEN ROAD,
KENMARE,
CO. KERRY

TEL: 064-41512 FAX: 064-42724

EMAIL: thelodgekenmare@eircom.net
WEB: www.thelodgekenmare.com

GUESTHOUSE ★★★★ MAP 1 D 3

Newly-built luxury guesthouse situated directly opposite Kenmare's 18 hole golf course. Within 3 minutes walk of some of the finest restaurants in Ireland. All rooms are elegantly furnished with kingsize beds and en suite bathrooms. The rooms are very well appointed with DD phone, TV, controllable central heating and safes. An ideal location for the active, with walking, horseriding and fishing nearby. 4 of the bedrooms are on ground level with one especially equipped for wheelchair use.

B&B from €45.00 to €55.00

ROSEMARIE QUILL
PROPRIETOR

Mastercard

Visa

🏠🐾☎️🖥️TC❄️🖐️J🅿️🍴♿
10 10

Closed 07 November - 17 March

O'DONNABHAIN'S

HENRY STREET,
KENMARE,
CO. KERRY

TEL: 064-42106 FAX: 064-42321

EMAIL: info@odonnabhain-kenmare.com
WEB: www.odonnabhain-kenmare.com

GUESTHOUSE ★★★ MAP 1 D 3

Conveniently located in the centre of Kenmare Town, providing affordable accommodation with lashings of old world charm. Spacious en suite rooms (direct dial phone, TV 6 channels, parking), some with king size beds, finished with the comfort of the guests in mind. Rooms are located away from the bar, so as to ensure no sleepless nights-quietness in the centre of town. Ideal base to discover the South's attractions.

B&B from €34.00 to €48.00

JEREMIAH FOLEY
OWNER

Mastercard

Visa

🏠🐾☎️🖥️TU🖐️♪PS🅰️ic Inet
10 10

IRISH
HOTELS
FEDERATION

Open All Year

Room rates are per room per night

PARK HOTEL KENMARE

KENMARE,
CO. KERRY

TEL: 064-41200 FAX: 064-41402
EMAIL: info@parkkenmare.com
WEB: www.parkkenmare.com

HOTEL ★★★★★ MAP 1 D 3

Standing proudly amidst some of Irelands most breathtaking scenery, the limestone building, dating from 1897 welcomes guests with renowned warmth. A deluxe base from which to tour the famous Ring of Kerry, Ring of Beara or simply enjoy the intimacy of your accommodations. The dining room overlooking Kenmare Bay is regarded as one of Ireland's most respected offering the finest cuisine and an extensive wine list from around the world. Privately owned and managed - a most pleasant stay is assured.

Member of Ireland's Blue Book

B&B from € 183.00 to € 223.00

FRANCIS BRENNAN
PROPRIETOR

American Express
Diners
Mastercard
Visa

Weekend specials from €295.00

47 47

Closed 02 January - 18 April

RIVERSDALE HOUSE HOTEL

KENMARE,
CO. KERRY

TEL: 064-41299 FAX: 064-41075
EMAIL: riversdale@eircom.net
WEB: www.kenmare.com/riversdale

HOTEL ★★★ MAP 1 D 3

Located on the scenic shores of Kenmare Bay and backed by the McGillycuddy Reeks and Caha Mountains the hotel is the ideal choice to tour the famous Ring of Kerry and beautiful West Cork. Recently refurbished, the hotel boasts 4 luxurious suites, each with panoramic views of the scenery beyond our seven acre garden. Our Waterfront Restaurant is renowned for its fine cuisine while local activities include an 18 hole golf course, deep sea angling, hill walking, cycling and water-skiing.

Member of Best Western Hotels

B&B from € 50.00 to € 80.00

PEGGY O'SULLIVAN
PROPRIETOR

American Express
Diners
Mastercard
Visa

Weekend specials from €99.00

64 64

Closed 06 November - 22 March

ROSEGARDEN GUESTHOUSE

SNEEM RD (N70),
KENMARE,
CO. KERRY

TEL: 064-42288 FAX: 064-42305
EMAIL: rosegard@iol.ie
WEB: www.euroka.com/rosegarden

GUESTHOUSE ★★★ MAP 1 D 3

The Rosegarden Guesthouse and Restaurant is situated within walking distance of Kenmare Town, Ring of Kerry (N70). Set in 1 acre of landscaped garden with 350 roses. Private car park. All rooms en suite, power showers, centrally heated. Restaurant open from 6.30 pm. Menu includes lamb, steaks, salmon, stuffed crab, mussels and wine list. Enjoy our peaceful and relaxed ambience. We are looking forward to your visit. Ask for our 3 and 7 day specials.

B&B from € 29.50 to € 39.50

INGRID & PETER RINGLEVER

American Express
Diners
Mastercard
Visa

Week partial board from €350.00

8 8

Closed 01 November - 17 March

B&B rates are per person sharing per night incl. Breakfast

SEA SHORE FARM

TUBRID,
KENMARE,
CO. KERRY

TEL: 064-41270 FAX: 064-41270
EMAIL: seashore@eircom.net
WEB: http://homepage.eircom.net/~seashore

GUESTHOUSE ★★★ MAP 1 D 3

Our setting on the Bay is uniquely peaceful and private yet only 1 mile from town. Our farm extends to the shore affording unspoilt field walks in natural habitat with plentiful bird/wildlife. Large en suite rooms with panoramic seascapes, king beds, phone, tea facilities, etc. AA ♦♦♦♦ Selected, Recommended Guide du Routard, Los Angeles Times. Sign posted 300m from Kenmare by Esso Station - junction N71/N70 Killarney/Ring of Kerry Sneem Road.

Member of Friendly Homes of Ireland

B&B from €40.00 to €60.00

MARY PATRICIA O'SULLIVAN
PROPRIETOR

Mastercard
Visa

🏠👤☎🖥TC❄♿🅿♿
6 6

Closed 10 November - 01 March

SHEEN FALLS LODGE

KENMARE,
CO. KERRY

TEL: 064-41600 FAX: 064-41386
EMAIL: info@sheenfallslodge.ie
WEB: www.sheenfallslodge.ie

HOTEL ★★★★★ MAP 1 D 3

Uniquely set on the shores of Kenmare Bay & Sheen River, only 2km from the Heritage Town of Kenmare, located on a 300-acre woodland estate. Our signature restaurant La Cascade, offers a distinctive fine dining experience overlooking the Sheen Waterfalls. Choose from an extensive array of Estate activities from salmon fishing to horse riding, or unwind with luxurious treatments in our Health Spa. Dedicated staff uphold the most outstanding service to make your stay as unforgettable & unique as Ireland itself.

Member of Relais & Châteaux

B&B from €152.00 to €220.00

ADRIAAN BARTELS
GENERAL MANAGER

American Express
Diners
Mastercard
Visa

☺ Weekend specials from €300.00

🏠👤☎🖥⚡T🅰©♣CM❄🔆🖥
61 61
🔲♿U♿♪🅿🚲♿♿

Closed 02 January - 07 February

Room rates are per room per night

VIRGINIA'S

HENRY STREET,
KENMARE,
CO. KERRY
TEL: 064-41021
EMAIL: virginias@eircom.net
WEB: www.virginias-kenmare.com

GUESTHOUSE N MAP 1 D 3

Welcome to Virginia's guesthouse and restaurant, ideally situated in the heart of Kenmare Town. The newly appointed spacious rooms are decorated and furnished to a very high standard with an emphasis on cleanliness and comfort. All are complete with DD telephone, cable TV, power shower, hairdryer and personal safe. Delicious varied 3-course breakfast. Enjoy lunch and dinner in Virginia's Restaurant, serving the best in local fresh produce.

B&B from €30.00 to €50.00

NEIL & NOREEN HARRINGTON

Mastercard
Visa

9 9

Closed 25 December - 01 March

19TH GREEN (THE)

LACKABANE,
FOSSA, KILLARNEY,
CO. KERRY
TEL: 064-32868 FAX: 064-32637
EMAIL: 19thgreen@eircom.net
WEB: www.19thgreen-bb.com

GUESTHOUSE ★★★ MAP 2 E 4

Family run guesthouse 3km from Killarney Town. Ring of Kerry Road; adjacent to Killarney's 3 x 18 hole championship courses. Ideal for golfers playing Killarney, Beaufort, Dooks, Waterville, Tralee or Ballybunion. All tee times arranged. Putting green for guests' use. Tours arranged: Gap of Dunloe, Ring of Kerry and Dingle Peninsula. All rooms en suite with direct dial phone and TV. Whether you are sightseeing, fishing, rambling or golfing, the 19th Green will suit you to a tee.

B&B from €30.00 to €45.00

TIMOTHY AND BRIDGET FOLEY
PROPRIETORS

Mastercard
Visa

10 10

Closed 01 November - 01 March

ABBEY LODGE

MUCKROSS ROAD,
KILLARNEY,
CO. KERRY
TEL: 064-34193 FAX: 064-35877
EMAIL: abbeylodgekly@eircom.net
WEB: www.abbeylodge.com

GUESTHOUSE ★★★★ MAP 2 E 4

A genuine Irish welcome awaits you at Abbey Lodge. Our guesthouse is family run and boasts 15 luxurious en suite rooms with TV, direct dial phone and central heating. We are conveniently located on the Muckross Road (N71) a mere three minute walk to the town centre. The house is tastefully decorated throughout and features many interesting antiques and art. With 30 years in the business - anywhere else is a compromise.

Member of Premier Guesthouses

B&B from €35.00 to €60.00

JOHN G KING
OWNER

Mastercard
Visa

15 15

Closed 20 - 28 December

B&B rates are per person sharing per night incl. Breakfast

AGHADOE HEIGHTS HOTEL

LAKES OF KILLARNEY,
KILLARNEY,
CO. KERRY
TEL: 064-31766 FAX: 064-31345
EMAIL: info@aghadoeheights.com
WEB: www.aghadoeheights.com

HOTEL ★★★★★ MAP 2 E 4

Quietly located 5 minutes from Killarney Town, with breathtaking views of the ever-changing lakes and mountains, this exceptional 5 star hotel is internationally renowned for outstanding standards of service, comfort and cuisine, and has recently been awarded the AA Irish Hotel of the Year for 2001-2002. A warm welcome on arrival, luxurious and oversized bedrooms, a superb private leisure centre and dedicated and professional staff, overseen by Pat & Marie Chawke, transform a special stay into one that is memorable.

Member of Preferred Hotels & Resorts Worldwide

B&B from €155.00 to €197.00

PAT & MARIE CHAWKE
GENERAL MANAGERS

American Express
Diners
Mastercard
Visa

Weekend specials from €245.00

69 69

Open All Year

AISLING HOUSE

COUNTESS ROAD,
KILLARNEY,
CO. KERRY
TEL: 064-31112 FAX: 064-30079
EMAIL: aislinghouse@eircom.net

GUESTHOUSE ★★★ MAP 2 E 4

Aisling House located in peaceful surroundings just 800 meters off Muckross Road and 8 minutes walk from the centre of Killarney. All bedrooms are en suite, with TV and central heating. Tea/coffee facilities available to guests at all times. There is private car parking and a garden for guests. Aisling House is well within walking distance of Killarney National Park, Ross Castle and Muckross House. Tours of the Ring of Kerry/Dingle may be arranged. Nearby facilities include golf, horse riding, angling.

Member of Premier Guesthouses

B&B from €28.00 to €35.00

PATRICK O'DONOGHUE/PATRICIA
O'DONOGHUE OWNER/MANAGER

Mastercard
Visa

10 10

Closed 20 - 27 December

Room rates are per room per night

ARBUTUS HOTEL

COLLEGE STREET,
KILLARNEY,
CO. KERRY
TEL: 064-31037 FAX: 064-34033
EMAIL: arbutushotel@eircom.net
WEB: www.arbutuskillarney.com

HOTEL ★★★ MAP 2 E 4

The Arbutus is a fine townhouse hotel in the heart of Killarney town. Here the Buckley family & their team have been welcoming guests since 1926. Constantly upgraded it now has 36 luxurious bedrooms, an award-winning restaurant & an oak panelled bar. There is a great atmosphere, character & care shown towards guests. The Arbutus is a superb place to base yourself, in the town centre close to all the best that Killarney and Kerry have to offer.

B&B from €60.00 to €85.00

SEÁN BUCKLEY
PROPRIETOR

Diners
Mastercard
Visa

36 36

Open All Year

ASHVILLE GUESTHOUSE

ROCK ROAD,
KILLARNEY,
CO. KERRY
TEL: 064-36405 FAX: 064-36778
EMAIL: ashvillehouse@eircom.net
WEB: www.ashvillekillarney.com

GUESTHOUSE ★★★ MAP 2 E 4

Ashville is a spacious family run guesthouse, 2 mins walk from town centre, on main Tralee Road (N22). Private car park. Comfortably furnished en suite rooms include orthopaedic beds, direct dial phone, multi channel TV, hairdryer. Sample our varied breakfast menu. Convenient to Killarney National Park, pony trekking, golf and fishing. Ideal touring base for Ring of Kerry, Dingle and Beara. Declan and Elma assure you of a warm welcome at Ashville. Awarded AA ♦♦♦, RAC ♦♦♦♦.

B&B from €28.00 to €39.00

DECLAN & ELMA WALSH
PROPRIETORS

American Express
Mastercard
Visa

12 12

Closed 18 - 30 December

BROOK LODGE HOTEL

HIGH STREET,
KILLARNEY,
CO. KERRY
TEL: 064-31800 FAX: 064-35001
EMAIL: brooklodgekillarney@eircom.net
WEB: www.brooklodgekillarney.com

HOTEL ★★★ MAP 2 E 4

Brook Lodge Hotel is a new hotel, family-run, situated in the heart of Killarney Town, set back from the street on over an acre of landscaped garden with private parking. Our large and tastefully decorated bedrooms are all en suite, including tea/coffee, direct dial phone, hairdryer, multichannel TV. Wheelchair facilities. Lift. Excellent cuisine in Brook Restaurant with wine licence and residents' bar.

B&B from €45.00 to €70.00

JOAN COUNIHAN
OWNER

American Express
Diners
Mastercard
Visa

18 18

Inet

Closed 01 November - 11 April

B&B rates are per person sharing per night incl. Breakfast

CAHERNANE HOUSE HOTEL

MUCKROSS ROAD,
KILLARNEY,
CO. KERRY
TEL: 064-31895 FAX: 064-34340
EMAIL: cahernane@eircom.net
WEB: www.cahernane.com

HOTEL ★★★★ MAP 2 E 4

Formerly the residence of the Herbert family, Earls of Pembroke, Cahernane House dates back to the 17th century. Cahernane House Hotel is situated on its own parklands on the edge of Killarney's National Park, an area of outstanding natural beauty with its untamed landscape of mountains, lakes and woodland walks and is only 10 minutes walk from Killarney town. All of the 42 bedrooms are beautifully appointed many with antique furniture, jacuzzis and private balconies.

Member of Manor House Hotels

B&B from € 106.00 to € 126.00

BROWNE FAMILY
PROPRIETORS

American Express
Diners
Mastercard
Visa

🛏️ 🔔 ☎️ 🖥️ ⬛T🅲🛒 CM❄️ ♨️ ⛵ 🅿️
🎿 🏠 a|c 🚴 Inet
42 42

Closed 23 December - 05 January

CASTLELODGE GUESTHOUSE

MUCKROSS ROAD,
KILLARNEY,
CO. KERRY
TEL: 064-31545 FAX: 064-32325
EMAIL: castlelodge@eircom.net
WEB: http://homepage.eircom.net/~castlelodge/

GUESTHOUSE U MAP 2 E 4

Conveniently located, just two minutes walk from Killarney Town Centre. Open all year round, our Guesthouse offers very friendly staff, a homely atmosphere and easy access to all the major attractions and magnificent scenery in Killarney. Good restaurants and live music will be recommended, come and see the sights, hear the music and taste the atmosphere.

B&B from € 26.00 to € 45.00

TONY O'SHEA

American Express
Diners
Mastercard
Visa

🎵

🛏️ 🔔 ☎️ 🖥️ ⬛T🅲 ❄️ ⛵ 🅿️ 🛗
25 25

Open All Year

Room rates are per room per night

CASTLEROSSE HOTEL & LEISURE CENTRE

KILLARNEY,
CO. KERRY

TEL: 064-31144 FAX: 064-31031
EMAIL: reservations@crhk.ie
WEB: www.castlerossehotelkillarney.com

HOTEL ★★★ MAP 2 E 4

A Tower Group Hotel - situated right on the lakeside, between the golf course and the National Park and a little over a mile from Killarney Town Centre, the Castlerosse commands magnificent views of the lakes and mountains, especially from the restaurant and panoramic bar. The impressive range of leisure facilities, including an on-site golf course, leisure centre with 20m swimming pool and 2 floodlit tennis courts, makes the Castlerosse the perfect location for a holiday or leisure break.

Member of Tower Hotel Group

B&B from €45.00 to €75.00

DANNY BOWE
GENERAL MANAGER

American Express
Diners
Mastercard
Visa

Weekend specials from €115.00

110 110

Closed 06 November - 17 March

COFFEY'S LOCH LEIN HOUSE HOTEL

GOLF COURSE ROAD,
FOSSA, KILLARNEY,
CO. KERRY

TEL: 064-31260 FAX: 064-36151
EMAIL: ecoffey@indigo.ie
WEB: www.lochlein.com

HOTEL U MAP 2 E 4

Superb family run hotel, uniquely situated by the shores of Killarney's Lower Lake. Magnificent views of lakes & mountains. Ideally located on the Ring of Kerry/Dingle roads, near the Gap of Dunloe. Tours personally arranged. Nearby four 18 hole championship golf courses, horseriding & fishing.
While you may be surprised by the delightful new building, you will be pleased that the hospitality, grade A service & relaxed atmosphere have not changed. A warm welcome awaits you here.

B&B from €35.00 to €80.00

EITHNE COFFEY
PROPRIETOR

Mastercard
Visa

16 16

Closed 27 October - 15 March

CRYSTAL SPRINGS

BALLYCASHEEN (OFF N22),
KILLARNEY,
CO. KERRY

TEL: 064-33272 FAX: 064-35518
EMAIL: crystalsprings@eircom.net
WEB: http://homepage.eircom.net/~doors/

GUESTHOUSE P MAP 2 E 4

Located on the banks of the peaceful River Flesk offering fishing on location. Just off N22/Cork Road only 10 minutes walk to town centre, where many traditional pubs and fine restaurants can be found. Close to lakes, national park, Ring of Kerry and I.N.E.C. Spacious en suite rooms, AA ♦♦♦♦ award. TV, tea/coffee facilities, hairdryers, DD phones, trouser press and refrigerators. Extensive menus including vegetarian and home specialities. Ample safe parking.

B&B from €30.00 to €40.00

EILEEN & TIM BROSNAN

Mastercard
Visa

7 7

Closed 20 - 29 December

B&B rates are per person sharing per night incl. Breakfast

DARBY O'GILLS COUNTRY HOUSE HOTEL

LISSIVIGEEN,
MALLOW ROAD, KILLARNEY,
CO. KERRY

TEL: 064-34168 FAX: 064-36794
EMAIL: darbyogill@eircom.net
WEB: www.darbyogillskillarney.com

HOTEL U MAP 2 E 4

Darby O'Gills Country House Hotel is a charming family run hotel located in a quiet rural setting just on the edge of Killarney Town. We are positioned ideally for touring the wonders of Kerry and Cork, playing golf, fishing, hillwalking or just plain relaxing. Killarney Town Centre is only a five minute drive. We are a family friendly hotel and personal attention is guaranteed. Open all year with excellent rates offering great value.

Member of MinOtel Ireland Hotel Group

B&B from €30.00 to €65.00

PAT & JOAN GILL & FAMILY

American Express
Diners
Mastercard
Visa

Midweek specials from €100.00pps
(2 B&B, 1 Dinner)

25 25

Open All Year

DROMHALL HOTEL

MUCKROSS ROAD,
KILLARNEY,
CO. KERRY

TEL: 064-39300 FAX: 064-39301
EMAIL: info@dromhall.com
WEB: www.dromhall.com

HOTEL U MAP 2 E 4

Killarney's famous mountain scenes provide a magnificent backdrop for the Dromhall Hotel. Located 5 minutes walk from town the hotel offers the comfort and service one associates with a first class hotel while retaining the friendliness and welcome of a family run hotel. From the moment you enter the elegant marbled lobby the scene is set for a special experience. Banquet and conference facilities for up to 300. Award winning Kaynes Bistro. Full leisure centre.

B&B from €45.00 to €95.00

DENISE BATT
GENERAL MANAGER

American Express
Diners
Mastercard
Visa

Weekend specials from €120.00

70 70

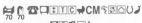

Closed 23 - 27 December

SWING

TEE-TIME RESERVATION SERVICE FOR ALL OF IRELAND

Ensure a hassle free golf vacation.

CONTACT US AT

Phone: +353 (0)66 7125733
Fax: +353 (0)66 7123651
Email: swing@iol.ie
Web: www.swinggolfireland.com
Address:
South West Ireland Golf Ltd,
24 Denny Street, Tralee, Co.
Kerry, Ireland.

Room rates are per room per night

EARLS COURT HOUSE

WOODLAWN JUNCTION,
MUCKROSS ROAD, KILLARNEY,
CO. KERRY
TEL: 064-34009 FAX: 064-34366
EMAIL: info@killarney-earlscourt.ie
WEB: www.killarney-earlscourt.ie

GUESTHOUSE ★★★★ MAP 2 E 4

Our family run 4**** hideaway is 5
minutes walk to town centre. Awarded
RAC "Small Hotel of the Year for
Ireland' 1998 and Little Gem 2001 &
2002. Your stay here will be the
"highlight" of your Irish visit.
Experience country house ambience
rich in tradition, a real warm Irish
welcome, home baking, open fires,
fine antiques & paintings. Breakfast is
special - a feast offering tempting
choices. Spacious bedrooms are
graced with antiques & soft
furnishings, king beds, full bathroom
and balconies. Four poster suites.
Private parking. AA♦♦♦♦♦.

B&B from €48.00 to €68.00

EMER & RAY MOYNIHAN
OWNERS

Mastercard
Visa

11 11

IRISH
HOTELS
FEDERATION

Closed 30 November - 01 February

EVISTON HOUSE HOTEL

NEW STREET,
KILLARNEY,
CO. KERRY
TEL: 064-31640 FAX: 064-33685
EMAIL: evishtl@eircom.net
WEB: www.killarney-hotel.com

HOTEL ★★★ MAP 2 E 4

Eviston House Hotel is located in the
centre of Killarney yet only a few
minutes away from the National Park
and championship golf courses. All
our luxurious bedrooms are complete
with private bathroom, direct dial
telephone, tea/coffee facilities, hair
dryer and satellite TV. The elegant
Colleen Bawn Restaurant offers fine
food in intimate surroundings.
Afterwards visit our famous pub, the
Danny Mann, for the best in
traditional music and great 'craic'.

Member of Best Western Hotels

B&B from €45.00 to €85.00

EDWARD EVISTON
PROPRIETOR

American Express
Diners
Mastercard
Visa

Weekend specials from €119.00

75 75

IRISH
HOTELS
FEDERATION

Open All Year

FAILTE HOTEL

COLLEGE STREET,
KILLARNEY,
CO. KERRY
TEL: 064-33404 FAX: 064-36599
EMAIL: failtehotel@eircom.net

HOTEL ★★ MAP 2 E 4

The Failte Hotel, recently refurbished
to a very high standard, is owned
and managed by the O'Callaghan
family. It is internationally known for
its high standard of cuisine. Paudie
supervises the award winning bar. It
is situated in the town centre,
adjacent to railway station, new
factory outlet, shopping complex. Also
close by are many local cabarets &
night clubs. Local amenities include
golfing, fishing, walking.

B&B from €40.00 to €65.00

DERMOT & EILEEN O'CALLAGHAN
PROPRIETORS

American Express
Mastercard
Visa

15 15

IRISH
HOTELS
FEDERATION

Closed 24 - 26 December

B&B rates are per person sharing per night incl. Breakfast

FAIRVIEW GUESTHOUSE

MICHAEL COLLINS PLACE,
COLLEGE STREET, KILLARNEY,
CO. KERRY
TEL: 064-34164 FAX: 064-71777
EMAIL: fvk@eircom.net
WEB: www.fairviewkillarney.com

GUESTHOUSE N   MAP 2 E 4

This premier purpose built guesthouse stands proudly in the heart of downtown Killarney, yet out of noise's way. Convenient to bus and rail stations. Easy to find, hard to leave. Parking, spacious rooms with optional jacuzzi facilities, and all modern amenities including elevator access and wheelchair facilities. A deluxe base from which to tour, golf or socialise. Privately owned and managed, we ensure a memorable and exceptional stay.

B&B from €35.00 to €55.00

JAMES & SHELLEY O' NEILL
PROPRIETORS

American Express
Mastercard
Visa

15 15

FAX

IRISH
HOTELS
FEDERATION

Open All Year

FOLEY'S TOWNHOUSE

23 HIGH STREET,
KILLARNEY,
CO. KERRY
TEL: 064-31217 FAX: 064-34683
EMAIL: info@foleystownhouse.com
WEB: www.foleystownhouse.com

GUESTHOUSE ★★★★   MAP 2 E 4

Originally a 19th century Coaching Inn, this old house has hosted generations of travellers. Newly refurbished, this is a 4**** family-run town centre located guesthouse. Luxury bedrooms are individually designed for comfort complete with every modern amenity. Downstairs is our award-winning seafood and steak restaurant. Chef/owner Carol provides meals from fresh local produce. Choose from approx 200 wines. Personal supervision. Private parking. Awarded AA ◆◆◆◆◆, RAC Highly Acclaimed.

B&B from €58.75 to €62.95

CAROL HARTNETT
PROPRIETOR

American Express
Mastercard
Visa

28 28

IRISH
HOTELS
FEDERATION

Closed 14 November - 01 March

Room rates are per room per night

FRIARS GLEN

MANGERTON ROAD,
MUCKROSS, KILLARNEY,
CO. KERRY
TEL: 064-37500 FAX: 064-37388
EMAIL: fullerj@indigo.ie
WEB: www.friarsglen.ie

GUESTHOUSE ★★★★ MAP 2 E 4

This 4**** Guesthouse, built in a traditional style, offers a haven of peace and tranquillity; set in its own 28 acres of wood and pastureland and located in the heart of Killarney National Park. Reception rooms have a rustic feel, with a warm and friendly atmosphere, finished in stone and wood with open fires and antiques. Bedrooms & bathrooms are finished to the highest standards. The dining room, patio & garden have a terrific mountain view. An ideal base in the South West. Highly recommended by Michelin.

B&B from €40.00 to €55.00

MARY & JOHN FULLER
PROPRIETORS

Mastercard
Visa

Midweek specials from €110.00

10 10

HOTELS
FEDERATION

Closed 30 November - 06 February

FUCHSIA HOUSE

MUCKROSS ROAD,
KILLARNEY,
CO. KERRY
TEL: 064-33743 FAX: 064-36588
EMAIL: fuchsiahouse@eircom.net
WEB: www.fuchsiahouse.com

GUESTHOUSE ★★★★ MAP 2 E 4

We invite you to enjoy the affordable luxury of Fuchsia House which is set well back from the road in mature, leafy gardens is only 7 mins walk from Killarney Town Centre. Purpose built to combine the amenities of a modern 4**** guest-house with the elegance of an earlier age, we offer spacious rooms with orthopaedic beds dressed in crisp cotton & linen, private bath with power shower, DD phone. Conservatory. Irish & vegetarian menu. Winner 1999 "Best Guesthouse" in Killarney Looking Good Competition. RAC Sparkling Diamond Award.

B&B from €38.00 to €58.00

MARY TREACY
OWNER

Mastercard
Visa

9 9

HOTELS
FEDERATION

Open All Year

GLEANN FIA COUNTRY HOUSE

DEERPARK,
KILLARNEY,
CO. KERRY
TEL: 064-35035 FAX: 064-35000
EMAIL: info@gleannfia.com
WEB: www.gleannfia.com

GUESTHOUSE ★★★ MAP 2 E 4

Set in a secluded 30 acre wooded river valley, 1 mile from Killarney - Gleann Fia is the perfect holiday setting. Our Victorian style country house offers tasteful en suite rooms, each with phone & orthopaedic beds. Stroll along the river walk admiring the wild flowers & Autumn colours. Relax by the peat fire or in the conservatory. Wholesome breakfasts include freshly squeezed oranges, scrambled eggs with smoked salmon, fresh fish, country cheeses, homemade preserves. A professional & friendly homestyle service. 300yds from Killarney's Ring road N22.

B&B from €32.00 to €62.00

CONOR & BRIDGET O'CONNELL
YOUR HOSTS

American Express
Mastercard
Visa

19 19

HOTELS
FEDERATION

Open All Year

B&B rates are per person sharing per night incl. Breakfast

GLENA GUESTHOUSE

MUCKROSS ROAD,
KILLARNEY,
CO. KERRY

TEL: 064-32705 FAX: 064-35611
EMAIL: glena@iol.ie
WEB: www.glenahouse.com

GUESTHOUSE ★★★ MAP 2 E 4

Glena House - Killarney's award winning 3 star guesthouse, AA ◆◆◆◆, Bord Failte approved. It's the simple things that make it a great place to stay, great location 5 minutes from town centre, evening meals available during season, orthopaedic beds to rest in, a shower/bath ensuite to invigorate, tea/coffee when you want, homebaking and preserves, healthy options breakfast, a bowl of ice, dispense bar service and a host and staff eager to make your stay happy and memorable. Parking on site.

B&B from €35.00 to €45.00

MARINA & TIM BUCKLEY
OWNERS/MANAGERS

American Express
Diners
Mastercard
Visa

26 26

IRISH HOTELS FEDERATION

Closed 01 December - 15 March

GLENEAGLE HOTEL

KILLARNEY,
CO. KERRY

TEL: 064-36000 FAX: 064-32646
EMAIL: info@gleneaglehotel.com
WEB: www.gleneaglehotel.com

HOTEL ★★★ MAP 2 E 4

Ireland's leading leisure and conference/convention hotel, adjacent to Killarney's National Park with beautifully furnished rooms. Ireland's National Events Centre is ideally suited for conventions, conferences, exhibitions, sporting events, concerts and theatrical productions. Our award winning chefs will delight you in both our restaurants. We have a great line-up of entertainment all year round. Relax and unwind using our indoor/outdoor leisure facilities.

B&B from €55.00 to €125.00

O'DONOGHUE FAMILY
PROPRIETORS

American Express
Diners
Mastercard
Visa

246 246

IRISH HOTELS FEDERATION

Open All Year

Room rates are per room per night

HOLIDAY INN KILLARNEY

MUCKROSS ROAD,
KILLARNEY,
CO. KERRY
TEL: 064-33000 FAX: 064-33001
EMAIL: reservations@holidayinnkillarney.com
WEB: www.holidayinnkillarney.com

HOTEL ★★★ MAP 2 E 4

Holiday Inn Killarney enjoys a quiet but central location close to Killarney Town Centre. Its 100 spacious en suite rooms including 24 suites, are tastefully decorated to the highest standard. Our fully-equipped leisure centre is the perfect place to relax and unwind. Our Library Point Restaurant serves the finest of local cuisine while Saddlers Pub serves food daily and has entertainment nightly. A haven for all seasons!

Member of Sweeney Hotel Group

Room Rate from €50.00 to €90.00

DAVID HENNESSY
GENERAL MANAGER

American Express
Diners
Mastercard
Visa

100 100

Open All Year

HOTEL DUNLOE CASTLE

KILLARNEY,
CO. KERRY

TEL: 064-44111 FAX: 064-44583
EMAIL: sales@kih.liebherr.com
WEB: www.iol.ie/khl

HOTEL ★★★★★ MAP 2 E 4

110 bedroomed resort near Killarney, facing the famous Gap of Dunloe. Historical park and botanic gardens with ruins of castle. Elegant décor with many valuable antiques. Luxurious lounges, cocktail bar, gourmet restaurant. Extensive leisure facilities: pool, sauna, gym, riding, putting green, tennis, jogging track. 10 championship courses nearby. Sister hotels: Ard-na-Sidhe and Hotel Europe. Central Reservations: Tel: 064-31900, Fax: 064-32118.

B&B from €80.00 to €100.00

MICHAEL BRENNAN
MANAGER

American Express
Diners
Mastercard
Visa

☺ Weekend specials from €210.00

110 110

Closed 01 October - 15 April

HOTEL EUROPE

KILLARNEY,
CO. KERRY

TEL: 064-31900 FAX: 064-32118
EMAIL: sales@kih.liebherr.com
WEB: www.iol.ie/khl

HOTEL ★★★★★ MAP 2 E 4

De luxe resort known internationally for its spectacular location on the Lakes of Killarney. 205 spacious bedrooms and suites of highest standards, many with lake view. Elegant lounges, cocktail bar, Panorama Restaurant. Boutique. Health/fitness centre, 25m indoor pool, sauna, gym. Tennis, horseriding, fishing, boating, cycling. 10 championship courses nearby. Sister hotels: Hotel Dunloe Castle and Ard-na-Sidhe.

B&B from €80.00 to €100.00

MICHAEL W. BRENNAN

American Express
Diners
Mastercard
Visa

205 205

Closed 15 November - 15 March

B&B rates are per person sharing per night incl. Breakfast

HUSSEYS TOWNHOUSE & BAR

43 HIGH STREET,
KILLARNEY,
CO. KERRY
TEL: 064-37454 FAX: 064-33144
EMAIL: husseys@iol.ie
WEB: www.husseystownhouse.com

GUESTHOUSE ★★★ MAP 2 E 4

Centrally located, within walking distance of Killarney National Park, the principal shopping areas & the best restaurants in town. This family owned house offers peaceful accommodation in tastefully decorated rooms, equipped to a high standard. Enjoy a choice of breakfast in our delightful dining room, relax in our comfortable guest lounge or cosy friendly bar. For walkers, cyclists, golfers or touring Kerry this is the discerning traveller's perfect choice. Private parking.

B&B from €28.00 to €40.00

GERALDINE O'LEARY
OWNER

American Express
Mastercard
Visa

5 5

IRISH HOTELS FEDERATION

Closed 31 October - 18 April

INTERNATIONAL BEST WESTERN HOTEL

KENMARE PLACE,
KILLARNEY,
CO. KERRY
TEL: 064-31816 FAX: 064-31837
EMAIL: inter@iol.ie
WEB: www.killarney-inter.com

HOTEL ★★★ MAP 2 E 4

A warm welcome awaits you at the International. This town centre hotel has been brought into the 21st century with carefully planned refurbishment. 79 luxurious bedrooms - 10 with Jacuzzi en suite - with modern facilities to make your stay a memorable one. Excellent cuisine served using only fresh local produce. Traditional music in our award winning Hannigans Pub. Guest facilities - snooker room, library & drying room. 100m from Killarney National Park. Killarney's three 18 hole championship golf courses nearby. Bus/Train Station 200m.

Member of Best Western Hotels

B&B from €50.00 to €100.00

TERENCE MULCAHY
GENERAL MANAGER

American Express
Diners
Mastercard
Visa

Weekend specials from €115.00

79 79

IRISH HOTELS FEDERATION

Closed 23 - 26 December

INVERARAY FARM GUESTHOUSE

BEAUFORT,
KILLARNEY,
CO. KERRY
TEL: 064-44224 FAX: 064-44775
EMAIL: inver@indigo.ie
WEB: www.inver-aray.com

GUESTHOUSE ★★ MAP 2 E 4

A luxury farm guesthouse in a quiet sylvan setting. Views of Killarney Lakes, Mountains and Gap of Dunloe. 9km west of Killarney, 1km off N72, left over bridge at Shop. Free private trout and salmon fishing on River Laune. Angling, walking and golfing tours arranged. Tea-room, playroom, playground and pony for children. Singing pubs, horse-riding locally. Home-baking, seafood and dinner a speciality with good, wholesome home cooking. Recommended Le Guide du Routard 2002.

B&B from €26.00 to €32.00

EILEEN & NOEL SPILLANE
PROPRIETORS

9 9

IRISH HOTELS FEDERATION

Closed 30 November - 20 February

Room rates are per room per night

KATHLEENS COUNTRY HOUSE

MADAMS HEIGHT, TRALEE ROAD,
KILLARNEY,
CO. KERRY
TEL: 064-32810 FAX: 064-32340
EMAIL: info@kathleens.net
WEB: www.kathleens.net

GUESTHOUSE ★★★★ MAP 2 E 4

Attentiveness, friendliness and traditional hospitality make Kathleens special. Romantic oasis in 3 acres of mature gardens yet only 3km from Killarney Town. RAC Small Hotel of the Year for Ireland, AA ◆◆◆◆◆. Elegant spacious bedrooms furnished in antique pine with bath tub/power shower, orthopaedic beds, tea/coffee makers, hairdryer, telephone. Contemporary paintings throughout. Non-Smoking. Singles welcome. Ideal golf base. Easy to get to! Hard to leave!

B&B from €45.00 to €65.00

KATHLEEN O'REGAN SHEPPARD
PROPRIETOR

American Express
Mastercard
Visa

17 17

Closed 01 November - 10 March

KILLARNEY AVENUE HOTEL

KENMARE PLACE,
KILLARNEY,
CO. KERRY
TEL: 064-32522 FAX: 064-33707
EMAIL: kavenue@odonoghue-ring-hotels.com
WEB: www.odonoghue-ring-hotels.com

HOTEL ★★★★ MAP 2 E 4

This boutique 4★★★★ hotel has an idyllic setting in the heart of downtown Killarney. Well appointed air-conditioned guestrooms provide guests with every care and comfort. Druids Restaurant provides a perfect blend of local and classical cuisine. The Kenmare Rooms is a distinctly different hotel bar. Guests are welcome to use the leisure facilities of our sister hotel (Killarney Towers Hotel), 100m away. Underground garage parking available.

B&B from €80.00 to €160.00

FRANK MC CARTHY
GENERAL MANAGER

American Express
Mastercard
Visa

66 66

Closed 01 December - 31 January

KILLARNEY COURT HOTEL

TRALEE ROAD,
KILLARNEY,
CO. KERRY
TEL: 064-37070 FAX: 064-37060
EMAIL: stay@irishcourthotels.com
WEB: www.irishcourthotels.com

HOTEL ★★★ MAP 2 E 4

Opened in April '98 the Killarney Court Hotel is a 5 minute walk from Killarney Town Centre, only 15km from Kerry International Airport and close to 3 world famous golf courses. Our 96 en suite bedrooms boast a tasteful neo-gothic style decor. Enjoy a meal in our Seasons Restaurant with traditional Irish and international cuisine or a drink in McGillicuddys traditional Irish pub with its wonderful 'ceol, ol agus craic' atmosphere. We assure you your stay will be enjoyable.

Member of Irish Court Hotels

B&B from €35.00 to €115.00

DEREK CARROLL
GENERAL MANAGER

American Express
Diners
Mastercard
Visa

96 96

Closed 25 December

B&B rates are per person sharing per night incl. Breakfast

KILLARNEY GREAT SOUTHERN HOTEL

KILLARNEY,
CO. KERRY

TEL: 064-31262 FAX: 064-31642
EMAIL: res@killarney-gsh.com
WEB: www.gshotels.com

HOTEL ★★★★ MAP 2 E 4

The Great Southern Hotel Killarney combines old world charm and modern elegance. Originally built in 1854 this Victorian hotel was extensively renovated in 2002. Facilities include Garden Room Restaurant, Peppers à la carte restaurant, Innisfallen Spa with swimming pool, steam room, monsoon shower, hydrotherapy bath, beauty treatments. Conference facilities for 800. Bookable worldwide through UTELL Intl or Central Reservations Tel: 01-214 4800

Room Rate from €150.00 to €250.00

CONOR HENNIGAN
GENERAL MANAGER

American Express
Diners
Mastercard
Visa

☺ Weekend specials from €195.00 pps

180 180

HOTELS FEDERATION

Open All Year

KILLARNEY HEIGHTS HOTEL

CORK ROAD,
KILLARNEY,
CO. KERRY

TEL: 064-31158 FAX: 064-35198
EMAIL: khh@iol.ie

HOTEL U MAP 2 E 4

Situated 1km from Killarney Town Centre on the Cork Road, this beautiful 70 bedroomed hotel overlooks the majestic Torc & Mangerton Mountains. Open fires, olde world flagstone floors and pitch pine furnishings create a unique nostalgic atmosphere in the bars, restaurants and bistro. The hotel is easily accessed by mainline rail or by flying into Kerry Airport, just 14km away. The Killarney Heights Hotel, the perfect venue for the perfect holiday, to begin your tour of our beautiful scenic country side.

Member of Logis of Ireland

B&B from €53.50 to €76.50

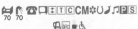

BERNARD O'RIORDAN

Diners
Mastercard
Visa

70 70

HOTELS FEDERATION

Closed 24 - 25 December

KILLARNEY LODGE

COUNTESS ROAD,
KILLARNEY,
CO. KERRY

TEL: 064-36499 FAX: 064-31070
EMAIL: klylodge@iol.ie
WEB: www.killarneylodge.net

GUESTHOUSE ★★★★ MAP 2 E 4

Welcome to Killarney Lodge, a purpose built four star guesthouse set in private walled-in gardens, yet only 2 minutes walk from Killarney town centre. The Lodge provides private parking, spacious en suite air conditioned bedrooms with all modern amenities including wheelchair facilities. Enjoy an extensive breakfast menu relax in comfortable lounges with open fires where traditional home baking is served. The Lodge has justifiably earned an outstanding reputation for quality of service, relaxed atmosphere and friendliness.

B&B from €40.00 to €65.00

CATHERINE TREACY
OWNER

American Express
Diners
Mastercard
Visa

16 16

HOTELS FEDERATION

Closed 15 November - 14 February

Room rates are per room per night

KILLARNEY PARK HOTEL

KENMARE PLACE,
KILLARNEY,
CO. KERRY
TEL: 064-35555 FAX: 064-35266
EMAIL: info@killarneyparkhotel.ie
WEB: www.killarneyparkhotel.ie

HOTEL ★★★★★ MAP 2 E 4

Superbly located on its own grounds in the heart of Killarney Town, this family owned hotel is renowned as a place of elegance laced with warmth and hospitality. The hotel offers 70 beautifully appointed guest rooms and suites each with a private entrance hall and air conditioning. 2003 will see the opening of a magnificent new health spa which will enhance the existing leisure facilities. Other guest areas include a library, drawing room, billiard room and a games room. Conference facilities available for up to 150 delegates.

B&B from €120.00 to €180.00

DONAGH DAVERN
GENERAL MANAGER

American Express
Mastercard
Visa

☺ Weekend specials from €240.00

70 70

Closed 09 - 26 December

KILLARNEY PLAZA HOTEL

KENMARE PLACE,
KILLARNEY,
CO. KERRY
TEL: 064-21100 FAX: 064-21190
EMAIL: kplaza@odonoghue-ring-hotels.com
WEB: www.odonoghue-ring-hotels.com

HOTEL U MAP 2 E 4

This premier hotel enjoys a wonderful location in downtown Killarney. All air-conditioned rooms have an atmosphere of tranquil, unhurried comfort and thoughtful colour schemes. A choice of restaurants and bars provide the perfect excuse to join us at this inviting address. The health and wellness centre allow guests to unwind and relax with a hint of luxury. Underground garage parking.

B&B from €100.00 to €230.00

FRANK MCCARTHY
GENERAL MANAGER

American Express
Diners
Mastercard
Visa

202 202

Open All Year

KILLARNEY ROYAL

COLLEGE STREET,
KILLARNEY,
CO. KERRY
TEL: 064-31853 FAX: 064-34001
EMAIL: royalhot@iol.ie
WEB: www.killarneyroyal.ie

HOTEL U MAP 2 E 4

Joe and Margaret Scally's charming Victorian townhouse recently awarded RAC 4**** grading and two ribbons for dining, is the older sister of their larger, Hayfield Manor, Cork City. Located in the heart of Killarney, it is the perfect base for golfers and touring the South West of Ireland. Each room has been individually designed, with air conditioning throughout, 24 hour personal service, elegant dining room & a local bar atmosphere.

B&B from €70.00 to €160.00

NICOLA DUGGAN
GENERAL MANAGER

American Express
Diners
Mastercard
Visa

29 29

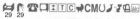
Closed 23 - 27 December

B&B rates are per person sharing per night incl. Breakfast

KILLARNEY RYAN (THE)

CORK ROAD,
KILLARNEY,
CO. KERRY
TEL: 064-31555 FAX: 064-32438
EMAIL: info@killarneyryan.com
WEB: www.ryan-hotels.com

HOTEL ★★★ MAP 2 E 4

Just 2km from Killarney Town Centre this hotel offers the perfect location for a leisure break. The extensive leisure facilities include an 18m pool, steam rooms, sauna, jacuzzi and sports hall. Many bedrooms were completely refurbished during 2002. Award winning creche and a childrens' activity programme during weekends & school holidays. Excellent dining, breakfast until noon and entertainment in the bar. Complimentary car parking. AA, RAC and Egon Ronay recommended.

B&B from €60.00 to €90.00

PAT GALVIN
GENERAL MANAGER

American Express
Diners
Mastercard
Visa

Weekend specials from €125.00

🏨🛏️☎️📺🛁🅿️🚫🍴🪑♿CMCS✷
❄️🛎️🍷☕️🎵♪PS🖥️🅰️🍺

168 168

Closed 01 January - 07 February

KILLARNEY VIEW HOUSE

MUCKROSS ROAD,
KILLARNEY,
CO. KERRY
TEL: 064-33122 FAX: 064-33122
EMAIL: killarneyviewhouse@eircom.net
WEB: www.killarneyviewhouse.com

GUESTHOUSE P MAP 2 E 4

We are very reasonably priced with a magnificent location overlooking our own river - your ideal base. Six minutes walk to Killarney Town, on main Muckross Road, at the gateway to Killarney's mountain/lake area. Wonderful river/mountain view from dining, lounge, bedroom areas. Guest lounge with open fire and tea making facilities. All 12 bedrooms en suite with TV. Large private car park. Adjacent Gleneagle Hotel with conference/leisure/entertainment complex.

B&B from €30.00 to €60.00

MARY GUERIN
PROPRIETOR

Mastercard
Visa

🏨🛏️🅿️📺TCM✷♪PS🍷

12 12

Open All Year

KILLEEN HOUSE HOTEL

AGHADOE,
LAKES OF KILLARNEY,
CO. KERRY
TEL: 064-31711 FAX: 064-31811
EMAIL: charming@indigo.ie
WEB: www.killeenhousehotel.com

HOTEL ★★★ MAP 2 E 4

The Killeen House is truly a charming little hotel. With only 23 rooms, 8 of them deluxe, it is the ideal base for touring 'God's own country', the magical Kingdom of Kerry. With our DIY Golf Pub and an elegant award-winning dining room you are assured a memorable experience. Go on, do the smart thing and call us now! We look forward to extending the 'hostility of the house' to you!

B&B from €60.00 to €120.00

GERALDINE & MICHAEL ROSNEY
OWNERS

American Express
Diners
Mastercard
Visa

Week partial board from €750.00

🏨🛏️☎️📺T❄️🍷🅿️🅰️🍷alc

23 23

Closed 01 November - 10 April

Room rates are per room per night

KINGFISHER LODGE GUESTHOUSE

LEWIS ROAD,
KILLARNEY,
CO. KERRY
TEL: 064-37131 FAX: 064-39871
EMAIL: kingfisherguesthouse@eircom.net
WEB: www.kingfisherkillarney.com

GUESTHOUSE ★★★   MAP 2 E 4

A warm welcome awaits you at Kingfisher Lodge, a family run luxury Irish Tourist Board registered guesthouse, 3 minutes walk from Killarney Town Centre with its excellent pubs, restaurants, entertainment and shopping. Our spacious bedrooms are beautifully decorated with TV, direct dial phone and hairdryers. Relaxing guest lounge with tea/coffee facilities and channel TV. Varied breakfast menu. Private parking. Tackle, drying rooms available for anglers, walkers and golfers. Tours arranged. Non-smoking guesthouse.

B&B from €30.00 to €45.00

ANN & DONAL CARROLL

Mastercard
Visa

9 9

Closed 14 December - 01 February

LAKE HOTEL

ON LAKE SHORE,
MUCKROSS ROAD, KILLARNEY,
CO. KERRY
TEL: 064-31035 FAX: 064-31902
EMAIL: lakehotel@eircom.net
WEB: www.lakehotel.com

HOTEL ★★★   MAP 2 E 4

The most beautiful location in Ireland. Set on Killarney's lake shore, open log fires, double height ceilings, relaxed and friendly atmosphere. Standard rooms, Luxury Lakeside Suites with jacuzzi, balcony and some four poster beds, plus Roman and Mediaeval Themed Rooms with jacuzzi and double steam shower. Check out our Master Roman Theme room for the ultimate treat. Just open, our adult fitness centre with outdoor hot tub on lake shore, sauna, steam room and exercise room. The Lake Hotel "A little bit of heaven on earth." See www.lakehotel.com

B&B from €50.00 to €130.00

TONY HUGGARD
MANAGING DIRECTOR

American Express
Diners
Mastercard
Visa

3 D+B&B from €164.00 Standard,
Suites from €240.00pps

70 70

Closed 09 December - 05 February

LINDEN HOUSE HOTEL

NEW ROAD,
KILLARNEY,
CO. KERRY
TEL: 064-31379 FAX: 064-31196

HOTEL ★★   MAP 2 E 4

Situated in a quiet tree lined avenue 2 minutes walk from the town centre. Linden House is under the personal supervision of Peter and Ann Knoblauch. The Linden Restaurant has an enviable reputation for good food prepared by owner chef. Year after year, guests return to Linden House, ample proof that you, too, will be made welcome and comfortable during your stay in beautiful Killarney.

B&B from €35.00 to €45.00

ANN & PETER KNOBLAUCH
OWNERS/CHEF

Mastercard
Visa

3 nights B&B & 2 Dinners from
€139.00 to €179.00 pps

20 19

Closed 15 November - 01 February

B&B rates are per person sharing per night incl. Breakfast

MCSWEENEY ARMS HOTEL

COLLEGE STREET,
KILLARNEY,
CO. KERRY
TEL: 064-31211 FAX: 064-34553
EMAIL: sales@mcsweeneyarms.com
WEB: www.mcsweeneyarms.com

HOTEL ★★★ MAP 2 E 4

McSweeney Arms Hotel is a superior 3 star hotel, situated in Killarney Town Centre, an ideal base for golfing, touring and shopping. It boasts 28 beautifully appointed bedrooms with private bathroom, TV and direct dial phone. Tonys Sandtrap Bar & Restaurant, where we boast our own lobster tank, specialises in fresh seafood and traditional Irish cuisine. Both the bar and the restaurant host a relaxed friendly atmosphere.

B&B from €55.00 to €95.00

TONY MCSWEENEY
PROPRIETOR

American Express
Diners
Mastercard
Visa

28 28

Open All Year

MOUNTAIN VIEW GUEST HOUSE

MUCKROSS ROAD,
KILLARNEY,
CO. KERRY
TEL: 064-33293 FAX: 064-37295
EMAIL: tguerin@indigo.ie

GUESTHOUSE ★★ MAP 2 E 4

Mountain View Guest House offers the highest standard of accommodation by friendly and efficient staff. All rooms are en suite with direct dial phone, tea/coffee making facilities, multi channel televisions and hairdryers. Mountain View Guest House is located only 6 minutes walk from Killarney Town Centre and 3 minutes from the Gleneagle Country Club on the famous Ring of Kerry scenic route close to Ross Castle, Ross Golf Club, Muckross House, Torc Waterfall.

B&B from €28.00 to €45.00

TIMOTHY GUERIN
OWNER

American Express
Mastercard
Visa

6 6

Closed 10 November - 10 March

MUCKROSS PARK HOTEL

LAKES OF KILLARNEY,
MUCKROSS VILLAGE, KILLARNEY,
CO. KERRY
TEL: 064-31938 FAX: 064-31965
EMAIL: muckrossparkhotel@eircom.net
WEB: www.muckrosspark.com

HOTEL ★★★★ MAP 2 E 4

Muckross Park Hotel is set in the heart of Killarney's National Park, comprising 27 superior rooms, including suites. Molly Darcy's, our award winning, traditional Irish pub and restaurant is an experience not to be missed. Situated 4km outside Killarney, and adjacent to Muckross House and Abbey. Local amenities include golf, boating, fishing, horse riding and hillwalking.

B&B from €75.00 to €100.00

PAUL CORRIDAN
GENERAL MANAGER

American Express
Diners
Mastercard
Visa

Weekend specials from €155.00

27 27

Closed 26 November - 01 February

Room rates are per room per night

MURPHYS OF KILLARNEY

COLLEGE STREET,
KILLARNEY,
CO. KERRY
TEL: 064-31294 FAX: 064-31294
EMAIL: info@murphysofkillarney.com
WEB: www.murphysofkillarney.com

GUESTHOUSE U MAP 2 E 4

Murphy's of Killarney: a town centre family run guesthouse with all rooms newly refurbished, adjacent to bus & rail stations, incorporating Lord Kenmare's renowned restaurant, Murphy's Traditional Irish Bar, where you can enjoy live Irish music and the more contemporary Squires Bar. Sean, Maire & the staff will make sure that your visit to "Murphy's" is enjoyable & memorable. Amenities include, golf, fishing, horse-riding, scenic walks and shopping. Local tours arranged. "Murphy's a sense of Tradition"

B&B from €40.00 to €55.00

SEÁN & MAIRE MURPHY
PROPRIETORS

American Express
Diners
Mastercard
Visa

🛏️ 👤 ☎️ 🖥️ ⬆️ T C 🏌️ ∪ ♫ 🔲 abc ⚓ ⛵ ♿
20 20

Closed 21 - 26 December

OAKLAND HOUSE

CORK ROAD,
KILLARNEY,
CO. KERRY
TEL: 064-37286 FAX: 064-37991
EMAIL: oakland@eircom.net

GUESTHOUSE ★★ MAP 2 E 4

Oakland House is a custom built guesthouse situated 1km from Killarney Town Centre, bus and train stations. All rooms en suite with TV and DD phone. All scenic tours arranged. Guest lounge with tea/coffee making facilities. Launderette, supermarket, post office, bureau de change, internet café approximately 100 metres. Visa, Amex, MasterCard, vouchers. Personal attention and a warm welcome awaits you at Oakland House.

B&B from €26.00 to €30.00

DAVID & NOREEN HEGARTY
PROPRIETORS

American Express
Mastercard
Visa

🛏️ 👤 ☎️ 🔲 ∪ P
8 8

IRISH
HOTELS
FEDERATION

Closed 24 - 26 December

OLD WEIR LODGE

MUCKROSS ROAD,
KILLARNEY,
CO. KERRY
TEL: 064-35593 FAX: 064-35583
EMAIL: oldweirlodge@eircom.net
WEB: www.oldweirlodge.com

GUESTHOUSE ★★★★ MAP 2 E 4

A purpose built, family-run, Tudor designed, magnificent house, conveniently located 500m from the centre of Killarney Town, within 1km of Killarney National Park. Set in landscaped garden with 30 en suite king sized bedrooms, with bath and power shower, DD phone, orthopaedic beds, multi-channel TV, hairdryer, tea/coffee facilities. 2 spacious lounges, private parking, with home baking a speciality. Friendly, relaxed atmosphere ensures an enjoyable stay. Elevator or ground floor rooms.

B&B from €38.00 to €58.00

MAUREEN & DERMOT O'DONOGHUE
PROPRIETORS

American Express
Diners
Mastercard
Visa

🛏️ 👤 ☎️ 🖥️ ⬆️ T C 🔲 C M ∪ J P 📺 ⚓
30 30

IRISH
HOTELS
FEDERATION

Closed 23 - 26 December

B&B rates are per person sharing per night incl. Breakfast

RANDLES COURT CLARION HOTEL

MUCKROSS ROAD,
KILLARNEY,
CO. KERRY
TEL: 064-35333 FAX: 064-39301
EMAIL: info@randlescourt.com
WEB: www.randlescourt.com

HOTEL ★★★★ MAP 2 E 4

This AA/RAC 4★★★★ hotel is one of
Killarney's gems. Family owned and
run, this deluxe hotel offers all the
elegance and charm of a country
house. Dating back to 1906, the
hotel has been tastefully restored with
beautiful furniture and open fires.
Checker's Restaurant is truly a unique
dining experience. The leisure club
offers the ultimate in relaxation with
its own treatment rooms. The fully
automated conference suite is ideal
for all events.

Member of Choice Hotels Ireland

B&B from €63.50 to €150.00

TOM RANDLES
GENERAL MANAGER

American Express
Diners
Mastercard
Visa

🙂 Weekend specials from €130.00

50 50

Closed 23 - 27 December

RIVERMERE

MUCKROSS ROAD,
KILLARNEY,
CO. KERRY
TEL: 064-37933 FAX: 064-37944
EMAIL: rivermereguesthouse@eircom.net

GUESTHOUSE ★★★★ MAP 2 E 4

Rivermere is a custom built, family
run 4★★★★ guesthouse within walking
distance of Lakes and National Park
and only 7 minutes walk from town
centre. All rooms are spacious with
TV, radio, direct dial phone,
orthopaedic beds, bath, power
showers, hairdryer. Rivermere is in a
delightful setting and combines luxury
with charm, elegance and serenity,
walkers' and golfers' paradise. Drying
room available. Private parking.
Choose from our delicious breakfast
menu. A warm welcome awaits you.

B&B from €35.00 to €56.00

HANNAH & ANDREW KISSANE
PROPRIETORS

Mastercard
Visa

8 8

Closed 05 November - 07 March

RIVERSIDE HOTEL

MUCKROSS ROAD,
KILLARNEY,
CO. KERRY
TEL: 064-39200 FAX: 064-39202
EMAIL: stay@riversidehotelkillarney.com
WEB: www.irishcourthotel.com

HOTEL U MAP 2 E 4

On the Muckross Road, the main road
to Killarney National Park and Lakes
and just 5 minutes from town centre.
The hotel offers 69 well appointed
bedrooms with many overlooking the
famous Flesk River against the back
drop of the beautiful MacGillycuddy
Reeks. Bedrooms are equipped with
telephone, TV, hairdryer, tea/coffee
making facilities, computer points and
24 hour room service menu. The
Bacchus Restaurant provides
traditional and international cuisine
prepared by our award winning chefs
with table d'hôte and à la carte
menus available.

Member of Irish Court Hotels

B&B from €40.00 to €180.00

UNA YOUNG
GENERAL MANAGER

American Express
Diners
Mastercard
Visa

69 69

Inet

Closed 24 - 26 December

Room rates are per room per night

ROSS HOTEL

KENMARE PLACE,
KILLARNEY,
CO. KERRY
TEL: 064-31855 FAX: 064-31139
EMAIL: ross@kph.iol.ie
WEB: www.rosshotel.ie

HOTEL ★★★ MAP 2 E 4

A warm and friendly welcome awaits you at the family owned Ross Hotel, established since 1929. Located directly within the town of Killarney, this elegant hotel has a perfect combination of old world character, superb cuisine and friendly attentive service. Private car parking and leisure facilties are available at our sister hotel, the Killarney Park Hotel. We are pleased to arrange for you golf on Kerry's premier courses, fishing, horseriding or guided walks.

B&B from €50.00 to €65.00

JANET & PÁDRAIG TREACY
PROPRIETORS

American Express
Mastercard
Visa

Weekend specials from €115.00

32 32

HOTELS

Closed 01 November - 31 December

SCOTTS GARDENS HOTEL

KILLARNEY,
CO. KERRY

TEL: 064-31060 FAX: 064-36656
EMAIL: scottskill@eircom.net
WEB: www.gleneagle-hotel.com

HOTEL ★★★ MAP 2 E 4

Newly refurbished town centre hotel with private carpark facilities. 52 3*** standard bedrooms with direct dial phone, hairdryer, satellite TV, tea/coffee facilities. Adjacent to shops, restaurants, pubs, churches and Killarney National Park. Tours, cruises, golf, and fishing arranged. Entertainment nightly July/August and on weekends during the rest of the year.

B&B from €50.00 to €90.00

MAURICE EOIN O'DONOGHUE
PROPRIETOR

American Express
Diners
Mastercard
Visa

52 52

HOTELS

Closed 24 - 26 December

SLIEVE BLOOM MANOR GUESTHOUSE

MUCKROSS ROAD,
KILLARNEY,
CO. KERRY

TEL: 064-34237 FAX: 064-35055
EMAIL: slievebloomanor@eircom.net
WEB: www.slievebloomkillarney.com

GUESTHOUSE ★★★ MAP 2 E 4

This charming 3*** guesthouse has a premier location on Muckross Road only 7 minutes walk to Killarney Town and gateway to Killarney's world famous National Park and lakes. Rooms are tastefully furnished with all facilities, varied breakfast menu available, private parking and store for bicycles etc. Local amenities include superb golf at Killarney's 2 renowned courses, horse riding and fishing. Leisure centre close by. All tours arranged. Looking forward to your visit.

B&B from €30.00 to €35.00

TERESA CLERY
PROPRIETOR

Mastercard
Visa

11 11

HOTELS

Closed 15 -30 December

B&B rates are per person sharing per night incl. Breakfast

TORC GREAT SOUTHERN HOTEL

KILLARNEY,
CO. KERRY

TEL: 064-31611 FAX: 064-31824
EMAIL: res@torc-gsh.com
WEB: www.gshotels.com

HOTEL ★★★ MAP 2 E 4

A modern 3*** hotel situated in extensive grounds in Killarney Town. It has 96 well appointed bedrooms. Leisure facilities include swimming pool, steamroom, jacuzzi, outdoor tennis court, childrens' playground. Superbly located for golfing at Killarney's championship courses. Bookable through UTELL International or Central Reservations Tel: 01-214 4800.

Room Rate from €69.00 to €165.00

FREDA DARCY
GENERAL MANAGER

American Express
Diners
Mastercard
Visa

☺ Weekend specials from €125.00

96 96

Closed 01 January - 01 April

TUSCAR LODGE

GOLF COURSE ROAD,
FOSSA, KILLARNEY,
CO. KERRY

TEL: 064-31978 FAX: 064-31978
EMAIL: tuscarlodge@eircom.net

GUESTHOUSE ★★ MAP 2 E 4

Tuscar Lodge is a family run guesthouse. The proprietress Mrs Fitzgerald and her family always ensure that the guests have an enjoyable stay. Situated in scenic surroundings overlooking Loch Lein, with a magnificent view of the Magillycuddy Reeks. With its own car park, it is very central for touring the beauty spots of West Cork and Kerry. Pony trekking, boating, fishing and mountain climbing, all nearby. Walking distance to Killarney's three championship golf courses.

B&B from €25.00 to €35.00

EILEEN FITZGERALD
PROPRIETOR

10 10

Closed 01 November - 28 February

VICTORIA HOUSE HOTEL

MUCKROSS ROAD,
KILLARNEY,
CO. KERRY

TEL: 064-35430 FAX: 064-35439
EMAIL: killarneylakes@eircom.net
WEB: www.victoriahousehotel.com

HOTEL ★★★ MAP 2 E 4

Set at the gateway to Killarney's National Park, this charming and cosy family owned and managed hotel offers the ambience of a country house, with first class personal and friendly staff. Attention to detail complements the elegantly furnished bedrooms and reception area. The restaurant maximises local produce with care and attention, where the menu changes in accordance with the seasons. Our hotel is a perfect base for exploring the sightseeing delights of Kerry.

B&B from €46.00 to €70.00

JOHN COURTNEY
PROPRIETOR

American Express
Diners
Mastercard
Visa

35 35

Closed 02 December - 01 February

Room rates are per room per night

WHITE GATES HOTEL

MUCKROSS ROAD,
KILLARNEY,
CO. KERRY
TEL: 064-31164 FAX: 064-34850
EMAIL: whitegates@iol.ie
WEB: www.whitegates.com

HOTEL ★★★ MAP 2 E 4

White Gates Hotel combines the friendliness and warmth of a family run hotel with the professional service and comfort of modern facilities. Enjoy the sparkling atmosphere of Kit Flaherty's Pub with a varied menu of quality food and traditional music nightly. White Gates Hotel is located on the Muckross Road - the main road to Killarney National Park and Muckross House.

Member of Irish Country Hotels

B&B from € 64.00 to € 77.50

BROWNE FAMILY
PROPRIETORS

American Express
Diners
Mastercard
Visa

27 27

Closed 01 December - 31 January

WOODLAWN HOUSE

WOODLAWN ROAD,
KILLARNEY,
CO. KERRY
TEL: 064-37844 FAX: 064-36116
EMAIL: awrenn@eircom.net
WEB: www.kerry-insight.com/woodlawnhouse

GUESTHOUSE ★★★ MAP 2 E 4

Old style charm and hospitality. Family run. Relaxed atmosphere. All modern conveniences. Ideally located 5 minutes walk from town centre. Near leisure centre, lakes and golf courses. Tours arranged. Private parking. Decorated with natural pine wood. Orthopaedic beds dressed in white cotton and linen. Irish and vegetarian menus. Our wholesome breakfasts include freshly squeezed orange juice, homemade preserves and bread. Early bird breakfast also available. A warm welcome assured.

B&B from € 35.00 to € 55.00

JAMES & ANNE WRENN

Mastercard
Visa

10 10

Closed 01 - 29 December

BIANCONI

KILLORGLIN,
RING OF KERRY,
CO. KERRY
TEL: 066-976 1146 FAX: 066-976 1950
EMAIL: bianconi1@eircom.net
WEB: www.bianconi-inn.com

GUESTHOUSE ★★★ MAP 1 D 4

Family run inn on the Ring of Kerry. Gateway to Dingle Peninsula, Killarney 18km. On the road to Glencar - famous for its scenery, lakes, hill walking and mountain climbing. Famous for its table. High standard of food in bar. Table d'hôte and à la carte available. 50 minutes to Waterville, Tralee & Ballybunion golf courses. 15 minutes to Dooks & Beaufort courses. 5 minutes to Killorglin course. 15 mins to Killarney course. Private access to Caragh Lake. Own boat. Mentioned by many guides.

B&B from € 42.50 to € 50.00

RAY SHEEHY
OWNER

American Express
Diners
Mastercard
Visa

15. 15

Closed 24 - 28 December

B&B rates are per person sharing per night incl. Breakfast

GROVE LODGE RIVERSIDE GUESTHOUSE

KILLARNEY ROAD,
KILLORGLIN,
CO. KERRY
TEL: 066-976 1157 FAX: 066-976 2330
EMAIL: info@grovelodge.com
WEB: www.grovelodge.com

GUESTHOUSE ★★★ MAP 1 D 4

Ideally located for all your holiday activities; golfing, fishing, hill walking, sightseeing, beaches, Ring of Kerry,Dingle, with local gourmet restaurants & pub entertainment. (5 min walk from town centre). We invite you to share your holiday with us in our newly refurbished, spacious & luxurious accommodation, situated on 3 acres of mature gardens & woodlands, fronted by the River Laune & McGillycuddy Reeks Mountains & savour our speciality gourmet breakfasts. RAC, AA ♦♦♦♦.

Member of Irish Premier Guesthouses

B&B from €40.00 to €55.00

DELIA & FERGUS FOLEY
OWNERS & MANAGERS

American Express
Diners
Mastercard
Visa

🏨 👤 ☎ 🖥 T C ❄ ♨ U J P
10 10

Closed 22 - 29 December

WESTFIELD HOUSE

KILLORGLIN,
CO. KERRY
TEL: 066-976 1909 FAX: 066-976 1996
EMAIL: westhse@iol.ie
WEB: www.westfieldhse.com

GUESTHOUSE ★★★ MAP 1 D 4

Westfield House is a family run guesthouse. All rooms are bright & spacious en suite, orthopaedic beds, direct dial telephone, TV, tea/coffee maker. Extra large family room available. We are situated on the Ring of Kerry in a quiet peaceful location only 5 minutes walk from town with panoramic views of MacGillycuddy Reeks. There are five 18 hole golf courses within 20 minutes drive. Recognised stop for many weary cyclists. Ideal location for the hillwalker and climber.

B&B from €33.00 to €45.00

LEONARD CLIFFORD
PROPRIETOR

Mastercard
Visa

🏨 👤 ☎ 🖥 T C C M ❄ 🖥 U J P 🔹 S
10 10

IRISH
HOTELS
FEDERATION

Closed 1 November - 01 March

LISTOWEL ARMS HOTEL

THE SQUARE,
LISTOWEL,
CO. KERRY
TEL: 068-21500 FAX: 068-22524
EMAIL: listowelarms@ireland.com

HOTEL ★★★ MAP 2 E 6

Ideally located in the corner of Listowels Old Square, The Listowel Arms Hotel is a haven of comfort & hospitality. An establishment with a proud tradition of fine food, a warm and intimate meeting place. Recently extended and refurbished to capitalise on its fine views of the River Feale and Listowel's race course. An ideal base to explore Listowel Town but also the nearby blue flag beaches and world famous golf courses at Ballybunion, The Ring of Kerry, Dingle Peninsula and Lakes of Killarney.

Member of Holiday Ireland Hotels

B&B from €45.00 to €150.00

KEVIN O'CALLAGHAN
DIRECTOR

American Express
Diners
Mastercard
Visa

🏨 👤 ☎ 🖥 T C ♥ C M ❄ U J ♫ P
37 37
🔹 S alc 🍴 Inet FAX

Closed 24 - 26 December

Room rates are per room per night

MOORINGS (THE)

PORTMAGEE,
CO. KERRY

TEL: 066-947 7108 FAX: 066-947 7220
EMAIL: moorings@iol.ie
WEB: www.moorings.ie

GUESTHOUSE ★★★ MAP 1 B 3

The Moorings is a family owned guesthouse & restaurant overlooking the picturesque fishing port in Portmagee. Excellent cuisine, specialising in locally caught seafood. Adjacent to the Moorings is the Bridge Bar, also run by the family, where you can enjoy a wonderful night of music, song & dance. The Moorings is central to all local amenities including angling, diving, watersports, 18 hole golf course etc. Trips to Skellig Michael can be arranged. Recently awarded RAC ◆◆◆◆.

B&B from €35.00 to €45.00

GERARD & PATRICIA KENNEDY
PROPRIETORS

Mastercard
Visa

14 14

Inet

Closed 01 November - 01 March

PARKNASILLA GREAT SOUTHERN HOTEL

SNEEM,
CO. KERRY

TEL: 064-45122 FAX: 064-45323
EMAIL: res@parknasilla-gsh.com
WEB: www.gshotels.com

HOTEL ★★★★ MAP 1 C 3

Acknowledged as one of Ireland's finest hotels, Parknasilla is a 19th century house set in 300 acres of grounds. A classically individual hotel with 84 bedrooms equipped with every modern amenity. Leisure facilities include indoor heated swimming pool, sauna, steam room, jacuzzi, hydrotherapy baths, outdoor hot tub, pony trekking, clay pigeon shooting, archery, water skiing, private 9 hole golf course - special green fees for guests. UTELL International or Central Reservations Tel; 01-214 4800.

Room Rate from €150.00 to €250.00

JIM FEENEY
GENERAL MANAGER

American Express
Diners
Mastercard
Visa

☺ Weekend specials from €200.00

84 84

Open All Year

TAHILLA COVE COUNTRY HOUSE

TAHILLA,
NEAR SNEEM,
CO. KERRY

TEL: 064-45204 FAX: 064-45104
EMAIL: tahillacove@eircom.net
WEB: www.tahillacove.com

GUESTHOUSE ★★★ MAP 1 D 3

Travel writers have described this family-run, fully licensed seashore guesthouse as the most idyllic spot in Ireland - the haunt of Irish/British dignitaries. Located on the Ring of Kerry seashore. 14 acre estate boasts mature gardens & private pier. Ideal place for a relaxing holiday/touring centre. Each room has en suite facilities, phone, TV, radio, hairdryer, iron and tea/coffee facilities. Log fires, superb views, home cooking. Take Sneem Road from Kenmare (N70).

B&B from €50.00 to €60.00

JAMES/DEIRDRE/CHAS WATERHOUSE
OWNERS

American Express
Diners
Mastercard
Visa

9 9

Closed 15 October - 01 April

B&B rates are per person sharing per night incl. Breakfast

LANTERNS HOTEL

COAST ROAD,
TARBERT,
CO. KERRY
TEL: 068-36210 FAX: 068-36553
EMAIL: reservations@thelanternshotel.ie
WEB: www.thelanternshotel.ie

HOTEL N MAP 5 E 7

The Lanterns Hotel is a superbly refurbished hotel overlooking the magnificent Shannon Estuary. An ideal tourist base we are central to world famous golf courses at Ballybunion, Adare, Killarney, Tralee and Lahinch. The Parsons Restaurant at the Lanterns Hotel has a reputation for excellent food and personal service. Under the personal supervision of owner Maureen Fitzgerald.

B&B from €32.50 to €45.00

MAUREEN FITZGERALD
OWNER

American Express
Mastercard
Visa

Midweek & weekend specials available

22 22

Inet

Closed 25 - 26 December

ABBEY GATE HOTEL

MAINE STREET,
TRALEE,
CO. KERRY
TEL: 066-712 9888 FAX: 066-712 9821
EMAIL: info@abbeygate-hotel.com
WEB: www.abbeygate-hotel.com

HOTEL ★★★ MAP 1 D 5

Welcome, the Abbey Gate Hotel is located in the heart of Tralee. All 100 rooms are spacious with full facilities. The Old Market Place Pub is Tralee's liveliest venue with great pub grub served all day and casual dining in our Bistro at night. Or try our fabulous Toscana Ristorante Italiano for the best in authentic Italian cuisine. The Abbey Gate Hotel is your gateway to the delights of Kerry.

B&B from €55.00 to €89.95

PATRICK DILLON
GENERAL MANAGER

American Express
Diners
Mastercard
Visa

Weekend specials from €99.00

100 100

Closed 24 - 26 December

BALLYGARRY HOUSE HOTEL

KILLARNEY ROAD,
TRALEE,
CO. KERRY
TEL: 066-712 3322 FAX: 066-712 7630
EMAIL: info@ballygarryhouse.com
WEB: www.ballygarryhouse.com

HOTEL ★★★★ MAP 1 D 5

Ballygarry House invites you to relax by open fires and experience an air of wellbeing. Ideally situated for Kerry's magnificent golf courses, we can be found less than 1.5km from Tralee en route to Kerry Airport and Killarney (N22). This country house boasts 46 luxurious rooms overlooking beautiful landscaped gardens. Our Riverside Restaurant offers modern and traditional cuisine in an intimate atmosphere. A warm welcome awaits you.

B&B from €65.00 to €130.00

PÁDRAIG MCGILLICUDDY
MANAGER

American Express
Mastercard
Visa

46 46

Closed 18 - 26 December

Room rates are per room per night

BALLYROE HEIGHTS HOTEL

BALLYROE,
TRALEE,
CO. KERRY

TEL: 066-712 6796 FAX: 066-712 5066

EMAIL: info@ballyroe.com
WEB: www.ballyroe.com

HOTEL ★★★ MAP 1 D 5

A modern luxurious hotel set in six and a half acres of woodland and sloping gardens. Situated 3km from Tralee Town it is the ideal base for touring, golfing or just relaxing. The views of the Sliabh Mish Mountains and Tralee Bay are breathtaking. Relax in our spectacular Summit Restaurant or Palace Bar while enjoying the view. All en suite bedrooms have satellite TV, hairdryer and tea/coffee making facilities.

B&B from € 50.00 to € 65.00

MARK SULLIVAN
GENERAL MANAGER

American Express
Mastercard
Visa

😊 Midweek specials from €146.00
(3 B&B, 2D)

25 25

IRISH HOTELS FEDERATION

Open All Year

BALLYSEEDE CASTLE HOTEL

BALLYSEEDY,
TRALEE,
CO. KERRY

TEL: 066-712 5799 FAX: 066-712 5287

EMAIL: ballyseede@eircom.net
WEB: www.ballyseedecastle.com

HOTEL ★★★ MAP 1 D 5

Ballyseede Castle Hotel is a casual, almost cosy 15th century castle on 35 hectares of parkland. The castle boasts a fine selection of continental cuisine as well as many traditional Irish dishes. Located on the main Tralee/Killarney Road within easy reach of Kerry's five magnificent golf courses, Ballybunion, Waterville, Killarney, Dooks and Barrow, the recently designed course for Tralee by Arnold Palmer. Ideally situated for touring the Ring of Kerry and Dingle Peninsula.

B&B from € 100.00 to € 150.00

BART W O'CONNOR
MANAGING DIRECTOR

Diners
Mastercard
Visa

12 12

IRISH HOTELS FEDERATION

Open All Year

BARROW COUNTRY HOUSE

WEST BARROW,
ARDFERT, TRALEE,
CO. KERRY

TEL: 066-7136437 FAX: 066-7136402

EMAIL: info@barrowhouse.com
WEB: www.barrowhouse.com

GUESTHOUSE ★★★★ MAP 1 D 5

Built in 1723, Barrow Country House is located on Barrow Harbour next to the Slieve Mish Mountains and the Dingle Peninsula. This period house has been elegantly renovated and refurbised to provide a combination of luxurious suites and deluxe rooms. Each bedroom enjoys the comfort of modern day living in a unique and tranquil setting. Golf, angling, golden beaches, sailing, award-winning restaurants and pubs close by. Former home of the Knight of Kerry.

Member of Spectra Hotel Group

B&B from € 50.00 to € 118.00

LORRAINE WALSH
MANAGER

American Express
Mastercard
Visa

16 16

IRISH HOTELS FEDERATION

Closed 20 December - 14 February

B&B rates are per person sharing per night incl. Breakfast

BRANDON COURT HOTEL

JAMES STREET,
TRALEE,
CO. KERRY
TEL: 066-712 9666 FAX: 066-712 5019
EMAIL: sales@brandonhotel.ie
WEB: www.brandonhotel.ie

HOTEL U MAP 1 D 5

The concept - quality at a fixed price. Bright, modern and spacious rooms, each en suite with tea/coffee making facilities. The room only price remains fixed whether the room is occupied by 1, 2 or 3 adults or 2 adults and 2 children. Guests at Brandon Court Hotel have full use of facilities at our sister hotel, Brandon Hotel, which is located close by.

Room Rate from €79.00 to €150.00

PETER MCDERMOTT
GENERAL MANAGER

American Express
Diners
Mastercard
Visa

49 49

Closed 01 October - 30 April

BRANDON HOTEL

PRINCES STREET,
TRALEE,
CO. KERRY
TEL: 066-712 3333 FAX: 066-712 5019
EMAIL: sales@brandonhotel.ie
WEB: www.brandonhotel.ie

HOTEL ★★★ MAP 1 D 5

Renowned, privately owned premises ideally located in the heart of Tralee Town, close to shopping and visitor attractions. The hotel offers a range of accommodation - standard rooms, deluxe rooms and suites, and a choice of bars and restaurants. It is also equipped with full leisure centre incorporating swimming pool, sauna, steamroom, jacuzzi, gymnasium and beauty treatment rooms, as well as extensive conference and banqueting facilities. Private Parking available. Tralee is accessible by mainline rail and air with Kerry Airport just 10 miles away.

B&B from €45.00 to €102.00

PETER MCDERMOTT
GENERAL MANAGER

American Express
Diners
Mastercard
Visa

182 182

IRISH
HOTELS
FEDERATION

Closed 22 - 28 December

Room rates are per room per night

BROOK MANOR LODGE

FENIT ROAD,
TRALEE,
CO. KERRY
TEL: 066-712 0406 FAX: 066-712 7552
EMAIL: brookmanor@eircom.net

GUESTHOUSE ★★★★ MAP 1 D 5

A warm welcome awaits you at our new 4**** luxurious, family-run lodge. Only minutes drive from Tralee, golden beaches and Arnold Palmer designed golf course. 30 minutes from Killarney. 40 minutes from Ballybunion. The Lodge is situated in acres of meadowlands and surrounded by a babbling brook. All our rooms are en suite with full facilities. Brook Manor Lodge is the ideal place for the perfect holiday.

Member of Premier Guesthouses

B&B from €45.00 to €65.00

MARGARET & VINCENT O'SULLIVAN
OWNERS

American Express
Mastercard
Visa

8 8

HOTELS
FEDERATION

Open All Year

COMFORT INN TRALEE

CASTLE STREET,
TRALEE,
CO. KERRY
TEL: 066-712 1877 FAX: 066-712 2273
EMAIL: comfortinntralee@eircom.net
WEB: www.choicehotelsireland.ie

HOTEL ★★★ MAP 1 D 5

Situated in the heart of bustling Tralee. The Comfort Inn Tralee exudes an air of hospitality that appeals to young and old. All rooms are en suite with multi channel TV, DD phone and tea/coffee making facilities. Enjoy live entertainment in McDades Bar and dance away in the Courthouse Nite Club. 2 minutes from the train and bus station. 15 minutes from Kerry Airport.

Member of Choice Hotels Ireland

B&B from €45.00 to €70.00

NANCY GALLAGHER
GENERAL MANAGER

American Express
Diners
Mastercard
Visa

45 45

HOTELS
FEDERATION

Closed 24 - 26 December

GLENDUFF HOUSE

KIELDUFF,
TRALEE,
CO. KERRY
TEL: 066-713 7105 FAX: 066-713 7099
EMAIL: glenduffhouse@eircom.net
WEB: www.tralee-insight.com/glenduff

GUESTHOUSE ★★★ MAP 1 D 5

Enter the old world charm of the 19th century in our family run period house set on 6 acres with mature gardens. Refurbished to give the comforts of the modern day, yet keeping its original character with antiques & paintings. Personal attention assured. Relax & enjoy a drink in our friendly bar. Also self catering cottages in courtyard. Ideally situated for golf and sports amenities. From Tralee take route to racecourse off N21 at Clash Roundabout, continue for 4.5 miles.

Member of Premier Guesthouses

B&B from €36.00 to €56.00

SHEILA SUGRUE
OWNER

Mastercard
Visa

5 5

HOTELS
FEDERATION

Closed 02 November - 16 March

B&B rates are per person sharing per night incl. Breakfast

GRAND HOTEL

DENNY STREET,
TRALEE,
CO. KERRY
TEL: 066-712 1499 FAX: 066-712 2877
EMAIL: info@grandhoteltralee.com
WEB: www.grandhoteltralee.com

HOTEL ★★★ MAP 1 D 5

The Grand Hotel is a 3*** hotel situated in Tralee Town Centre. Established in 1928, its open fires, ornate ceilings & mahogany furnishings offer guests old world charm in comfortable surroundings. All our rooms are equipped with direct dial phone, computer point, satellite TV and tea/coffee welcoming trays. Residents can avail of green fee reductions at Tralee Golf Club. Also reduced rates to the fabulous Aqua Dome Waterworld complex. Family rooms are available at discounted rates.

B&B from €45.00 to €85.00

DICK BOYLE
GENERAL MANAGER

American Express
Diners
Mastercard
Visa

☺ Weekend special from €120.00

44 44
alc inet

IRISH HOTELS FEDERATION

Closed 24 - 27 December

MEADOWLANDS HOTEL

OAKPARK,
TRALEE,
CO. KERRY
TEL: 066-718 0444 FAX: 066-718 0964
EMAIL: medlands@iol.ie
WEB: www.meadowlands-hotel.com

HOTEL ★★★★ MAP 1 D 5

A charming and intimate hotel, set in a tranquil corner of Tralee, on its own beautiful landscaped gardens. This luxurious hotel comprises 58 superbly appointed rooms, including suites. Our award winning restaurant specialises in the freshest of locally-caught seafood and shellfish cuisine. State of the art conference centre. Ideal base for golfing enthusiasts and touring the Dingle Peninsula, The Ring of Kerry. Experience an experience.

Member of Platinum Hotels

B&B from €50.00 to €150.00

CAROL KENNELLY
GENERAL MANAGER

American Express
Diners
Mastercard
Visa

☺ Weekend specials from €145.00

58 58
alc

IRISH HOTELS FEDERATION

Closed 24 - 26 December

OAKLEY HOUSE

BALLYMULLEN,
TRALEE,
CO. KERRY
TEL: 066-712 1727 FAX: 066-712 1727
EMAIL: info@oakleyguesthouse.com
WEB: www.oakleyguesthouse.com

GUESTHOUSE ★★ MAP 1 D 5

Spacious period house with old world charm and character. Situated on road to Dingle, Killorglin and Ring of Kerry. On N70 Road, turn right at Ballymullen Roundabout, right at next junction, situated on left. Situated on the outskirts of Tralee Town. Overlooking Slieve Mish Mountains. Ideal touring base. 8 minutes walk from town centre, National Folk Theatre, Medieval Experience. 10 minutes walk from Aqua Dome. Private car park. Convenient to beaches, angling, golf, horseriding and pony trekking. A cead mile failte awaits you.

B&B from €30.00 to €32.00

MICHAEL & PHILOMENA BENNIS
PROPRIETORS

Mastercard
Visa

☺ Midweek specials from €84.00

7 7

IRISH HOTELS FEDERATION

Closed 01 - 31 December

Room rates are per room per night

TRALEE TOWNHOUSE

HIGH STREET,
TRALEE,
CO. KERRY

TEL: 066-718 1111 FAX: 066-718 1112
EMAIL: townhouse@iolfree.ie
WEB: www.traleetownhouse.com

GUESTHOUSE ★★★ MAP 1 D 5

Centrally located beside all of Tralee's visitor attractions; - Siamsa Tire, Aqua Dome, Tralee Superbowl, Geraldine Experience, Kerry County Museum, Blennerville Windmill, Steam Train and the new Tralee Marina. Local amenities include - for the golf enthusiast, the world renowned Tralee & Ballybunion Golf Courses are only a few miles away. 2 excellent 9 hole courses are within 1 mile of the town centre. Fishing, horse riding, hillwalking, sports centre with indoor pool, etc. 3*** AA.

B&B from €29.50 to €48.00

ELEANOR COLLINS
MANAGER

Mastercard
Visa

19 19

HOTELS
FEDERATION

Closed 24 - 28 December

BAY VIEW HOTEL

WATERVILLE,
CO. KERRY

TEL: 066-947 4122 FAX: 066-947 4504
EMAIL: bayviewwaterville@eircom.net
WEB: www.bayviewwaterville.com

HOTEL CR MAP 1 B 3

The Bay View Hotel has old world charm with beautiful spacious bedrooms with front rooms facing the Atlantic. On the Ring of Kerry in the middle of the village of Waterville the hotel is an ideal location for exploring the peninsula with its breathtaking scenery and archaeological sites. Make sure you visit the Sceilig Rock.

B&B from €30.00 to €58.00

MICHAEL O'SHEA
MANAGER

American Express
Mastercard
Visa

69 69

HOTELS
FEDERATION

Closed 01 November - 01 March

BROOKHAVEN COUNTRY HOUSE

NEW LINE ROAD,
WATERVILLE,
CO. KERRY

TEL: 066-947 4431 FAX: 066-947 4724
EMAIL: brookhaven@esatclear.ie
WEB: www.stayatbrookhaven.com

GUESTHOUSE ★★★★ MAP 1 B 3

New purpose built 4**** country house, overlooking the Atlantic Ocean, and the Waterville golf course. Luxury spacious en suite rooms, with all modern facilities. Centrally located to all amenities, e.g. golf, fishing, (lake and sea) beaches, surfing, horse riding, walking Kerry Way, cycling, Skellig Islands and gourmet restaurants. Private parking and drying room available for golfers, anglers and walkers. On Ring of Kerry route, surrounded by colourful gardens. AA & RAC ♦♦♦♦, plus repeated Sparkling Diamond Accolades.

B&B from €35.00 to €60.00

MARY CLIFFORD
PROPRIETOR

5 5

Inet

HOTELS
FEDERATION

Closed 01 January - 01 March

B&B rates are per person sharing per night incl. Breakfast

BUTLER ARMS HOTEL

WATERVILLE,
CO. KERRY

TEL: 066-947 4144 FAX: 066-947 4520
EMAIL: reservations@butlerarms.com
WEB: www.butlerarms.com

HOTEL ★★★★ MAP 1 B 3

This charming hotel, on the scenic Ring of Kerry, has been run by 4 generations of the Huggard Family. Tastefully furnished bedrooms, many with magnificent seaviews, cosy lounges, award-winning restaurant specializing in local seafood (AA 2 Red Rosettes) and the Fishermens Bar with its cosmopolitan ambience. Only 1 mile from Waterville's Championship Golf Links. Renowned salmon & seatrout fishing, sandy beaches, horseriding, hill-walking.

Member of Manor House Hotels

B&B from €89.00 to €120.00

MARY & PETER HUGGARD
PROPRIETORS

American Express
Diners
Mastercard
Visa

☺ Weekend specials from €150.00

40 40

Closed 20 October - 13 April

LAKELANDS FARM GUESTHOUSE

LAKE ROAD,
WATERVILLE,
CO. KERRY

TEL: 066-947 4303 FAX: 066-947 4678
EMAIL: lakelands@eircom.net
WEB: www.kerrygems.ie/lakelands/

GUESTHOUSE ★★★ MAP 1 B 3

Luxury family run guesthouse in unique location set on 100 acre estate on the south shore of Europe's best free salmon and sea trout lake. Smoking and non smoking lounges. Comfortable spacious en suite bedrooms with all mod cons, some with balcony or jacuzzi. Proprietor professional angler with 10 motor boats. Private pools on River Inny. Convenient to Waterville Golf Course. For the golf enthusiast we have a complimentary 250 yards practice range.

B&B from €30.00 to €40.00

FRANK & ANNE DONNELLY
PROPRIETORS

Mastercard
Visa

☺ Week partial board from €420.00

12 12

Closed 25 December

SMUGGLERS INN

CLIFF ROAD,
WATERVILLE,
CO. KERRY

TEL: 066-947 4330 FAX: 066-947 4422
EMAIL: thesmugglersinn@eircom.net
WEB: www.welcome.to/thesmugglersinn

GUESTHOUSE ★★★ MAP 1 B 3

The Smugglers Inn, a family run inn with old world charm and character, quiet location on 2km sandy beach. Adjacent to Waterville Golf Course, near lake and sea fishing facilities and sporting activities. Very high standard in our gourmet seafood restaurant, meals prepared by Harry Hunt, son Henry and daughter Lucy. Dining room under supervision of his wife Lucille. Comfortable en suite accommodation. Recommended by many good food guides. Breathtaking sea views and spectacular sunsets.

B&B from €38.00 to €55.00

LUCILLE & HARRY HUNT
PROPRIETORS

American Express
Diners
Mastercard
Visa

☺ 3 B&B + 3 Dinners from €225.00

17 17

Closed 31 October - 01 March

Room rates are per room per night

SHANNON
Romantic and Exciting

Your holiday in the Shannon Region can be as active or as placid as you choose. Whichever you choose, you are guaranteed relaxation and enjoyment. All the ingredients are there: the towering cliffs and golden beaches of Clare and North Kerry; the enigmatic rockscapes of the Burren; the gentle beauty of the rolling Slieve Bloom Mountains in South Offaly; Tipperary's fertile pastures and the woodland estates in the heart of County Limerick. And, of course, the mighty Shannon River, which has bestowed its riches on the surrounding countryside and glories in its beauty.

This is one of the few remaining places on earth where clean, unpolluted air is taken for granted.

You have the space to breathe, to refresh your spirit a universe away from frenetic and crowded cities.

There is a sense of timelessness aided by the many physical reminders of Ireland's turbulent past. Castles, forts and ancient churches, spanning centuries of history, abound, many have been lovingly restored.

At the famous Bunratty Castle, visitors can slip back in time and take part in a 15th century Mediaeval Banquet of romance and merriment. The Bunratty Folk Park, in the castle grounds, accurately recreates Irish village life at the turn of the century.

Sporting facilities, in contrast, are very much up to date. Imagine golfing in a magnificent, scenic setting or fishing some of the most productive and versatile fishing waters in Europe. Take to the saddle on horse-back and the countryside is yours.

If boating is your pleasure, the possibilities are, literally, limitless.

There are many elements to a really memorable holiday and the Shannon Region can provide them all. One of the most important is the feeling of being really welcome, of being valued. This intangible but very real feature of a Shannon holiday will be immediately evident in the sense of fun which you will encounter and an eagerness to treat you as an honoured guest.

In Ireland, enjoyment is an art form. Go to one of the many festivals in the Shannon Region and you will experience the art at its best. Entertainment, spontaneous or organised, is everywhere, so too is good food and good company. For further information contact: Tourist Information Office, Arthur's Quay, Limerick. Tel: 061 317522. Fax: 061 317939.
Visit our website: www.shannon-dev.ie/tourism

BALLYVAUGHAN LODGE

BALLYVAUGHAN,
CO. CLARE

TEL: 065-707 7292 FAX: 065-707 7287
EMAIL: ballyvau@iol.ie
WEB: www.ballyvaughanlodge.com

GUESTHOUSE ★★★ MAP 6 F 10

Located in the heart of Ballyvaughan, a small fishing village overlooking Galway Bay. A custom built modern guesthouse, dedicated to the comfort and relaxation of our guests. Each room is en suite having TV, direct dial phone, tea/coffee making facilities, etc. Allow us to plan your carefree days in the most unspoilt natural environment imaginable, The Burren, including Neolithic caves, sea fishing, hill walking, cycling, Cliffs of Moher and the Aran Islands.

B&B from €28.00 to €38.00

PAULINE BURKE
OWNER

Mastercard

Visa

🛏 🐾 ☎ 🖥 TC 🍴 CM ✿ ∪ J P S 🕳
11 11

Closed 25 - 26 December

CAPPABHAILE HOUSE

BALLYVAUGHAN,
CO. CLARE

TEL: 065-707 7260 FAX: 065-707 7300
EMAIL: cappabhaile@oceanfree.net
WEB: www.cappabhaile.com

GUESTHOUSE ★★★ MAP 6 F 9

Relax, enjoy the peace & quiet, luxury & comfort and a warm family welcome at Cappabhaile House. All rooms generously sized with private bathrooms. We have scenic views of the Burren Mountains, Newtown Castle & Ailwee Cave. We have a private carpark, pitch & putt course, games room & the Burren Gallery, all FREE to our guests. Courtesy bus to facilitate hill walking, beaches, nature trails, pubs & restaurants. Perfect base for touring The Burren, Aran Islands, Galway and Connemara.

B&B from €25.00 to €39.00

MARGARET & CONOR FAHY
PROPRIETORS

Mastercard

Visa

☺ Walks & Archaeological tours from €50.00

🛏 🐾 ☎ 🖥 TC 🍴 CM ✿ ∪ J P
8 8

S ⬛ Inet

Closed 30 November - 01 March

DRUMCREEHY HOUSE

BALLYVAUGHAN,
CO. CLARE

TEL: 065-707 7377 FAX: 065-707 7379
EMAIL: B&B@drumcreehyhouse.com
WEB: www.drumcreehyhouse.com

GUESTHOUSE ★★★ MAP 6 F 10

Delightful country style house overlooking Galway Bay and the surrounding Burren landscape. Open fires, antique furnishings plus a friendly and personal service by conscientious hosts Armin and Bernadette who help to make your stay both enjoyable and memorable. Tastefully decorated rooms, all en suite and equipped with TV and direct dial phone. Extensive breakfast menu and simple country style cooking in a relaxed and homely atmosphere. Ideally located for touring Clare, Kerry and Galway.

B&B from €28.00 to €40.00

A & B MOLONEY-GREFKES
PROPRIETORS

Mastercard

Visa

🛏 🐾 ☎ 🖥 TC 🍴 CM ✿ ∪ J P 🕳 S 📺
10 10

Open All Year

Room rates are per room per night

GREGANS CASTLE HOTEL

THE BURREN,
BALLYVAUGHAN,
CO. CLARE
TEL: 065-707 7005 FAX: 065-707 7111
EMAIL: res@gregans.ie
WEB: www.gregans.ie

HOTEL ★★★★ MAP 6 F 10

4**** luxury hotel amid splendid Burren mountain scenery, overlooking Galway Bay. Country house comforts, turf fires, tranquillity, no TV in rooms. Award winning gardens, food, service, accommodations. Individually designed superior rooms/suites. Nearby ocean swimming, horse riding, hillwalking. Golf at Lahinch. Halfway between Kerry and Connemara using ferry. RAC Blue Ribbon winner. AA Red Stars award. 1 hour to Shannon Airport. Excellence of private ownership for 27 years. On-line booking available on website.

Member of Ireland's Blue Book

B&B from € 77.50 to € 99.00

SIMON HADEN
MANAGER & DIRECTOR

American Express
Mastercard
Visa

☺ 3 days half board

22 22

Closed 18 November - 13 February

HYLAND'S BURREN HOTEL

BALLYVAUGHAN,
CO. CLARE
TEL: 065-707 7037 FAX: 065-707 7131
EMAIL: hylandsburren@eircom.net
WEB: www.hylandsburren.com

HOTEL ★★★ MAP 6 F 10

Hyland's Burren Hotel is a charming hotel, dating back to the 18th Century and now tastefully modernised. It is located in the picturesque village of Ballyvaughan, nestling in the unique Burren landscapes of County Clare. Experience bygone charm with the best of modern facilities, open turf fires, informal bars and restaurants specialising in the finest local seafood. An ideal base for golfing and walking enthusiasts and truly an artists haven.

Member of Irish Country Hotels

B&B from € 45.00 to € 66.00

DOROTHY COSTELLO
MANAGER

American Express
Diners
Mastercard
Visa

☺ Weekend specials from €115.00

30 30

Closed 22 - 26 December

RUSHEEN LODGE

BALLYVAUGHAN,
CO. CLARE
TEL: 065-707 7092 FAX: 065-707 7152
EMAIL: rusheen@iol.ie
WEB: www.rusheenlodge.com

GUESTHOUSE ★★★★ MAP 6 F 10

Rusheen Lodge is a 4****, AA ♦♦♦♦ and RAC ♦♦♦♦ highly acclaimed luxury guest house nestling in the Burren mountains. The Lodge provides elegant and tastefully designed en suite bedrooms, suites, dining room and residents' lounge ensuring a comfortable and relaxing stay. Recent winner Guesthouse of the Year Jameson Guide, RAC Sparkling Diamond, previous winner RAC Small Hotel & Guesthouse of the Year. Ideally located for touring the Shannon Region, Aran Islands and Connemara. Non Smoking.

B&B from € 35.00 to € 45.00

KAREN MCGANN
PROPRIETOR

Mastercard
Visa

☺ Midweek specials from €103.00

9 9

Closed 18 November - 13 February

B&B rates are per person sharing per night incl. Breakfast

BUNRATTY CASTLE HOTEL

BUNRATTY,
CO. CLARE

TEL: 061-478700 FAX: 061-364891
EMAIL: info@bunrattycastlehotel.com
WEB: www.bunrattycastlehotel.com

HOTEL ★★★ MAP 6 G 7

The new Bunratty Castle Hotel is a 3*** Georgian hotel. Situated in the centre of Bunratty Village overlooking the historic Bunratty Castle and just across the road from Ireland's oldest pub, Durty Nellies. The rooms have been tastefully decorated in the traditional style. All rooms have air conditioning, satellite TV and have every modern comfort. Relax in Kathleens Pub and Restaurant and enjoy great food. We welcome you to experience the warmth and hospitality here.

B&B from €88.00 to €145.00

DEIRDRE WELCH
GENERAL MANAGER

American Express
Diners
Mastercard
Visa

79 79

Closed 24 - 26 December

BUNRATTY GROVE

CASTLE ROAD,
BUNRATTY,
CO. CLARE

TEL: 061-369579 FAX: 061-369561
EMAIL: bunrattygrove@eircom.net
WEB: http://homepage.eircom.net/~bunrattygrove

GUESTHOUSE ★★★ MAP 6 G 7

Bunratty Grove is a purpose built luxurious guest house. This guesthouse is located within 3 minutes drive from Bunratty Castle and Folk Park and 10 minutes from Shannon Airport. Fishing, golfing, historical interests within a short distance. Ideally located for tourists arriving or departing Shannon Airport. Bookings for Bunratty and Knappogue Banquets taken on request. All rooms en suite with multi-channel TV, hair dryer, tea/coffee facilities and direct dial phone.

B&B from €35.50 to €46.00

PETER & PATSY GOLDEN
OWNERS

Mastercard
Visa

9 9

Closed 01 November - 31 March

BUNRATTY MANOR HOTEL

BUNRATTY,
CO. CLARE

TEL: 061-707984 FAX: 061-360588
EMAIL: bunrattymanor@eircom.net
WEB: www.bunrattymanor.net

HOTEL ★★★ MAP 6 G 7

A Manor House hotel designed to reflect the ambience and comforts associated with elegant living. Beautiful gardens, superb classical Italian cuisine prepared by David (including vegetarian), renowned for friendliness, comfort, tranquillity and hospitality. Bunratty Village - excellent restaurants, fun pubs, the Castle and shopping - is two minutes walk! Within easy reach of eleven Championship golf courses and breathtaking scenery. Tea/coffee facilities, ice, TV and ISDN.

B&B from €55.00 to €63.00

GERRY HUGHES
HOST

American Express
Diners
Mastercard
Visa

14 14

Closed 31 October - 01 November

Room rates are per room per night

BUNRATTY VIEW GUESTHOUSE

CRATLOE,
NEAR BUNRATTY,
CO. CLARE
TEL: 061-357352 FAX: 061-357491
EMAIL: bunrattyview@eircom.net

GUESTHOUSE ★★★ MAP 6 G 7

Bunratty View is a 3*** guesthouse located 10 minutes from Shannon Airport, 2 km from Bunratty Castle. Bedrooms have private bathroom, satellite TV, direct dial telephone, hair dryer, tea/coffee facilities, orthopaedic beds. Ideal for tourists arriving or departing Shannon Airport. Excellent location for touring Cliffs of Moher, Ailwee Caves, Lakes of Killaloe. Banquets for Bunratty and Knappogue booked on request. Recommended by leading guides for accommodation and hospitality.

B&B from €27.00 to €40.00

JOE & MAURA BRODIE
PROPRIETORS

American Express
Mastercard
Visa

☺ Midweek specials from €84.00

6   6

Open All Year

BUNRATTY WOODS COUNTRY HOUSE

LOW ROAD,
BUNRATTY,
CO. CLARE
TEL: 061-369689 FAX: 061-369454
EMAIL: bunratty@iol.ie
WEB: www.iol.ie/~bunratty

GUESTHOUSE ★★★ MAP 6 G 7

Bunratty Woods is a 3*** luxurious guesthouse situated in the old grounds of Bunratty Castle (2 minutes drive) to Bunratty Castle and Folk Park and the renowned Durty Nellies Pub. All rooms are en suite with direct dial phone, TV, tea/coffee making facilities and hair dryer. Magnificent mountain views. Bunratty Woods is furnished with style and taste of a bygone era - featuring items such as a settle bed and a famine pot and many, many other items from yesteryear. Recommended by Frommer.

B&B from €32.00 to €36.00

MAUREEN & PADDY O'DONOVAN
OWNERS

Diners
Mastercard
Visa

15   15

Closed 10 November - 15 March

COURTYARD (THE)

BUNRATTY VILLAGE,
CO. CLARE

TEL: 061-361444 FAX: 061-364498
EMAIL: info@bunrattycourtyard.com
WEB: www.bunrattycourtyard.com

GUESTHOUSE P MAP 6 G 7

The Courtyard is the ideal location for convenience and comfort when visiting the Mid West region. We are adjacent to a variety of pubs and restaurants and of course the Medieval Castle and Folk Park. Shannon Airport is just 4 miles away. With regular bus and taxi service. For the golf enthusiast we have a variety of top class courses available locally. Recommended by Michelin.

B&B from €32.00 to €48.00

MICHAEL & MARY WALSH
PROPRIETORS

American Express
Mastercard
Visa

11   11

Open All Year

B&B rates are per person sharing per night incl. Breakfast

FITZPATRICK BUNRATTY

BUNRATTY,
CO. CLARE

TEL: 061-361177 FAX: 061-471252
EMAIL: info@bunratty.fitzpatricks.com
WEB: www.fitzpatrickhotels.com

HOTEL U MAP 6 G 7

Situated in wooded grounds in Bunratty Village against the backdrop of the medieval castle and folk park. Discover village life with lively pubs, colourful restaurants and shops. 4 miles from Shannon. Hotel facilities include excellent bar and restaurant, fitness centre and rooms with bath, satellite TV and direct dial phone. Four 18 hole championship golf courses within easy drive. Horse riding available locally. The ideal choice for your stay in the Mid West.

B&B from €99.00 to €126.00

DENIS DEERY
GENERAL MANAGER

American Express
Diners
Mastercard
Visa

Weekend specials from €100.00

115 115

Closed 24 - 26 December

ARAN VIEW HOUSE HOTEL & RESTAURANT

COAST ROAD,
DOOLIN,
CO. CLARE

TEL: 065-707 4061 FAX: 065-707 4540
EMAIL: bookings@aranview.com
WEB: www.aranview.com

HOTEL ★★★ MAP 5 E 9

A Georgian house built in 1736, has a unique position commanding panoramic views of the Aran Islands, the Burren region and the Cliffs of Moher. Situated on 100 acres of farmland, Aran View echoes spaciousness, comfort and atmosphere in its restaurant and bar. Menus are based on the best of local produce, fish being a speciality. All rooms with private bathroom, colour TV and direct dial phone. Visitors are assured of a warm and embracing welcome at the Aran View House Hotel.

B&B from €50.00 to €80.00

THERESA & JOHN LINNANE
PROPRIETORS

American Express
Diners
Mastercard
Visa

Weekend specials from €120.00

19 19

Closed 31 October - 18 April

BALLINALACKEN CASTLE COUNTRY HOUSE & RESTAURANT

COAST ROAD,
DOOLIN,
CO. CLARE

TEL: 065-707 4025 FAX: 065-707 4025
EMAIL: ballinalackencastle@eircom.net
WEB: www.ballinalackencastle.com

HOTEL ★★★ MAP 5 E 9

A romantic peaceful oasis steeped in history and ambience offering the most spectacular views of the Cliffs of Moher, Aran Islands, Atlantic Ocean & Connemara Hills. Built in 1840 as the home of Lord O'Brien. Family members radiate a warm friendly welcome. Award winning chef Frank Sheedy (son-in-law) makes dining here an experience to remember. Peat and log fires add to the cosy atmosphere. Ideal base for exploring Clare. Recommended by Egon Ronay, Michelin, Fodor, Frommer. Charming Hotels of Ireland. New York Times, Washington Post, London Times.

B&B from €50.00 to €100.00

MARY AND DENIS O'CALLAGHAN
PROPRIETORS

American Express
Diners
Mastercard
Visa

12 12

Closed 31 October - 19 April

Room rates are per room per night

CULLINAN'S SEAFOOD RESTAURANT & GUESTHOUSE

DOOLIN,
CO. CLARE

TEL: 065-707 4183 FAX: 065-707 4239
EMAIL: cullinans@eircom.net
WEB: www.cullinansdoolin.com

GUESTHOUSE ★★★ MAP 5 E 9

Cullinan's Restaurant and Guesthouse, centrally located in the heart of Doolin provides spacious and elegant bedrooms, all en suite with tea/coffee making facilities, direct dial phone, hairdryers and a comfortable TV lounge. Idyllic setting with highly acclaimed restaurant overlooking the Aille River. Imaginative menus are carefully chosen by the chef/owner, specialising in the freshest of locally caught seafood. Natural stone and wood combined gives Cullinan's a cozy, comfortable atmosphere.

B&B from €25.00 to €40.00

CAROL & JAMES CULLINAN
OWNERS

Mastercard
Visa

🛏 🐾 ☎ T C CM ✲ ∪ ⌒ P Y abc 🛁
6   6

Closed 23 - 26 December

DOONMACFELIM HOUSE

DOOLIN,
CO. CLARE

TEL: 065-707 4503 FAX: 065-707 4129

WEB: www.kingsway.ie/doonmacfelim

GUESTHOUSE ★★★ MAP 5 E 9

Doonmacfelim House is a 3*** guesthouse, situated on our farm in the village of Doolin, famous for traditional Irish music. Excellent location for visiting Cliffs of Moher, boat to Aran Islands, visiting prehistoric ruins. Its geology, flora, caves, archaeology and history set it apart as a place of mystery and beauty. All rooms en suite, with hairdryers, direct dial telephone. Shannon Airport & Killimer Car Ferry 70km. Hard tennis court, rackets supplied.

B&B from €28.00 to €34.00

MAJELLA & FRANK MOLONEY
OWNERS

Mastercard
Visa

🛏 🐾 ☎ ⌨ T C ➻ ✲ 🔍 ∪ ⌒ 🛁
8   8

Closed 22 - 28 December

ARDILAUN GUESTHOUSE

GALWAY ROAD,
ENNIS,
CO. CLARE

TEL: 065-682 2311 FAX: 065-684 3989
EMAIL: purcells.ennis@eircom.net
WEB: www.ardilaun.com

GUESTHOUSE ★★★ MAP 6 F 8

Ardilaun is a modern, architect designed 3*** guesthouse overlooking the River Fergus and Ballyallia Lake amenity area. Most rooms enjoy panoramic views of the river and all are superbly decorated with en suite, phone, TV, hairdryer, tea and coffee facilities. Our gymnasium, sauna and fishing facilities also overlook the river and are available to guests only. Ardilaun is just 2 mins drive to the fabulous new Ennis swimming pool. Situated 20 mins drive from Shannon Airport on N18 and is an ideal touring base for Clare, Limerick and Galway.

B&B from €32.50 to €35.00

ANNE PURCELL
PROPRIETRESS

Mastercard
Visa

🛏 🐾 ☎ ⌨ T C ➻ ✲ 🔥 © ∪ ⌒ P S 🛁
10   10

FAX

Closed 23 - 27 December

B&B rates are per person sharing per night incl. Breakfast

Room rates are per room per night

CILL EOIN HOUSE

KILDYSERT CROSS,
CLARE ROAD, ENNIS,
CO. CLARE
TEL: 065-684 1668 FAX: 065-684 1669
EMAIL: cilleoin@iol.ie
WEB: www.euroka.com/cilleoin

GUESTHOUSE ★★★ MAP 6 F 8

Cill Eoin, named after the nearby 13th century Abbey, is a 3*** guesthouse on the main tourist route to the west coast of Clare, with its unparalleled beauty in the scenery of the desolate Burren and the majestic vistas, that are the Cliffs of Moher. Golf, with a links and three courses nearby, is abundantly available. Horse riding, fishing and many other pastimes are well provided for in the area. Call and see us soon, you will feel at home.

B&B from €32.00 to €37.00

PAT & BRIDGET GLYNN LUCEY

American Express
Diners
Mastercard
Visa

14 14

Closed 24 December - 02 January

FOUNTAIN COURT

LAHINCH ROAD,
ENNIS,
CO. CLARE
TEL: 065-682 9845 FAX: 065-684 5030
EMAIL: kyran@fountain-court.com
WEB: www.fountain-court.com

GUESTHOUSE ★★★ MAP 6 F 8

Peaceful rural setting yet only 4 minutes drive to Ennis. Superb bedrooms with king sized beds, TV, tea making facilities, Hi Fi, bath and power shower. Family run with delicious breakfasts. Beautiful reception rooms and the personal service of the owners make Fountain Court the ideal base to tour The Burren National Park, Cliffs of Moher and Bunratty Castle and Folk Park. Golf, fishing and horse riding all within easy reach. Shannon Airport 15km. Fax & Internet access from all rooms.

Member of Premier Guesthouses

B&B from €32.00 to €50.00

KYRAN & BREED CARR

Mastercard
Visa

☺ Midweek specials from €95.00

12 12

Inet FAX

Closed 20 December - 07 January

MAGOWNA HOUSE HOTEL

INCH,
KILMALEY, ENNIS,
CO. CLARE
TEL: 065-683 9009 FAX: 065-683 9258
EMAIL: info@magowna.com
WEB: www.magowna.com

HOTEL ★★★ MAP 6 F 8

We are a beautifully located, family managed, country house hotel with extensive gardens and lovely views. Ideal for an active or purely relaxing break. Close to excellent golf courses, angling and walks. (Mid-Clare Way 1.5km) Shannon Airport, Cliffs of Moher, The Burren, Doolin, Bunratty Castle, Killimer Car Ferry to Kerry within easy reach. Conference room (capacity 200). Enjoy hospitality, comfort, good food and a genuine welcome in the heart of County Clare.

Member of Irish Family Hotels

B&B from €44.00 to €50.00

GAY MURPHY
PROPRIETOR

American Express
Diners
Mastercard
Visa

☺ Weekend specials from €110.00

10 10

Closed 24 - 26 December

B&B rates are per person sharing per night incl. Breakfast

OLD GROUND HOTEL

O'CONNELL STREET,
ENNIS,
CO. CLARE

TEL: 065-682 8127 FAX: 065-682 8112
EMAIL: reservations@oldgroundhotel.ie
WEB: www.flynnhotels.com

HOTEL ★★★ MAP 6 F 8

Ivy clad manor house dates to the 18th century. The hotel offers 83 de luxe rooms and superior suites. Our elegant formal dining room is renowned for excellent cuisine. Visit our recently opened Town Hall Café. The hotel is located in the heart of Ennis, 20 minutes drive from Shannon Airport, close to the Cliffs of Moher, The Burren, Bunratty Castle and many superb challenging golf courses, such as Doonbeg and Lahinch. GDS Access LE. Online reservations at www.flynnhotels.com.

Member of Flynn Hotels

B&B from €52.50 to €95.00

ALLEN FLYNN, MANAGING DIR
MARY GLEESON, GEN MANAGER

American Express
Diners
Mastercard
Visa

☺ Weekend specials from €115.00

83 83

S ⓐ alc

IRISH HOTELS FEDERATION

Closed 24 - 26 December

QUEENS HOTEL

ABBEY STREET,
ENNIS,
CO. CLARE

TEL: 065-682 8963 FAX: 065-682 8628
EMAIL: stay@irishcourthotels.com
WEB: www.irishcourthotels.com

HOTEL ★★★ MAP 6 F 8

The Queen's Town Centre Hotel is an ideal base for touring Bunratty Castle and Folk Park, Cliffs of Moher and The Burren. All bedrooms are en suite, with satellite TV, video, radio, phone, hairdryer, tea/coffee. Overlooking the 13th century Franciscan Abbey from which Ennis takes its origin. Adjoins the famous Cruise's Pub and Restaurant built circa 1658. Renowned for its authentic old world charm, superb home cooked Fayre and traditional music nightly. Shannon International Airport 15km.

Member of Irish Court Hotels

B&B from €35.00 to €115.00

MAURICE WALSH
GENERAL MANAGER

American Express
Diners
Mastercard
Visa

50 50

alc

IRISH HOTELS FEDERATION

Closed 25 December

Room rates are per room per night

TEMPLE GATE HOTEL

THE SQUARE,
ENNIS,
CO. CLARE
TEL: 065-682 3300 FAX: 065-682 3322
EMAIL: info@templegatehotel.com
WEB: www.templegatehotel.com

HOTEL ★★★ MAP 6 F 8

Resting on the site of a 19th Century Convent, the gothic style combines with luxurious charm in this town house hotel. Situated just off the main street, a short walk through the cobblestone courtyard leads to the town centre. Exceptional bedrooms, include executive and junior suites. AA Rosette for JM's Bistro 6 years. Acclaimed bar menu in award-winning pub. Near Shannon Airport, Burren, Cliffs of Moher, Bunratty and renowed Lahinch and Doonbeg golf courses.

B&B from €65.00 to €115.00

VERA & JOHN MADDEN
PROPRIETORS

American Express
Diners
Mastercard
Visa

☺ Weekend specials from €130.00

70 70

Closed 24 - 27 December

WESTBROOK HOUSE

GALWAY ROAD,
ENNIS,
CO. CLARE
TEL: 065-684 0173 FAX: 065-686 7777
EMAIL: westbrook.ennis@eircom.net
WEB: www.westbrookhouse.net

GUESTHOUSE ★★★ MAP 6 F 8

Westbrook House is a recently built luxury guesthouse in Ennis. All rooms are fitted to exceptionally high standards. Within walking distance of the centre of historic Ennis, with its friendly traditional pubs and fantastic shopping. Ideal base for golfing holidays, special discounts with local golf courses. A short drive to the majestic Cliffs of Moher, The Burren or Bunratty Castle and Folk Park. Only 15 minutes from Shannon Airport.

B&B from €35.00 to €40.00

SHEELAGH & DOMHNALL LYNCH
PROPRIETORS

Mastercard
Visa

10 10

Closed 23 - 26 December

WOODSTOCK HOTEL

SHANAWAY ROAD,
ENNIS,
CO. CLARE
TEL: 065-684 6600 FAX: 065-684 6611
EMAIL: info@woodstockhotel.com
WEB: www.woodstockhotel.com

HOTEL ★★★★ MAP 6 F 8

The hotel is set amidst its own 18 hole parkland golf course. Each room luxuriously appointed with colour multi channel TV, tea/coffee making facilities & exclusive toiletries. Full leisure centre on site. Modern Irish dishes served in hotels restaurant & drinks in Spikes Bar. A wonderful base to explore Clare - visit The Burren & Cliffs of Moher. Hotel close to Doonbeg & Lahinch Golf Courses. Sister hotel of Hibernian Hotel, Dublin and McCausland Hotel, Belfast. GDS Acc code LX. UK Toll free: 00 800 525 48000.

Member of Small Luxury Hotels of the World

B&B from €100.00 to €145.00

EDWARD FARRELL
RESIDENT MANAGER

American Express
Diners
Mastercard
Visa

☺ Weekend specials from €169.00

67 67

Closed 24 - 26 December

B&B rates are per person sharing per night incl. Breakfast

FALLS HOTEL

ENNISTYMON,
CO. CLARE

TEL: 065-707 1004 FAX: 065-707 1367
EMAIL: falls@iol.ie
WEB: www.fallshotel.net

HOTEL ★★★ MAP 5 E 9

A superior 3★★★ hotel, its manor entrance gives a welcoming warmth leading to 140 spacious en suite bedrooms. The grounds extend to 50 acres of gardens, woodland and glen with river walks and woodland pathways which offer a haven of peace and tranquillity. An ideal base to explore The Burren, Cliffs of Moher, Ailwee Caves. For the sportsman there is the world famous Lahinch Golf Club close by.

B&B from €49.80 to €63.00

BILL CHAMBERS
MANAGER

American Express
Diners
Mastercard
Visa

☺ Weekend specials from €120.00

140 140

Open All Year

GROVEMOUNT HOUSE

LAHINCH ROAD,
ENNISTYMON,
CO. CLARE

TEL: 065-707 1431 FAX: 065-707 1823
EMAIL: grovmnt@gofree.indigo.ie
WEB: www.tourclare.com/grovemount

GUESTHOUSE ★★★ MAP 5 E 9

Grovemount House is a family run guesthouse situated on the outskirts of Ennistymon town. From here you can access with ease the renowned Cliffs of Moher and the spectacular and unique Burren. Just 5mins drive away is Lahinch championship golf links and blue flag beach. Whatever is your pleasure: fishing, golfing, sightseeing, horse-riding or the best Traditional Music, enjoy and then return to luxurious tranquility in Grovemount House.

Member of Premier Guesthouses

B&B from €32.00 to €42.00

SHEILA LINNANE
OWNER

Mastercard
Visa

☺ Midweek specials from €81.00

8 8

Closed 28 October - 30 April

HALPIN'S TOWNHOUSE HOTEL

ERIN STREET,
KILKEE,
CO. CLARE

TEL: 065-905 6032 FAX: 065-905 6317
EMAIL: halpinshotel@iol.ie
WEB: www.halpinsprivatehotels.com

HOTEL ★★★ MAP 5 D 7

Highly acclaimed 3★★★ town house hotel. Combination of old world charm, fine food, vintage wines & modern comforts - overlooking old Victorian Kilkee, near Shannon Airport & Killimer car ferry. Ideal base for touring - Cliffs of Moher, Bunratty, The Burren & Loop drive. Nearby golf courses- Lahinch, Doonbeg & Ballybunion. Accolades- RAC, AA, Times, Best Loved Hotels, Johansens. Sister property of Aberdeen Lodge and Merrion Hall. USA toll free 1800 617 3178. UK free phone 0800 096 4748. Direct Dial 353 65 905 6032.

Member of Green Book of Ireland

B&B from €35.00 to €60.00

PAT HALPIN
PROPRIETOR

American Express
Diners
Mastercard
Visa

12. 12

Closed 15 November - 15 March

Room rates are per room per night

KILKEE BAY HOTEL

KILRUSH ROAD,
KILKEE,
CO. CLARE
TEL: 065-906 0060 FAX: 065-906 0062
EMAIL: info@kilkee-bay.com
WEB: www.kilkee-bay.com

HOTEL ★★★ MAP 5 D 7

A superb location - 3 minutes walk from Kilkee's renowned Blue Flag beach and town centre. This modern hotel has 41 spacious en suite bedrooms with direct dial phone, tea/coffee facilities and TV. On site tennis court, multiplex cinema, nite club, bar and seafood bistro. The perfect base for touring the Cliffs of Moher, Burren and Ailwee Caves. Shannon Airport/Limerick City within an hour's drive. Reduced rates at local dolphin watching, golf, diving centre, thalassotherapy, pony trekking and waterworld.

B&B from €35.00 to €55.00

MARIE SPICER
GENERAL MANAGER

American Express
Mastercard
Visa

Weekend specials from €100.00

41 41

IRISH HOTELS FEDERATION

Closed 03 January - 10 March

STRAND GUEST HOUSE

THE STRAND LINE,
KILKEE,
CO. CLARE
TEL: 065-905 6177 FAX: 065-905 6177
EMAIL: thestrandkilkee@eircom.net
WEB: www.clareguesthouse.com

GUESTHOUSE ★★★ MAP 5 O 7

Situated on the seafront in Kilkee, one of the most westerly seaside resorts in Europe. Kilkee is built around a 1.5km beach, considered one of the best and safest bathing places in the west with breathtaking coastal walks. The Strand makes an ideal touring base - visit The Burren, Cliffs of Moher, Ailwee Caves. For golf enthusiasts there is a local 18 hole course, Kilrush 13km, Lahinch 42km or Ballybunion 40km (via car ferry). Restaurant fully licenced, specialises in local seafood.

B&B from €32.00 to €46.00

JOHNNY & CAROLINE REDMOND

Mastercard
Visa

6 6

IRISH HOTELS FEDERATION

Open All Year

THOMOND GUESTHOUSE & KILKEE THALASSOTHERAPY CENTRE

GRATTAN STREET,
KILKEE,
CO. CLARE
TEL: 065-905 6742 FAX: 065-905 6762
EMAIL: info@kilkeethalasso.com
WEB: www.kilkeethalasso.com

GUESTHOUSE ★★★ MAP 5 D 7

Thomond Guesthouse is a magnificent premises with 5 en suite rooms coupled with Kilkee Thalassotherapy Centre, offering natural seaweed baths, algae body wraps, beauty salon & other thalassotherapy treatments. Non-smoking. Children over 16 welcome. Ideal get-away for those looking for a totally unique & relaxing break. Situated in beautiful Kilkee with golfing, scuba diving, deep sea angling, dolphin watching, swimming, pony trekking & spectacular cliff walks, all within walking distance. Private Car Parking.

B&B from €32.00 to €45.00

EILEEN MULCAHY
PROPRIETOR

Mastercard
Visa

Specials available

5 5

IRISH HOTELS FEDERATION

Closed 20 December - 10 January

B&B rates are per person sharing per night incl. Breakfast

KINCORA HALL HOTEL

ON THE LAKE,
KILLALOE,
CO. CLARE

TEL: 061-376000 FAX: 061-376665
EMAIL: info@kincorahall.com
WEB: www.kincorahall.com

HOTEL N MAP 6 H 8

Beautifully situated, overlooking our own picturesque Harbour & Yachting Marina on the shores of Lough Derg. This friendly, family run hotel exudes a warmth from the minute you enter and view the blazing open hearth fire, and the welcoming smile of the reception staff, you are assured of a memorable visit. Peaceful, relaxing, luxurious bedrooms with modern day facilities-many with views of River Shannon. Enjoy lunch time carvery and candlelight dining. Scenic walks & nature trails, fishing, horseriding, watersports & golf, all within minutes. Conference facilities are available.

Member of Select Hotels

B&B from €55.00 to €95.00

MATT SHERLOCK
GENERAL MANAGER

American Express
Mastercard
Visa

☺ Midweek specials from €49.00 per night pps

30 30

Closed 25 December

LAKESIDE HOTEL & LEISURE CENTRE

KILLALOE,
CO. CLARE

TEL: 061-376122 FAX: 061-376431
EMAIL: lakesidehotelkillaloe@eircom.net
WEB: www.lakesidekillaloe.com

HOTEL ★★★ MAP 6 H 8

On the banks of the River Shannon, overlooking Lough Derg, the Lakeside is the ideal base for touring Counties Clare, Limerick and Tipperary. Enjoy our fabulous indoor leisure centre with its 40 metre water-slide, swimming pools, sauna and steam rooms, jacuzzi, gym, snooker and creche rooms. Our 3*** hotel has 46 en suite bedrooms, including 10 superior family suites. Fully licensed restaurant and conference facilities available.

Member of Irish Country Hotels

B&B from €57.00 to €67.50

CHRISTOPHER BYRNES
GENERAL MANAGER

American Express
Diners
Mastercard
Visa

46 46

Closed 23 - 26 December

LANTERN HOUSE

OGONNELLOE,
KILLALOE,
CO. CLARE

TEL: 061-923034 FAX: 061-923139
EMAIL: phil@lanternhouse.com
WEB: www.lanternhouse.com

GUESTHOUSE ★★★ MAP 6 H 8

Ideally situated overlooking Lough Derg in a beautiful part of East Clare, 6 miles north of historic Killaloe and 45 minutes drive from Shannon Airport. Our en suite rooms are non-smoking, have semi-orthopaedic beds, direct dial phone, TV and radio. Residents' lounge, homely atmosphere and safe car parking. Enjoy the wonderful views from our fully licenced restaurant. Owner chef. Local activities include golf, watersports, fishing, pony trekking and walking.

B&B from €32.00 to €34.00

ELIZABETH COPPEN/PHILIP HOGAN
OWNERS

American Express
Mastercard
Visa

6 6

Closed 01 November - 01 March

B&B rates are per person sharing per night incl. Breakfast

WATERMAN'S LODGE COUNTRY HOUSE HOTEL

BALLINA,
KILLALOE,
CO. CLARE
TEL: 061-376333 FAX: 061-375445
EMAIL: info@watermanslodge.ie
WEB: www.watermanslodge.ie

HOTEL ★★★ MAP 6 H 8

Perched on a hill overlooking the River Shannon, Watermans Lodge Country House Hotel offers with simplicity and taste, the attractions of high ceilings and large comfy beds and open fires. Less that 2 hours from Dublin and Cork, it is an ideal venue for business and pleasure (only 15 minutes from Limerick). It boasts one of the finest restaurants in Killaloe - The Courtyard - and a relaxing bar - The Derg Lounge. Fishing, golf, shooting all on our doorstep.

Member of Manor House Hotels

B&B from €75.00 to €90.00

JOHN DOWNES
MANAGER

American Express
Mastercard
Visa

Off season midweek + weekend specials available

10 10

Closed 23 - 27 December

CENTRAL GUESTHOUSE

46 HENRY STREET,
KILRUSH,
CO. CLARE
TEL: 065-905 1332 FAX: 065-905 1332
EMAIL: centralguesthouse@eircom.net
WEB: http://kilrushcentral.port5.com

GUESTHOUSE ★★★ MAP 5 E 7

Family run attractive Georgian town house on N67 route (Kilrush-Heritage town). Close to Shannon Airport - Killimer / Tarbert Car Ferry - Cliffs of Moher - The Burren and Loop Head Drive. Major golf courses nearby - Kilrush/Kilkee/Doonbeg/Lahinch/Ballybunion. Attractive woodlands with walled gardens and walks. Marina within walking distance, boat trips to Scattery Island. Also, Dolphin watching on River Shannon. Close to all restaurants and amenities.

Member of Premier Guesthouses

B&B from €32.00 to €44.00

SEÁN & MARY COTTER
PROPRIETORS

Mastercard
Visa

Midweek specials negotiable

6 6

Closed 23 - 26 December

Room rates are per room per night

ATLANTIC HOTEL

MAIN STREET,
LAHINCH,
CO. CLARE

TEL: 065-708 1049 FAX: 065-708 1029
EMAIL: atlantichotel@eircom.net
WEB: www.atlantichotel.ie

HOTEL ★★★ MAP 5 E 9

The Atlantic Hotel is a family run hotel where comfort and friendliness are our priority. Intimate dining room offering the very best in local seafood. All rooms are en suite and have direct dial phone, TV, hairdryer and tea/coffee making facilities. 51km from Shannon Airport, 5 minutes from the famous Lahinch championship golf courses, Cliffs of Moher and the Burren. Recently refurbished and upgraded, this charming little hotel has much to offer our special guests. A warm welcome awaits you.

B&B from €50.50 to €56.00

ALAN LOGUE
YOUR HOST

Diners
Mastercard
Visa

14 14

Closed 02 November - 01 March

DOUGH MOR LODGE

STATION ROAD,
LAHINCH,
CO. CLARE

TEL: 065-708 2063 FAX: 065-707 1384
EMAIL: dough@gofree.indigo.ie

GUESTHOUSE ★★★ MAP 5 E 9

Purpose-built family run guesthouse with residents' lounge and dining room. Private car parking and large garden. You can see Lahinch's famous golf links from the house. Tee times can be booked and arranged for guests. This is an ideal location for golfing, touring the Burren or visiting the Cliffs of Moher. The beach is within 5 mins walk. Lahinch Sea World has a fine heated indoor swimming pool. The ideal place to unwind and enjoy your holiday.

Member of Premier Guesthouses of Ireland

B&B from €30.00 to €55.00

JIM FOLEY

Mastercard
Visa

6 6

Closed 31 October - 31 March

GREENBRIER INN GUESTHOUSE

LAHINCH,
CO. CLARE

TEL: 065-708 1242 FAX: 065-708 1247
EMAIL: gbrier@indigo.ie
WEB: www.greenbrierinn.com

GUESTHOUSE ★★★ MAP 5 E 9

Luxurious 3*** guesthouse, overlooking Lahinch Golf Links & the Atlantic Ocean. Situated 300 yards from Lahinch Village with its excellent restaurants, pubs & shops. All rooms are en suite with antique style pine furnishings, pressurised showers, orthopaedic beds, DD phones, multi-channel TV, tea/coffee making facilities. An excellent base from which to visit the Cliffs of Moher, play the famous Lahinch Golf Links or the spectacular Greg Norman designed Doonbeg Golf Links 18 miles away. "Come & enjoy our home while away from your own".

Member of Premier Guesthouses of Ireland

B&B from €35.00 to €75.00

MARGARET & VICTOR MULCAHY
PROPRIETORS

Mastercard
Visa

14 14

Closed 07 January - 07 March

B&B rates are per person sharing per night incl. Breakfast

MOY HOUSE

LAHINCH,
CO. CLARE

TEL: 065-708 2800 FAX: 065-708 2500
EMAIL: moyhouse@eircom.net
WEB: www.moyhouse.com

GUESTHOUSE ★★★★ MAP 5 E 9

Moy House prevails over the breathtaking seascape of Lahinch Bay, set on 15 acres of grounds, adorned by mature woodland and a picturesque river. Major restoration has transformed this 18th century country house in keeping with present day expectations of superior standards, yet preserving its unique character style and period ambience. Personal attention and the relaxation of a sanctuary, yet minutes away from the many amenities available, are the hallmarks that distinguish us.

Member of Ireland's Blue Book

B&B from €97.50 to €114.50

BERNADETTE MERRY
GENERAL MANAGER

American Express
Mastercard
Visa

9 9

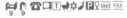

Closed 23 - 27 December

SANCTA MARIA HOTEL

LAHINCH,
CO. CLARE

TEL: 065-708 1041 FAX: 065-708 1529
EMAIL: sanctamaria01@eircom.net

HOTEL ★★ MAP 5 E 9

The McInerney Family have welcomed holiday makers to the Sancta Maria for over 40 years. Many of the attractive bedrooms overlook the famous Lahinch Golf Links and golden beach, which are within 100 metres of the hotel. Our restaurant specialises in fresh produce and special emphasis is placed on local seafoods and home baking. The Sancta Maria is the ideal base for touring the Burren or visiting the Cliffs of Moher and Aran Islands.

B&B from €36.00 to €42.50

THOMAS MCINERNEY
PROPRIETOR

Mastercard
Visa

☺ Weekend specials from €92.00

24 24

Closed 01 November - 01 March

SHAMROCK INN HOTEL

MAIN STREET,
LAHINCH,
CO. CLARE

TEL: 065-708 1700 FAX: 065-708 1029
EMAIL: atlantichotel@eircom.net
WEB: www.atlantichotel.ie

HOTEL ★★ MAP 5 E 9

Situated right in the heart of charming Lahinch. All tastefully decorated rooms have direct dial phone, TV, hairdryer and tea/coffee making facilities. Our restaurant is renowned for its warm and intimate atmosphere offering a choice of excellent cuisine, catering for all tastes. Delicious home cooked bar food is served daily and by night the bar comes to life with the sound of music. Whatever your interest, golf, fishing or horseriding, we can arrange it for you.

B&B from €50.50 to €56.00

ALAN LOGUE
YOUR HOST

Diners
Mastercard
Visa

10 10

Closed 24 - 26 December

Room rates are per room per night

LISCANNOR BAY HOTEL

LISCANNOR,
CO. CLARE

TEL: 065-708 6000 FAX: 065-708 1713
EMAIL: info@liscannorbayhotel.com
WEB: www.liscannorbayhotel.com

HOTEL ★★★ MAP 5 E 9

The Liscannor Bay Hotel is situated in the picturesque village of Liscannor, nestling between the rugged Burren, the Cliffs of Moher and Lahinch. The hotel offers panoramic views of the Atlantic Ocean. The elegant bedrooms are an invitation to relax and unwind. Fresh fish from the bay, succulent "Burren" lamb and locally grown organic vegetables are combined by our award winning chefs to create a memorable dining experience. Lahinch 18-hole golf course is 1km. 25m leisure complex is 3km away.

B&B from €35.00 to €100.00

BRIAN J O'HIGGINS
PROPRIETOR

American Express
Diners
Mastercard
Visa

:/🍴

Weekend specials from €99.00

🙂

🛏🐾☎🖥📺🅲◀CM🌙🎵🄿🆂
49 49
🄰🅰🖨

Closed 01 October - 30 April

CARRIGANN HOTEL

LISDOONVARNA,
CO. CLARE

TEL: 065-707 4036 FAX: 065-707 4567
EMAIL: carrigannhotel@eircom.net
WEB: www.gateway-to-the-burren.com

HOTEL ★★★ MAP 5 E 9

Quiet, friendly and relaxing family run hotel, set in its own landscaped grounds, just two minutes from village centre. Our restaurant, with views of the gardens, is the place to relax and enjoy fresh local produce expertly cooked and served. Perfect base for touring the Burren, Clare, Galway, Limerick. Burren walking holiday specialists - own maps/notes. One hour Shannon Airport. Ground floor rooms. Private parking.

B&B from €42.00 to €60.00

MARY & GERARD HOWARD
PROPRIETORS

Mastercard
Visa

🛏🐾☎🖥📺🅲◀CM❄🌙🄿🄰🅰🖨
20 20

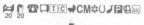

Closed 01 November - 28 February

B&B rates are per person sharing per night incl. Breakfast

KINCORA HOUSE AND GALLERY RESTAURANT

LISDOONVARNA,
CO. CLARE

TEL: 065-707 4300 FAX: 065-707 4490
EMAIL: kincorahotel@eircom.net
WEB: www.kincora-hotel.com

GUESTHOUSE ★★★ MAP 5 E 9

Relax in peace and tranquillity in our award-winning Country Inn, where the Drennan Family offers a warm welcome to our guests. A landmark building since 1860, the house exudes charm, character and a lovely ambience. Enjoy fine food and fine art in our Gallery Restaurant, which is set in beautiful gardens. Relax in our old atmospheric pub with open turf fires. Ideal base, for the Burren, near the Cliffs of Moher and Lahinch Golf Course, Shannon Airport 1 hour. Painting holidays a speciality. AA ◆◆◆◆ RAC ◆◆◆◆. Irish Inn of the year '98 & '01.

Member of Signpost Premier Hotels

B&B from €35.00 to €60.00

DOREEN & DIARMUID DRENNAN
PROPRIETORS

Mastercard
Visa

✓

Weekend specials from €110.00

🙂

🛏🐾☎🖥📺🅃❄🌙🎵🄿🆂🄰🅰🖨
14 14

Closed 31 October - 15 March

LYNCHS HOTEL

THE SQUARE,
LISDOONVARNA,
CO. CLARE

TEL: 065-707 4010

EMAIL: lynchshotel@eircom.net
WEB: http://homepage.eircom.net/njoelynch

HOTEL ★ MAP 5 E 9

Comfortable family run hotel situated on the square providing 12 en suite rooms with TV and hairdryers. Centrally located for all of North Clare's tourist attractions, golf courses and sea / river angling. Cozy and relaxing bar with real fires and extensive homecooked bar/restaurant menu. Providing live entertainment at weekends.

B&B from €25.00 to €45.00

BRIGID BYRNE
MANAGER

Mastercard

Visa

12 12

Open All Year

SHEEDY'S COUNTRY HOUSE HOTEL

LISDOONVARNA,
CO. CLARE

TEL: 065-707 4026 FAX: 065-707 4555
EMAIL: enquiries@sheedys.com
WEB: www.sheedys.com

HOTEL ★★★ MAP 5 E 9

Sheedys Country House offers award winning cuisine, beautiful gardens and an unrivalled location on the edge of the Burren. Each of the 11 beautifully appointed guest rooms and suites have been individually designed with comfort in mind. Our restaurant is recognised very favourably in "The Good Food Guide" and holds 2 AA Rosettes. Recommended by the New York Times. Close to Doolin, Lahinch and 1 hour from Shannon.

Member of Irish Country Hotels

B&B from €60.00 to €90.00

JOHN AND MARTINA SHEEDY

Mastercard

Visa

11 11

Closed 10 October - 15 March

THE BURREN Centre

Discover the unique magic of

the Burren Region in 'A Walk Through Time' at the New Burren Centre. The new visitor centre in the historic village of Kilfenora boosts a fantastic new exhibition, audio visual film theatre, local craft shop and tea room.

Opening Times:
Mid March to May
10am to 5pm,
June, July & August
9:30am to 6pm,
September to October
10am to 5pm,
Last Admission 30 min before closing,

Explore the flora, fauna, archaeology and natural history of the Burren in the all new Burren Centre.

Services: Tourist Information Point, Free parking, Beside Kilfenora High Crosses, all Burren reference Maps & Guides available in new craft shop.

Burren Centre, Kilfenora, Co. Clare.
Tel: 065-7088030
Fax: 065-7088102
e-mail: info@theburrencentre.ie
website: www.theburrencentre.ie

Room rates are per room per night

BAY VIEW GUESTHOUSE

SPANISH POINT,
MILLTOWN MALBAY,
CO. CLARE
TEL: 065-708 4006
EMAIL: bayviewguesthouse@eircom.net

GUESTHOUSE ★★★ MAP 5 E 8

A family run guesthouse overlooking the Atlantic Ocean. All rooms en suite with TV, DD phone, hair dryer and tea/coffee facilities. Also, private guest lounge. Nearby beaches, angling, golf, watersports, pubs and restaurants. Ideal for touring the Burren, Cliffs of Moher, etc. Private car park, garden for visitors' use and walk to rocky shore.

B&B from € 30.00 to € 38.00

ANN LAHIFF
PROPRIETOR

Mastercard

Visa

9   9

☺ Midweek specials from €87.00

Closed 20 - 30 December

BELLBRIDGE HOUSE HOTEL

SPANISH POINT,
MILLTOWN MALBAY,
CO. CLARE
TEL: 065-708 4038 FAX: 065-708 4830
EMAIL: bellbridge@eircom.net
WEB: www.bellbridgehotelclare.com

HOTEL ★★★ MAP 5 E 8

Situated on the West Clare coastline, this new hotel offers excellent accommodation and cuisine. Adjacent to Spanish Point Golf Course, sandy beaches, horse riding, fishing, tennis and water sports. Ideal base for touring the Burren, Cliffs of Moher, Ailwee Caves, Bunratty Castle and Folk Park. A hotel with friendly and efficient staff whose aim is to make your stay enjoyable and memorable. All rooms have hairdryer, tea/coffee making facilities, DD phone and colour TV. World famous Lahinch and Doonbeg Golf Courses are within a 10 min drive.

B&B from € 51.00 to € 70.00

DEREK LOGUE
PROPRIETOR

American Express

Mastercard

Visa

60   60

Open All Year

BURKES ARMADA HOTEL

SPANISH POINT,
MILLTOWN MALBAY,
CO. CLARE
TEL: 065-708 4110 FAX: 065-708 4632
EMAIL: info@burkesarmadahotel.com
WEB: www.burkesarmadahotel.com

HOTEL ★★★ MAP 5 E 8

The redeveloped Burkes Armada Hotel commands a superb oceanfront setting in the beautiful seaside resort of Spanish Point. All rooms are furnished to a very high standard with suites and superior rooms available. The Cape Restaurant offers exceptional cuisine under the attention of an award winning culinary team, in contemporary modern surroundings with private bar area. The hotel also offers private garden area, fitness room, reading room, with holiday packages available. Also extensive conference and banqueting facilities.

Member of MinOtel Ireland Hotel Group

B&B from € 30.00 to € 75.00

JOHN J.BURKE
GENERAL MANAGER

Mastercard

Visa

61   61

Open All Year

B&B rates are per person sharing per night incl. Breakfast

MOUNTSHANNON HOTEL

MOUNTSHANNON,
CO. CLARE

TEL: 061-927162 FAX: 061-927272
EMAIL: info@mountshannon-hotel.ie

HOTEL ★★ MAP 6 H 9

The Mountshannon Hotel, situated in the rural and peaceful village of Mountshannon, offers you first class accommodation in friendly surroundings. All bedrooms are en suite with direct dial phone, TV, tea/coffee making facilities and hairdryer. Our continental style restaurant, which is known for excellent and reasonably priced cuisine, overlooks our garden and Lough Derg. Private car park. Mountshannon Harbour is four minutes walk away. Fishing, pony trekking and golf are available.

Member of Irish Family Hotels

B&B from € 38.00 to € 44.00

PAULINE AND MICHAEL MADDEN
DIRECTOR/OWNER

American Express
Mastercard
Visa

14 14

alc 📷

IRISH HOTELS FEDERATION

Closed 25 December

DROMOLAND CASTLE

NEWMARKET-ON-FERGUS,
CO. CLARE

TEL: 061-368144 FAX: 061-363355
EMAIL: sales@dromoland.ie
WEB: www.dromoland.ie

HOTEL ★★★★★ MAP 6 G 8

Located 13km from Shannon Airport. Stately halls, elegant public areas & beautifully furnished guest rooms are steeped in a timeless atmosphere that is unique to Dromoland. The international reputation for excellence is reflected in the award-winning cuisine in the castle's Earl of Thomond & The Fig Tree Restaurant in the Dromoland Golf & Country Club. A meticulously maintained 18-hole golf course, fishing, horse-riding, clay shooting, health & beauty clinic & much more.

Member of Preferred Hotels & Resorts WW

Room Rate from € 277.00 to € 520.00

MARK NOLAN
GENERAL MANAGER

American Express
Diners
Mastercard
Visa

100 100

IRISH HOTELS FEDERATION

Open All Year

GOLF VIEW

LATOON, QUIN ROAD,
NEWMARKET-ON-FERGUS,
CO. CLARE

TEL: 061-368095 FAX: 065-682 8624
EMAIL: mhogangolfviewbandb@eircom.net
WEB: www.clarelive.com/golfview

GUESTHOUSE ★★★ MAP 6 G 8

New purpose built family run 3*** guesthouse, overlooking Dromoland Castle and Clare Inn Golf Course, one hundred metres off N18 on Quin Road at the entrance to the Clare Inn Hotel. Non smoking en suite rooms on the ground floor with phone, multi-channel TV and hair dryers. Local tourist attractions include Bunratty and Knappogue Castles, many 18 hole golf courses and horse riding schools. Castle banquets can be arranged. Shannon Airport 10 minutes. Private car park.

B&B from € 35.00 to € 45.00

MAUREEN HOGAN
PROPRIETOR

Mastercard
Visa

6 6

IRISH HOTELS FEDERATION

Closed 20 - 28 December

B&B rates are per person sharing per night incl. Breakfast

HUNTERS LODGE

THE SQUARE,
NEWMARKET-ON-FERGUS,
CO. CLARE
TEL: 061-368577 FAX: 061-368057

GUESTHOUSE ★★★ MAP 6 G 8

Ideally situated for visitors arriving or departing from Shannon Airport (12km). We offer 6 comfortable bedrooms en suite with telephone and TV. Our olde worlde pub and restaurant specialises in good quality fresh food served in a relaxed atmosphere with a friendly and efficient service. Local tourist attractions include Bunratty Folk Park, castle banquets and many 18 hole golf courses. Ideal stopover for touring Co. Clare or commencing your trip to the West of Ireland.

B&B from € 37.50 to € 42.50

ROBERT & KATHLEEN HEALY
PROPRIETORS

American Express
Diners
Mastercard
Visa

6   6

Open All Year

COMFORT INN SHANNON

BALLYCASEY,
SHANNON,
CO. CLARE
TEL: 061-364588 FAX: 061-364045
EMAIL: sales@qualityshannon.com
WEB: www.choicehotelsireland.ie

HOTEL U MAP 6 G 7

Just minutes from Shannon International Airport and Industrial area, Quality Hotel Shannon serves as an ideal base for exploring the surrounding Clare and Limerick region. The Olde Lodge themed bar and Lannigans Restaurant make a lively centre of activity, complemented by superb accommodation of a 3*** standard. The rich hinterland around Shannon is full of heritage and culture. Mediaeval banquets at Bunratty Castle, the spectacular Cliffs of Moher and Cragganowen will keep you intrigued during your stay.

B&B from € 50.00 to € 120.00

DAMIAN CALDWELL
GENERAL MANAGER

American Express
Diners
Mastercard
Visa

54   54

alc 🍴 ♿ inet

IRISH
HOTELS
FEDERATION

Closed 24 - 25 December

GREAT SOUTHERN HOTEL

SHANNON AIRPORT,
SHANNON,
CO. CLARE
TEL: 061-471122 FAX: 061-471982
EMAIL: res@shannon-gsh.com
WEB: www.gshotels.com

HOTEL ★★★ MAP 6 G 7

Shannon Great Southern is a hotel with exceptional style and comfort within walking distance of the terminal building at Shannon Airport. All 115 rooms are en suite with direct dial phone, TV, tea/coffee making facilities, hairdryer and trouser press. Leisure facilities include a gym and steam room. Bookable worldwide through UTELL International or central reservations Telephone Number: 01-214 4800.

Room Rate from € 90.00 to € 150.00

UNA MCMAHON
GENERAL MANAGER

American Express
Diners
Mastercard
Visa

115 115

alc 🍴 ♿

IRISH
HOTELS
FEDERATION

Closed 24 - 26 December

Room rates are per room per night

OAK WOOD ARMS HOTEL

SHANNON,
CO. CLARE

TEL: 061-361500 FAX: 061-361414
EMAIL: reservations@oakwoodarms.com
WEB: www.oakwoodarms.com

HOTEL ★★★ MAP 6 G 7

Located on the Airport Road, the recently refurbished Oak Wood Arms Hotel is convenient to Bunratty, the Aviation Park, Shannon Free Zone, golf club and town centre. Setting the standard on quality, the Oak Wood Arms has just completed renovations to the award winning "Sophies Lounge", maintaining its standard of excellence. Experience our superior bedrooms, many air-conditioned, our new private fitness centre and our Chef Aidan McCarthy's excellent menu.

B&B from €58.00 to €86.00

VICTOR O'SULLIVAN
MANAGING DIRECTOR

American Express
Diners
Mastercard
Visa

100 100

Closed 24 - 26 December

LEENS HOTEL

MAIN STREET,
ABBEYFEALE,
CO. LIMERICK

TEL: 068-31121 FAX: 068-32550
EMAIL: leenshotelabbeyfeale@eircom.net
WEB: www.leenshotel.com

HOTEL ★★ MAP 5 E 6

Leens Hotel is located in the Square, Abbeyfeale in the heart of West Limerick. It has been recently refurbished to the highest standard and is under the personal supervision of Maurice and Olive Sheehan. It has 19 new bedrooms, tastefully finished to a very high standard. There is a carvery lunch served daily and a wide selection of bar food available throughout the day. There is a very warm atmosphere in the Oak Bar and a very intimate restaurant offering the best in local produce.

B&B from €40.00 to €60.00

OLIVE AND MAURICE SHEEHAN

American Express
Mastercard
Visa

19 19

Closed 24 - 26 December

ADARE MANOR HOTEL & GOLF RESORT

ADARE,
CO. LIMERICK

TEL: 061-396566 FAX: 061-396124
EMAIL: reservations@adaremanor.com
WEB: www.adaremanor.com

HOTEL ★★★★★ MAP 6 G 7

Located 20 miles from Shannon Airport. Adare Manor Hotel & Golf Resort, set on the banks of the River Maigue, boasts splendour in its luxuriously finished rooms. The Oak Room Restaurant provides haute cuisine laced with Irish charm. Indoor heated pool, fitness centre and the recent addition, the spa. Outdoor pursuits include fishing, horseriding, clay pigeon shooting and the Robert Trent Jones Senior championship golf course. New clubhouse with state of the art conference centre.

Member of Leading Small Hotels of the World

Room Rate from €210.00 to €670.00

ANITA CAREY
GENERAL MANAGER

American Express
Diners
Mastercard
Visa

74 74

Open All Year

B&B rates are per person sharing per night incl. Breakfast

CARRABAWN HOUSE

KILLARNEY ROAD (N21),
ADARE,
CO. LIMERICK
TEL: 061-396067 FAX: 061-396925
EMAIL: carrabaw@indigo.ie
WEB: www.carrabawnhouseadare.com

GUESTHOUSE ★★★ MAP 6 G 7

Only 20 miles from Shannon Airport, beside Adare Manor Golf Resort. This superior quality guest accommodation is a must for the weary traveller. We take pride in caring for you as though you were a member of our family. Tastefully decorated, Carrabawn House is ideally located within a few minutes walk of the village centre. Set among award winning gardens, a delight in all seasons, your stay is assured of being memorable indeed. Many of our guests return year to year such is our friendly service. So come stay a while and "be our guest".

Member of Premier Guesthouses

B&B from €35.00 to €45.00

BRIDGET LOHAN
PROPRIETOR

Mastercard
Visa

☺ Midweek specials from €90.00

7 7

IRISH HOTELS FEDERATION

Closed 24 - 26 December

DUNRAVEN ARMS HOTEL

ADARE,
CO. LIMERICK
TEL: 061-396633 FAX: 061-396541
EMAIL: reservations@dunravenhotel.com
WEB: www.dunravenhotel.com

HOTEL ★★★★ MAP 6 G 7

Established in 1792 a 4**** old world hotel surrounded by ornate thatched cottages, in Ireland's prettiest village. Each bedroom, including twelve suites, is beautifully appointed with antique furniture, dressing room and bathroom en suite. Award-winning restaurant, AA Three Red Rosettes. Leisure centre comprised of a 17m pool, steam room and gym studio. Equestrian and golf holidays a speciality. 30 mins from Shannon Airport. GDS Access Code UI Toll Free 1-800-44 UTELL.

Member of Small Luxury Hotels of the World

B&B from €105.00 to €130.00

LOUIS MURPHY
PROPRIETOR

American Express
Diners
Mastercard
Visa

76 76

IRISH HOTELS FEDERATION

Open All Year

ADARE
heritage
CENTRE

Main Street, Adare, Co. Limerick

Tel: 061-396666
Fax: 061-396932

Email: adareheritage@eircom.net

Opened to the public in 1994, the Centre offers the following exciting range of facilities for the discerning traveller:

Tourist Information Office

Kerry Woollen Mills

Black Abbey Crafts

Curren Heraldry

The Dovecot Restaurant

The Historical Exhibition

Open all year round

FITZGERALDS WOODLANDS HOUSE HOTEL AND LEISURE SPA

KNOCKANES,
ADARE,
CO. LIMERICK
TEL: 061-605100 FAX: 061-396073
EMAIL: reception@woodlands-hotel.ie
WEB: www.woodlands-hotel.ie

HOTEL ★★★ MAP 6 G 7

Luxurious 94 bedroom hotel located in the Splendour of Adare, Co. Limerick on its own grounds of 44 acres. Superior and Executive Suites available boasting Jacuzzi baths. Award winning Brennan Room Restaurant, Timmy Mac's Traditional Bar and Bistro, Trad sessions and storytelling. Reva's Hair, Beauty & Relaxation Spa boasting Balneotherapy spa baths & Stone therapy massage. State of the art Health & Leisure Spa. Golf & health spa breaks a speciality. Excellent Wedding and Conference Facilities.

Member of Irish Country Hotels

B&B from €55.00 to €108.00

DICK, MARY & DAVID FITZGERALD
HOSTS

American Express
Diners
Mastercard
Visa

Weekend specials from €125.00

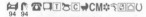

Closed 24 - 25 December

CASTLE OAKS HOUSE HOTEL & COUNTRY CLUB

CASTLECONNELL,
CO. LIMERICK

TEL: 061-377666 FAX: 061-377717
EMAIL: info@castleoaks.ie
WEB: www.castleoaks.ie

HOTEL ★★★ MAP 6 H 7

Located 10 minutes from Limerick City just off the main Dublin Road (N7), the newly refurbished Castle Oaks House Hotel & Country Leisure Club is situated on 26 acres of mature gardens. The hotel boasts 20 lavishly appointed bedrooms and 20 superior executive suites with individual private lounges. Extensive conference and banqueting facilities. Award winning Acorn Restaurant. Fishing on site, golf, equestrian, water sports nearby. Shannon Airport 40 minutes. We welcome you to experience the warmth and hospitality of our Georgian mansion.

Member of Great Fishing House's of Ireland

B&B from €57.50 to €70.00

GOBNAIT O'CONNELL
MANAGING DIRECTOR

American Express
Diners
Mastercard
Visa

Closed 24 - 26 December

ALEXANDRA GUEST HOUSE

5-6 O'CONNELL AVENUE,
LIMERICK

TEL: 061-318472 FAX: 061-400433
EMAIL: info@alexandra.iol.ie

GUESTHOUSE ★★ MAP 6 H 7

Elegant Victorian house, 5 minutes walk to the heart of the city centre and located on the Angela's Ashes trail. Many beautiful architecturally renowned churches nearby. Comfortable spacious rooms, en suite with multi channel TV, direct dial phone. Relaxing guest lounge with tea/coffee facilities provided. Conveniently located for bus and rail stations and 20 minutes drive to Shannon and Bunratty. Multi guide recommendations.

B&B from €32.00 to €60.00

AGNES DONOVAN
GENERAL MANAGER

Mastercard
Visa

Closed 23 December - 06 March

B&B rates are per person sharing per night incl. Breakfast

Room rates are per room per night

CLIFTON HOUSE GUEST HOUSE

ENNIS ROAD,
LIMERICK

TEL: 061-451166 FAX: 061-451224
EMAIL: cliftonhouse@eircom.net

GUESTHOUSE ★★★ MAP 6 H 7

Set in 1 acre of landscape gardens.
All sixteen rooms en suite, with multi-channel TV, trouser press, hair dryers,
direct dial telephone. Complimentary
tea/coffee available in our spacious
TV lounge. We are situated on the
main Limerick/ Shannon Road. Within
15 minutes walk of city centre. 22
space car park. AA listed. Friendly
welcome awaits you.

Member of Premier Guesthouses

B&B from €35.00 to €35.00

MICHAEL & MARY POWELL
PROPRIETOR

Mastercard

Visa

16 16

IRISH HOTELS FEDERATION

Closed 19 December - 06 January

CLONMACKEN HOUSE GUEST HOUSE

CLONMACKEN,
OFF ENNIS ROAD (AT IVANS),
LIMERICK

TEL: 061-327007 FAX: 061-327785
EMAIL: clonmac@indigo.ie
WEB: www.euroka.com/clonmacken

GUESTHOUSE ★★★ MAP 6 H 7

A purpose built, family run guest
house, built to the highest standards,
with multi-channel TV, direct dial
phone, tea/coffee making facilities
and hair dryer in each of its ten en
suite superbly decorated bedrooms.
Limerick City and King John's Castle
are 5 minutes drive, Bunratty and
Shannon Airport are situated nearby.
Golf outings, coach tours, car hire &
Bunratty Banquet can be arranged.
Private secure car parking on our own
1 acre site. Home to the Cranberries
and Frank McCourt.

Member of Premier Guesthouses

B&B from €35.00 to €35.00

BRID AND GERRY MCDONALD
PROPRIETORS

American Express

Diners

Mastercard

Visa

10 10

IRISH HOTELS FEDERATION

Closed 19 December - 06 January

CRUISES HOUSE

DENMARK STREET,
LIMERICK

TEL: 061-315320 FAX: 061-316995
EMAIL: cruiseshouse@eircom.net
WEB: www.premierguesthouses.com/cruises.htm

GUESTHOUSE ★★★ MAP 6 H 7

Limerick's largest guesthouse,
situated in the heart of the city centre.
Offering luxurious en suite
accommodation with direct dial
phone, TV, tea/coffee making facilities
and hairdryer in each room.
Convenient to Limerick's finest
restaurants, pubs and shops.
Additional facilities include a business
meeting room. Reception services -
fax, photocoping and bureau de
change available.

Member of Premier Guesthouses

B&B from €30.00 to €38.00

CAROLE KELLY
MANAGER

American Express

Diners

Mastercard

Visa

29 29

Closed 24 December - 02 January

B&B rates are per person sharing per night incl. Breakfast

FORTE TRAVELODGE

COONAGH ROUNDABOUT,
ENNIS ROAD,
LIMERICK
TEL: 1800-709709 FAX: 061-454991

WEB: www.travelodge.co.uk

HOTEL U   MAP 6 H 7

This superb modern hotel offers comfortable, yet affordable, accommodation. Each room is large enough to sleep up to three adults, a child under 12 and a baby in a cot. Excellent range of facilities, from en suite bathroom to colour TV. Unbeatable value for business or leisure. From UK call free: 0800 850950 or from Ireland Freephone 1800 709709.

Room Rate from €69.00 to €79.00

MARY HAYES
MANAGER

American Express
Diners
Mastercard
Visa

40 40

Open All Year

GLENTWORTH HOTEL

GLENTWORTH STREET,
LIMERICK

TEL: 061-413822 FAX: 061-413073
EMAIL: glentworthhotel@oceanfree.net

HOTEL ★★★   MAP 6 H 7

The Glentworth Hotel established in 1878 and situated in the city centre is the perfect location for entertainment & shopping. Our hotel features 62 newly refurbished en suite rooms with multi channel TV, hairdryer, tea/coffee facilities & trouser press. Superb restaurant, coffee shop, lounge bar, banqueting & conference facilities. 5 mins walk from bus/train, 25 mins from Shannon and private lock-up carpark. The Glentworth where people matter - Limerick's friendliest hotel.

B&B from €40.00 to €70.00

JEREMIAH FLYNN
DIRECTOR/GENERAL MANAGER

American Express
Diners
Mastercard
Visa

☺   Weekend specials from €100.00

62 62

IRISH
HOTELS
FEDERATION

Closed 25 - 26 December

GREENHILLS HOTEL CONFERENCE/LEISURE

ENNIS ROAD,
LIMERICK

TEL: 061-453033 FAX: 061-453307
EMAIL: info@greenhillsgroup.com
WEB: www.greenhillsgroup.com

HOTEL ★★★   MAP 6 H 7

The Greenhills Hotel is set in 3.5 acres of tended gardens. Just 5 minutes from Limerick City and 15 minutes from Shannon Airport. Enjoy our popular bar and our award winning restaurant. Lamb a speciality from our own farm. Relax in our residents lounge or workout in our health and leisure centre, including 18m indoor swimming pool. State of the art conference and meeting facilities. Local amenities include golf, bowling and horseriding.

B&B from €65.00 to €85.00

ROGER BECK
GENERAL MANAGER

American Express
Diners
Mastercard
Visa

☺   Weekend specials from €130 .00

57 57

IRISH
HOTELS
FEDERATION

Closed 24 - 26 December

Room rates are per room per night

GRESHAM ARDHU

ENNIS ROAD,
LIMERICK

TEL: 061-453922 FAX: 061-326333
EMAIL: info@gresham-ardhuhotel.com
WEB: www.gresham-hotels.com

HOTEL ★★★ MAP 6 H 7

Formely known as The Limerick Ryan Hotel, the original hotel dates back to 1780. Restored to combine the grace and spaciousness of an earlier age with the comforts of today. 179 bedrooms, two suites, including two executive floors designed for business guests, the award winning Ardhu Restaurant, gym, superior meeting rooms, Toddy's Bar, Cocktail Bar, business centre and complimentary car parking. AA, RAC and Egon Ronay recommended.

B&B from €51.00 to €112.00

DERMOT FEHILY
GENERAL MANAGER

American Express
Diners
Mastercard
Visa

😊 Weekend specials from €125.00

 181 181

Open All Year

JURYS INN LIMERICK

LOWER MALLOW STREET,
LIMERICK

TEL: 061-207000 FAX: 061-400966
EMAIL: jurysinnlimerick@jurysdoyle.com
WEB: www.jurysdoyle.com

HOTEL ★★★ MAP 6 H 7

Set in the heart of the city along the banks of the Shannon and just a two-minute stroll from the shopping and cultural centre of Limerick. This very welcoming inn provides an excellent base from which to explore many scenic delights in Co. Limerick and Co. Clare.

Room Rate from €75.00 to €82.00

DEREK MCDONAGH
GENERAL MANAGER

American Express
Diners
Mastercard
Visa

 151 151

Closed 24 - 26 December

JURYS LIMERICK HOTEL

ENNIS ROAD,
LIMERICK

TEL: 061-327777 FAX: 061-326400
EMAIL: limerick@jurysdoyle.com
WEB: www.jurysdoyle.com

HOTEL ★★★★ MAP 6 H 7

Set in a green leafy garden on the banks of the mighty Shannon and just a 2-minute walk to the principal shopping and business districts, Jurys Limerick Hotel is at once contemporary and timeless in its appeal. It is also within short driving distance of some of Ireland's most dramatic scenic attractions.

B&B from €60.00 to €121.00

AILEEN PHELAN
GENERAL MANAGER

American Express
Diners
Mastercard
Visa

  95 95

Closed 24 - 27 December

B&B rates are per person sharing per night incl. Breakfast

RADISSON SAS HOTEL

ENNIS ROAD,
LIMERICK

TEL: 061-326666 FAX: 061-327418
EMAIL: sales.limerick@radissonsas.com
WEB: www.radissonsas.com

HOTEL ★★★★ MAP 6 H 7

The Radisson SAS Hotel in Limerick is strategically located on the Ennis Road (N18) just 5 minutes drive from Limerick City Centre and 20 minutes from Shannon International Airport. The hotel boasts 154 deluxe newly refurbished rooms and suites, Porters Restaurant, Heron's Irish Pub, Lobby Bar and leisure centre including indoor swimming pool, sauna, steam room, gym and treatments.

Member of Radisson SAS Hotels & Resorts

B&B from € 82.50 to € 105.00

EIVIND DALVANG
GENERAL MANAGER

American Express
Diners
Mastercard
Visa

154 154

Open All Year

RAILWAY HOTEL

PARNELL STREET,
LIMERICK

TEL: 061-413653 FAX: 061-419762
EMAIL: sales@railwayhotel.ie
WEB: www.railwayhotel.ie

HOTEL ★★ MAP 6 H 7

Family run hotel, owned and managed by the McEnery/Collins Family, this hotel offers Irish hospitality at its best. Personal attention is a way of life, along with an attractive lounge/bar, comfortable en suite accommodation and good home cooked food, one can't ask for more. Ideally situated, opposite rail/bus station, convenient to city centre, it is the perfect stop for the tourist and businessman alike. All major credit cards accepted.

B&B from € 35.00 to € 45.00

PAT & MICHELE MCENERY
OWNERS/MANAGERS

American Express
Diners
Mastercard
Visa

30 25

Closed 24 - 26 December

ROYAL GEORGE HOTEL

O'CONNELL STREET,
LIMERICK

TEL: 061-414566 FAX: 061-317171
EMAIL: royalgeorgehotel@eircom.net
WEB: www.royalgeorge.com

HOTEL R MAP 6 H 7

This 3*** hotel is ideally suited for business or pleasure situated in the heart of Limerick City. Enjoy a night in our traditional Irish pub of distinction, The Sibin, with nightly entertainment. 15 minutes drive from Shannon International Airport. Local attractions include St. Johns Castle, Bunratty Folk Park, the Hunt Museum, Cliffs of Moher and Adare. Secure lock-up carpark. Niteclub - Thursday, Friday, Saturday, complimentary to all residents.

Room Rate from € 50.00 to € 90.00

DERMOT HARTIGAN
GENERAL MANAGER

American Express
Diners
Mastercard
Visa

54 54

Closed 24 - 26 December

Room rates are per room per night

WOODFIELD HOUSE HOTEL

ENNIS ROAD,
LIMERICK

TEL: 061-453022 FAX: 061-326755
EMAIL: woodfieldhotel@eircom.net
WEB: www.woodfieldhousehotel.com

HOTEL ★★★ MAP 6 H 7

Woodfield House Hotel ideally located within strolling distance of Limerick city centre, Georgian streets, lovely quays, along the Shannon and King John's Castle, St. Mary's cathedral and the Hunt Museum. Complete your evening in our Bistro where fine cuisine and attentive service create a special dining experience. Our Lansdowne Bar offers a welcoming retreat for both locals and visitors alike.

Member of MinOtel Ireland Hotel Group

B&B from €53.00 to €72.50

AUSTIN GIBBONS
PROPRIETOR

American Express
Diners
Mastercard
Visa

26 26

Ⓑ inet FAX

HOTELS FEDERATION

Closed 24 - 26 December

COURTENAY LODGE HOTEL

NEWCASTLE WEST,
CO. LIMERICK

TEL: 069-62244 FAX: 069-77184
EMAIL: res@courtenaylodge.iol.ie
WEB: www.courtenaylodgehotel.com

HOTEL ★★★ MAP 2 F 6

A warm welcome awaits you at the Courtenay Lodge Hotel situated on the main Limerick to Killarney Road and only 15 mins from the picturesque village of Adare. The newly-built, tastefully decorated, en suite rooms complete with TV, direct dial phone, power showers, trouser press, tea/coffee facilities, etc. ensure a level of comfort second to none. The ideal base for touring the Shannon and South West region and the perfect location for golfers to enjoy some of the most renowned courses.

B&B from €45.00 to €75.00

DECLAN O'GRADY
GENERAL MANAGER

American Express
Diners
Mastercard
Visa

39 39
alc

HOTELS FEDERATION

Closed 25 December

DEVON INN HOTEL

TEMPLEGLANTINE,
NEWCASTLE WEST,
CO. LIMERICK

TEL: 069-84122 FAX: 069-84255
EMAIL: devoninnhotel@eircom.net

HOTEL ★★★ MAP 6 F 6

The newly refurbished Devon Inn Hotel offers a superb base to explore the wonderful attractions of the South West. Situated midway between Limerick City and Killarney in the heart of West Limerick. The hotel features 40 excellent bedrooms, a superb restaurant featuring the best of local produce, a choice of two bars and conference and banqueting for up to 400 guests. Private car park. Just over an hour's drive from Shannon Airport and under an hour to Killarney.

Member of Irish Family Hotels

B&B from €45.00 to €65.00

WILLIAM SHEEHAN
MANAGER

American Express
Diners
Mastercard
Visa

40 40
alc

HOTELS FEDERATION

Closed 24 - 28 December

B&B rates are per person sharing per night incl. Breakfast

RATHKEALE HOUSE HOTEL

RATHKEALE,
CO. LIMERICK

TEL: 069-63333 FAX: 069-63300
EMAIL: rhh@iol.ie

HOTEL ★★★ MAP 6 G 6

Rathkeale House Hotel, located just off the N21 Limerick to Killarney route and 4 miles west of Ireland's prettiest village, Adare. 26 superior en suite rooms, O'Deas Bistro open each evening 6-9.30pm. Chestnut Tree Bar where carvery lunch is available each day. Conference & banqueting facilities for 300 guests. Golf packages a speciality. Local courses, Adare, Adare Manor, Newcastle West (Ardagh), Charleville. Spacious gardens for your relaxation. A warm welcome awaits you.

B&B from €50.00 to €63.00

GERRY O'CONNOR
GENERAL MANAGER

American Express
Diners
Mastercard
Visa

Weekend specials from €150.00

26 26

Closed 25 December

ABBEY COURT HOTEL AND TRINITY LEISURE CLUB

DUBLIN ROAD,
NENAGH,
CO. TIPPERARY

TEL: 067-41111 FAX: 067-41022
EMAIL: info@abbeycourt.ie
WEB: www.abbeycourt.ie

HOTEL ★★★ MAP 6 I 8

Ideally situated off the main Dublin to Limerick road (N7). The hotel consists of 82 bedrooms, all tastefully decorated with emphasis on luxury and relaxation. Superb conference and banqueting facilities available with secretarial backup. Award winning Cloister Restaurant. Lively Abbots Bar and nite club complete with a unique techno gym and 20 meter heated pool. Golf, angling, horseriding and boating available nearby.

B&B from €60.00 to €95.00

TOM WALSH
MANAGING DIRECTOR

American Express
Diners
Mastercard
Visa

82 82

Open All Year

DROMINEER BAY HOTEL

DROMINEER,
NENAGH,
CO. TIPPERARY

TEL: 067-24114 FAX: 067-24444
EMAIL: info@dromineerbay.com
WEB: www.dromineerbay.com

HOTEL ★★★ MAP 6 I 8

Situated on the shores of Lough Derg, in Dromineer, the capital of Lough Dergh, we offer the perfect getaway from it all. Our facilities include 24 fully equipped en suite bedrooms, Captains Deck Restaurant, home of great food & great views of the lake, newly opened Crows Nest Bar & Restaurant and conference and banqueting facilities for up to 200 people. Easy access to sailing, angling, walking and numerous other leisure activities.

B&B from €35.00 to €100.00

ALAN ANDREWS
GENERAL MANAGER

American Express
Diners
Mastercard
Visa

Weekend specials from €100.00

24 24

Open All Year

Room rates are per room per night

GRANT'S HOTEL

CASTLE STREET,
ROSCREA,
CO. TIPPERARY
TEL: 0505-23300 FAX: 0505-23209
EMAIL: grantshotel@eircom.net
WEB: www.grantshotel.com

HOTEL ★★★ MAP 7 J 9

Located on the main link road from Dublin to Kerry, Limerick and Clare (N7). Visit Grant's Hotel, 3*** Hotel in the heart of the heritage town of Roscrea. The hotel features 25 en suite bedrooms pleasantly furbished in warm toned colours. Lunch and evening meals served in Kitty's Tavern daily. The award-winning Lemon Tree Restaurant is the ideal place to relax after a day's golfing, fishing or exploring Ely O'Carroll country. Special golf packages available.

B&B from €50.00 to €55.00

SHARON GRANT
PROPRIETOR

American Express
Diners
Mastercard
Visa

Closed 25 December

TOWER GUESTHOUSE, BAR & RESTAURANT

CHURCH STREET,
ROSCREA,
CO. TIPPERARY
TEL: 0505-21774 FAX: 0505-22425
EMAIL: thetower@eircom.net

GUESTHOUSE ★★★ MAP 7 J 9

Tucked away on the side of the road beside a medieval round tower this is a wonderful combination of a guesthouse, restaurant & bar. Situated in the centre of the town, with ample car parking, this is an ideal touring base with golfing, hill walking, horse riding and fishing all within close proximity. The en suite bedrooms are beautifully appointed and tastefully decorated. Overall this establishment has everything for lovers of good food, quality accommodation and classical bars.

Member of Premier Guesthouses

B&B from €28.00 to €45.00

GERARD & BRIDIE COUGHLAN
PROPRIETORS

American Express
Diners
Mastercard
Visa

Closed 25 - 26 December

TEMPLEMORE ARMS HOTEL

MAIN STREET,
TEMPLEMORE,
CO. TIPPERARY
TEL: 0504-31423 FAX: 0504-31343
EMAIL: info@templemorearmshotel.com
WEB: www.templemorearmshotel.com

HOTEL ★★ MAP 7 J 8

The Templemore Arms Hotel, located in the shadow of one of Ireland's most prominent landmarks, The Devil's Bit, in the centre of the town of Templemore. Recently rebuilt to match the demands of the most discerning guests, it boasts lounge bars, carvery, restaurant, banqueting suite and conference room, providing first class service. Visit the Templemore Arms Hotel and experience an enjoyable getaway.

B&B from €50.00 to €65.00

DAN WARD

Mastercard
Visa

Closed 18 April & 25 December

B&B rates are per person sharing per night incl. Breakfast

ANNER HOTEL & LEISURE CENTRE

DUBLIN ROAD,
THURLES,
CO. TIPPERARY

TEL: 0504-21799 FAX: 0504-22111
EMAIL: info@annerhotel.com
WEB: www.annerhotel.com

HOTEL ★★★ MAP 7 | 7

The Anner Hotel located on the outskirts of Thurles, 5 minutes walk from the town centre with beautiful landscaped gardens. We offer our guests a warm welcome, excellent food and a friendly service in comfortable surroundings. Superb leisure facilities boasts 18m pool, kiddies pool, jacuzzi, sauna and gym. Close to Holy Cross Abbey and The Rock of Cashel. Ideal base for touring, golf, walking, leisure breaks, conference and meetings.

B&B from €55.00 to €120.00

CATHERINE HARRINGTON

American Express
Diners
Mastercard
Visa

Weekend specials from €105.00

64   64

Closed 25 - 27 December

INCH HOUSE COUNTRY HOUSE AND RESTAURANT

THURLES,
CO. TIPPERARY

TEL: 0504-51348 FAX: 0504-51754
EMAIL: info@inch-house.com
WEB: www.inch-house.com

GUESTHOUSE ★★★★ MAP 3 | 7

Historic 300 year old manor set in a demesne of 250 acres, with fully licenced award winning restaurant. Relax in peace and tranquillity in front of open log fires. Each room has its own individual style with antique furniture combined with modern comforts for the discerning guests. Recommended in Bridgestone 100 Best in Ireland, the Good Hotel Guide, AA 5◆◆◆◆◆. Golf, fishing, shooting and horse-riding can be arranged.

B&B from €52.50 to €52.50

NORA EGAN

American Express
Mastercard
Visa

5   5

Closed 20 - 30 December

Room rates are per room per night

Galway, Mayo and Roscommon

There is a special quality about these three counties in the West of Ireland which is unique in Europe. The welcome is heartwarming, the quality of life, people and landscapes are all there for the visitor to enjoy.

The spectaculury beautiful countryside, the coast that has been etched by the Atlantic, the rambling hills and mountains and the lovely lakes and bays that mirror that special light from the clear skies over the countryside. Each county has its own special attractions and rich in all that is best in Irish folklore, music and song. There is something here for everyone. You will not be disappointed

MAJOR ATTRACTIONS

Galway City has a host of attractions on offer, including Galway Irish Crystal Heritage Centre, Royal Tara China, Lynch's Castle, the Spanish Arch, Nora Barnacle House and the Talbhdhearc – Ireland's only Irish-speaking theatre. In Co. Galway you have Thoor Ballylee, the home of the poet W.B. Yeats, and Coole Park Visitor Centre, former home of Lady Gregory, both located just north of Gort. The Battle of Aughrim Interpretative Centre near Ballinasloe gives a fascinating account of one of the most decisive battles in European history. Other major attractions include Dartfield Ireland's Horse Museum near Loughrea, Aughnanure Castle in Oughterard, Dan O'Hara's Pre-Famine Farm near Clifden, Leenane Cultural Centre, Kylemore Abbey in Letterfrack, Connemara, Glengowla Mines near Oughterard and Ionad Arann, Aran's Heritage Centre on Inishmore.

Amongst the attractions worth a visit in Co. Mayo are the Ceide Fields in Ballycastle, Foxford Woollen Mills, Turlough Park House, Knock Shrine and Folk Museum, Ballintubber Abbey and the Westport Heritage Centre. Westport Heritage Centre Ballintubber Abbey and Westport House and Country Park.

While Roscommon can boast the County Heritage

and Genealogical centre in Strokestown, Strokestown Park House, Gardens and Famine Museum, Clonalis House in Castlerea, Douglas Hyde Interpretative Centre in Porthard, King House and Boyle Abbey in Boyle and the magnificent Lough Key Forest Park.

For information and accommodation bookings in Counties Galway, Mayo and Roscommon contact:

Ireland West Tourism,
Aras Fáilte, Forster Street, Galway.
Tel: 00353 91 537700
Fax: 00353 91 537733
Email: info@irelandwest.ie
web: www.irelandwest.ie

Tourist Information Office,
James Street, Westport, Co. Mayo.
Tel: 00353 98 25711
Fax: 00353 98 26709
Email: westport@irelandwest.ie
web: www.visitmayo.com

Tourist Information Office,
Boyle, Co. Roscommon.
Tel: 00353 79 62145.
web: www.visitroscommon.ie

Galway Arts Festival, Co. Galway.
July

Guinness Galway Races, Co. Galway.
July / August

Galway International Oyster Festival, Co. Galway.
September

Guinness Ballinasloe International October Fair & Festival, Co. Galway.
September / October

ARD EINNE GUESTHOUSE

INISMOR,
ARAN ISLANDS,
CO. GALWAY
TEL: 099-61126 FAX: 099-61388
EMAIL: ardeinne@eircom.net
WEB: www.galway.net/pages/ardeinne

GUESTHOUSE ★★★ MAP 5 D 10

Ard Einne 3*** guesthouse is situated in an area of unrivalled beauty with sweeping panoramic views of Galway/Clare coastlines and Galway Bay from bedroom windows. The warmest of welcomes await you in this family-run, high quality guesthouse. Conveniently situated. Suitable base for cyclists, walkers and tours. Overlooks own beach. Ideal getaway for those looking for a totally unique, relaxing break. Quality home cooked food. Attractive group/individual rates.

B&B from € 36.00 to € 36.00

CLODAGH NÍ GHOILL
MANAGER

Mastercard

Visa

☺ 2 nights B&B and 1 Dinner from €84.00pps

🛏🐾☎️T❄♨️🎵P🍷⬛
14   14

IRISH HOTELS FEDERATION

Closed 12 December - 01 February

KILMURVEY HOUSE

KILRONAN,
INISMOR, ARAN ISLANDS,
CO. GALWAY
TEL: 099-61218 FAX: 099-61397
EMAIL: kilmurveyhouse@eircom.net
WEB: www.kilmurveyhouse.com

GUESTHOUSE ★★★ MAP 5 D 10

Kilmurvey House is a 150 year-old country house situated at the foot of Dun Aonghus, beside Dun Aongusa visitor centre. 3 minutes walk from a Blue Flag beach in one of the more peaceful locations on the island. We are the ideal setting for cyclists, walkers, botanists and those who just want to relax. Special group rates available.

B&B from € 35.00 to € 40.00

TREASA JOYCE
PROPRIETOR

Mastercard

Visa

🛏🐾☎️TC❄UP🍷
12   12

IRISH HOTELS FEDERATION

Closed 31 October - 01 April

PIER HOUSE GUESTHOUSE

LOWER KILRONAN,
ARAN ISLANDS,
CO. GALWAY
TEL: 099-61417 FAX: 099-61122
EMAIL: pierh@iol.ie

GUESTHOUSE ★★★ MAP 5 D 10

Pier House is perfectly located less than 100m from Kilronan Harbour and Village, within walking distance of sandy beaches, pubs, restaurants and historical remains. This modern house is finished to a very high standard, has a private gym for guest use and many other extra facilities. Its bedrooms are well appointed and have perfect sea and landscape views. If it is comfort and old fashioned warmth and hospitality you expect, then Pier House is the perfect location to enjoy it.

B&B from € 35.00 to € 55.00

MAURA & PÁDRAIG JOYCE
PROPRIETORS

Mastercard

Visa

🛏🐾☎️🖥TC❄JP🅿️S🕶
12   12

IRISH HOTELS FEDERATION

Closed 01 November - 01 March

Room rates are per room per night

TIGH FITZ

**KILLEANY, KILRONAN,
INISHMORE, ARAN ISLANDS,
CO. GALWAY**
TEL: 099-61213 FAX: 099-61386
EMAIL: penny@tighfitz.com
WEB: www.tighfitz.com

GUESTHOUSE ★★★ MAP 5 D 10

Tigh Fitz, a family run guest house, bar, lounge, is in Killeany, Inishmore. Offering luxurious accommodation in this unspoilt area of the Aran Isles. Tigh Fitz is unique in its situation, in its spaciousness and proximity to beaches and areas of archaeological and historical remains. In this area are the tall cliffs of Aran and the magnificent pre-historic forts. Tigh Fitz is 1.6km from the Island capital Kilronan and close to the Aer Arann Airstrip.

B&B from €38.10 to €50.00

PENNY FITZPATRICK
PROPRIETOR

Mastercard
Visa

11 11

IRISH HOTELS FEDERATION

Closed 01 November - 28 December

CASTLEGATE HOTEL

**NORTHGATE STREET,
ATHENRY,
CO. GALWAY**
TEL: 091-845111 FAX: 091-845154
EMAIL: info@castlegatehotel.com
WEB: www.castlegatehotel.com

HOTEL ★★ MAP 6 G 10

Small family run hotel situated in the heart of mediaeval Athenry, a heritage status town with 14 well appointed comfortable en suite bedrooms with TV. 15 minutes from Galway City in close proximity to the train station. Cinema centre and tea/coffee facilities available in residents' lounge. Live traditional music three nights a week.

B&B from €30.00 to €55.00

APHRIA COFFEY
MARKETING MANAGER

Mastercard
Visa

14 14

IRISH HOTELS FEDERATION

Closed 01 November - 31 January

BALLYNAHINCH CASTLE HOTEL

**BALLYNAHINCH,
RECESS, CONNEMARA,
CO. GALWAY**
TEL: 095-31006 FAX: 095-31085
EMAIL: bhinch@iol.ie
WEB: www.ballynahinch-castle.com

HOTEL ★★★★ MAP 5 D 11

Once home to the O'Flaherty Chieftains, pirate queen Grace O'Malley, Humanity Dick Martin & Maharajah Ranjitsinji, Ballynahinch is now a 4**** hotel. With casual country elegance overlooking the river & ringed by mountains, Ballynahinch offers an unpretentious service and is an ideal centre from which to tour the West. Log fires and a friendly fisherman's pub complement a restaurant offering the best in fresh game, fish & produce. Ballynahinch, the Jewel in Connemara's Crown. AA 2 rosettes. Member of Manor House Hotels.

Member of Great Fishing Houses of Ireland

B&B from €80.00 to €195.00

PATRICK O'FLAHERTY
GENERAL MANAGER

American Express
Diners
Mastercard
Visa

40 40

IRISH HOTELS FEDERATION

Closed Christmas Week & February

B&B rates are per person sharing per night incl. Breakfast

SILVERSEAS

CAPPAGH ROAD,
BARNA,
CO. GALWAY
TEL: 091-590575 FAX: 091-590575
EMAIL: silverseas@eircom.net

GUESTHOUSE ★★★ MAP 5 F 10

Luxurious quality residence, on coast road between Salthill & Barna Village, overlooking Galway Bay and landscaped gardens. AA Selected ◆◆◆, family run guesthouse with high standard of accommodation. All rooms en suite with power showers, TV, clock radio, hairdryer & trouser press. Guest sitting room with tea/coffee making facilities, large private car park. Breakfast menu available. Horse riding, golf, surfing, beach nearby, cycling, nature walks, angling, historical tours, Burren, sea cruise, Connemara & Aran Island trips arranged.

B&B from €27.00 to €40.00

GEULAH MCGRATH
PROPRIETOR

Mastercard
Visa

🛏️🅁☎️🖥️❄️🅅🅹🅿️
8 8

Open All Year

CARNA BAY HOTEL

CARNA,
CONNEMARA,
CO. GALWAY
TEL: 095-32255 FAX: 095-32530
EMAIL: carnabay@iol.ie
WEB: www.carnabay.com

HOTEL ★★★ MAP 9 D 11

Are you looking for somewhere special? Allow us to plan your carefree days in the most magical scenery in Ireland. Connemara, unique landscape, flora and fauna, unspoilt beaches, mountain ranges. Beautiful Western Way walking routes. Cycling, bicycles provided free. Our kitchen offers the finest fresh Irish produce. 26 well appointed rooms, most with sea or mountain views. Locally: St. McDara's Island, Connemara National Park, Kylemore Abbey, Aran and Inisbofin Ferry 40 mins drive.

Member of Irish Country Hotels

B&B from €50.00 to €90.00

PARAIC & MARY CLOHERTY
PROPRIETORS

American Express
Mastercard
Visa

🛏️🅁☎️🖥️🆃🅲🅲🅼🅹🅿️🆂🅰️🅲
26 26

🏛️🅁

IRISH
HOTELS
FEDERATION

Closed 23 -27 December

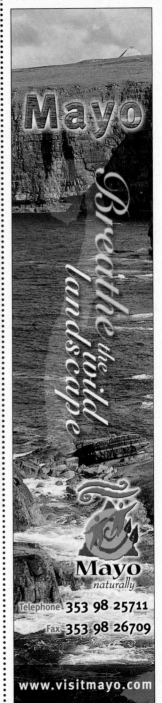

Mayo

Breathe the wild landscape

Mayo
naturally

Telephone **353 98 25711**
Fax **353 98 26709**

www.visitmayo.com

Room rates are per room per night

HOTEL CARRAROE

CARRAROE,
CO. GALWAY

TEL: 091-595116 FAX: 091-595187
EMAIL: hotelcarraroe@eircom.net

HOTEL ★★ MAP 5 D 10

The Hotel Carraroe is a 25 bedroomed en suite family run hotel situated in the heart of the Connemara Gaeltacht. The village of Carraroe itself is renowned for its traditional values and music. Daily boat trips to the Aran Islands are from nearby Rossaveal Harbour. Our local friendly staff will provide information on where to fish, play golf, horse ride or tour beautiful Connemara. Enjoy our new Irish Themed Bar.

B&B from €38.00 to €60.00

SEOSAMH Ó LOIDEÁIN

Mastercard
Visa

🖼 🏠 ☎ ▢ ▢ C CM ♪ ▢ P S 🔲 🔲 ▣
25 25

CASHEL HOUSE HOTEL

CASHEL,
CO. GALWAY

TEL: 095-31001 FAX: 095-31077
EMAIL: info@cashel-house-hotel.com
WEB: www.cashel-house-hotel.com

HOTEL ★★★★ MAP 5 D 11

Elegance in a wilderness on the shores of the Atlantic. It is set amidst the most beautiful garden in Ireland. Enjoy long walks, bicycle or horseback rides, and fishing. Later, relax in front of a peat fire in this elegant residence appointed with antique furniture and period paintings. Most guestrooms look onto the gardens and some onto the sea. Dine on bounty from the sea and garden - enjoy vintage wine. Also member of Ireland's Blue Book.

Member of Relais & Châteaux

B&B from €90.00 to €135.00

MCEVILLY FAMILY
PROPRIETORS

American Express
Mastercard
Visa

☺ Weekend specials from €178.87

🖼 🏠 ☎ ▢ T C ♨ CM ❄ ⚲ ∪ ▢ 🔲
32 32

🔲 🔲 Inet

IRISH
HOTELS
FEDERATION

ZETLAND COUNTRY HOUSE HOTEL

CASHEL BAY,
CONNEMARA,
CO. GALWAY

TEL: 095-31111 FAX: 095-31117
EMAIL: zetland@iol.ie
WEB: www.zetland.com

HOTEL ★★★★ MAP 5 D 11

Overlooking Cashel Bay this 19th century manor house is renowned for its peace and commanding views. The bedrooms and superb seafood restaurant overlook the gardens and Cashel Bay. Facilities include tennis court and billiard room and there are many activities, hill walking and golf in the surrounding area. Good Hotel Guide recommended, AA Courtesy of Care Award and Gilbeys Gold Medal Winner. 4**** Manor House Hotel, GDS Access Code: US 1-800-44-UTELL.

Member of Manor House Hotels

B&B from €88.00 to €105.00

JOHN & MONA PRENDERGAST
PROPRIETORS

American Express
Diners
Mastercard
Visa

✓ 🎣

☺ Weekend specials from €199.00

🖼 🏠 ☎ ▢ T C ♨ CM ❄ ⚲ ∪ ▢
19 19

🔲 🔲

IRISH
HOTELS
FEDERATION

B&B rates are per person sharing per night incl. Breakfast

QUALITY HOTEL CLARINBRIDGE

CLARINBRIDGE,
CO. GALWAY

TEL: 091-796988 FAX: 091-796884
EMAIL: info.galway@qualityhotels.ie
WEB: www.qualityhotels.ie/galway

HOTEL U   MAP 6 F 10

Superb Country House Hotel, 10 minutes from Galway City, on Galway/Limerick road, set in splendid woodlands in the famous Oyster village of Clarinbridge. Facilities include 51 luxurious bedrooms, an elegant restaurant offering a creative dining experience & Mollie Greaney's bar providing regular entertainment & an excellent bar food menu. Leisure facilities available complimentary at our sister hotel 5 minutes away. Family rooms available. An ideal choice for both business & pleasure. Golfing, fishing & equestrian facilities nearby.

Member of Choice Hotels Ireland

Room Rate from €65.00 to €169.00

RHONA KEARNEY
SALES & MARKETING MANAGER

American Express
Diners
Mastercard
Visa

Midweek special 3 B&B + 2 Dinners
from €139.00pps

51 51 CM P S

alc

IRISH HOTELS FEDERATION

Closed 24 - 26 December

ABBEYGLEN CASTLE HOTEL

SKY ROAD,
CLIFDEN,
CO. GALWAY

TEL: 095-22832 FAX: 095-21797
EMAIL: info@abbeyglen.ie
WEB: www.abbeyglen.ie

HOTEL ★★★★   MAP 9 C 12

Abbeyglen Castle Hotel was built in 1832 in the heart of Connemara by John D'Arcy of Clifden Castle. It is romantically set in beautiful gardens with waterfalls and streams, has a panoramic view of Clifden and the bay with a backdrop of the Twelve Bens. Abbeyglen provides a long list of indoor/outdoor facilities, cuisine of international fame, unique qualities of peace, serenity and ambience. Complimentary afternoon tea a speciality. AA 2 rosettes for good food and service. Reservations from USA 011 353 95 22832, from Europe 00 353 95 22832.

Member of Manor House Hotels

B&B from €89.00 to €107.00

BRIAN/PAUL HUGHES
MANAGER/PROPRIETOR

American Express
Diners
Mastercard
Visa

38 38 T P S

alc

IRISH HOTELS FEDERATION

Closed 06 - 31 January

Room rates are per room per night

ALCOCK AND BROWN HOTEL

CLIFDEN,
CONNEMARA,
CO. GALWAY
TEL: 095-21206 FAX: 095-21842
EMAIL: alcockandbrown@eircom.net
WEB: www.alcockandbrown-hotel.com

HOTEL ★★★ MAP 9 C 12

Alcock and Brown Hotel is family owned and operated. Situated in the centre of Clifden Village, featuring Brownes Restaurant with AA Rosette and 2 RAC ribbons for food and service. Ideal base for touring Connemara. Pursuits to be enjoyed are pony trekking, golfing on Connemara championship links course. Sea angling, guided heritage walks and mountain climbing. Numerous sandy beaches nearby. Member of Best Western Hotels - Central Reservations 01-6766776.

Member of Best Western Hotels

B&B from €50.00 to €65.00

DEIRDRE KEOGH
MANAGER

American Express
Diners
Mastercard
Visa

✓

19 19

Closed 22 - 26 December

ARDAGH HOTEL & RESTAURANT

BALLYCONNEELY ROAD,
CLIFDEN,
CO. GALWAY
TEL: 095-21384 FAX: 095-21314
EMAIL: ardaghhotel@eircom.net
WEB: www.ardaghhotel.com

HOTEL ★★★ MAP 9 C 12

A quiet family-run 3*** hotel, 2km from Clifden on Ardbear Bay, AA and RAC recommended. Bedrooms individually decorated with television, telephone and tea/coffee facilities. Award-winning restaurant, 3 AA rosettes & 3 dining seals by RAC, specialises in lobsters, salmon, oysters and Connemara lamb with homegrown vegetables and a wide selection of wines. Local amenities: golf, fishing and beaches. Reservations by post, phone, fax, email and website. Superior suites with bay view available.

Member of Irish Country Hotels

B&B from €69.50 to €82.50

STEPHANE & MONIQUE BAUVET
PROPRIETOR/MANAGER/CHEF

American Express
Diners
Mastercard
Visa

✓

☺ Weekend specials from €135.00

17 17

Closed 28 October - 17 April

BEN VIEW HOUSE

BRIDGE STREET,
CLIFDEN, CONNEMARA,
CO. GALWAY
TEL: 095-21256 FAX: 095-21226
EMAIL: benviewhouse@ireland.com
WEB: www.connemara-tourism.org

GUESTHOUSE ★★ MAP 9 C 12

Dating from 1848 Benview has been owned and managed by our family since 1926. See our history on web site. Recommended by Frommer and Le Petit Fute Guides. RAC and AA approved. Enjoy all the modern comforts of this elegant guesthouse, surrounded by antiques and old world atmosphere. Walking distance to all amenities, harbour and seaside. Free on street parking. Lockup garage available for motorcycles and bicycles. Your hostess Eileen wishes everyone a safe and pleasant journey.

B&B from €25.00 to €35.00

EILEEN MORRIS
PROPRIETOR

American Express
Mastercard
Visa

✓

9 9

Closed 24 - 26 December

B&B rates are per person sharing per night incl. Breakfast

Room rates are per room per night

BYRNE'S MAL DUA HOUSE

GALWAY ROAD,
CLIFDEN, CONNEMARA,
CO. GALWAY
TEL: 095-21171 FAX: 095-21739
EMAIL: info@maldua.com
WEB: www.maldua.com

GUESTHOUSE ★★★★ MAP 9 C 12

Awarded Guesthouse of the Year Ireland by Les Routiers, RAC Little Gem Award. Luxury & personalised hospitality in a relaxed, friendly atmosphere. All facilities for your comfort. Reception rooms & balcony overlooking landscaped gardens, invite you to enjoy our light menu, afternoon tea & select wines. RAC ◆◆◆◆◆. AA ◆◆◆◆◆ Karen Brown's Guide. Courtesy minibus. Bicycles for rental. Use of nearby health & leisure centre. Some ground floor rooms. Non smoking. Small conferences. USA Toll Free 1 866 891 9420, UK Free Phone 1 800 904 7532.

Member of Premier Guesthouses

B&B from €43.00 to €69.00

THE BYRNE FAMILY

American Express
Diners
Mastercard
Visa

Any 3 nights from €120.00

14 14

Inet

Open All Year

CLIFDEN HOUSE

BRIDGE STREET,
CLIFDEN,
CO. GALWAY
TEL: 095-21187 FAX: 095-21701
EMAIL: resv@clifden.info
WEB: www.clifden.info

GUESTHOUSE P MAP 6 F 10

This period town house of almost 200 years offers spacious airy rooms with views over the Twelve Bens. Newly renovated in 2001 it is an ideal base for touring Connemara, fishing and golfing or simply enjoying the delights of Clifden's bars and restaurants which is just a short walk away. We have private car parking. The treasures of Connemara await you. Welcome to Clifden House.

B&B from €35.00 to €70.00

MICHAEL & SHARON PRENDERGAST

American Express
Mastercard
Visa

12 12

Closed 10 January - 01 March

CONNEMARA COUNTRY LODGE

WESTPORT ROAD,
CLIFDEN,
CO. GALWAY
TEL: 095-22122 FAX: 095-21122
EMAIL: connemara@unison.ie
WEB: www.bedandbreakfastgalway.com

GUESTHOUSE ★★ MAP 6 F 10

Delightful Georgian home with spacious bedrooms, 2 mins walk from Clifden, on extensive grounds with large private car park. All bedrooms are en suite with TV, tea/coffee making facilities, telephones and hairdryers. Why not join Mary for an evening of traditional Irish music and song in her large lounge - a truly unique experience - as Mary is a well known performer. Her home and ballad singing have recently been recorded for broadcasting on American TV. French and German spoken.

B&B from €30.00 to €45.00

MARY CORBETT
PROPRIETRESS

10 10

Open All Year

B&B rates are per person sharing per night incl. Breakfast

DUN RI GUESTHOUSE

HULK STREET,
CLIFDEN,
CO. GALWAY
TEL: 095-21625 FAX: 095-21635
EMAIL: dunri@anu.ie
WEB: www.connemara.net/dun-ri

GUESTHOUSE ★★★ MAP 9 C 12

Centrally located in picturesque Clifden. Dun Ri is newly built and specially designed to offer a high standard of accommodation. The spacious and luxurious bedrooms are all en suite. Facilities include TV, phone, hairdryer and tea/coffee. Private parking is available. Ideal base to enjoy all Connemara has to offer - golf, fishing, walking, sandy beaches, cycling, horse riding, excellent restaurants and pubs. Secure motorcycle parking.

B&B from €25.00 to €35.00

MICHAEL KING
PROPRIETOR

Mastercard
Visa

10   10

Closed 01 November - 01 March

ERRISEASK HOUSE HOTEL & RESTAURANT

BALLYCONNEELY,
CLIFDEN,
CO. GALWAY
TEL: 095-23553 FAX: 095-23639
EMAIL: erriseask@connemara-ireland.com
WEB: www.erriseask.connemara-ireland.com

HOTEL ★★★ MAP 9 C 11

This 3*** hotel is situated on the shores of Mannin Bay with its own private beach. Only 10 minutes drive from Clifden on the R341, ideally situated for exploring the Galway coast, walk along the numerous sandy beaches & bay for hours. An extensive à la carte menu is available in our restaurant or you may enjoy a snack in the bar. Open to residents and non residents. Local amenities include guided heritage walks, climbing, sea angling, Connemara Link Course, pony trekking, cycling, and deep sea diving.

B&B from €45.00 to €85.00

PEADAR NEVIN & FABRICE GALAND
PROPRIETORS

Mastercard
Visa

12   12

Closed 05 January - 12 February

Room rates are per room per night

FOYLES HOTEL

CLIFDEN,
CONNEMARA,
CO. GALWAY
TEL: 095-21801 FAX: 095-21458
EMAIL: info@foyleshotel.com
WEB: www.foyleshotel.com

HOTEL U   MAP 9 C 12

Foyles Hotel, formerly Clifden Bay Hotel, is situated on the square in Clifden. Connemara's longest established hotel, it has been owned and managed by the Foyle Family since 1917. Facilities include direct dial phone, tea/coffee tray, multi-channel colour TV and hair dryers in all bedrooms. There is a pleasant patio garden to the rear of the hotel. Golf, horse riding, deep sea fishing and tennis are all available locally. Logis of Ireland, Central Reservations tel. 01-668 9743.

B&B from €45.00 to €70.00

EDDIE FOYLE
PROPRIETOR

Diners
Mastercard
Visa

☺ Weekend specials from €119.00

28 28

IRISH HOTELS FEDERATION

Closed 01 November - 04 April

JOYCES WATERLOO HOUSE

GALWAY ROAD,
CLIFDEN, CONNEMARA,
CO. GALWAY
TEL: 095-21688 FAX: 095-22044
EMAIL: pkp@joyces-waterloo.com
WEB: www.joyces-waterloo.com

GUESTHOUSE ★★★   MAP 9 C 12

Romantic lodge on edge of Clifden Town (12 mins walk). Relax with a genuine Irish coffee in front of a glowing fire after settling into your spacious 4 poster or 6' king-size en suite room embellished with special touches. South facing superior rooms furnished with sofas in bay windows to enjoy glorious countryside views. A refreshing relaxed home, tempered with our knowledge of local activities. Superb breakfast menu & our evening meals are a must. Secure private parking. Most bedrooms with 20" colour TV & VCR. Now with outdoor Hot-Tub & sauna.

Member of Premier Guesthouses of Ireland

B&B from €38.00 to €52.00

PATRICIA & P.K. JOYCE
HOSTS

American Express
Mastercard
Visa

8 8

IRISH HOTELS FEDERATION

Closed 24 - 27 December

QUAY HOUSE (THE)

BEACH ROAD,
CLIFDEN,
CO. GALWAY
TEL: 095-21369 FAX: 095-21608
EMAIL: thequay@iol.ie
WEB: www.thequayhouse.com

GUESTHOUSE ★★★★   MAP 9 C 12

The Quay House is Clifden's oldest building, c.1820. It now comprises 14 individually furnished rooms, some with balconies and working fireplaces, and has a wonderful collection of Georgian furniture and family portraits. It's just 7 minutes walk into town. Fishing, golf, pony-trekking, etc. are all nearby. Owned by Julia and Paddy Foyle whose family have been innkeepers in Connemara since 1917. Staying at the Quay House is a completely different experience. Outright winner of "Ceasar" Award for Ireland 2003.

Room Rate from €140.00 to €160.00

JULIA & PADDY FOYLE
OWNERS

Mastercard
Visa

14 14

IRISH HOTELS FEDERATION

Closed 07 November - 12 March

B&B rates are per person sharing per night incl. Breakfast

Room rates are per room per night

STATION HOUSE HOTEL

CLIFDEN,
CONNEMARA,
CO. GALWAY
TEL: 095-21699 FAX: 095-21667
EMAIL: info@stationhousehotel.com
WEB: www.stationhousehotel.com

HOTEL ★★★ MAP 9 C 12

Modern hotel adjacent to the old station house which has been restored as a pub and restaurant. Rooms are spacious, warm and designed for the modern traveller. Leisure centre with indoor pool and conference facilities for 250. A heritage site complete with museum, old railway buildings, a village of crafts, antique and designer shops and 11 holiday homes complete what is the most exciting resort complex in Ireland. A warm, friendly and relaxed atmosphere awaits you at the Station House.

Member of Sweeney Hotels

B&B from € 50.00 to € 100.00

CIAN LANDERS
GENERAL MANAGER

American Express
Diners
Mastercard
Visa

78 78

Closed 24 - 25 December

PASS INN HOTEL

KYLEMORE,
CONNEMARA,
CO. GALWAY
TEL: 095-41141 FAX: 095-41377
EMAIL: passinn@indigo.ie
WEB: www.kylemore-pass-inn-hotel.com

HOTEL ★★ MAP 9 D 12

Family owned and managed where you are assured a warm welcome, comfortable & restful holiday. Beautifully situated on a 4 acre site overlooking mountains and Kylemore Lake. Ideal base for leisure activities including fishing, diving, pony trekking and hiking. In both restaurant & lounge bar each window affords a view of magnificent scenery, serves vegetarian menu & local caught fish a speciality, also when available organic produce. Restaurant (and 1st Floor Bedrooms) Non-Smoking.

B&B from € 45.00 to € 63.00

ROSE RIMA
OWNER

American Express
Diners
Mastercard
Visa

11 11

Closed 01 November - 15 March

BALLINDIFF BAY LODGE

LUIMNAGH,
CORRANDULLA,
CO. GALWAY
TEL: 091-791195 FAX: 091-791099
EMAIL: mickrey@gofreeindigo.ie

GUESTHOUSE P MAP 6 F 11

A fully licensed guesthouse on the shores of Lough Corrib 20 minutes from Galway City in a peaceful rural setting. Ideally situated for touring Connemara or The Burren country. Boats, Ghillies are available by prior arrangement on Lough Corrib. There are several golf courses within 30 minutes drive. In the evening relax in our lounge bar and patio overlooking the lake and enjoy our award winning bar food.

Member of Premier Guesthouses

B&B from € 35.00 to € 40.00

KATHLEEN REYNOLDS
PROPRIETOR

Mastercard
Visa

6 6

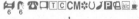

Closed 31 October - 01 March

B&B rates are per person sharing per night incl. Breakfast

CONNEMARA COAST HOTEL

FURBO,
CO. GALWAY

TEL: 091-592108 FAX: 091-592065
EMAIL: sinnott@iol.ie
WEB: www.sinnotthotels.com

HOTEL ★★★★ MAP 6 F 10

Perched on the shores of Galway Bay, just 10 minutes from the city this is the ideal base for your precious leisure time. View unspoilt sea and landscapes of the Aran Islands and the Clare Hills from the comfort of our Canadian hot tub. Luxurious public areas, an award winning bar and leisure centre, ample grounds and car parking provide a unique setting to relax and enjoy Galway City and County at its best.

Member of Sinnott Hotels Ireland

B&B from €57.00 to €115.00

PAUL O'MEARA
GENERAL MANAGER

American Express
Diners
Mastercard
Visa

Weekend specials from €115.00

112 112

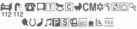

Open All Year

A STAR OF THE SEA

125 UPPER SALTHILL,
SALTHILL,
GALWAY

TEL: 091-525900 FAX: 091-589563
EMAIL: astarsea@iol.ie
WEB: www.astarofthesea.com

GUESTHOUSE N MAP 6 F 10

Luxury family managed guesthouse overlooking Galway Bay, within walking distance of Galway's medieval city and Salthill's sandy beach. An ideal base for holiday makers and business people, offering a very high standard of accommodation. All rooms have en suite, cable TV, hairdryers, tea/coffee. Some of our rooms have stunning views of the sea with balconies. Convenient to Leisureland, tennis, windsurfing, fishing, horseriding and golf. Safe facilities and carpark available.

B&B from €25.00 to €45.00

LORRAINE MCEVADDY
OWNER

American Express
Mastercard
Visa

8 8

Open All Year

Ireland's Horse Museum and Park

The Irish Horse Museum is housed in restored farm buildings on the old Dartfield Estate. Newly built galleries house fascinating and informative displays and AV presentations.

A unique feature of Dartfield is the stable area where some of the horses can be seen at rest and work.

Enjoy the wonderful flora and fauna and a variety of farm animals in the natural setting of old and young woodlands, bog, streams and parkland.

- Open all year
- Cafe and gift shop
- Extensive car and coach parking
- School tours and groups welcome
- Educational videos and computer games
- Picnic areas and nature trails
- 350 acres of beautiful parkland to explore
- Located on the main Dublin Galway road the N6, 4 miles from Loughrea near the village of Kilreekill.

DARTFIELD
Ireland's Horse Museum and Park

Dartfield, Kilreekill, Loughrea,
Co. Galway, Ireland.
Ph: 353 - 91 843 968
Fax: 353 - 91 843 969
Email: info@dartfieldhorsemuseum.com
Web: www.dartfieldhorsemuseum.com

Room rates are per room per night

ABBEY HOUSE

113 UPPER NEWCASTLE,
GALWAY

TEL: 091-524394 FAX: 091-528217
EMAIL: johndarby@eircom.net
WEB: www.abbeyhousegalway.com

GUESTHOUSE ★★ MAP 6 F 10

Family run guest house located on the N59 leading to Connemara. Convenient to city centre. Rooms are en suite with cable TV, and direct dial phones. Private car parking. Close to golf, fishing, tennis, swimming pool, horse riding, seaside and city centre. Excellent location for touring Connemara, Aran Islands and the Burren. A warm welcome awaits you from the Darby family.

B&B from €35.00 to €50.00

JOHN DARBY

Mastercard
Visa

12 12

IRISH HOTELS FEDERATION

Closed 20 - 28 December

ADARE GUEST HOUSE

9 FATHER GRIFFIN PLACE,
GALWAY

TEL: 091-582638 FAX: 091-583963
EMAIL: adare@iol.ie
WEB: www.adarebedandbreakfast.com

GUESTHOUSE ★★★ MAP 6 F 10

Adare Guesthouse is a family managed guesthouse, within 5 minutes of city centre (train/bus). Refurbished with old time pine furniture & floors, you can enjoy your multi choice breakfast in our dining room overlooking our beautiful patio area. All bedrooms have en suite, direct dial phones, cable TV & hairdryers. Tea/coffee & ironing facilities are available. 2 new suites built to a high standard with baths, direct dial fax phone, trouser press/iron, tea/coffee, cable TV/radio. Safe facilities available.

B&B from €35.00 to €49.00

GRAINNE & PADRAIC CONROY
PROPRIETORS

American Express
Mastercard
Visa

11 11

IRISH HOTELS FEDERATION

Closed 21 - 27 December

ANNO SANTO HOTEL

THREADNEEDLE ROAD,
SALTHILL,
GALWAY

TEL: 091-523011 FAX: 091-522110
EMAIL: annosant@iol.ie
WEB: www.annosantosalthill.com

HOTEL ★★ MAP 6 F 10

Small family run hotel located in quiet residential area. Galway's major tennis/badminton and squash club lies opposite the hotel. The golf club is also close by (1km), while Galway City and beaches are within easy reach. We are also on a main bus route. All rooms are en suite, TV, tea/coffee and direct dial telephone. Your hosts, the Vaughan Family, provide high class service in comfortable bedrooms at budget prices.

B&B from €35.00 to €65.00

GERARD & JOANNA VAUGHAN
PROPRIETORS

American Express
Diners
Mastercard
Visa

14 14

IRISH HOTELS FEDERATION

Closed 20 December - 20 January

B&B rates are per person sharing per night incl. Breakfast

ARDAWN HOUSE

31 COLLEGE ROAD,
GALWAY

TEL: 091-568833 FAX: 091-563454
EMAIL: ardawn@iol.ie
WEB: www.galway.net/pages/ardawn-house/

GUESTHOUSE ★★★★ MAP 6 F 10

Ardawn House is a luxurious haven for the discerning visitor to Galway. Located within five minutes walking of city centre, train & bus. Antiques, fresh flowers, silver and china help to make our multi choice home cooked breakfast famous. All bedrooms have en suite, direct dial phones, cable TV & hairdryers. Tea/coffee & ironing facilities are also available. Highly recommended in Guide du Routard, AA and many other guide books.

B&B from €35.00 to €70.00

MIKE & BREDA GUILFOYLE
PROPRIETORS

American Express
Mastercard
Visa

8   8

HOTELS
FEDERATION

Closed 22 - 26 December

ARDILAUN HOUSE HOTEL, CONFERENCE CENTRE & LEISURE CLUB

TAYLOR'S HILL,
GALWAY

TEL: 091-521433 FAX: 091-521546
EMAIL: info@ardilaunhousehotel.ie
WEB: www.ardilaunhousehotel.ie

HOTEL ★★★★ MAP 6 F 10

The Ardilaun is a privately owned 89 bedroomed 4**** hotel, in 5 acres of beautiful grounds. All rooms are en suite with *direct dial phone *TV *Trouser press *Tea and coffee making facilities *Hairdryer *Award winning restaurant *Superb leisure club *Deck level pool *Hydro-spa *Jacuzzi *Sauna *Steamroom *Aerobics *Hi-tech gym *Sun-room* therapy suites *Billiard room *Golf *Tennis *Beach & city within 5 minutes drive. Conference facilities for 2 - 400 delegates, banqueting facilities up to 300 guests.

B&B from €70.00 to €115.00

JOHN RYAN
MANAGING DIRECTOR

American Express
Diners
Mastercard
Visa

😊 Midweek specials from €190.00

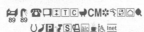
89   89

HOTELS
FEDERATION

Closed 22 - 28 December

ASHFORD MANOR

NO 7 COLLEGE ROAD,
GALWAY

TEL: 091-563941 FAX: 091-563941
EMAIL: ashfordmanor@esatclear.ie
WEB: www.galway.net/pages/ashford

GUESTHOUSE ★★★ MAP 6 F 10

Centrally located in the heart of Galway's City centre, Ashford Manor offers a unique combination of stylish en suite accommodation in a prestigious location at affordable prices. All rooms include multi-channel TV, radio, direct dial phone, professional hairdryer and tea/coffee facilities. Car parking. Credit cards accepted. Featured in holiday programme "Bon Voyage". Beside train and bus station. Ideal base for touring Connemara, The Burren and The Aran Islands.

B&B from €30.00 to €55.00

CORINNE MANNION
PROPRIETOR

American Express
Mastercard
Visa

5   5

HOTELS
FEDERATION

Open All Year

Room rates are per room per night

ATLANTIC VIEW HOUSE

4 OCEAN WAVE,
GALWAY

TEL: 091-582109 FAX: 091-528566
EMAIL: jennifer.treacy@nuigalway.ie

GUESTHOUSE ★★★ MAP 6 F 10

Atlantic View House is a luxurious haven overlooking Galway Bay with a large sun balcony. Some of our rooms have stunning views of the sea, with balconies. The house overlooks the beach with spectacular views of the Aran Islands and the Burren Mountains. We are only a short walk from the mediaeval City of Galway and the seaside resort of Salthill. Our rooms are luxuriously decorated with direct dial phone, satellite TV, trouser press, hair dryer, hospitality tray and clock-radio. Mobile: 086 - 8524579.

Room Rate from €30.00 to €100.00

JENNIFER TREACY
PROPRIETOR

Mastercard

Visa

⌂ 🛏 ☎ T C ∪ J P S 🔔
5 5

Closed 23 - 28 December

BRENNANS YARD HOTEL

LOWER MERCHANTS ROAD,
GALWAY

TEL: 091-568166 FAX: 091-568262
EMAIL: info@brennansyardhotel.com
WEB: www.brennansyardhotel.com

HOTEL ★★★ MAP 6 F 10

Brennans Yard Hotel situated in Galway City Centre, is a charming intimate hotel with excellent standards of accommodation, food and service. Our en suite bedrooms furnished with antique pine furniture have direct dial telephone, TV, radio, hairdryer, tea/coffee making facilities. In Terry's Restaurant, you can dine in discreet elegance and choose from a wide range of dishes prepared from the freshest ingredients. The Spanish Bar offers an intimate, warm and lively atmosphere. Bookable worldwide through UTELL International.

B&B from €47.50 to €85.50

CONNIE FENNELL
GENERAL MANAGER

American Express

Diners

Mastercard

Visa

☺ Midweek special offer 3 nights B&B plus 2 Dinners from €159.00

⌂ 🛏 ☎ 🖥 C ●CM J 🎵 P 🄰 🔔
45 45

Closed 24 - 29 December

CORRIB GREAT SOUTHERN HOTEL

RENMORE,
GALWAY

TEL: 091-755281 FAX: 091-751390
EMAIL: res@corrib-gsh.com
WEB: www.gshotels.com

HOTEL ★★★★ MAP 6 F 10

This 4**** hotel overlooks Galway Bay. It has 180 well appointed guest rooms. Leisure facilities include indoor heated swimming pool, steam room, jacuzzi, gym. Evening entertainment and childrens' play centre during summer months. Currach Restaurant and O'Malley's Bar. Convention centre accommodates up to 750 delegates. Bookable through central reservations 01-214 4800 or UTELL International.

Room Rate from €100.00 to €240.00

MICHEAL CUNNINGHAM
GENERAL MANAGER

American Express

Diners

Mastercard

Visa

☺ Weekend specials from €150.00

⌂ 🛏 ☎ 🖥 T ◬ ⬡ C ●CM ❄ 🕃
180 180
◐ ∪ J P S 🄰 🔔 ⅋ inet FAX

Closed 24 - 26 December

B&B rates are per person sharing per night incl. Breakfast

CORRIB HAVEN

**107 UPPER NEWCASTLE,
GALWAY**

**TEL: 091-524171 FAX: 091-582414
EMAIL: corribhaven@eircom.net**

GUESTHOUSE ★★★   MAP 6 F 10

Corrib Haven's motto is quality hospitality for discerning people. AA Selected ◆◆◆◆. It is new, purpose built, located in Galway City on the N59 leading to Connemara. All rooms en suite, power showers, posture sprung beds, cable TV, video, direct dial phones. Tea/coffee facility, breakfast menu, private parking. Convenient to city centre, good restaurants, nightly entertainment. Ideal for touring Connemara, Aran Islands. Smooth professionalism with personal warmth to our visitors. Non-smoking.

B&B from €25.00 to €45.00

TOM & ANGELA HILLARY
OWNERS

Mastercard
Visa

🖐 🎅 ☎ 🖥 T P S
9   9

Closed 24 - 27 December

EYRE SQUARE HOTEL

**FORSTER STREET,
OFF EYRE SQUARE,
GALWAY**

**TEL: 091-569633 FAX: 091-569641
EMAIL: eyresquarehotel@eircom.net
WEB: www.byrne-hotels-ireland.com**

HOTEL ★★★   MAP 6 F 10

The Eyre Square Hotel is situated right in the heart of Galway adjacent to both bus and rail stations. The Eyre Square Hotel caters for both the tourist and business person offering a very high standard of accommodation, rooms en suite with direct dial phone, satellite TV and tea/coffee making facilities. Enjoy excellent cuisine in our Red's Bistro or visit the lively Red Square pub. A warm and friendly welcome awaits you at the Eyre Square Hotel.

Member of Byrne Hotel Group

B&B from €45.00 to €100.00

JOHN HUGHES
GENERAL MANAGER

American Express
Diners
Mastercard
Visa

☺ Weekend specials from €125.00

🖐 🎅 ☎ 🖥 ⬍ T C CM ♫ ♪ 🔊 🖵 abc 🖥
52 52

Inet

IRISH
HOTELS
FEDERATION

Closed 25 - 26 December

FLANNERYS HOTEL

**DUBLIN ROAD,
GALWAY**

**TEL: 091-755111 FAX: 091-753078
EMAIL: flanneryshotel@eircom.net
WEB: www.flanneryshotel.net**

HOTEL ★★★   MAP 6 F 10

Flannerys Hotel is long established in Galway as an hotel offering comfort and style within relaxed surroundings. A welcome choice for business traveller or leisure guest. We take pride in ensuring that a special emphasis is placed on guest comfort enhanced by a genuinely caring and efficient service. Recently refurbished, the interior features tasteful décor, excellent restaurant and relaxing bar offering all day food service. Sample a selection of 136 rooms and suites. Member of Best Western.

Member of Best Western Hotels

B&B from €55.00 to €100.00

MARY FLANNERY
PROPRIETOR

American Express
Mastercard
Visa

☺ Weekend specials from €125.00

🖐 🎅 ☎ 🖥 ⬍ T C ♿ CM ♫ ♪ P S
136 136

🖥 abc 🍴 ♿

IRISH
HOTELS
FEDERATION

Closed 22 - 29 December

Room rates are per room per night

FORSTER COURT HOTEL

FORSTER STREET,
GALWAY

TEL: 091-564111 FAX: 091-539839
EMAIL: sales@forstercourthotel.com
WEB: www.forstercourthotel.com

HOTEL ★★★ MAP 6 F 10

This new hotel is excellently located in Galway City Centre and is easily accessed by all major approach roads. The hotel is impeccably finished incorporating every comfort for our guests. It comprises 48 stylish en suite guest rooms, all designed to cater for your every need. Enjoy dining in the intimacy of Elwood's Restaurant or why not relax in our extensive bar. The Forster Court Hotel gives you Freedom of the City.

Member of Select Hotels of Ireland

B&B from €45.00 to €120.00

RONAN LAWLESS
PROPRIETOR

American Express
Mastercard
Visa

48 48

Inet FAX

IRISH
HOTELS
FEDERATION

Open All Year

GALWAY BAY HOTEL, CONFERENCE & LEISURE CENTRE

THE PROMENADE,
SALTHILL,
GALWAY

TEL: 091-520520 FAX: 091-520530
EMAIL: info@galwaybayhotel.net
WEB: www.galwaybayhotel.net

HOTEL ★★★★ MAP 6 F 10

This AA**** Hotel situated on Galway City's Seafront at the Promenade, Salthill, has all the advantages of a city location while being situated on a beautiful beach overlooking the famous Galway Bay. All bedrooms are designed for maximum guest comfort. The hotel has a fully equipped leisure centre and swimming pool. Enjoy dining in The Lobster Pot Restaurant which offers modern style cuisine with strong emphasis on fresh fish and lobster from the lobster tank.

B&B from €70.00 to €125.00

DAN MURPHY
GENERAL MANAGER

American Express
Diners
Mastercard
Visa

Weekend specials from €110.00

153 153

IRISH
HOTELS
FEDERATION

Open All Year

GALWAY GREAT SOUTHERN HOTEL

EYRE SQUARE,
GALWAY

TEL: 091-564041 FAX: 091-566704
EMAIL: res@galway-gsh.com
WEB: www.gshotels.com

UNDER REFURBISHMENT - RE-OPENING MARCH 03

HOTEL R MAP 6 F 10

Originally built in 1845 this deluxe hotel has 99 guest rooms, incorporating Level 5, a range of luxury suites. Facilities include The Oyster Room Restaurant, O'Flaherty's Bar, Cocktail Bar. Leisure facilities include rooftop Canadian hot tub, sauna, steamroom, gym. Bookable through UTELL International or Central Reservations Tel: 01-2144800.

Room Rate from €150.00 to €250.00

FERGAL O'CONNELL
GENERAL MANAGER

American Express
Diners
Mastercard
Visa

Weekend specials from €170.00

99 99

IRISH
HOTELS
FEDERATION

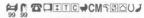

Closed 01 January - 18 March

B&B rates are per person sharing per night incl. Breakfast

GALWAY RADISSON SAS HOTEL

LOUGH ATALIA ROAD,
GALWAY

TEL: 091-538300 FAX: 091-538380
EMAIL: sales.galway@radissonsas.com
WEB: www.radissonsas.com

HOTEL N   MAP 6 F 10

The Radisson SAS Hotel located overlooking Lough Atalia Road, just a few steps from Eyre Square & main railway & bus stations. Choose from three room styles: Scandinavian, Maritime or Classic. Restaurant Marinas specialises in both seafood & international cuisine & the Atrium Bar & Lounge serves a selection of light meals. The Backstage Bar is a lively venue which attracts sports enthusiasts & the entertainment centre hosts a variety of musical & theatrical performances. The leisure centre with outdoor Canadian Hot Tub overlooks Galway Bay.

Member of Radisson SAS Hotels and Resorts

B&B from €72.50 to €182.50

MICHAEL DE HAAST
GENERAL MANAGER

American Express
Diners
Mastercard
Visa

200 200

Open All Year

GALWAY RYAN (THE)

DUBLIN ROAD,
GALWAY CITY EAST,
GALWAY

TEL: 091-753181 FAX: 091-753187
EMAIL: info@galwayryan.com
WEB: www.ryan-hotels.com

HOTEL ★★★   MAP 6 F 10

We offer the ultimate in relaxation and leisure facilities. 96 en suite rooms, newly refurbished in 2002, to ensure your stay is comfortable and restful. A magnificent leisure centre with a 2,500 sq. ft pool with 60ft swimming lanes, geyser pool, toddlers pool, loungers, jacuzzi, sauna, sports hall, aerobics studio, gym and floodlit tennis courts. Oranmore Room Restaurant, Toddys' Bar, Lobby Lounge and two meeting rooms. Complimentary parking. AA, RAC and Egon Ronay Recommended.

B&B from €92.00 to €111.00

SIOBHAN BURKE
GENERAL MANAGER

American Express
Diners
Mastercard
Visa

☺ Weekend specials from €140.00

96 96

Open All Year

GLENLO ABBEY HOTEL

BUSHYPARK,
GALWAY

TEL: 091-526666 FAX: 091-527800
EMAIL: info@glenloabbey.ie
WEB: www.glenlo.com

HOTEL ★★★★★   MAP 6 F 10

Glenlo Abbey Hotel - an 18th century country residence, is located on a 138 acre lake side golf estate just 4km from Galway City. A Bord Failte rated 5***** hotel, Glenlo Abbey is a haven for all discerning travellers. All 46 rooms have a marbled bathroom, personal safe, direct dial phone, trouser press, cable TV, radio and 24 hour room service. The Pullman Restaurant, two unique Orient Express carriages, offers a totally new dining experience. Other activities include fishing, etc.

Member of Small Luxury Hotels

Room Rate from €145.00 to €320.00

PEGGY & JOHN BOURKE
PROPRIETORS

American Express
Diners
Mastercard
Visa

46 46

Open All Year

Room rates are per room per night

GLENOAKS HOTEL

BISHOP O'DONNELL ROAD,
GALWAY

TEL: 091-589680 FAX: 091-589509
EMAIL: info@glenoakshotel.com
WEB: www.glenoakshotel.com

HOTEL ★★ MAP 6 F 10

A new family run hotel offering the visitor a warm welcome. Situated 1.5 miles from Eyre Square and a leisurely walk from the shores of Galway Bay, making this the ideal location for business or pleasure. All bedrooms are en suite with multi channel TV, direct dial telephone, hairdryer and tea/coffee making facilities.

B&B from €48.00 to €93.00

HANLEY BROTHERS

American Express
Mastercard
Visa

🛏🚪☎🖥⬆TCMPS🛗♿
20   20

Closed 23 - 28 December

HARBOUR HOTEL

NEW DOCK ROAD,
GALWAY

TEL: 091-569466 FAX: 091-569455
EMAIL: stay@harbour.ie
WEB: www.harbour.ie

HOTEL U MAP 6 F 10

The Harbour Hotel opened in March 2001. Located in the city centre adjacent to the waterfront area. Offering guests secure, complimentary on-site parking, this contemporary hotel offers 96 spacious rooms including 14 "Harbour" executive rooms. The hotel also has a chic bar & restaurant along with meeting rooms to cater for up to 75 people. The Harbour prides itself on its outstanding levels of service and quality in refreshingly unique surroundings.

B&B from €65.00 to €170.00

SEAMUS DOOLEY
GENERAL MANAGER

American Express
Diners
Mastercard
Visa

🛏🚪☎🖥T♿CM❄☀♫🎵P🛗
96   96
alc 🍽 Inet FAX

Open All Year

HOTEL SACRE COEUR

LENABOY GARDENS,
SALTHILL,
GALWAY

TEL: 091-523355 FAX: 091-523553

HOTEL ★★ MAP 6 F 10

Hotel Sacre Coeur is a family owned and managed hotel where a Cead Mile Failte awaits you. All of our 40 rooms are en suite, direct dial telephone, with colour TV and tea/coffee making facilities. Within five minutes walk of the hotel we have Salthill's magnificent promenade, tennis club and a wonderful 18 hole golf course. Renowned for its friendly service and excellent food you will enjoy your stay at the Sacre Coeur.

B&B from €45.00 to €52.00

SEÁN OG DUNLEAVY
MANAGER

Mastercard
Visa

🛏🚪☎🖥CMU♫🎵PS🛗alc Inet
40   40

Closed 22 - 31 December

B&B rates are per person sharing per night incl. Breakfast

HOTEL SPANISH ARCH

**QUAY STREET,
GALWAY**

TEL: 091-569600 FAX: 091-569191
EMAIL: emcdgall@iol.ie
WEB: www.iol.ie/~spanish_arch

HOTEL U MAP 6 F 10

Situated in the heart of Galway this is a 20 bedroomed boutique style hotel. Rooms of unsurpassed elegance designed by Easter McDonagh. Victorian bar features original wooden panelled walls from the home of Lilly Langtree, confidante to King Edward VII. The original 16th Century stone wall can be found in the bar where locals and visitors mingle and enjoy late nightly music. Claddagh Loft Organic Restaurant & Cogars Organic Bistro. Secure car park nearby. (Reduced fee payable).

Room Rate from €190.50 to €228.60

EASTER MCDONAGH
MANAGING DIRECTOR

American Express
Mastercard
Visa

20 20

Closed 25 - 26 December

IMPERIAL HOTEL

**EYRE SQUARE,
GALWAY**

TEL: 091-563033 FAX: 091-568410
EMAIL: imperialhtl@hotmail.com
WEB: www.imperialhotelgalway.ie

HOTEL ★★★ MAP 6 F 10

A bustling hotel in the centre of Galway City with modern comfortable 3 star bedrooms. Located in the main shopping area surrounded by a large choice of restaurants, pubs and quality shops. Five minutes walk from the new Galway Theatre, main bus and rail terminals. Beside main taxi rank with multi storey parking nearby. Full service hotel; friendly and informative staff. No service charge. R.A.C. 3 ***.

B&B from €50.00 to €85.00

KEVIN FLANNERY
GENERAL MANAGER

American Express
Diners
Mastercard
Visa

84 84

Closed 24 - 27 December

INISHMORE GUESTHOUSE

**109 FR. GRIFFIN ROAD,
LOWER SALTHILL,
GALWAY**

TEL: 091-582639 FAX: 091-589311
EMAIL: inishmorehouse@eircom.net
WEB: www.galwaybaygolfholidays.com

GUESTHOUSE ★★★ MAP 6 F 10

A charming family residence with secure carpark within 5 minutes walk of city and beach. All rooms contain direct dial phone, multi-channel TV and hairdryers. Tea/coffee and ironing facilities available. German spoken. An ideal base for touring the Aran Islands, Burren and Connemara. All day tours can be organised. Golf holidays, sea angling trips and coarse or game fishing arranged. Recommended by many leading travel guides. Specialise in Golf Package Holidays.

B&B from €30.00 to €60.00

MARIE & PETER
PROPRIETORS

Mastercard
Visa

Midweek specials from €100.00

8 8

Closed 23 December - 07 January

Room rates are per room per night

JAMESONS HOTEL

SALTHILL,
GALWAY

TEL: 091-528666 FAX: 091-528626
EMAIL: jamesons@iol.ie
WEB: www.galway.net/pages/jamesons

HOTEL ★★★ MAP 6 F 10

Jamesons Hotel is located in the heart of Salthill, overlooking Galway Bay. All rooms are en suite with special jacuzzi suites available. We offer excellent cuisine in the pleasant surroundings of our restaurant. Live entertainment 7 nights a week in summer and at weekends over the winter period. Conference suites facilitating up to 60 people. Private car parking. Special midweek rates available.

B&B from €31.00 to €100.00

JONATHAN POWELL
GENERAL MANAGER

American Express
Diners
Mastercard
Visa

20 20

alc

IRISH HOTELS FEDERATION

Open All Year

JURYS INN GALWAY

QUAY STREET,
GALWAY

TEL: 091-566444 FAX: 091-568415
EMAIL: jurysinngalway@jurysdoyle.com
WEB: www.jurysdoyle.com

HOTEL ★★★ MAP 6 F 10

Beside the historic Spanish Arch, overlooking Galway Bay and just a few minutes walk through twisting medieval streets to the buzz of Galway's commercial and shopping districts. Convenient also to main access routes to the haunting landscape of Connemara and the Atlantic Coast. There couldn't be a better location!

Room Rate from €72.00 to €170.00

KAREN CREMINS
GENERAL MANAGER

American Express
Diners
Mastercard
Visa

128 128

IRISH HOTELS FEDERATION

Closed 24 - 26 December

KNOCKREA GUEST HOUSE

55 LOWER SALTHILL,
GALWAY

TEL: 091-520145 FAX: 091-529985
EMAIL: knockrea@eircom.net
WEB: www.galway.net/pages/knockrea/

GUESTHOUSE ★★★ MAP 6 F 10

A 3*** family run guesthouse established 1950. Refurbished to a high standard with pine floors throughout. Car park at rear. 1km from city centre on bus route. 300 metres from Salthill Promenade. Restaurants, theatres, golf, tennis, horseriding close by. Perfect base for touring Connemara, Burren and Aran Islands. Within walking distance of Spanish Arch and Quay Street. Irish pub music entertainment available locally. All rooms en suite, TV and direct dial phone, tea making facilities, hairdryer. Frommers Guide recommended.

B&B from €27.00 to €45.00

EILEEN STORAN
PROPRIETOR

Mastercard
Visa

6 6

IRISH HOTELS FEDERATION

Closed 23 - 26 December

B&B rates are per person sharing per night incl. Breakfast

LOCHLURGAIN HOTEL

22 MONKSFIELD,
UPPER SALTHILL,
GALWAY
TEL: 091-529595 FAX: 091-522399
EMAIL: lochlurgain@eircom.net
WEB: www.lochlurgain.com

HOTEL U MAP 6 F 10

Welcome to Lochlurgain. Completely refurbished elegant Town House Hotel, AA***. Beside church off Main St, 5 minutes beach and leisure centre. City centre 5 minutes. Fresh home cooked food served. Seafood also featured. Enjoy comfort, peace, tranquillity and relaxation. Lochlurgain is 62 miles/100km north of Shannon Airport. One hour from the Burren and Connemara. On parle francais. Bed, breakfast and dinner breaks, please ask for details. Peadar and Joan Cunningham welcome you.

B&B from €45.00 to €95.00

PEADAR & JOAN CUNNINGHAM
PROPRIETORS

Mastercard

Visa

⊙ 2 B&B & 2 Dinner from €135.00pps

10 10

Closed 28 October - 11 March

MARIAN LODGE GUESTHOUSE

KNOCKNACARRA ROAD,
SALTHILL UPPER,
GALWAY
TEL: 091-521678 FAX: 091-528103
EMAIL: celine@iol.ie
WEB: www.marian-lodge.com

GUESTHOUSE ★★★ MAP 6 F 10

AA ♦♦♦♦ "A home from home". Family run. Period furniture. Adjacent to promenade/beach in Salthill Upr. Private parking. Daily tours arranged Connemara/Burren/Aran Islands. City bus route. Home baking. Bedrooms en suite, cable TV, DD phone, clock radio, orthopaedic beds, hairdryers, tea/coffee facilities. Iron, trouser press available. Large family rooms. Children welcome. Convenient to nightly entertainment, Leisureland, Aquarium, tennis, windsurfing, fishing, horse-riding, bird sanctuary. Beside golf course, driving range, hair salon, restaurant, pubs and shops.

B&B from €32.00 to €44.00

CELINE MOLLOY

Mastercard

Visa

6 6

Closed 23 - 28 December

MENLO PARK HOTEL AND CONFERENCE CENTRE

TERRYLAND,
HEADFORD ROAD,
GALWAY
TEL: 091-761122 FAX: 091-761222
EMAIL: menlopkh@iol.ie
WEB: www.menloparkhotel.com

HOTEL ★★★ MAP 6 F 10

Situated near Galway's City centre the Menlo Park offers the best of modern facilities with old fashioned hospitality. All rooms have TV/satellite, welcome tray, power showers, ironing centres, rich colour schemes. Executive rooms also feature king beds, sofas, work desks. Contemporary chic but casual restaurant; MP's Bar and Lounge. Bar food/carvery all day. Entertainment, traditional and folk at weekends. Easy access, free parking. Computer point in some bedrooms.

B&B from €50.00 to €110.00

DAVID KEANE
MANAGER

American Express

Diners

Mastercard

Visa

64 64

Closed 24 - 26 December

Room rates are per room per night

OCEAN CREST HOUSE

NO 6 OCEAN WAVE,
SEAPOINT PROMENADE, SALTHILL,
GALWAY
TEL: 091-589028 FAX: 091-529399
EMAIL: oceanbb@iol.ie
WEB: www.oceanbb.com

GUESTHOUSE ★★★ MAP 6 F 10

We chose this site and built this guesthouse to provide what our guests love, a taste of subtropical elegance, overlooking Galway Bay and beaches with panoramic views of the Burren Mountains. We are walking distance from the bustling medieval city of Galway and across the road we have the Promenade. Our bedrooms are beautifully appointed with multi channel TV, en suite facilities, phone, trouser press, hair dryers, hospitality tray and armchairs.

B&B from € 25.00 to € 45.00

LORRAINE MCEVADDY
MANAGER

American Express
Mastercard
Visa

🛏️ ⚟ ▢ T C P ▪
6   6

Closed 24 - 28 December

PARK HOUSE HOTEL & PARK ROOM RESTAURANT

FORSTER STREET,
EYRE SQUARE,
GALWAY
TEL: 091-564924 FAX: 091-569219
EMAIL: parkhousehotel@eircom.net
WEB: www.parkhousehotel.ie

HOTEL ★★★★ MAP 6 F 10

An oasis of luxury and hospitality in the heart of Galway City centre. We are Bord Failte 4★★★★, AA 4 star and RAC 4 star. All 57 rooms are en suite with bath and shower, direct dial phone, ISDN line, multi channel TV, tea/coffee making facilities, trouser press, awards of excellence winning restaurant over many years. Les Routiers Restaurant of the Year Ireland 1998-1999. Our high standards are your guarantee. Private residents' car park on hotel grounds.

B&B from € 60.00 to € 140.00

EAMON DOYLE & KITTY CARR
PROPRIETORS

American Express
Diners
Mastercard
Visa

☺ Weekend specials from €135.00

🛏️ ⚟ ☎ ▢ ↕ T C C M P 🔒 ▪
57   57

IRISH
HOTELS
FEDERATION

Closed 24 - 26 December

ROCKBARTON PARK HOTEL

ROCKBARTON PARK,
SALTHILL,
GALWAY
TEL: 091-522286 FAX: 091-527692
EMAIL: tyson'shotel@eircom.net
WEB: www.rockbartonhotel.com

HOTEL ★★ MAP 6 F 10

Owned and managed by the Tyson Family, fully licensed, in a quiet residential cul de sac. 200 metres from seafront and Leisureland Centre. Golf, tennis, badminton and squash just 5 minutes walk. Tyson's Restaurant offers a homely comfortable atmosphere noted for fresh local fish and prime steaks, prepared and cooked delightfully by chef/proprietor Terry. Bar food also available. Friendly service.

Member of Logis of Ireland

B&B from € 40.00 to € 50.00

PATRICIA AND TERRY TYSON
PROPRIETORS

American Express
Diners
Mastercard
Visa

☺ Weekend specials from €96.00

🛏️ ⚟ ☎ ▢ T C ⌖ C M ∪ J P S 🔒 ▪
10   10

IRISH
HOTELS
FEDERATION

Closed 23 - 31 December

B&B rates are per person sharing per night incl. Breakfast

SALT LAKE GUESTHOUSE

40 LOUGH ATALIA ROAD, GALWAY

TEL: 091-564572 FAX: 091-569544
EMAIL: oceanbb@iol.ie
WEB: www.oceanbb.com

GUESTHOUSE ★★★   MAP 6 F 10

Salt Lake House is a beautifully purpose-built guesthouse with exquisite views of Lough Atalia (inlet of Galway Bay). We offer luxurious accommodation within easy reach of Galway City centre, only minutes from bus/train station. Each room is beautifully appointed with en suite facilities, multi-channel TV (12 channels), armchairs and table, hospitality tray, iron and board and hairdryer.

B&B from €25.00 to €45.00

LORRAINE MCEVADDY
MANAGER

American Express
Mastercard
Visa

7   7

Closed 24 - 30 December

SALTHILL COURT HOTEL

THE PROMENADE, SALTHILL, GALWAY

TEL: 091-522711 FAX: 091-521855
EMAIL: salthillhotel@eircom.net
WEB: www.byrne-hotels-ireland.com

HOTEL ★★★   MAP 6 F 10

A Byrne Hotel, 50m from Salthill's sandy beach. Live entertainment most nights, every night from June to Sept (Thu-Sun rest of year). All rooms en suite, direct dial phone, tea making facilities, hair dryer. Excellent cuisine and service. 100m from Leisureland and indoor swimming pool. Overlooking Galway Bay with large car park. Ideal location for family holidays and over 55s in off season. Less than 2 miles from the medieval city of Galway. Many sporting activities nearby.

Member of Byrne Hotel Group

B&B from €55.00 to €105.00

PAULINE GRIFFIN
MANAGER

American Express
Diners
Mastercard
Visa

75   75

IRISH HOTELS FEDERATION

Closed 23 - 26 December

SKEFFINGTON ARMS HOTEL

EYRE SQUARE, GALWAY

TEL: 091-563173 FAX: 091-561679
EMAIL: info@skeffington.ie
WEB: www.skeffington.ie

HOTEL ★★★   MAP 6 F 10

The Skeffington Arms Hotel has been caring for guests for over 100 years. Overlooking Eyre Square, within walking distance of rail and bus terminals, it enjoys an enviable position in the heart of Galway. This privately owned hotel is justifiably proud of its new bars and à la carte menu which is very popular with both locals and guests alike. The bedrooms, which are newly refurbished have multi-channel TV, tea/coffee making facilities, direct dial phone and bath/shower en suite.

B&B from €50.00 to €120.00

SINEAD LALLY
RESERVATIONS MANAGER

American Express
Mastercard
Visa

23   23

IRISH HOTELS FEDERATION

Closed 25 - 26 December

Room rates are per room per night

SPINNAKER HOUSE HOTEL

KNOCKNACARRA,
SALTHILL,
GALWAY
TEL: 091-525425 FAX: 091-526650
EMAIL: spinnakerhousehotel@eircom.net

HOTEL ★★ MAP 6 F 10

The newly refurbished Spinnaker Hotel is a family run hotel overlooking Galway Golf Course and has spectacular views of Galway Bay and the Burren. All 20 rooms, most with private balconies, are newly built with en suite facilities, telephone, TV and tea/coffee maker. Within 2km of the hotel we have beaches, fishing, horse riding, golf and tennis clubs, Leisureland complex and the ferry port to the Aran Islands.

B&B from €35.00 to €77.50

TOM O'DWYER
PROPRIETOR

American Express
Mastercard
Visa

🛏️📞 T C M ♻ J P S 🔋 📶 ⚡
20 20

Closed 25 - 26 December

SUNRISE LODGE

3 OCEAN WAVE,
DR. COLOHAN ROAD, SALTHILL,
GALWAY
TEL: 091-527275 FAX: 091-583130
EMAIL: kheery@eircom.net
WEB: www.galway.net/pages/sunrise

GUESTHOUSE N MAP 6 F 10

Sunrise Lodge 3*** Irish Tourist Board rated / 4**** AA rated purpose built (1996) guesthouse. All en suite rooms, tea/coffee, hairdryer, DD phone, cable TV. Located overlooking Galway Bay just 5 minutes cab ride from Galway City Centre. Beautiful, unique views of Galway Bay, the Burren & Aran Islands. Ideal location to tour these regions as all are within 1.5 hrs - including Connemara, Cliffs of Moher & Westport/Clew Bay. The best of both worlds - your stay at Sunrise Lodge is at the heart of it all - for business or for a relaxing break.

B&B from €35.00 to €45.00

VALERIE HEERY

Mastercard
Visa

🛏️📞 C M ❄ J P S 🔋 ♿
9 9

Open All Year

VICTORIA HOTEL

VICTORIA PLACE,
EYRE SQUARE,
GALWAY
TEL: 091-567433 FAX: 091-565880
EMAIL: victoriahotel@eircom.net
WEB: www.byrnehotel.com

HOTEL ★★★ MAP 6 F 10

The Victoria Hotel is centrally located just 100 yards off Eyre Square, within walking distance of all shops, theatres, pubs and cinemas. Each of the 57 spacious en suite rooms is beautifully appointed with direct dial phone, trouserpress and hairdryer. The hotel restaurant serving à la carte dinner along with a lively bar serving lunches will all add up to make your stay at the Victoria as enjoyable as possible. The Victoria is your enclave in the city, dedicated to pleasing you.

Member of Byrne Hotel Group

B&B from €45.00 to €100.00

VINCENT HOBAN
GENERAL MANAGER

American Express
Diners
Mastercard
Visa

🛏️📞 T C M J 🔋 ⚡
57 57

Closed 24 - 26 December

B&B rates are per person sharing per night incl. Breakfast

WARDS HOTEL

LOWER SALTHILL,
GALWAY

TEL: 091-581508 FAX: 091-520353

HOTEL ★ MAP 6 F 10

Wards comfortable family run hotel is located 5 minutes from Galway's City Centre, a short stroll from Salthill's picturesque promenade, aquarium, swimming, bowling & golf. The hotel has a secure car park, cosy bar in which you'll get a taste of true Salthill life from our friendly staff. All our rooms are en suite with hairdryer, multi channel TV with remote control & direct dial telephone. Ironing facilities available on request. Additional Tel No: 091 523312

B&B from €35.00 to €50.00

ANTHONY FINNERTY
HOST

Mastercard
Visa

🙂 🍴🛏️☎️🖥️TCP🅿️
10 10

IRISH
HOTELS
FEDERATION

Closed 19 December - 02 January

WATERFRONT HOTEL

SALTHILL,
GALWAY

TEL: 091-588100 FAX: 091-588107
EMAIL: info@waterfront.ie
WEB: www.waterfront.ie

HOTEL U MAP 6 F 10

Our superbly located Hotel sits on the shores of Galway Bay in the delightful suburb of Salthill, just 5 minutes from Galway's vibrant city centre. Each of our spacious 64 en suite rooms offers a dazzling, panoramic ocean view, and is amply furnished with a large lounge or kitchenette. Adjacent to the Hotel is the famous Kitty O'Shea's Bar and Restaurant. Family rooms and free, secure car parking. Reservations: Call Save 1850 588 488

Room Rate from €57.00 to €105.00

KEN BERGIN
GENERAL MANAGER

American Express
Mastercard
Visa

🙂 Weekend specials from €99.00

🍴🛏️☎️🖥️TC♦CMU🎵🎶🅿️
64 64

aic Inet

IRISH
HOTELS
FEDERATION

Closed 21 - 28 December

WEST WINDS

5 OCEAN WAVE,
SALTHILL,
GALWAY

TEL: 091-520223 FAX: 091-520223
EMAIL: westwinds@eircom.net
WEB: www.travelaccommodation.co.uk/westwind.htm

GUESTHOUSE ★★★ MAP 6 F 10

Westwinds is a charming family-managed guesthouse overlooking Galway Bay, 10 minutes walk from Galway City, an ideal base for all travellers wishing to explore the Burren, Connemara and the Aran Islands. We are situated at the city end of Salthill Promenade, restaurants, nightly entertainment and all other amenities 5-10 minutes walk. All rooms have en suite bathrooms with power shower, hairdryer, cable TV, tea/coffee making facilities. Our hospitality awaits!

€75 per room per night Parking.

B&B from €27.50 to €50.00

RITA & PATRICK JOYCE
PROPRIETORS

American Express
Mastercard
Visa

🙂 Midweek specials from €73.66

🍴🛏️☎️🖥️CCM🎵P🅂♿
8 8

Closed 1 December - 10 March

WESTWOOD HOUSE HOTEL

DANGAN,
UPPER NEWCASTLE,
GALWAY
TEL: 091-521442 FAX: 091-521400
EMAIL: reservations@westwoodhousehotel.com
WEB: www.westwoodhousehotel.com

HOTEL ★★★★ MAP 6 F 10

The 4**** Westwood House Hotel stands amidst a rural landscape of greenery combining a mellow taste of the countryside with the city's cutting edge. Air conditioned throughout, the hotel features 58 superbly appointed bedrooms, the Meridian Restaurant, split level bar, conference and banqueting facilities and complimentary private car parking.

Member of Sweeney Hotels

B&B from €50.00 to €130.00

RACHAEL COYLE
GENERAL MANAGER

American Express
Diners
Mastercard
Visa

Weekend specials from €129.00

58 58

Inet FAX

Closed 24 - 26 December

WHITE HOUSE

2 OCEAN WAVE,
SEAPOINT PROMENADE, SALTHILL,
GALWAY
TEL: 091-529399 FAX: 091-529399
EMAIL: oceanbb@iol.ie
WEB: www.oceanbb.com

GUESTHOUSE ★★★ MAP 6 F 10

New and beautiful purpose-built guest house in Galway's finest location, overlooking Galway Bay and the Burren Mountains, minutes walk to Galway's medieval city and Salthill's new hotel, the Galway Bay. Large bedrooms with armchairs and tables, iron and board, multi-channel TV, hospitality tray and hairdryer.

€80 per night.

B&B from €25.00 to €45.00

LORRAINE MCEVADDY
MANAGER

American Express
Mastercard
Visa

6 6

Closed 24 - 28 December

LADY GREGORY HOTEL

ENNIS ROAD,
GORT,
CO. GALWAY
TEL: 091-632333 FAX: 091-632332
EMAIL: info@ladygregoryhotel.ie
WEB: www.ladygregoryhotel.ie

HOTEL ★★★ MAP 6 G 9

Situated in the west of Ireland near Coole Park, home of Lady Gregory in the town of Gort, with its many historic and local attractions. A warm friendly welcome awaits you as you enter the architectural splendour of the Lady Gregory Hotel. 48 beautifully appointed rooms, Copper Beech Restaurant, lively Jack B Yeats Bar and magnificent Gregory Suite. Relax in our Kiltatan Reading Room. Discounted green fees available from reception for Gort Golf Course located less than 1 hour from Shannon Airport. www.ladygregoryhotel.ie

B&B from €55.00 to €120.00

LEONARD MURPHY
GENERAL MANAGER

American Express
Diners
Mastercard
Visa

48 48

Inet FAX

Closed 24 - 27 December

B&B rates are per person sharing per night incl. Breakfast

SULLIVAN'S ROYAL HOTEL

THE SQUARE,
GORT,
CO. GALWAY

TEL: 091-631257 FAX: 091-631916
EMAIL: jsullinsauc@eircom.net
WEB: www.irelandmidwest.com

HOTEL ★★ MAP 6 G 9

Sullivan's Hotel is family run and managed, fully licensed and open all year round. Situated on main west of Ireland road, in close proximity to Coole Park, home of Lady Gregory, Thoore Ballylee, Kilmacduagh and the Burren. TV and telephone in all bedrooms, en suite rooms, meals served all day - bar food, à la carte dinner at reasonable rates. Available locally: golf, pony trekking, fishing. Dining Pub of the Year Award 2000 & 2001.

Room Rate from €40.00 to €70.00

JOHNNY & ANNIE SULLIVAN
PROPRIETORS

American Express
Diners
Mastercard
Visa

🛏🔥☎🖥Ⓣ🅲🍴CM🚶🌙🆂🅰alc🚬
12 12

IRISH HOTELS FEDERATION

Open All Year

ANGLERS REST HOTEL

HEADFORD,
CO. GALWAY

TEL: 093-35528 FAX: 093-35749
EMAIL: anglersrest@eircom.net

HOTEL ★★ MAP 10 F 12

The Anglers Rest Hotel has been owned and managed by the Heneghan family since 1905. Just 3 miles from the eastern shore of Lough Corrib and 16 miles from Galway City. It is an ideal centre for the tourist or angler. With 20 bedrooms, dining room, 2 bars, open lounge, residents lounge and a function room with dining facilities for more than 200. David Heneghan, and his son Frank, grandson of the founder are now the proprietors and most genial hosts.

B&B from €45.00 to €65.00

FRANK HENEGHAN
MANAGER

American Express
Mastercard
Visa

🛏🔥☎🖥🅲CM🌙🆂🅰alc🚬♿
20 20

IRISH HOTELS FEDERATION

Open All Year

DOONMORE HOTEL

INISHBOFIN ISLAND,
CO. GALWAY

TEL: 095-45804 FAX: 095-45804
EMAIL: info@doonmorehotel.com
WEB: www.doonmorehotel.com

HOTEL ★★ MAP 9 C 12

Uniquely situated on a beautiful and historic island, commanding magnificent views of the surrounding sea and islands. Inishbofin, a haven for artists, fishermen, bird watchers, nature lovers or those who just wish to escape from the hectic pace of life. Fine sandy beaches. Sea trips and boat angling can be arranged. Facilities for divers. Excellent shore fishing. Doonmore Hotel is owned and managed by the Murray Family, unpretentious but friendly and comfortable.

B&B from €38.00 to €55.00

AILEEN MURRAY
MANAGER

American Express
Mastercard
Visa

🛏🔥☎🖥Ⓣ🅲🍴CM❄🌙🆂🅰alc
19 19
☕

Closed 30 September - 18 April

Room rates are per room per night

MERRIMAN INN & RESTAURANT

MAIN STREET,
KINVARA,
CO. GALWAY
TEL: 091-638222 FAX: 091-637686
EMAIL: merrimanhotel@eircom.net
WEB: www.merrimanhotel.com

HOTEL ★★★ MAP 6 G 10

Located in the picturesque fishing village of Kinvara, The Merriman opened in April '97. Named after the famous Irish Poet, Brian Merriman, this 32 bedroomed hotel has one of the largest thatched roofs in Ireland. Overlooking Galway Bay, the Burren, the hills of Connemara, Kinvara is an ideal touring base. Dunguaire Castle, a short stroll away, where an enjoyable medieval banquet can be experienced. Excellent restaurant & bar provides for a friendly, comfortable & value for money hotel.

B&B from €47.50 to €60.00

RITA HUBAN
MANAGER

American Express
Diners
Mastercard
Visa

32 32

Closed 22 December - 31 January

LEENANE HOTEL

LEENANE,
CONNEMARA,
CO. GALWAY
TEL: 095-42249 FAX: 095-42376
EMAIL: leenanehotel@eircom.net
WEB: www.connemara.net/leenanehotel

HOTEL U MAP 9 D 12

On the shores of Killary Harbour, Ireland's only Fjord, lies Ireland's oldest Coaching Inn. The Leenane Hotel, recently refurbished to the highest of standards, boasts the most spectacular views in Ireland. Being a family-run hotel, we understand the appreciation for traditional home-cooking. Fresh seafood from the harbour and vegetables and herbs from the hotel garden are brought in every day. The hotel's position makes it without doubt the best base for exploring Connemara, the most romantic and unspoiled region of Ireland.

B&B from €35.00 to €70.00

CONOR FOYLE
MANAGER

Mastercard
Visa

☺ Week partial board from €375.00

29 29

Closed 02 November - 15 April

PORTFINN LODGE

LEENANE,
CO. GALWAY
TEL: 095-42265 FAX: 095-42315
EMAIL: rorydaly@anu.ie
WEB: www.portfinn.com

GUESTHOUSE ★★ MAP 9 D 12

Portfinn Lodge is a family run guest house offering 8 comfortable rooms en suite including double and triple bedrooms, a guest lounge and a restaurant which has an international reputation for its fresh seafood. Rory and Brid Daly will be delighted to make you feel welcome. An ideal centre from which beaches, walking, angling, watersports etc. are within easy reach. When in Connemara, stay at Portfinn.

Member of Premier Guesthouses

B&B from €35.00 to €45.00

BRID & RORY DALY
OWNERS

Mastercard
Visa

8 8

Closed 01 November - 31 March

B&B rates are per person sharing per night incl. Breakfast

ROSLEAGUE MANOR HOTEL

LETTERFRACK,
CONNEMARA,
CO. GALWAY

TEL: 095-41101 FAX: 095-41168

EMAIL: rosleaguemanor@eircom.net
WEB: www.rosleague.com

HOTEL ★★★★ MAP 9 C 12

Rosleague is a Regency manor now run as a first class country house hotel by Mark Foyle and Eddie Foyle. It lies 7 miles north west of Clifden on the coast overlooking a sheltered bay and surrounded by the Connemara Mountains, beside the National Park. It is renowned for its superb cuisine personally supervised by the owners with all the amenities expected by today's discerning guest. Also a member of Ireland's Blue Book.

Member of I.C.H.R.A. (Blue Book)

B&B from €80.00 to €115.00

MARK FOYLE/EDDIE FOYLE
MANAGER/OWNER

American Express
Mastercard
Visa

Weekend specials from €170.00

20 20

Closed 01 November - 14 March

MEADOW COURT HOTEL

CLOSTOKEN,
LOUGHREA,
CO. GALWAY

TEL: 091-841051 FAX: 091-842406

EMAIL: meadowcourthotel@eircom.net
WEB: www.meadowcourthotel.com

HOTEL ★★★ MAP 6 H 10

Newly extended and refurbished the Meadow Court Hotel's en suite rooms have full facilities, multi channel TV, hair dryer and garment press. Superb dining is on offer in our award-winning restaurant renowned for its outstanding cuisine. Enjoy after dinner drinks in our Derby Bar. Situated on the main Galway Dublin Road 2 miles from Loughrea, 18 miles from Galway, convenient to all local 18-hole golf courses, angling, horseriding, water sports. Banqueting & conference facilities. Carpark.

B&B from €45.00 to €82.50

TOM & DAVID CORBETT
DIRECTORS

American Express
Mastercard
Visa

Midweek room only rate available

21 21

Closed 25 December

O'DEAS HOTEL

BRIDE STREET,
LOUGHREA,
CO. GALWAY

TEL: 091-841611 FAX: 091-842635

EMAIL: odeashotel@eircom.net
WEB: www.commerce.ie/odeashotel

HOTEL ★★★ MAP 6 H 10

O'Deas Hotel is a family hotel, a Georgian town house hotel, of character with open fires and within walking distance of Loughrea's game fishing lake. It is an ideal touring base situated on the N6 (exactly halfway between Clonmacnoise, 35 miles to the east and the Cliffs of Moher, 35 miles to the west). The start of the Burren country is just 12 miles away. Galway City 20 miles.

Member of MinOtel of Ireland

B&B from €50.00 to €55.00

MARY O'NEILL
PROPRIETOR/MANAGER

American Express
Mastercard
Visa

32 32

Closed 24 - 26 December

Room rates are per room per night

PEACOCKES HOTEL & COMPLEX

MAAM CROSS,
CONNEMARA,
CO. GALWAY
TEL: 091-552306 FAX: 091-552216
EMAIL: peacockes@eircom.net
WEB: www.peacockeshotel.com

HOTEL ★★★ MAP 6 F 10

Newly built, nestling between the lakes and mountains at the crossroads to Connemara. Peacockes Hotel is the ideal base for hillwalking, cycling, golfing, fishing, horse riding or watersports. After a day's travel, relax with a drink by the open turf fire in the Bogdale Bar or enjoy a sumptuous meal in our Quiet Man Restaurant. Visit our 20m high viewing tower, extensive craft shop and replica Quiet Man cottage.

B&B from €50.00 to €90.00

EIMEAR KILLIAN
GENERAL MANAGER

American Express
Diners
Mastercard
Visa

☺ Weekend specials from €125.00

25 25

Closed 23 - 26 December

ORANMORE LODGE HOTEL, CONFERENCE & LEISURE CENTRE

ORANMORE,
CO. GALWAY

TEL: 091-794400 FAX: 091-790227
EMAIL: orlodge@eircom.net
WEB: www.oranmorelodge.com

HOTEL ★★★ MAP 6 G 10

This manor house hotel 8km from Galway City in the picturesque village of Oranmore, overlooking Galway Bay and on the edge of oyster country. 3km from Galway Airport. Equestrian, golfing and walking pursuits all within 3km of the hotel. Full leisure facilities with a 17m swimming pool and computerised TechnoGym. Your host and his efficient staff radiate a welcome and warmth reminiscent of the old country houses of Ireland.

B&B from €50.00 to €130.00

BRIAN J. O'HIGGINS
PROPRIETOR

American Express
Diners
Mastercard
Visa

☺ Weekend specials from €99.00

56 56

Closed 22 - 27 December

QUALITY HOTEL AND LEISURE CENTRE GALWAY

ORANMORE,
CO. GALWAY

TEL: 091-792244 FAX: 091-792246
EMAIL: info.galway@qualityhotels.ie
WEB: www.qualityhotels.ie/galway

HOTEL ★★★ MAP 6 G 10

This luxury hotel is ideally located on the N6 approach to Galway, adjacent to the picturesque village of Oranmore & just 5 mins drive from Galway City. Facilities include 113 spacious rooms, a traditional pub with regular entertainment & all day menu, Lannigans Restaurant, residents' lounge & a superb leisure centre with a 20m pool, jacuzzi, hi-tech gym, steamroom, sauna, therapy suite & solarium. Rooms to accommodate up to 2 adults & 3 children. Golf, karting, horseriding nearby.

Member of Choice Hotels Ireland

Room Rate from €65.00 to €169.00

DERMOT COMERFORD
GENERAL MANAGER

American Express
Diners
Mastercard
Visa

☺ Midweek specials 3 B&B + 2 Dinners from €139.00pps

113 113

Closed 24 - 26 December

B&B rates are per person sharing per night incl. Breakfast

BOAT INN

THE SQUARE,
OUGHTERARD,
CO. GALWAY

TEL: 091-552196 FAX: 091-552694
EMAIL: info@theboatinn.com
WEB: www.theboatinn.com

GUESTHOUSE ★★★ MAP 5 E 11

3*** guesthouse in the heart of Oughterard, just 25 minutes from Galway. 5 minutes to Lough Corrib and redesigned 18 hole golf course. Ideal base to explore Connemara. The Boat Bar and Restaurant offer an imaginative choice of food, drink and wine. Enjoy the continental feel of our terrace and rear gardens. Live music in the bar. All bedrooms en suite with TV, radio, phone and tea coffee making facilities.

B&B from € 32.00 to € 38.00

MICHAEL MURPHY
PROPRIETOR

American Express
Diners
Mastercard
Visa

10 10

Closed 25 - 26 December

CONNEMARA GATEWAY HOTEL

OUGHTERARD,
CO. GALWAY

TEL: 091-552328 FAX: 091-552332
EMAIL: gateway@iol.ie
WEB: www.sinnotthotels.com

HOTEL ★★★ MAP 5 E 11

Set in its own grounds, just 16 miles from Galway City at the gateway to Connemara. The emphasis here is on warmth and hospitality. Full of character and style, turf fires, a pine panelled lobby, Cottage Bar, indoor heated swimming pool, meeting facilities and all bedrooms en suite with tea/coffee making facilities, make this an ideal place from which to explore all that Galway/Connemara has to offer. Excellent golf and fishing nearby.

Member of Sinnott Hotels Ireland

B&B from € 49.00 to € 110.00

JOHN BRODERICK
MANAGER

American Express
Diners
Mastercard
Visa

Weekend specials from €115.00

62 62

Open All Year

CORRIB HOUSE HOTEL

BRIDGE STREET,
OUGHTERARD,
CO. GALWAY

TEL: 091-552329 FAX: 091-552522
EMAIL: info@corribhotel.com
WEB: www.corribhotel.com

HOTEL U MAP 5 E 11

Character at the gateway to Connemara is the Corrib House Hotel situated 17 miles from Galway City. 27 comfortable en suite rooms, turf fires and our renowned Owenriff Restaurant with superb food and wine list. 4 championship golf courses within 30 miles, the world famous fishing on Lough Corrib (1 mile) and magnificent walking and hiking - a few of the pastimes available while staying with us.

B&B from € 36.00 to € 55.00

CAROLINE FAHY CONNEELY
MANAGER

American Express
Diners
Mastercard
Visa

Weekend specials from €90.00

27 27

Closed 23 - 28 December

Room rates are per room per night

CORRIB WAVE GUEST HOUSE

PORTACARRON,
OUGHTERARD, CONNEMARA,
CO. GALWAY
TEL: 091-552147 FAX: 091-552736
EMAIL: cwh@gofree.indigo.ie
WEB: www.corribwave.com

GUESTHOUSE ★★★ MAP 5 E 11

Panoramic lakeside guest house - the home of Michael & Maria Healy. As our guests, you are assured of a warm welcome to a family home with every comfort and Irish hospitality, superb home cooking, excellent wines, beautiful en suite bedrooms (all with double and single beds), TVs, hairdryers. Spectacular views, turf fire, peace & tranquillity. Angling specialists, boats, engines. Boatmen for hire. Wild brown trout, salmon, pike, lakeside walks. 18 hole golf 1km. Colour brochure on request.

B&B from €32.50 to €35.00

MARIA & MICHAEL HEALY
PROPRIETORS

Mastercard
Visa

Midweek specials from €155.00

9 9

Closed 15 November - 01 March

CURRAREVAGH HOUSE

OUGHTERARD,
CONNEMARA,
CO. GALWAY
TEL: 091-552312 FAX: 091-552731
EMAIL: currarevagh@ireland.com
WEB: www.currarevagh.com

GUESTHOUSE ★★★★ MAP 5 E 11

A charming country mansion, built in 1842, situated beside Lough Corrib in 60 hect. of private woodlands. The relaxing atmosphere & classically simple menus receive much international praise. Own fishing, boats, tennis court, with golf & riding locally. Recommendations: Egon Ronay, Guide Michelin, Footprint Guide, Lonely Planet, Karen Brown's Irish Country Inn's, Good Food Guide, Good Hotel Guide & many other international hotel & food guides. You should stay at least 3 nights to absorb the atmosphere and gently explore Connemara.

Member of Ireland's Blue Book

B&B from €77.00 to €97.00

HARRY & JUNE HODGSON
PROPRIETORS

Mastercard
Visa

Week partial board from €682.00

15 15

Closed 20 October - 01 April

LAKE HOTEL

OUGHTERARD,
CO. GALWAY

TEL: 091-552275 FAX: 091-552794

HOTEL ★★ MAP 5 E 11

Family Run Hotel under the personal supervision of Frank & Mary O' Meara. There are 4 championship golf courses, Oughterard, Connemara, Barna, Galway Bay Golf & Country Club close by. Oughterard is within easy access to Connemara's rugged hills and hidden lakes, only 20 minutes drive to Galway City. Wild Brown Trout, Salmon in the beautiful Lough Corrib. We cater for shooting groups. Special group rates. All rooms en suite with TV and phone.

B&B from €45.00 to €55.00

FRANK & MARY O'MEARA
PROPRIETORS

American Express
Diners
Mastercard
Visa

Weekend specials from €109.00

18 18

Open All Year

B&B rates are per person sharing per night incl. Breakfast

MOUNTAIN VIEW GUEST HOUSE

AUGHNANURE,
OUGHTERARD,
CO. GALWAY
TEL: 091-550306 FAX: 091-550133
EMAIL: tricia.oconnor@eircom.net

GUESTHOUSE ★★★ MAP 5 E 11

Situated just off the N59, 24km from Galway City and within 2.4km of Oughterard, with the Connemara Mountains in the distance and Lough Corrib nearby. Leisure activities include; golf at the renowned Oughterard Golf Club, established walks along scenic routes, boating or fishing on Lough Corrib. Guests can relax in the lounge with open turf fire and sample some of the cuisine before retiring to en suite bedrooms with TV, direct dial phone, tea/coffee making facilities and hairdryer.

B&B from €26.00 to €35.00

RICHARD & PATRICIA O'CONNOR
PROPRIETORS

Mastercard
Visa

😊 Weekend specials from €75.00

10 10

Closed 23 - 28 December

RIVER RUN LODGE

GLANN ROAD,
OUGHTERARD,
CO. GALWAY
TEL: 091-552697 FAX: 091-552669
EMAIL: rivrun@indigo.ie
WEB: www.connemara-bedandbreakfast.com

GUESTHOUSE ★★★★ MAP 5 E 11

River Run Lodge sits on the Owenriff which flows into Lough Corrib. Just minutes walk from the heart of Oughterard you'll find landscaped gardens, patios and riverside walks. A lodge warmed by light wood and lit by natural hues. Comfortably traditional spacious bedrooms and cosy lounges. A riverside restaurant with menus to rival any city repertoire. Book your slice of peace and quiet in the ideal base for exploring Connemara. AA ◆◆◆◆◆.

B&B from €35.00 to €55.00

TOM & ANNE LITTLE
PROPRIETORS

American Express
Mastercard
Visa

😊 weekend specials from €119.00

6 6

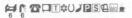

Open All Year

ROSS LAKE HOUSE HOTEL

ROSSCAHILL,
OUGHTERARD,
CO. GALWAY
TEL: 091-550109 FAX: 091-550184
EMAIL: rosslake@iol.ie
WEB: www.rosslakehotel.com

HOTEL ★★★ MAP 5 E 11

Ross Lake House is a wonderful Georgian house set in the magnificent wilderness of Connemara. Six acres of mature gardens surround the house creating an air of peace and tranquillity. Hosts Henry and Elaine Reid have beautifully restored this manor house to its former glory. A high quality Irish menu is prepared daily featuring a tempting variety of fresh produce from nearby Connemara hills, streams and lakes as well as fish straight from the Atlantic.

Member of Green Book of Ireland

B&B from €75.00 to €150.00

ELAINE & HENRY REID
PROPRIETORS

American Express
Diners
Mastercard
Visa

😊 Midweek specials from €170.00

13 13

Closed 31 October - 15 March

Room rates are per room per night

SHANNON OAKS HOTEL & COUNTRY CLUB

PORTUMNA,
CO. GALWAY

TEL: 0509-41777 FAX: 0509-41357
EMAIL: sales@shannonoaks.ie
WEB: www.shannonoaks.ie

HOTEL ★★★ MAP 6 I 9

Shannon Oaks Hotel & Country Club lies adjacent to the 17th century Portumna Castle and estate, by the shores of Lough Derg. All our rooms have satellite television, D.D. phone and an en suite bathroom. A distinguished menu of classic and fusion Irish dishes are available each evening. Our leisure centre, with its indoor heated swimming pool, sauna, steam room and gymnasium provides the stress free atmosphere in which to relax and unwind.

Member of Signature Hotels

B&B from €75.00 to €82.50

BARRY MAHER
GENERAL MANAGER

American Express
Diners
Mastercard
Visa

Weekend specials from €160.00

Open All Year

LOUGH INAGH LODGE

RECESS,
CONNEMARA,
CO. GALWAY
TEL: 095-34706 FAX: 095-34708
EMAIL: inagh@iol.ie
WEB: www.commerce.ie/inagh

HOTEL ★★★★ MAP 5 D 11

Lough Inagh Lodge was built in 1880. It offers all the comforts of an elegant modern hotel in an old world atmosphere, open log fires in the library and oak panelled bar symbolises the warmth of Inagh hospitality. The lodge is surrounded by famous beauty spots including the Twelve Bens Mountain Range and the Connemara National Park. Kylemore Abbey is also nearby.

Member of Manor House Hotels

B&B from €89.10 to €107.00

MAIRE O'CONNOR
PROPRIETOR

American Express
Diners
Mastercard
Visa

Weekend specials from €187.00

Closed 07 December - 14 March

MAOL REIDH LODGE

TULLYCROSS,
RENVYLE,
CO. GALWAY
TEL: 095-43844

HOTEL P MAP 9 C 12

Situated in the delightful village of Tullycross, Renvyle the new Maol Reidh Lodge offers guests a high standard of luxury. We are close to Connemara National Park and Kylemore Abbey. For the active guest, we are nestled in the Twelve Bens and Maamturk Mountains, and only a few minutes drive from Scuba-Dive West and Oceans Alive sealife centre. A perfect place to enjoy the natural paradise of Connemara.

B&B from €50.00 to €80.00

MONICA LYDON
PROPRIETOR

Mastercard
Visa

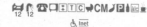

Open All Year

B&B rates are per person sharing per night incl. Breakfast

RENVYLE HOUSE HOTEL

RENVYLE,
CONNEMARA,
CO. GALWAY
TEL: 095-43511 FAX: 095-43515
EMAIL: renvyle@iol.ie
WEB: www.renvyle.com

HOTEL ★★★ MAP 9 C 12

Historic coastal hotel set amid the magical beauty of sea, lake and mountains, the keynotes are warmth and comfort with award winning fine fare. Turf fires and cosy lounges make you relax and feel at home. Golf, tennis, horse riding, swimming pool, snooker, boating, fishing are the facilities to name but a few. Wonderful walking and cycling routes throughout an area that hosts a vast National Park. Additional facilities include claypigeon shooting and archery.

B&B from €40.00 to €105.00

ZOE COYLE
SALES & MARKETING MANAGER

American Express
Diners
Mastercard
Visa

Midweek specials from €175.00
(3 B&B+2D)

56 56

Closed 02 January - 13 February

ELDONS HOTEL

ROUNDSTONE,
CONNEMARA,
CO. GALWAY
TEL: 095-35933 FAX: 095-35722
EMAIL: eldonshotel@eircom.net
WEB: www.connemara.net

HOTEL ★★ MAP 9 C 11

Situated in the village of Roundstone, has a view of the harbour and Twelve Bens mountain range. We are a newly built, family run hotel, offering all bedrooms with private bathrooms, colour TV and D.D. phones. Locally; 18 hole golf course and sea angling. Our Beola Restaurant has been operating successfully for many years and is renowned for its fine food, with lobster being its speciality. Credit cards taken. New annexe consisting of 6 superior rooms with a lift.

B&B from €50.00 to €65.00

ANN & NOLEEN CONNEELY
OWNER/CHEF

American Express
Diners
Mastercard
Visa

19 19

Closed 30 October - 13 March

ROUNDSTONE HOUSE HOTEL

ROUNDSTONE,
CONNEMARA,
CO. GALWAY
TEL: 095-35864 FAX: 095-35944
EMAIL: diar@eircom.net
WEB: www.irishcountryhotels.com

HOTEL ★★ MAP 9 C 11

Roundstone House Hotel is a family hotel situated in the picturesque village of Roundstone. Roundstone is a fascinating place for a holiday offering a wide range of interests for the holiday makers. Many outdoor activities are available locally including sea angling, watersports, hillwalking, pony trekking and a championship 18 hole golf course nearby. Come to beautiful Roundstone for a holiday to remember.

Member of Irish Country hotels

B&B from €42.00 to €52.00

MAUREEN VAUGHAN
PROPRIETOR

American Express
Mastercard
Visa

13 13

Closed 01 November - 30 March

Room rates are per room per night

AN CRUISCIN LAN HOTEL

SPIDDAL,
CO. GALWAY

TEL: 091-553148 FAX: 091-553712
EMAIL: info@cruiscinlanhotel.com
WEB: www.cruiscinlanhotel.com

HOTEL N MAP 5 E 10

The Cruiscin Lan Hotel offers the warmth and personal attention of a family-run business together with a highly professional banqueting team both with a commitment to service and quality. The property is located in the heart of Spiddal village, the gateway to the Gaeltacht, Connemara and "The Islands". All rooms are en suite with a colour TV and direct dial phone line. The hotel offers a snug, lounge bar, dining conservatory and beer garden with spectacular views of Galway Bay.

B&B from €55.00 to €75.00

JOHN FOYE

Mastercard
Visa

14 14

Closed 23 - 28 December

PARK LODGE HOTEL

PARK,
SPIDDAL,
CO. GALWAY

TEL: 091-553159 FAX: 091-553494
EMAIL: parklodgehotel@eircom.net
WEB: www.parklodgehotelandrentacottage.com

HOTEL U MAP 5 E 10

The Park Lodge Hotel is owned and run by the Foyle Family. It is situated on the coast road from Galway to Connemara, 16km west of Galway City and just east of Spiddal Village. Most of the 23 bedrooms have a view of Galway Bay. There are also seven detached cottages on the grounds, each self-catering and fully equipped for 5 persons. Cottages open all year.

B&B from €40.00 to €60.00

JANE MARIE FOYLE
MANAGER

American Express
Diners
Mastercard
Visa

23 23

Closed 01 October - 31 May

TIGH CHUALAIN

KILROE EAST,
SPIDDAL,
CO. GALWAY

TEL: 091-553609 FAX: 091-553049

GUESTHOUSE ★★★ MAP 5 E 10

Tigh Chualain is a charming, family run 3*** guesthouse, 16km west of Galway City and 2km west of Spiddal Village, en route to the Aran Islands' Ferry. Overlooking Galway Bay, with a nearby Blue Flag beach, it is in the heart of the Connemara Gaeltacht. An obvious starting point for exploring the rugged beauty of Connemara with its manifold attractions. All bedrooms are en suite with direct dial telephone and colour TV.

B&B from €26.00 to €32.00

NORA & COLM FOLAN
PROPRIETORS

Midweek specials from €75.00

9 9

Closed 31 October - 31 March

B&B rates are per person sharing per night incl. Breakfast

ACHILL CLIFF HOUSE HOTEL

KEEL,
ACHILL ISLAND,
CO. MAYO
TEL: 098-43400 FAX: 098-43007
EMAIL: info@achillcliff.com
WEB: www.achillcliff.com

HOTEL ★★★   MAP 9 C 14

AA ***, situated in a superb location with all facilities nearby. Beautifully decorated non-smoking bedrooms. The restaurant serves fresh homemade food with seafood and local lamb a speciality. This is complemented with fine wines or a drink from the bar. The relaxed ambience is a bonus to the spectacular views and the excellent cuisine. Friendly host recommends 3 day stay for walking, fishing, golf, painting, photography, Deserted Village, House of Prayer. No Disco.

Member of Premier Guesthouses

B&B from € 40.00 to € 70.00

JJ & TERESA MCNAMARA
PROPRIETORS

American Express
Mastercard
Visa

Weekend specials from €90.00

10 10

Closed 23 -27 December

GRAYS GUEST HOUSE

DUGORT,
ACHILL ISLAND,
CO. MAYO
TEL: 098-43244

GUESTHOUSE ★★★   MAP 9 C 14

Vi McDowell welcomes you to Grays where you are assured of a restful holiday, with good food, comfort and personal attention. Turf fires and electric blankets. Late dinner is served at 7pm. There are three lounges, colour TV, table tennis room and croquet lawn and swings in an enclosed garden. Art Gallery for use of artists staying in guesthouse.

B&B from € 35.00 to € 40.00

VI MCDOWELL
OWNER/MANAGER

15 15

Closed 24 - 26 December

ÓSTÁN OILEÁN ACLA

ACHILL SOUND,
CO. MAYO

TEL: 098-45138 FAX: 098-45198
EMAIL: reservations@achillislandhotel.com
WEB: www.achillislandhotel.com

HOTEL U   MAP 9 C 14

Enjoy the panoramic views of Achill Island from our new luxury hotel situated at the gateway to Achill Island. In our elegant Seafood Restaurant choose from a wide range of local produce. Relax and enjoy a drink in our friendly traditional bar. Convenient to Blue Flag beaches, the highest cliffs in Europe, golf courses, pitch and putt course, outdoor activities. A warm friendly welcome awaits you at Óstán Oileán Acla.

B&B from € 40.00 to € 65.00

MICHAEL MCLOUGHLIN

American Express
Mastercard
Visa

Weekend/Midweek specials
from €110.00

26 26

Open All Year

Room rates are per room per night

BELLEEK CASTLE

BELEEK,
BALLINA,
CO. MAYO

TEL: 096-22400 FAX: 096-71750
EMAIL: belleekcastlehotel@eircom.net
WEB: www.belleekcastle.com

HOTEL U MAP 10 F 15

Historic, romantic, set in 1000 acres of woodland on banks of River Moy - Wine/dine till midnight - Gourmet organic food enthusiasts welcomed - 'Perchance to Dream' in a four poster. For your added pleasure: tour of 16c castle armoury, giant fossil exhibits, Spanish Armada Bar, dramatic artefacts and timbers salvaged from Galleons wrecked off Irish west coast 1588. Sporting: international surfing, golf, fishing, tennis, riding, ten stables in castle.

B&B from € 70.00 to € 120.00

MARSHALL & JACQUELINE DORAN

American Express
Mastercard
Visa

15 15

Closed 24 - 27 December

DOWNHILL HOUSE HOTEL

BALLINA,
CO. MAYO

TEL: 096-21033 FAX: 096-21338
EMAIL: thedownhillhotel@eircom.net
WEB: www.downhillhotel.ie

HOTEL ★★★ MAP 10 F 15

3*** Downhill House Hotel, privately owned country house hotel beside Europe's best salmon fishing River Moy. The addition of the new garden wing offers the guest a perfect blend of olde world charm and new world comfort. Set in tranquil gardens, offering excellent cuisine with superb facilities on site. Eagles Leisure Club incorporates two swimming pools, steamroom, sauna, jacuzzi and floodlit tennis courts. Conference centre, piano bar with national and international entertainment. Six 18-hole golf courses nearby. Fishing - river, lake and deep sea.

Member of D'Arcy Marketing

B&B from € 70.00 to € 85.00

MICHAEL MCKEIGUE
GENERAL MANAGER

American Express
Diners
Mastercard
Visa

Weekend specials from € 152.50

62 62

Closed 22 - 27 December

DOWNHILL INN

SLIGO ROAD,
BALLINA,
CO. MAYO

TEL: 096-73444 FAX: 096-73411
EMAIL: thedownhillinn@eircom.net
WEB: www.downhillinn.com

HOTEL ★★★ MAP 10 F 15

A family-run 3*** hotel, located 1 mile outside Ballina Town on the main Sligo Road (N59). Contemporary in its design with 45 well-appointed triple rooms. All rooms are en suite with multi-channel TV, hairdryer, tea/coffee facilities and DD phone. The region offers superb fishing on the River Moy, Lough Conn and Killala Bay. An excellent selection of golf courses: Enniscrone, Ballina, Carne, to mention but a few. Enjoy a drink at the bar or a meal in our Terrace Restaurant. Rest assured!

Member of Holiday Ireland Hotels

B&B from € 45.00 to € 70.00

JOHN RAFTERY/NICOLA MOYLETT
PROPRIETORS

American Express
Mastercard
Visa

Weekend specials from € 100.00

45 45

Closed 22 December - 03 January

B&B rates are per person sharing per night incl. Breakfast

REGANS BARTRA HOUSE HOTEL

PEARSE STREET,
BALLINA,
CO. MAYO
TEL: 096-22200 FAX: 096-22111
EMAIL: bartrahotel@eircom.net

HOTEL ★★   MAP 10 F 15

Bartra House Hotel, situated in Ballina, is a family business run by brothers Paul and Noel Regan. Located near the famous River Moy and with two golf courses within easy reach, it is the ideal base for such holidays. The hotel boasts 22 bedrooms all en suite, with colour television and telephone. Our restaurant is famous for its superb food and service and our function room can cater for up to 200 people for dinner.

B&B from €50.00 to €70.00

PAUL AND NOEL REGAN
DIRECTORS

American Express
Diners
Mastercard
Visa

Closed 25 December

STELLA MARIS HOTEL

BALLYCASTLE,
CO. MAYO

TEL: 096-43322 FAX: 096-43965
EMAIL: info@StellaMarisIreland.com
WEB: www.StellaMarisIreland.com

HOTEL N   MAP 9 E 16

Overlooking Bunatrahir Bay and picturesque Downpatrick Head, Stella Maris is a luxurious boutique hotel in tranquil Ballycastle, Co. Mayo. The 1853 Coast Guard fortress and subsequent convent is strategically located between the world-renowned links of Enniscrone and Carne/Belmullet. High quality linens complement tasteful antique furnishings in well appointed oceanfront rooms. Stella Maris features a gourmet restaurant and inviting lounge. Sea and fresh water fishing nearby.

Member of Emerald Links

B&B from €90.00 to €115.00

TERENCE MCSWEENEY/FRANCES KELLY
PROPRIETORS

Mastercard
Visa

Closed 02 January - 31 March

Room rates are per room per night

SEA ROD INN

DOOHOMA,
BELMULLET, BALLINA,
CO. MAYO
TEL: 097-86767
EMAIL: info@thesearodinn.ie
WEB: www.thesearodinn.ie

GUESTHOUSE ★★ MAP 10 F 15

Located on the southern shore of Doohoma Peninsula, The Sea Rod Inn is a fully licensed premises with a beautifully decorated bar and lounge and nine magnificent bedrooms all of which are en suite with TV and central heating. Tea/coffee making facilities are all available in a separate sitting room, exclusive to guests, where you can enjoy panoramic views of Achill Island and the Atlantic Ocean. Our in-house entertainment during the summer months ensures that parents with young families can have a carefree holiday with no childcare worries.

B&B from €30.00 to €35.00

MICHAEL & BERNADETTE BARRETT

American Express
Mastercard
Visa

🛏🔥🖥🅰🅼©CM🔌♪♫🅿🆂🔒
9   9

Open All Year

TF ROYAL HOTEL & THEATRE

OLD WESTPORT ROAD,
CASTLEBAR,
CO. MAYO
TEL: 094-23111 FAX: 094-23111
EMAIL: patj@anu.ie
WEB: www.tfroyalhotel.com

HOTEL ★★★ MAP 9 E 14

The TF Royal Hotel & Theatre is a luxury family 3*** facility at Castlebar town centre. New extension 2002 provides for luxurious bedrooms newly decorated with air conditioning, security safe, ISDN lines, TV, VCR, trouser press, hair dryer and baby listening facility. Executive/master suites and connecting family rooms on request. Modern conference and theatre facility. Café Bar and Bistro. Adjacent to Institute of Technology, Mayo General Hospital, Harlequinn Shopping Centre. Member of MinOtel Ireland, Green Book of Ireland.

Member of MinOtel Ireland Hotel Group

B&B from €60.00 to €75.00

PAT AND MARY JENNINGS
PROPRIETORS

American Express
Mastercard
Visa

:/ 🍴

🛏🔥☎🖥TC🔌CM☺♪♫🅿🆂🔒
27   27

alc Inet

Closed 24 - 25 December

RIVERSIDE GUESTHOUSE & RESTAURANT

CHURCH STREET,
CHARLESTOWN,
CO. MAYO
TEL: 094-54200 FAX: 094-54207
EMAIL: riversiderestaurant@eircom.net
WEB: www.riversiderest.com

GUESTHOUSE ★★ MAP 10 G 14

Situated on the intersection of N17 & N5 primary routes. 10 minutes to Knock International Airport, 20 minutes to Knock Shrine. Ideal base for touring Mayo, Sligo, Roscommon and Galway. A charming family run guesthouse with all rooms en suite and with TV. Modern Irish food served and prepared in our Olde World restaurant by award winning chef/owner Anthony Kelly and his wife Anne. Special restaurant licence to serve all alcohol to diners. A warm Irish welcome awaits you. Member of Restaurant Association of Ireland.

B&B from €37.00 to €60.00

ANTHONY & ANNE KELLY
PROPRIETORS

Mastercard
Visa

🛏🔥🖥TCCMP🔒alc
10   10

Closed 01 - 25 November

B&B rates are per person sharing per night incl. Breakfast

ASHFORD CASTLE

CONG,
CO. MAYO

TEL: 094-954 6003 FAX: 094-954 6260
EMAIL: ashford@ashford.ie
WEB: www.ashford.ie

HOTEL ★★★★★ MAP 9 E 12

5***** Ashford Castle has long been considered one of Ireland's most outstanding properties - and has adapted the facilities to cater for the demands of today's discerning clientele. Now a total resort, guests can enjoy complimentary golf and the health club facilities which comprise a fully equipped gymnasium, sauna, steamroom and whirlpool. Other sports to be enjoyed are horseback riding outdoor & indoor, falconry, cruising and fishing on Lough Corrib. Nightly entertainment is provided.

Room Rate from €204.00 to €489.00

NIALL ROCHFORD
GENERAL MANAGER

American Express
Diners
Mastercard
Visa

83 83

Open All Year

LYDONS LODGE HOTEL

CONG,
CO. MAYO

TEL: 092-46053 FAX: 092-46523
EMAIL: lydonslodge@eircom.net
WEB: www.lydonslodgefreeservers.com

HOTEL ★★ MAP 9 E 12

Lydons Lodge combines the most modern amenities with old world charm. Located in Cong, village of 'Quiet Man' film fame it offers salmon, pike and famous Lough Corrib wild brown trout fishing. Boats, engines and boatmen can be arranged. Choice of 3 local golf clubs, horse riding and tennis. Minutes' walk from Ashford Castle and Gardens. Hill walks and mountain climbing with spectacular lake views, an archaeological and geological paradise. Traditional music and bar food.

B&B from €32.00 to €50.00

FRANK & CARMEL LYDON
OWNERS

American Express
Diners
Mastercard
Visa

11 11

Closed 05 November - 01 February

GOLFING
at
Ballinrobe Golf Club

Established 1895.
"This must be the finest championship course in the west of Ireland. The par Threes, in particular are a delight. My favourite hole is the fifth which has a marvellous green inset into the river Robe. The tenth hole is a hole which professionals will love with its island green needing a very precise choice of club."

Padraig Harrington

4 km from Ballinrobe on the main Claremorris Road. 45 minutes from Knock International Airport and Galway Airport.

Course length 6234 M, Par 73

Opening Hours: Daylight hours from 8am. Clubhouse open 8am to 10pm. Weekdays are best for visitors but booking is advisable.

Green Fees: Oct - March: €20 - April - Sept: €30

**Ballinrobe Golf Club
Clooncastle
Co Mayo
Ireland
Tel: ++ 353 (0) 92 41118
Fax: ++ 353 (0) 92 41889
E-mail bgcgolf@iol.ie**

Room rates are per room per night

RYAN'S HOTEL

CONG,
CO. MAYO

TEL: 092-46243 FAX: 092-46634
EMAIL: michaelv@indigo.ie

HOTEL ★★ MAP 9 E 12

The idyllic riverside setting of Ryan's Hotel is more than matched by the outstanding service and lovely surroundings inside. Just a few minutes' walk from the famous free brown trout fishing lake Lough Corrib, the hotel is ideally situated for touring the west coast including the breathtaking views of Connemara. Because of its unique beauty, Cong was chosen by John Ford for his film The Quiet Man.

Member of MinOtel Ireland Hotel Group

B&B from €40.00 to €57.00

MICHAEL & GERALDINE RYAN
OWNERS

Mastercard
Visa

12 12

TEACH IORRAIS

GEESALA,
BALLINA,
CO.MAYO

TEL: 097-86888 FAX: 097-86855
EMAIL: teachior@iol.ie
WEB: www.teachiorrais.com

HOTEL ★★★ MAP 10 F 15

Situated in an area of unrivalled beauty, Teach Iorrais is an exclusive and luxurious hotel in Co. Mayo. The hotel boasts 31 exquisite en suite bedrooms which are decorated to the highest standard and offer awe-inspiring views of the surrounding Neiphinn Mountains and the Atlantic Ocean. An Neiphinn Restaurant offers the best of fine dining in a relaxing and intimate environment. Our theme bar, Béar Synge, is one of the Irish Pubs of Distinction. Carne Links Golf Course located 15 minutes drive from hotel.

B&B from €46.00 to €62.00

PATRICIA GAUGHAN
MANAGER

American Express
Diners
Mastercard
Visa

Weekend specials from €109.00

31 31

CILL AODAIN HOTEL

MAIN STREET,
KILTIMAGH,
CO. MAYO

TEL: 094-81761 FAX: 094-81838
EMAIL: cillaodain@eircom.net

HOTEL ★★ MAP 10 F 14

This RAC 3*** hotel is set in the centre of historic Kiltimagh. Furnished with flair and imagination, panelled lounges and open fires. The restaurant which has received many accolades is open each evening. The rooms, with all amenities, are individually furnished and decorated. Kiltimagh is one of Ireland's most famous small towns. 5km off Galway to Sligo Road. Ideally situated for visiting Knock Village. Member of Irish Country Hotels.

Member of Irish Country Hotels

B&B from €37.00 to €57.00

MARY HALLIGAN
PROPRIETOR

American Express
Diners
Mastercard
Visa

12 12

B&B rates are per person sharing per night incl. Breakfast

BELMONT HOTEL

KNOCK,
CO. MAYO

TEL: 094-88122 FAX: 094-88532
EMAIL: reception@belmonthotel.ie
WEB: www.belmonthotel.ie

HOTEL ★★★ MAP 10 G 13

A haven of hospitality nestled at the rear entrance to Knock Shrine off N17. The hotel radiates Old Country Warmth from the moment you arrive. RAC 3***, Irish Tourist Board 3*** and AA 3*** status. Daily Cavery and sumptuous bar food menu complement our award winning Bialann Restaurant. Our specially developed Natural Health Therapy packages are very professional and attractive. Tastefully furnished bedrooms with facilities.

Member of Logis of Ireland

B&B from €42.00 to €56.00

JOE MELODY
GENERAL MANAGER

American Express
Diners
Mastercard
Visa

63 63

Open All Year

KNOCK HOUSE HOTEL

BALLYHAUNIS ROAD,
KNOCK,
CO. MAYO

TEL: 094-938 8088 FAX: 094-938 8044
EMAIL: hotel@knockhousehotel.ie
WEB: www.knockhousehotel.ie

HOTEL ★★★ MAP 10 G 13

Located in over 100 acres of parkland and nestling behind the Basilica, this 3 year old hotel is a gem! With 68 comfortable bedrooms, of which 6 are designed for Wheelchair users, every need is catered for. The superb Four Seasons Restaurant - open all day - and the glazed reception and lounge areas, surrounded by local limestone, overlook countryside. This well run, tranquil hotel, will be hard to leave.

B&B from €49.00 to €65.00

BRIAN CROWLEY
MANAGER

Mastercard
Visa

68 68

Open All Year

KNOCK INTERNATIONAL HOTEL

MAIN STREET,
KNOCK,
CO. MAYO

TEL: 094-88466 FAX: 094-88428
EMAIL: info@knockinternationalhotel.com
WEB: www.knockinternationalhotel.com

HOTEL ★★ MAP 10 G 13

Knock International Hotel was opened in 1986 by Mary and Edward Curry, who have been catering for pilgrims for years at Fairfield Restaurant. Set in its own gardens only minutes from Knock Shrine. Also only 10 minutes from Knock Airport. The Currys are joined in the operations by their family and the hotel is especially suited for weddings and functions. Credit cards: Mastercard, Visa.

B&B from €35.00 to €50.00

MR & MRS EDWARD CURRY
OWNERS

Mastercard
Visa

10 10

Closed 13 October - 29 March

Room rates are per room per night

HEALYS RESTAURANT & COUNTRY HOUSE HOTEL

PONTOON,
FOXFORD,
CO. MAYO
TEL: 094-56443 FAX: 094-56572
EMAIL: info@healyspontoon.com
WEB: www.healyspontoon.com

HOTEL ★★ MAP 9 F 14

Healys in the heart of Mayo, Ireland's best location for golf, fishing, cycling, shooting & walking. Our restaurant boasts "probably the best food in the west" with over 100 wines to choose from our winelist/cellar. Scenically overlooking Lough Cullin and Conn, 10 minutes from the world famous River Moy, one of Western Europe's best salmon rivers, 30 minutes from Enniscrone golflinks, Westport championship golf-links parkland and numerous class golf courses in the area, a hotel for all seasons.

B&B from €49.00 to €65.00

JOHN DEVER
PROPRIETOR

American Express
Diners
Mastercard
Visa

Closed 25 December

PONTOON BRIDGE HOTEL

PONTOON,
FOXFORD,
CO. MAYO
TEL: 094-925 6120 FAX: 094-925 6688
EMAIL: relax@pontoonbridge.com
WEB: www.pontoonbridge.com

HOTEL ★★★ MAP 10 F 14

Family managed hotel on the shores of Lough Conn and Cullin in the centre of Mayo. Famous for trout and salmon fishing - River Moy, golf, horseriding, scenery, central for touring. Twin Lakes Restaurant boasts the best food in Mayo. Geary's Waterfront Bar & Bistro with live musical entertainment nightly during season. Tennis court, sandy beaches, conference facilities. Families welcome. School of flyfishing, landscape painting and cookery. Leisure Centre opening mid-season. Bedrooms with panoramic views of Lough Conn & Cullin.

B&B from €55.00 to €95.00

BREETA GEARY
GENERAL MANAGER

American Express
Mastercard
Visa

Closed 24 - 26 December

ARDMORE COUNTRY HOUSE HOTEL AND RESTAURANT

THE QUAY,
WESTPORT,
CO. MAYO
TEL: 098-25994 FAX: 098-27795
EMAIL: ardmorehotel@eircom.net
WEB: www.ardmorecountryhouse.com

HOTEL ★★★★ MAP 9 E 13

Ardmore Country House and Restaurant is a small luxurious 4**** hotel, owned and managed by Pat & Noreen Hoban and family, offering warm hospitality. Ardmore House is idyllically situated overlooking Clew Bay with breathtaking sunsets, in the shadow of Croagh Patrick. The Restaurant offers the best of local produce, including fresh fish from Clew Bay, organic vegetables and herbs from local producers and a selection of Irish farmhouse cheeses. All bedrooms are non-smoking.

B&B from €85.00 to €125.00

NOREEN & PAT HOBAN

American Express
Mastercard
Visa

Closed 01 February - 01 March

B&B rates are per person sharing per night incl. Breakfast

ATLANTIC COAST HOTEL

THE QUAY,
WESTPORT,
CO. MAYO
TEL: 098-29000 FAX: 098-29111
EMAIL: reservations@atlanticcoasthotel.com
WEB: www.atlanticcoasthotel.com

HOTEL ★★★★ MAP 9 E 13

Recently established as one of Westport's finest and most popular hotels, situated on the waterfront at Westport Quay overlooking Clew Bay. Superb contemporary cuisine in our unique top floor award winning restaurant -The Blue Wave. The Atlantic Club features pool, gym, sauna, steamroom & massage, including seaweed hydrotherapy bath treatments. Championship golf, angling, scenic walks, islands & Blue Flag beaches nearby. Your perfect base to explore beautiful Westport. Callsave: 1850 229000. Awarded Ireland's Best Service Award 2002.

Member of Select Hotels of Ireland

B&B from € 110.00 to € 135.00

JOHN VARLEY
GENERAL MANAGER

American Express
Mastercard
Visa

85 85

Closed 23 - 27 December

AUGUSTA LODGE

GOLF LINKS ROAD,
WESTPORT,
CO. MAYO
TEL: 098-28900 FAX: 098-28995
EMAIL: info@augustalodge.ie
WEB: www.augustalodge.ie

GUESTHOUSE ★★★ MAP 9 E 13

Augusta Lodge is a purpose-built 3*** guesthouse situated just 5 minutes walk from the town centre of Westport. A warm and friendly welcome awaits you in this family run guesthouse and Liz and Dave will ensure that your stay is a memorable one. A golfer's haven with tee times and green fees arranged at Westport and adjacent courses. Putting green on-site for guests' use. Listed in all leading guides.

B&B from € 32.00 to € 45.00

LIZ O'REGAN

Mastercard
Visa

10 10

Closed 23 - 27 December

Room rates are per room per night

CASTLECOURT HOTEL CONFERENCE AND LEISURE CENTRE

CASTLEBAR STREET,
WESTPORT,
CO. MAYO
TEL: 098-55088 FAX: 098-28622
EMAIL: info@castlecourthotel.ie
WEB: www.castlecourthotel.ie

HOTEL ★★★ MAP 9 E 13

Perfectly located in the heart of Westport, the tourist haven of Mayo, a genuine welcome & special warm atmosphere await you at this spectacular hotel which is run by the Corcoran family since 1971. The hotel has been completely refurbished & extended & guests can enjoy 140 bedrooms (deluxe rooms available), indoor heated swimming pool, children's pool, spa, sauna, steamroom, sunbed, childrens' creche, health suites for aromatherapy & massage, hairdressing salon, large car park, conservatory concourse & an award-winning restaurant.

Member of Holiday Ireland Hotels

B&B from €55.00 to €105.00

MR.JOSEPH CORCORAN/ MS.ANNE CORCORAN

American Express
Diners
Mastercard
Visa

Weekend specials from €135.00

140 140

Closed 24 - 26 December

CLEW BAY HOTEL

JAMES STREET,
WESTPORT,
CO. MAYO
TEL: 098-28088 FAX: 098-25783
EMAIL: info@clewbayhotel.com
WEB: www.clewbayhotel.com

HOTEL ★★★ MAP 9 E 13

Enjoy our warm friendly family run hotel situated in Westport Town centre. Our newly renovated hotel has 28 en suite rooms finished to the highest standard of comfort. Guests can enjoy the Old World charm of the Tubber Bar that features traditional music. The Riverside Restaurant overlooking the Carrowbeg River offers an imaginative menu, modestly priced. Local attractions include Westport Leisure Park, golfing, angling, pony trekking, scenic walks/drives, beaches.

Member of Irish Country Hotels

B&B from €50.00 to €80.00

MARIA RUDDY & DARREN MADDEN PROPRIETORS

American Express
Mastercard
Visa

Weekend specials from €126.00

28   28

Closed 22 - 27 December

HOTEL WESTPORT, CONFERENCE & LEISURE CENTRE

THE DEMESNE,
NEWPORT ROAD, WESTPORT,
CO. MAYO
TEL: 098-25122 FAX: 098-26739
EMAIL: reservations@hotelwestport.ie
WEB: www.hotelwestport.ie

HOTEL ★★★ MAP 9 E 13

Award winning, RAC 4 star, hotel set in the heart of Westport. An enviable reputation for friendly, professional service and excellent food. Westport's premier leisure centre. A variety of theme and leisure holidays to enjoy as part of your precious relaxation and leisure time - golf, murder mystery intrigue, golden holidays, bridge and bowls. Childrens' 'Panda Club' a daily activity programme organised by the 'Fun Fellows' - seasonal. Hotel Westport - One of Ireland's Best Loved Hotels. Call Save 1850 53 63 73.

B&B from €85.00 to €115.00

GERRY WALSHE
GENERAL MANAGER

American Express
Diners
Mastercard
Visa

Weekend specials from €139.00

129 129

Open All Year

B&B rates are per person sharing per night incl. Breakfast

KNOCKRANNY HOUSE HOTEL

WESTPORT,
CO. MAYO

TEL: 098-28600 FAX: 098-28611
EMAIL: info@khh.ie
WEB: www.khh.ie

HOTEL ★★★★ MAP 9 E 13

Knockranny House Hotel is beautifully located on an elevated site overlooking Westport Town, Clew Bay & Croagh Patrick. The hotel is full of character with log fires creating a warm and relaxed atmosphere. 'La Fougère' Restaurant offers the finest of cuisine in luxurious surroundings, served by our friendly and welcoming staff. Guests have complimentary use of C Club Leisure Centre, located a short distance from the hotel. Recent developments within the hotel and grounds include Helipad, Gift Shop and Organic Herb Garden.

Member of Best Loved Hotels

B&B from €80.00 to €115.00

GERALDINE & ADRIAN NOONAN
PROPRIETORS

American Express
Mastercard
Visa

☺ Weekend specials from €165.00

54   54

Closed 22 - 27 December

KNOCKRANNY LODGE

KNOCKRANNY,
WESTPORT,
CO. MAYO

TEL: 098-28595 FAX: 098-28805
EMAIL: knockranny@anu.ie
WEB: www.anu.ie/knockrannylodge

GUESTHOUSE ★★★★ MAP 9 E 13

Knockranny Lodge is a beautifully appointed 4**** guesthouse. It has the peace and tranquillity of the country and yet is only 5 minutes walk to town. Relax and enjoy a cup of tea or coffee in our welcoming lounge. All of our en suite bedrooms have direct dial phone, multi-channel TV, trouserpress and hairdryer. Private tennis court and car park. We have full use of swimming pool and leisure complex in nearby sister hotel. AA ◆◆◆◆◆.

B&B from €35.00 to €60.00

MARY MCDERMOTT

American Express
Diners
Mastercard
Visa

☺ Weekend specials from €115.00

16   16

Closed 01 December - 30 January

OLDE RAILWAY HOTEL

THE MALL,
WESTPORT,
CO. MAYO

TEL: 098-25166 FAX: 098-25090
EMAIL: railway@anu.ie
WEB: www.anu.ie/railwayhotel

HOTEL ★★★ MAP 9 E 13

Get away from it all and be pampered in this tastefully appointed 18th century coaching inn. Standard and superior accommodation. Renowned for traditional country fare and fine wines. Genuine hospitality and warm welcome in relaxing intimate surroundings with conservatory restaurant, residents' lounge and library, turf fires & original antique furniture. Patio and garden area. Organic vegetable garden for restaurant. Recommended in all leading guides, Egon Ronay, AA Rosette winner.

B&B from €40.00 to €90.00

KARL ROSENKRANZ
OWNER/MANAGER

American Express
Diners
Mastercard
Visa

15   15

Open All Year

Room rates are per room per night

QUAY WEST

QUAY ROAD,
WESTPORT,
CO. MAYO
TEL: 098-27863 FAX: 098-28379
EMAIL: quaywest@eircom.net

GUESTHOUSE ★★ MAP 9 E 13

Quay West is a purpose built house situated 10 minutes walk from town and 5 minutes from the harbour and directly opposite Westport Woods Hotel where guests can enjoy the superb leisure facilities at discounted rates. Rooms are en suite with power showers, orthopaedic beds and TV. Lounge for guest comfort with tea/coffee facilities. Perfect base for touring beautiful Mayo, Connemara and relaxing in some of Westport's famous pubs and restaurants.

B&B from €25.00 to €38.00

DAVID KELLY
PROPRIETOR

Mastercard
Visa

Closed 24 - 27 December

WESTPORT INN HOTEL

TOWN CENTRE,
MILL STREET, WESTPORT,
CO. MAYO
TEL: 098-29200 FAX: 098-29250
EMAIL: info@westportinn.ie
WEB: www.westportinn.ie

HOTEL ★★ MAP 9 E 13

Westport's liveliest hotel offering a rate per room. Located in the centre of Westport, this charming 2** hotel has well equipped bedrooms and use of antique pine and neutral tones in the luxurious bedrooms ensures that they provide a relaxing haven for guests. Secure underground parking available. Home of WITS late night venue. Up to 3 adults or 2 adults and 2 children per room. Phone now for your rate.

Room Rate from €50.00 to €175.00

BRENDAN KEALY
PROPRIETOR

American Express
Diners
Mastercard
Visa

Open All Year

WESTPORT WOODS HOTEL & LEISURE CENTRE

QUAY ROAD,
WESTPORT,
CO. MAYO
TEL: 098-25811 FAX: 098-26212
EMAIL: info@westportwoodshotel.com
WEB: www.westportwoodshotel.com

HOTEL ★★★ MAP 9 E 13

Friendly, cosy hotel with fabulous 'Beech Club' leisure centre, set in mature woodland, overlooking private lake. Enjoy unforgettable family holidays with our famous Kiddies Club or treat yourself to a terrific themed break, ranging from golf and murder mystery to bridge and short mat bowls. Glorious "young at heart" getaways are a speciality in this welcoming establishment. Situated on the road to the harbour, the hotel is ideally located for lots of fascinating day trips - Kylemore Abbey, Achill, Clare Island, Croagh Patrick plus lots more.

Member of Brian McEniff Hotels

B&B from €50.00 to €110.00

MICHAEL LENNON & JOANNE MCENIFF

American Express
Mastercard
Visa

Weekend specials from €149.00

Open All Year

B&B rates are per person sharing per night incl. Breakfast

WYATT HOTEL

THE OCTAGON,
WESTPORT,
CO. MAYO

TEL: 098-25027 FAX: 098-26316

EMAIL: wyatthotel@anu.ie
WEB: www.wyatthotel.com

HOTEL ★★★ MAP 9 E 13

Westport is one of Ireland's most popular short break destinations and the Wyatt, one of its most popular hotels. Nestled on the famous Octagon, we invite you to discover the many delights, sights and sounds which you will find, literally, on our doorstep. Croagh Patrick, Westport Leisure Park, Blue Flag beaches, championship golf, islands, scenic drives, lively bars and restaurants, The Wyatt Hotel - your perfect Westport base. FREEPHONE 1800 205270.

B&B from €40.00 to €100.00

BRIAN FAHY
GENERAL MANAGER

American Express
Mastercard
Visa

☺ Weekend specials from €100.00

🛏📞☎🖥📶TC🛒CMⓊ♪🎵PS
🔲ac📶Inet FAX

HOTELS
FEDERATION

Closed 24 - 26 December

WHITEHOUSE HOTEL

BALLINLOUGH,
CO. ROSCOMMON

TEL: 094-964 0112 FAX: 094-964 0993

EMAIL: thewhitehousehotel@eircom.net
WEB: www.white-house-hotel.com

HOTEL N MAP 10 H 13

Located on the Roscommon Mayo border stands the all-new luxurious Whitehouse Hotel. Enjoy our lunchtime carvery in the bar whilst our Blue Room Restaurant offers the finest in contemporary and traditional cuisine. Frequent live music and traditional sessions throughout the year add to the ambience of this unique hotel. The hotel is just a short drive from Lough O'Flynn and within 6 miles of Ballyhaunis and Castlerea Golf Clubs.

B&B from €55.00 to €100.00

MARTIN DALY
GENERAL MANAGER

Mastercard
Visa

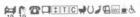

☺ Weekend specials from €125.00

🛏📞☎🖥📶TC🛒Ⓤ🔲ac
Inet

HOTELS
FEDERATION

Closed 25 December

ROYAL HOTEL

BRIDGE STREET,
BOYLE,
CO. ROSCOMMON

TEL: 079-62016 FAX: 079-64949

HOTEL ★★ MAP 10 I 14

Royal Hotel is over 250 years old. Under the new ownership since December 1999 of Nelson Chung & Adrian Bouchier, General Manager, it consists of 16 en suite bedrooms. Coffee shop open daily serving hot food from 8 a.m to 6 p.m. Chung's famous Chinese restaurant is also part of the hotel opening at 6 p.m. nightly until late. AA***. Private car park. Member of MinOtel Marketing Group, Ballycanew, Co. Wexford. Tel:+353-55-27291. Fax:+353-55-27398

Member of MinOtel Ireland Hotel Group

B&B from €50.00 to €65.00

ADRIAN BOUCHIER & NELSON CHUNG

Mastercard
Visa

☺ Weekend specials from €100.00pps

🛏📞☎🖥TCⓊ♪🎵PS🔲ac🛒
Inet

HOTELS
FEDERATION

Open All Year

ABBEY HOTEL, LEISURE & CONFERENCE CENTRE

GALWAY ROAD,
ROSCOMMON TOWN

TEL: 0903-26240 FAX: 0903-26021
EMAIL: sales@abbeyhotel.ie

HOTEL ★★★ MAP 10 | 12

A superb new leisure and fitness centre complemented by spacious new bedrooms puts this eighteenth century manor house into the leisure break market for the first time. The Abbey now also offers a newly designed business and conference centre with a choice of suites to suit large and small groups. A new restaurant and bar complete the transformation of this long established midland hotel which is still owned and managed by the Grealy family now in their fourth generation of hotelkeeping in Roscommon.

Member of Irish Country Hotels

B&B from €85.00 to €95.00

TOMMY & ANYA GREALY
MANAGER/MANAGERESS

American Express
Diners
Mastercard
Visa

50 50

Closed 25 - 26 December

GLEESONS TOWNHOUSE & RESTAURANT

MARKET SQUARE,
ROSCOMMON TOWN

TEL: 0906-626954 FAX: 0906-627425
EMAIL: info@gleesonstownhouse.com
WEB: www.gleesonstownhouse.com

GUESTHOUSE ★★★ MAP 10 | 12

Magnificent Townhouse/Restaurant in a tastefully restored listed 19th century Town House with an attractive finish of cut limestone & blue Bangor quarry slates. In the town centre next door to the Tourist Office/Museum. We offer superb accommodation with all 19 rooms built to a 4 star standard. Private car parking. Dine in our award winning "Manse" Restaurant where all the old values of guest satisfaction comfort and value for money prevail. Fully licensed for beers/spirits/wine. Anglers/Golf facility centre on-site. Conference facilities available. RAC♦♦♦♦

Member of Premier Guesthouses of Ireland

B&B from €45.00 to €75.00

MARY & EAMONN GLEESON
PROPRIETORS

American Express
Diners
Mastercard
Visa

Weekend specials from €109.00

19 19

Closed 25 - 26 December

O'GARA'S ROYAL HOTEL

CASTLE STREET,
ROSCOMMON TOWN

TEL: 0903-26317 FAX: 0903-26225
EMAIL: royalhotelros@eircom.net

HOTEL ★★ MAP 10 | 12

O'Gara's Royal Hotel family run, situated on the Dublin to Castlebar/Westport route. 19 bedrooms en suite, radio, direct dial phone, TV, video, hair dryer. Comfortable modern dining room with good food and friendly service. Coffee dock/carvery. Spacious lounge bar with pleasant surroundings. Private car park. A warm welcome awaits you. 3 new conference rooms are available, fully equipped with the latest facilities. Golfing holidays a speciality with a number of top golf courses locally.

B&B from €35.00 to €55.00

AILEEN & LARRY O'GARA
PROPRIETORS

American Express
Mastercard
Visa

19 19

Closed 25 December

B&B rates are per person sharing per night incl. Breakfast

REGANS

**MARKET SQUARE,
ROSCOMMON TOWN**

TEL: 0903-25339 FAX: 0903-27833
EMAIL: info@regans.com
WEB: www.regansbar.com

GUESTHOUSE ★★★   MAP 10 | 12

Regans is a family run 3*** licenced guesthouse situated in Roscommon Town Centre. It provides a central base to explore the town and environs. Regans boasts a fine bar, restaurant and 14 en suite bedrooms, all with satellite TV and direct dial phone facilities. We have also added a new dimension by way of two bedroom self-catering apartments. Our restaurant offers good quality food at a reasonable price. Also available is a fully equipped conference room. A warm welcome awaits you.

B&B from €35.00 to €40.00

EAMON & DOMINIC REGAN
MANAGERS

American Express
Mastercard
Visa

14 14

Closed 24 - 26 December

Room rates are per room per night

Ireland's North West spans a huge variety of landscape, from the rolling drumlins and tranquil lakes of counties Cavan and Monaghan in the east, to the lovely valleys of Leitrim and Sligo and the dramatic wild landscape of Co. Donegal in the west. Three of the counties, Donegal, Leitrim and Sligo bathe their feet in the restless Atlantic and the Shannon Erne Waterway connects the other great water courses in the region, the Shannon and the Erne Rivers.

FESTIVALS AND EVENTS
The North West offers many unexplored peaceful beauty spots, but lively action too. Festivals and events abound, from the Letterkenny and Ballyshannon Folk Festivals, Sligo International Choral Festival, the Mary from Dungloe International Festival, to the Yeats International Summer School and the North Leitrim Walking Festival and the Monaghan Jazz Festival.

MAJOR ATTRACTIONS
Two major attractions are Bundoran's Waterworld and the Visitor Centre at Carrowmore near Sligo, the largest and most important megalithic site in Europe.

Lough Muckno Park, Co. Monaghan

Not to be missed in Co. Donegal are the Lakeside Museum at Dunlewy, Glencolumbkille Folk Museum, Glenveagh National Park, Donegal Castle, the Vintage Car Museum in Buncrana and Parian China and Celtic Weave in Ballyshannon.

In Co. Cavan, visit the Cavan Crystal and Cavan County Museum and explore Swan Island Visitor Farm and Moon River Cruises on the Shannon in Co. Leitrim. In Co. Monaghan, visit the Patrick Kavanagh Centre in Inniskeen, also worth a visit are Ireland's only motor sport activity centre at Rally School Ireland in Scotstown and the award winning Monaghan County Museum. Near Sligo town, follow the sculpture trail through Hazelwood Forest, pamper yourself at the Celtic Seaweed Baths at Strandhill and visit Yeats Grave at Drumcliffe Church and Heritage Centre.

Tra Na Rosann Bay, Co. Donegal

Alternatively, discover our culture in the lively traditional music sessions that are held in pubs throughout the region.

For further information and assistance in planning your holiday and making accommodation reservations please contact:-
The North West Tourism Authority,
Temple Street, Sligo.
Tel: 071 916 1201. Fax: 071 916 0360
Email: irelandnorthwest@eircom.net
Web: www.irelandnorthwest.ie
OR
Tourist Information Office,
Neil T Blaney Road, Letterkenny, Co. Donegal.
Tel: 074 912 1160 Fax: 074 912 5180

Mary from Dungloe International Festival, Co. Donegal.
July / August

Yeats International Summer School, Co. Sligo.
July / August

Smithwicks Ballyshannon Folk Festival, Ballyshannon, Co. Donegal
August

Sligo International Choral Festival
November

Event details correct at time of going to press

NESBITT ARMS HOTEL

MAIN STREET,
ARDARA,
CO. DONEGAL.
TEL: 075-41103 FAX: 075-41895
EMAIL: nesbitta@indigo.ie

HOTEL ★★ MAP 13 H 18

Built in 1838 and named after the last Whaling family in Ireland, The Nesbitt Arms lies at the hub of the heritage town of Ardara, famed for its handwoven tweeds and handknits. Unspoilt sandy beaches and scenery, Maghera Caves, Glencolmcille, Slieve League and Glenveigh National Park. Choice of dining in Weavers à la carte Restaurant or in our Bar Bistro. Seafood specialities. Traditional Music and Lively Bar. Golf, fishing, hillwalking, horse riding neaby.

B&B from €40.00 to €60.00

PAUL & MARIE GALLAGHER

Diners
Mastercard
Visa

19 19

Open All Year

WOODHILL HOUSE

ARDARA,
CO. DONEGAL

TEL: 074-954 1112 FAX: 074-954 1516
EMAIL: yates@iol.ie
WEB: www.woodhillhouse.com

GUESTHOUSE ★★★ MAP 13 H 18

An historic country house, the site dates back to the 17th century. The house is set in its own grounds, overlooking the Donegal Highlands. There is a quality restaurant, with fully licensed bar and occasional music. The area, famous for its Donegal tweeds and woollen goods, also offers salmon and trout fishing, pony trekking, golf, boating, cycling, bathing beaches, many archaeological sites, Sheskinmore Wildlife Reserve, Slieve League and some of the most unspoiled scenery in Europe.

B&B from €45.00 to €60.00

NANCY & JOHN YATES
OWNERS

American Express
Diners
Mastercard
Visa

9 9

Closed 24 - 27 December

JACKSON'S HOTEL

BALLYBOFEY,
CO. DONEGAL

TEL: 074-31021 FAX: 074-31096
EMAIL: bjackson@iol.ie
WEB: www.jacksons-hotel.ie

HOTEL ★★★ MAP 13 J 19

Jackson's award winning family run hotel is situated in its own gardens with all 87 bedrooms en suite with mod cons. Relax at the log fire at reception or enjoy breathtaking views of the River Finn and Drumboe Woods. Close to Glenveagh National Park and ideal for golf, fishing, hillwalking and horse riding. Indulge in fine cuisine in the Bally Buffet Bistro or Garden Restaurant. Leisure club with swimming pool, jacuzzi, sauna, sun beds, massage and gym.

B&B from €58.00 to €70.00

MARGARET & BARRY JACKSON
PROPRIETORS

American Express
Diners
Mastercard
Visa

87 87

Open All Year

Room rates are per room per night

KEE'S HOTEL

STRANORLAR,
BALLYBOFEY
CO. DONEGAL
TEL: 074-913 1018 FAX: 074-913 1917
EMAIL: info@keeshotel.ie
WEB: www.keeshotel.ie

HOTEL ★★★ MAP 13 J 19

This charming historic family run hotel in its pleasant village situation overlooking the Blue Stack Mountains has that special atmosphere, a combination of excellent facilities, caring staff and management, which draws guests back time and again. The elegant Looking Glass Restaurant awarded 2 AA Rosettes of Excellence. The Old Gallery Restaurant for more casual dining. Delightful en suite rooms with TV, tea/coffee facilities, hairdryer, trouser press. Comprehensive leisure club.

B&B from €69.00 to €80.00

RICHARD & VICKY KEE
PROPRIETORS/MANAGERS

American Express
Diners
Mastercard
Visa

☺ Weekend specials from €139.00

53 53

Open All Year

DOHERTY'S POLLAN BEACH HOTEL

ARDAGH,
BALLYLIFFIN,
CO. DONEGAL
TEL: 074-937 8840 FAX: 074-937 8844
EMAIL: pollanbeachhotel@eircom.net
WEB: www.pollanbeachhotel.com

HOTEL N MAP 14 K 21

Doherty's Pollan Beach Hotel is situated 100yds from sandy beach with childrens playground. All bedrooms are en suite, equipped with modern facilities. Most bedrooms have sea views. Spacious dining room and bar overlooking the beach and Atlantic Ocean. The hotel overlooks the two 18 hole golf courses in Ballyliffin, the Classic Old Links and the New Glasheady Links. Ideal for: golf, fishing, cycling and walking. 40 minutes drive from city of Derry Airport, 2 hours drive from Belfast International. Perfect retreat for short break.

B&B from €50.00 to €60.00

KATHLEEN AND VINCENT DOHERTY
PROPRIETORS

American Express
Diners
Mastercard
Visa

20 20
alc Inet

Open All Year

DORRIANS IMPERIAL HOTEL

MAIN STREET,
BALLYSHANNON,
CO. DONEGAL
TEL: 071-985 1147 FAX: 071-985 1001
EMAIL: info@dorriansimperialhotel.com
WEB: www.dorriansimperialhotel.com

HOTEL ★★★ MAP 13 1 17

Town centre family run hotel (built 1781). All rooms en suite, TV, telephone, tea/coffee facilities. Private car park. Open fire. Hotel recently renovated, embracing old and new décor, elevator. Ideally suited for touring North West and North East Ireland and ideally located for golfing, fishing & beaches. Sligo 45km, Belfast 202km, Dublin 216km.

Member of Emerald Hotels of Ireland

B&B from €51.00 to €85.00

BEN & MARY DORRIAN
PROPRIETORS

Mastercard
Visa

47 47

Closed 22 - 29 December

B&B rates are per person sharing per night incl. Breakfast

FORGE (THE)

ROSSNOWLAGH ROAD,
BALLYSHANNON,
CO. DONEGAL

TEL: 071-982 2070 FAX: 071-982 2075

EMAIL: theforgeguesthouse@eircom.net

GUESTHOUSE ★★ MAP 13 I 17

Crafted with care, easy on the eye, this unique Irish country guesthouse and restaurant is definitely worth a visit. Ideally located about 3 miles from Ballyshannon and the same from Rossnowlagh Beach. With 10 superb en suite bedrooms you can relax in comfort. We have combined traditional charm, modern design and gracious hospitality. Dedicated to the highest standard 'The Forge' Restaurant features contemporary creative cuisine that will excite your palate.

B&B from €40.00 to €45.00

COLM & FIONA ROPER

American Express
Mastercard
Visa

☺ Weekend specials from €100.00

10 10

Closed 31 October - 30 November

OSTAN GWEEDORE HOTEL & LEISURE COMPLEX

BUNBEG,
CO. DONEGAL

TEL: 075-31177 FAX: 075-31726

EMAIL: reservations@ostangweedore.com
WEB: www.ostangweedore.com

HOTEL ★★★ MAP 13 I 20

Luxury hotel, all major guides approved, with 36 bedrooms & 3 executive suites, leisure centre with 19m swimming pool, children's pool, sauna, steam room & jacuzzi. Our award winning restaurant, overlooking the Atlantic, specialises in salmon & lobster fresh from the ocean. The Library Bar is the ideal place to relax with a quiet drink and a good book. 9-hole golf course & fishing available locally.

B&B from €62.50 to €80.00

CHARLES BOYLE
MANAGING DIRECTOR

American Express
Mastercard
Visa

☺ Weekend specials from €168.00

39 39

IRISH HOTELS FEDERATION

Closed 04 November - 13 Febuary

OSTAN RADHARC NA MARA

SEA VIEW HOTEL,
BUNBEG,
CO. DONEGAL

TEL: 074-953 1159 FAX: 074-953 2238

EMAIL: ostanradharcnamara@eircom.net

HOTEL ★★ MAP 13 I 20

In an area where nature remains untouched, the air is rich and pure, ensuring a heavy appetite. In the Seaview Hotel, guests are treated to wonderful food. The à la carte menu always includes a seasonal selection of fresh, local seafood dishes, with salmon, trout, lobster and oysters a speciality.

B&B from €55.00 to €65.00

JAMES BOYLE
GENERAL MANAGER

Mastercard
Visa

37 37

IRISH HOTELS FEDERATION

Closed 23 - 28 December

Room rates are per room per night

INISHOWEN GATEWAY HOTEL

RAILWAY ROAD,
BUNCRANA, INISHOWEN,
CO. DONEGAL
TEL: 074-936 1144 FAX: 074-936 2278
EMAIL: info@inishowengateway.com
WEB: www.inishowengateway.com

HOTEL ★★★ MAP 14 K 20

Elegant, contemporary-style hotel situated on the sandy shores of Lough Swilly. Superb leisure centre adjoining, plus free golf for our residents on adjacent course. Many activities catered for e.g. fishing, painting, walking, murder mystery breaks. Sister hotel, the Lake of Shadows, located near to town centre.

Member of Les Routiers

B&B from €55.00 to €60.00

PATRICK DOHERTY
PROPRIETOR

American Express
Diners
Mastercard
Visa

63 63

Open All Year

GRAND CENTRAL HOTEL

MAIN STREET,
BUNDORAN,
CO. DONEGAL
TEL: 072-42722 FAX: 072-42656
EMAIL: grandcentral@eircom.net

HOTEL ★★ MAP 13 I 17

Situated in Bundoran, Co. Donegal we provide the perfect base for touring Donegal, Sligo, Leitrim and Northern Ireland. The hotel consists of 62 bedrooms decorated with the emphasis on luxury and relaxation. Large family rooms and rooms with facilities for the disabled are also available. Our restaurant is known locally for its varied and interesting dishes and boasts a reputation for excellence in both cuisine and service. Multi purpose gym available with steam room.

B&B from €45.00 to €75.00

BRENDAN RUANE
MANAGER

American Express
Diners
Mastercard
Visa

62 62

Open All Year

GREAT NORTHERN HOTEL

BUNDORAN,
CO. DONEGAL

TEL: 072-41204 FAX: 072-41114
EMAIL: reservations@greatnorthernhotel.com
WEB: www.greatnorthernhotel.com

HOTEL ★★★★ MAP 13 I 17

Great Northern Hotel, Conference & Leisure Centre Bundoran. Hotel situated in the middle of 18 hole championship golf course overlooking Donegal Bay. 4**** hotel with 96 bedrooms with top leisure facilities for all the family. This hotel has all en suite bedrooms, a restaurant, grill room, lounge, ballroom and syndicate rooms. Leisure centre with swimming pool, gymnasium, private jacuzzi, sauna, steam room, plunge pool, beauty salon and hairdressing salon. We now offer a new state of the art conference centre.

Member of Brian McEniff Hotels

B&B from €90.00 to €110.00

PHILIP MCGLYNN
GENERAL MANAGER

American Express
Mastercard
Visa

Weekend specials from €175.00

96 96

Closed 20 - 26 December

B&B rates are per person sharing per night incl. Breakfast

HOLYROOD HOTEL

MAIN STREET,
BUNDORAN,
CO. DONEGAL

TEL: 072-41232 FAX: 072-41100
EMAIL: hrood@indigo.ie
WEB: www.holyroodhotel.com

HOTEL ★★★ MAP 13 I 17

The Holyrood Hotel situated on the main street of Bundoran, just a few minutes walk from the beach. All rooms are luxuriously furnished with multi-channel TV, DD phone, bath/shower, hairdryer and tea/coffee making facilities. Entertainment available at our Waterfront Bar. Leisure centre available at sister hotel nearby.

Member of Brian McEniff Hotels

B&B from €61.00 to €65.00

SEÁNNIE & AUDREY MCENIFF

American Express
Diners
Mastercard
Visa

Weekend specials from €110.00

100 100

Closed 23 - 26 December

MCGRORYS OF CULDAFF

CULDAFF,
INISHOWEN,
CO. DONEGAL

TEL: 074-937 9104 FAX: 074-937 9235
EMAIL: mcgr@eircom.net
WEB: www.mcgrorys.ie

GUESTHOUSE ★★★ MAP 14 L 21

This popular premises offering quality accommodation, award winning bar and restaurant is the ideal base for exploring the Inishowen Peninsula or golf at Ballyliffin. Our stylish restaurant serves excellent seafood, steaks, lamb and vegetarian choices. The front bar, Black and White Ulster Hotel Bar 2001, serves food daily. Macs Backroom Bar famous music venue, features acts such as Altan, Albert Lee, Brian Kennedy, Peter Green and many more.

B&B from €45.00 to €60.00

JOHN & NEIL MCGRORY/
ANNE DOHERTY

American Express
Mastercard
Visa

Midweek specials from €130.00

10 10

Closed 23 - 27 December

CENTRAL HOTEL, CONFERENCE & LEISURE CENTRE

THE DIAMOND,
DONEGAL

TEL: 073-21027 FAX: 073-22295
EMAIL: centralhotel@eircom.net
WEB: www.whites-hotelsireland.com

HOTEL ★★★ MAP 13 I 18

The Central Hotel, Conference & Leisure Centre is a 3*** hotel based in the centre of Donegal Town, with views of Donegal Bay. It is an ideal base for discovering our beautiful countryside and unspoilt beaches. There is also horse riding, golfing and angling near by. Our leisure centre has a fully equipped gym, indoor swimming pool, steam room, jacuzzi and solarium. An experience you won't forget. Newly refurbished hotel.

Member of White's and Associated Hotels

B&B from €65.00 to €85.00

MICHAEL NAUGHTON
GENERAL MANAGER

American Express
Diners
Mastercard
Visa

Weekend specials from €145.00

96 96

Open All Year

HARVEY'S POINT COUNTRY HOTEL

LOUGH ESKE,
DONEGAL TOWN,
CO. DONEGAL
TEL: 073-22208 FAX: 073-22352
EMAIL: reservations@harveyspoint.com
WEB: www.harveyspoint.com

HOTEL ★★★ MAP 13 I 18

If you enjoy fine food cooked with flair and attention to detail, coupled with a warm Irish welcome, then Harvey's Point is your destination. Hidden in the hills of Donegal, this exclusive, 30 bedroomed hotel is situated on the shores of Lough Eske, 6km from Donegal Town. Michelin Guide & food guide listed, AA 2 Rosette award 2002, RAC Blue Ribbon award 2002. Closed Sunday, Monday & Tuesday nights from 1st November to 31st March.

B&B from €99.00 to €145.00

DEIRDRE MCGLONE & MARC GYSLING
PROPRIETORS

American Express
Diners
Mastercard
Visa

Weekend specials from €200.00

30 30

Open All Year

MILL PARK HOTEL, CONFERENCE CENTRE & LEISURE CLUB

THE MULLINS, KILLYBEGS ROAD,
DONEGAL TOWN,
CO. DONEGAL
TEL: 073-22880 FAX: 073-22640
EMAIL: millparkhotel@eircom.net
WEB: www.millparkhotel.com

HOTEL ★★★ MAP 13 I 18

The warm welcome of an open fire mixed with the tranquil gentle flow of the millstream welcomes you to the Mill Park Hotel. A few minutes from Donegal Town the hotel is a perfect base for touring the North West of Ireland & its many attractions. The hotel has 43 luxurious bedrooms. With a fully equipped Leisure Centre. The heart of the hotel is the unique styled Granary, along with the restaurant, bars & lounges. Cead Mile Failte.

Member of Irish Country Hotels

B&B from €55.00 to €90.00

TONY MCDERMOTT

American Express
Diners
Mastercard
Visa

43 43

Closed 22 - 27 December

SAINT ERNAN'S HOUSE HOTEL

DONEGAL TOWN,
CO. DONEGAL

TEL: 074-972 1065 FAX: 074-972 2098
EMAIL: info@sainternans.com
WEB: www.sainternans.com

HOTEL ★★★★ MAP 13 I 18

Saint Ernan's House Hotel is situated on its own wooded island and joined to the mainland by a causeway. This graceful house offers a homely atmosphere where good food and tranquillity is a way of life. Golfing, swimming and angling are close by. The surrounding countryside offers beautiful scenic tours of mountains, sea and lakes. Saint Ernan's is the perfect respite from the hectic pace of life. Children under 6 not catered for. Member of Irish Country Houses and Restaurants Association.

Member of Ireland's Blue Book

B&B from €125.00 to €135.00

BRIAN O'DOWD
PROPRIETOR

Mastercard
Visa

10 10

Closed 29 October - 10 April

B&B rates are per person sharing per night incl. Breakfast

OSTAN NA TRA (BEACH HOTEL)

**DOWNINGS,
LETTERKENNY,
CO. DONEGAL**

TEL: 074-55303 FAX: 074-55907

HOTEL ★ MAP 13 J 21

The Beach Hotel is family run, situated on the breathtaking Atlantic Drive, having safe Downings Beach at the back door. In the heart of Rosguill, golf enthusiasts can avail of both Carrigart and Rosapenna 18 hole championship course. Ideally placed for angling, diving and walking, within easy driving distance of Glenveagh National Park, Glebe Gallery, Horn Head and Letterkenny. Sea trips to Tory Island, and diving for wrecks and shark fishing easily arranged.

B&B from €35.00 to €45.00

CHARLIE & MAIREAD MCCLAFFERTY

Mastercard

Visa

☺ Week partial board from €415.00

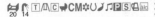

20 14

Closed 01 November - 01 April

ROSAPENNA HOTEL

**DOWNINGS,
CO. DONEGAL**

**TEL: 074-915 5301 FAX: 074-915 5128
EMAIL: rosapenna@eircom.net
WEB: www.rosapenna.ie**

HOTEL ★★★★ MAP 13 J 21

Rosapenna is a 4**** hotel situated in North West Donegal beside the fishing village of Downings. Set in 700 acres between Sheephaven Bay and Mulroy Bay, the hotel has its own 18 hole course designed by Old Tom Morris of St. Andrews in 1893. A new 18 hole links designed by Pat Ruddy is due to open in June 2003. Private pool, whirlpool, steam room, spacious lounges and a magnificent dining room overlooking the bay all contribute to a relaxing atmosphere. Rosapenna, a place to remember ...and return to.

B&B from €80.00 to €90.00

HILARY & FRANK CASEY
OWNERS

American Express

Diners

Mastercard

Visa

☺ 3 Dinners/3 B&B/Green Fees Old Course from €345.00

53 53

Closed 27 October - 14 March

ARNOLDS HOTEL

**DUNFANAGHY,
CO. DONEGAL**

**TEL: 074-913 6208 FAX: 074-913 6352
EMAIL: arnoldshotel@eircom.net
WEB: www.arnoldshotel.com**

HOTEL ★★★ MAP 13 J 21

Situated at the entrance to the village and overlooking Sheephaven Bay and Horn Head, the hotel has been in the Arnold Family for three generations. Good food, the friendly relaxed atmosphere and our helpful staff are just some of the compliments we receive from our guests who return each year. We are an ideal base for touring North West Donegal, Glenveagh National Park and Gardens.

Member of Irish Country Hotels

B&B from €65.00 to €80.00

ARNOLD FAMILY
PROPRIETORS

American Express

Diners

Mastercard

Visa

☺ Midweek specials from €150.00

30 30

Closed 03 November - 15 March

CO. DONEGAL
DUNGLOE / GLENCOLMCILLE / GLENTIES

ATLANTIC HOUSE

MAIN STREET,
DUNGLOE,
CO. DONEGAL
TEL: 074-952 1061 FAX: 074-952 1061
EMAIL: jcannon@iol.ie
WEB: www.atlantichousedungloe.com

GUESTHOUSE ★★ MAP 13 I 19

The Atlantic House is family run. It is within easy access of the airport, golf courses, pitch 'n' putt course, shopping and lots of beaches to choose from. There is also lake fishing, sea angling and hill walking close by. We have one of the most beautiful coastlines in Ireland as well as some of the most beautiful scenery to offer the tourist who just wants a quiet, peaceful holiday. We are also close to Dunlewey activity centre and Glenveagh National Park.

B&B from €26.00 to €50.00

JAMES & MARY CANNON OWNERS

Mastercard
Visa

Closed 20 - 30 December

OSTAN GHLEANN CHOLM CÌLLE

MALINMORE,
GLENCOLMCILLE,
CO. DONEGAL
TEL: 073-30003 FAX: 073-30222
EMAIL: reception@glenhotel.com
WEB: www.glenhotel.com

HOTEL ★★ MAP 13 G 18

Renowned as having the most beautiful location of any hotel in Ireland. This historic coastal hotel is set amid the magical scenery of sea, lake & mountains. Keynotes are warmth, comfort, excellent cuisine & a relaxed friendly Gaeltacht atmosphere. We have 37 modern & spacious guest bedrooms. Our unique unspoiled location makes the ideal base to explore Donegal, with a wide choice of interesting day trips and activities available.

B&B from €49.00 to €78.00

SHARON O'HARE

Mastercard
Visa

Weekend specials from €119.00

Closed 01 November - 15 March

HIGHLANDS HOTEL

GLENTIES,
CO. DONEGAL
TEL: 074-955 1111 FAX: 074-955 1564
EMAIL: highlandhotel@eircom.net
WEB: www.thehighlandshotel.com

HOTEL ★★ MAP 13 I 19

The Highlands Hotel is renowned for its warm and friendly atmosphere and good food. An attractive family run hotel ideally situated depending on what pastime you prefer, whether it be fishing, golfing, horse-riding or relaxing on the beautiful sandy beach of Narin. Famous for its excellent cuisine the hotel offers a wide ranging choice of à la carte menus. Special rates for families and golfing weekends are our speciality.

B&B from €46.20 to €55.00

JOHNNY, CHRISTINE & SINEAD BOYLE

Mastercard
Visa

Weekend specials from €105.00

Closed 24 - 28 December

378 **NORTH WEST**

B&B rates are per person sharing per night incl. Breakfast

BAY VIEW HOTEL & LEISURE CENTRE

MAIN STREET,
KILLYBEGS,
CO. DONEGAL
TEL: 073-31950 FAX: 073-31856
EMAIL: bvhotel@iol.ie
WEB: www.bayviewhotel.ie

HOTEL ★★★ MAP 13 H 18

One of Donegal's newest hotels, overlooking the splendour of Donegal Bay. We offer 40 en suite bedrooms with satellite TV, hair dryer, trouser press, tea/coffee makers, DD phone. Theme bar and carvery, seafood restaurant. Fully equipped leisure centre, indoor swimming pool. Deep sea angling, fresh water fishing, golf, hill walking. Scenic boat trips. An ideal touring base. Wheelchair accessible rooms. Lift.

B&B from €55.00 to €80.00

AIDAN MCHUGH
MANAGER

American Express
Mastercard
Visa

Weekend specials from €100.00

40 40

Closed 25 - 27 December

MOORLAND GUESTHOUSE

LAGHEY, R.232,
DONEGAL TOWN,
CO. DONEGAL
TEL: 074-973 4319 FAX: 074-973 4319
EMAIL: moorland@eircom.net

GUESTHOUSE ★★★ MAP 13 I 18

Have a break from the hustle and bustle. A guesthouse with family character, situated in a wild, high moor/hill landscape. We offer good cuisine. Available on the premises: Treatment with reflexology, body massage, cosmetic salon and sauna. Lounge with open fire and TV. Special relaxing and riding weeks. Arrangements made for golf and fishing. Excellent 18-hole golf links not far away. Ideal place for relaxation. Very quiet and remote. German spoken.

B&B from €25.00 to €40.00

ROSEMARIE & WALTER SCHAFFNER
PROPRIETORS

Mastercard
Visa

8 8

Open All Year

CASTLE GROVE COUNTRY HOUSE HOTEL

BALLYMALEEL,
LETTERKENNY,
CO. DONEGAL
TEL: 074-51118 FAX: 074-51384
EMAIL: enquires@castlegrove.com
WEB: www.castlegrove.com

HOTEL ★★★★ MAP 13 J 19

Castle Grove is a 17th century country house set on its own rolling estate overlooking Lough Swilly. Its bedrooms are spacious and with all modern facilities. Downstairs in both drawing room and library you find a perfect blend of old and new. The dining room offers excellent cuisine, much of its produce from the Walled Garden. To the discerning guest Castle Grove has to be visited to be appreciated. While here you can fish, golf, or simply enjoy the locality.

B&B from €75.00 to €95.00

RAYMOND & MARY T. SWEENEY
OWNERS

American Express
Diners
Mastercard
Visa

Weekend specials from €166.00

15 15

Closed 23 - 28 December

Room rates are per room per night

GLENEANY HOUSE

PORT ROAD,
LETTERKENNY,
CO. DONEGAL
TEL: 074-912 6088 FAX: 074-912 6090
EMAIL: gleneanyhouse@eircom.net
WEB: www.gleneany.com

GUESTHOUSE ★★★ MAP 13 J 19

Gleaneany House TOWN CENTER location opposite bus station in the heart of Letterkenny, offers both corporate and leisure clientele an excellent level of personal and friendly service. Renowned for its consistency in excellent cuisine, food is served all day. Our 19 en suite bedrooms have satellite TV and direct dial telephone. Our Lounge bar the ideal place for a quiet relaxing drink. An ideal base for touring beautiful Donegal, private car parking available.

B&B from €55.00 to €70.00

PAUL KELLY

Mastercard
Visa

19 19

HOLIDAY INN LETTERKENNY

DERRY ROAD,
LETTERKENNY,
CO. DONEGAL
TEL: 074-912 4369 FAX: 074-912 5389
EMAIL: info@holidayinnletterkenny.net
WEB: www.holidayinnletterkenny.net

HOTEL ★★★ MAP 13 J 19

Conveniently located on the outskirts of Letterkenny Town, the Holiday Inn Letterkenny is the ideal stopover for exploring County Donegal and the North West region of Ireland. All 121 superbly appointed en suite guest bedrooms are fully equipped and decorated to exceptionally high standards. Experience the latest leisure facilities at our health and fitness club. Our Aileach Restaurant serves a wide range of International cuisine while the Tara Bar and Lounge serves light meals and live music can be enjoyed at weekends.

B&B from €40.00 to €130.00

PETER BRADY
GENERAL MANAGER

American Express
Mastercard
Visa

Midweek specials from €160.00

121 121

PS🅰️ ♿ Inet

IRISH
HOTELS
FEDERATION

QUALITY HOTEL LETTERKENNY

MAIN STREET,
LETTERKENNY,
CO. DONEGAL
TEL: 074-912 2977 FAX: 074-912 2928
EMAIL: patricia@qualitydonegal.com
WEB: www.qualitydonegal.com

HOTEL ★★★ MAP 13 J 19

Prime location in the heart of Letterkenny Town. Quality Hotel comprises 84 luxurious en suite bedrooms, 26 of which are 1 & 2 bedroom apartment-style luxury suites. Its tastefully decorated bistro style restaurant "Lannigans" offers its patrons a delicately selective menu to suit all tastes. Quality Hotel has also gained its reputation with its famous bar "Dillons". Other facilities include masseur service, meeting room & business centre suite.

B&B from €50.00 to €80.00

PATRICIA PEOPLES

American Express
Diners
Mastercard
Visa

Weekend specials from €135.00

84 84

IRISH
HOTELS
FEDERATION

B&B rates are per person sharing per night incl. Breakfast

SILVER TASSIE HOTEL

RAMELTON ROAD,
LETTERKENNY,
CO. DONEGAL
TEL: 074-912 5619 FAX: 074-912 4473
EMAIL: silvertassie@eircom.net
WEB: www.silvertassiehotel.com

HOTEL ★★★ MAP 13 J 19

Nestled in the beautiful hills of Donegal overlooking Lough Swilly. The Silver Tassie Hotel combines old world charm with modern comfort and elegance. Our spacious and plush bedrooms (standard, superior or family) offer unrivalled comfort and luxury with an old country house feel. Our restaurant has a reputation for the best food around. Friendly service in relaxed surroundings with open fires. Ideal touring base with local golf courses, fishing and hill walking.

B&B from €55.00 to €95.00

CIARAN & ROSE BLANEY

Mastercard
Visa

😊 Weekend specials from €130.00

🛏 👤 ☎ 📺 🔥 T C M ♻ 🎵 P S 🔧 alc
36   36
♿ &

Closed 24 - 25 December

LAKE HOUSE HOTEL

NARIN,
PORTNOO,
CO. DONEGAL
TEL: 074-954 5123 FAX: 074-954 5444
EMAIL: lakehouse@iol.ie

HOTEL ★★★ MAP 13 H 19

The Lake House Hotel is a perfect base from which to tour our beautiful Donegal. Enjoy the delights of our award winning restaurant overlooking Clooney Lake. All of our bedrooms are en suite equipped with DD Telephone, remote control TV and hair dryer. Our conference centre comprises one main suite, which divides into two smaller suites for meetings - ideal location for weddings, functions, conferences & meetings.

B&B from €50.00 to €55.00

GERALDINE HEGARTY
GENERAL MANAGER

American Express
Mastercard
Visa

🛏 👤 ☎ T 🔥 C ♻ CM ❄ ♿ 🎵 P
14   14
S 🔧 alc ♿ &

Closed 24 - 26 December

FORT ROYAL HOTEL

RATHMULLAN,
CO. DONEGAL
TEL: 074-915 8100 FAX: 074-915 8103
EMAIL: fortroyal@eircom.net
WEB: www.fortroyalhotel.com

HOTEL ★★★ MAP 14 K 20

One of the most beautifully situated hotels in Ireland with 7 hectares of lovely grounds and gardens beside Lough Swilly include a sandy beach, hard tennis court, par 3 golf course. Especially friendly welcome accounts for the large number of regular visitors from all parts of the world to this peaceful unspoilt part of Donegal. Awarded two rosettes for food by AA. Member of Manor House Hotels, Irish Tourist Board and AA ***. GDS Access Code: UI Toll Free 1-800-44-UTELL.

Member of Manor House Hotels

B&B from €72.00 to €85.00

TIM & TINA FLETCHER
PROPRIETOR/MANAGER

American Express
Diners
Mastercard
Visa

😊 Midweek specials from €200.00

🛏 👤 ☎ T C ♻ CM ❄ ♿ P
15   15

Closed 01 November - 31 March

Room rates are per room per night

RATHMULLAN HOUSE

LOUGH SWILLY,
RATHMULLAN,
CO. DONEGAL

TEL: 074-915 8188 FAX: 074-915 8200
EMAIL: info@rathmullanhouse.com
WEB: www.rathmullanhouse.com

HOTEL ★★★★ MAP 14 K 20

A country house with a glorious seaside setting on Lough Swilly amid award winning gardens which stretch down to a sandy beach. Inside, elegant sitting-rooms are in period style. Bedrooms vary in size and cost from singles, families to superiors. Renowned for good food. Indoor heated pool, steamroom and tennis. 4 golf courses nearby. Special weekend and half board rates on request. Member of Blue Book. RAC★★★★ (Comfort Award). Dublin - 3.5 hours, Belfast - 2 hours.

Member of Ireland's Blue Book

B&B from €88.00 to €115.50

ROBIN & BOB WHEELER
HOSTS

American Express
Diners
Mastercard
Visa

24 24

Closed 02 January - 15 February

SANDHOUSE HOTEL

ROSSNOWLAGH,
CO. DONEGAL

TEL: 071-985 1777 FAX: 071-985 2100
EMAIL: info@sandhouse-hotel.ie
WEB: www.sandhouse-hotel.ie

HOTEL ★★★★ MAP 13 I 17

A delightful seaside setting overlooking the Atlantic Ocean on Donegal Bay. This small 4* luxury hotel, a transformed mid 19th century fishing lodge, is an oasis of comfort and relaxation on a 2 mile golden sandy beach. It combines elegant accommodation, open log fires, a marine spa and an award winning restaurant. A splendid location to explore the spectacular Donegal landscapes. Nearby 3 Ch'ship golf links courses. Described as one of Ireland's west coast treasures. Dublin 3hrs, Shannon 4hrs.

Member of Manor House Hotels

B&B from €80.00 to €150.00

PAUL DIVER
MANAGER

American Express
Diners
Mastercard
Visa

61 61

Closed 01 December - 01 February

COMMERCIAL & TOURIST HOTEL

BALLINAMORE,
CO. LEITRIM

TEL: 071-964 4675 FAX: 071-964 4679
EMAIL: commercialhotel@oceanfree.net
WEB: www.hotelcommercial.com

HOTEL ★★ MAP 11 J 15

Ideally situated in the centre of the beautiful town of Ballinamore in the heart of Lovely Leitrim. Completely rebuilt to 3*** standard. Large comfortable bedrooms with queen size beds, all en suite with DD phone. Your ideal base for breathtaking tours or business. Special rates for golfers.

B&B from €30.00 to €50.00

KAREN WALSH
MANAGERESS

American Express
Mastercard
Visa

28 28

FAX

Closed 25 December

GLENVIEW GUESTHOUSE

AUGHOO,
BALLINAMORE,
CO. LEITRIM

TEL: 078-44157 FAX: 078-44814
EMAIL: glenvhse@iol.ie

GUESTHOUSE ★★ MAP 11 J 15

Glenview House, 2 miles south of Ballinamore is a holiday haven, 500m from the Shannon-Erne Waterway. Exclusive fully licensed restaurant with extensive wine list. Enjoy Riverbus and boat trips, country drives, horse riding, cycling, animal farm, golf and hill walking. Glenview has its own private tennis court, games room, museum and play area. Self catering houses within grounds.

B&B from €38.00 to €45.00

TERESA KENNEDY

Mastercard
Visa

☺ Midweek specials from €108.00

6   6

a|c

IRISH HOTELS FEDERATION

Open All Year

RIVERSDALE FARM GUESTHOUSE

BALLINAMORE,
CO. LEITRIM

TEL: 071-964 4122 FAX: 071-964 4813
EMAIL: riversdaleguesthouse@eircom.net
WEB: www.riversdaleguesthouse.com

GUESTHOUSE ★★★ MAP 11 J 15

Riversdale is an impressive residence beautifully situated in parkland overlooking the Shannon-Erne Waterway. Spacious rooms and lounges mean a comfortable and peaceful ambience. We have our own heated indoor pool, squash court, sauna and fitness suite for when the weather is unkind - or hot! Local golf, horse riding, walking, riverbus, boat trips and scenic drives. Wide choice of interesting day trips. Brochure available - special family suites.

B&B from €38.00 to €45.00

THE THOMAS FAMILY
OWNERS

Mastercard
Visa

☺ Midweek Specials from €99.00

13   13

IRISH HOTELS FEDERATION

Closed 15 - 31 December

AISLEIGH GUEST HOUSE

DUBLIN ROAD,
CARRICK-ON-SHANNON,
CO. LEITRIM

TEL: 078-20313 FAX: 078-20675
EMAIL: aisleigh@eircom.net
WEB: http://homepage.eircom.net/~aisleigh

GUESTHOUSE ★★★ MAP 10 I 14

A warm welcome awaits you at our family run guest house situated 1km from the centre of the picturesque town of Carrick on Shannon, Ireland's best kept secret. Facilities include en suite bedrooms with TV, direct dial telephones (fax also available) games room and sauna. Local genealogy a speciality. Nearby there is golfing, swimming, tennis, squash, cruising, fishing (tackle & bait supplies) horse riding, walking, cycling, etc.

B&B from €26.00 to €30.00

SEÁN & CHARLOTTE FEARON
OWNERS

American Express
Mastercard
Visa

10   10

a|c

IRISH HOTELS FEDERATION

Open All Year

Room rates are per room per night

BUSH HOTEL

CARRICK-ON-SHANNON,
CO. LEITRIM

TEL: 078-20014 FAX: 078-21180
EMAIL: info@bushhotel.com
WEB: www.bushhotel.com

HOTEL ★★★ MAP 10 I 14

An hotel of ambience, style and comfort, the Bush Hotel (one of Ireland's oldest) has recently undergone major refurbishment whilst retaining its olde world character and charm. Centrally located in the town centre, the hotel backs onto courtyard, gardens and N4 by-pass with private access and parking. 26 en suite bedrooms, theme bars, coffee shop, restaurant overlooking courtyard. Amenities: National Parks, period houses, River Shannon.

B&B from €55.00 to €65.00

JOSEPH DOLAN
MANAGING DIRECTOR

American Express
Mastercard
Visa

26 26

Closed 24 - 31 December

LANDMARK HOTEL

CARRICK-ON-SHANNON,
CO. LEITRIM

TEL: 078-22222 FAX: 078-22233
EMAIL: landmarkhotel@eircom.net
WEB: www.thelandmarkhotel.com

HOTEL U MAP 10 I 14

Overlooking the River Shannon and its picturesque marinas. This beautifully appointed new luxury AA and RAC 4**** hotel is just a stroll from the town. Luxurious accommodation, fitness suite, Boardwalk Café & Bar, choice of 2 restaurants Ferrari's and CJ's. This unique unspoilt location invites you to enjoy river cruising, golf, hill walking, horse riding, watersports, scenic drives and places of historic interest. Located on the N4 Route, 2hrs Dublin, 2.5hrs Belfast.

B&B from €90.00 to €125.00

NOEL MEENAGHAN
MANAGER

American Express
Mastercard
Visa

☺ Midweek specials from €190.00

50 50

Closed 24 - 25 December

GLEBE HOUSE

BALLINAMORE ROAD,
MOHILL,
CO. LEITRIM

TEL: 071-963 1086 FAX: 071-963 1886
EMAIL: glebe@iol.ie
WEB: www.glebehouse.com

GUESTHOUSE ★★★ MAP 11 J 14

Dating back to 1823 this lovely Georgian former rectory set in fifty acres of woods and farmland has been completely restored by the Maloney Family. Enjoy the tranquillity of this peaceful part of Ireland. Plenty to see and do. Visit the stately homes and gardens, sample golf, horse riding, pony trekking, fishing and cruising. Or take to the country roads by bike or on foot. Assistance given with genealogy. 10% discount on bookings if more than one night. Special discount for seniors.

B&B from €38.00 to €45.00

LAURA MALONEY
MANAGER

American Express
Mastercard
Visa

☺ Weekend specials from €105.00

8 8

Open All Year

B&B rates are per person sharing per night incl. Breakfast

SHANNON KEY WEST HOTEL

THE RIVER EDGE,
ROOSKEY,
CO. LEITRIM
TEL: 071-963 8800 FAX: 071-963 8811
EMAIL: shnkywst@iol.ie
WEB: www.keywest.firebird.net

HOTEL ★★★ MAP 11 J 13

Situated on N4 Dublin Sligo route. Rooskey is an elegant marina village nestling between Carrick-On-Shannon and Longford Town. Dromod Train Station only 2km from Hotel. This beautiful 39 bedroom hotel with Greek, Georgian and modern architecture offers panoramic views of the River Shannon from both bedrooms and roof gardens. Excellent cuisine and personal service. Facilities include gymnasium, steamroom, jacuzzi, sunbed and outdoor tennis/basketball. Rooskey is a stress free comfort zone.

Member of Best Western Hotels

B&B from € 50.00 to € 59.00

JOHN LIKELY
MANAGING DIRECTOR

American Express
Mastercard
Visa

39 39

Closed 24 - 26 December

MARKREE CASTLE

COLLOONEY,
CO. SLIGO
TEL: 071-67800 FAX: 071-67840
EMAIL: markree@iol.ie
WEB: www.markreecastle.ie

HOTEL ★★★ MAP 10 H 15

Charles and Mary Cooper have restored Sligo's oldest inhabited house and made it a spectacular family hotel. Home of the Cooper family since 1640 and set in the middle of a large estate, Markree boasts spectacular plasterwork, a fine Irish oak staircase yet has all the comforts of a 3*** hotel. Good food, peace, quiet, lots of space and warm family welcome. Riding is also available on the estate.

B&B from € 92.00 to € 157.50

CHARLES COOPER
OWNER

American Express
Diners
Mastercard
Visa

30 30

Closed 24 - 27 December

CASTLE ARMS HOTEL

ENNISCRONE,
CO. SLIGO
TEL: 096-36156 FAX: 096-36156
EMAIL: castlearmshotel@eircom.net
WEB: www.castlearmshotel.com

HOTEL ★★ MAP 10 F 15

The Castle Arms Hotel is a family run hotel and upholds the tradition of offering a warm and friendly welcome with excellent home cooking. It is adjacent to a three mile long sandy beach, an 18 hole championship golf links, aqua leisure centre, seaweed and steam health baths, tennis courts and many other amenities. For more information contact a member of the Grimes family at 096-36156.

B&B from € 40.00 to € 40.00

LIAM & SHANE GRIMES

Mastercard
Visa

27 27

Closed 01 November - 01 March

Room rates are per room per night

BEACH HOTEL AND LEISURE CLUB

THE HARBOUR,
MULLAGHMORE,
CO. SLIGO

TEL: 071-916 6103 FAX: 071-916 6448
EMAIL: beachhot@iol.ie
WEB: www.beachhotelmullaghmore.com

HOTEL ★★ MAP 13 H 17

Set in the centre of the picturesque seaside village of Mullaghmore, overlooking the Atlantic Ocean. All rooms en suite (bath & shower), direct dial phone, TV & tea/coffee facilities. The hotel boasts an excellent leisure club; heated indoor swimming pool, jacuzzi, sauna, steam room & gymnasium. Discount at 5 golf courses, sea, game & coarse angling, horse riding, watersports & boat trips locally. Free Kiddies Club. Murder Mystery & activity weekends. "Fall under the spell of the Beach Hotel".

B&B from €35.00 to €80.00

COLM & AUDRI HERRON
PROPRIETORS

American Express
Mastercard
Visa

☺ Weekend specials from €85.00

23 23

Open All Year

PIER HEAD HOTEL

MULLAGHMORE,
CO. SLIGO

TEL: 071-66171 FAX: 071-66473
EMAIL: pierhead@eircom.net
WEB: www.pierheadhotel.com

HOTEL ★★ MAP 13 H 17

Boasting a unique setting at the edge of Mullaghmore Harbour, this family owned hotel stands majestically within this picturesque fishing & seaside resort. Located just 20 minutes from Sligo it offers guests panoramic views of the harbour and bay and features all en suite rooms, public bar, restaurant, function and conference facilities. Adjoining the hotel is the renowned Olde Quay Bar and Seafood Restaurant combining an old world nautical charm with the finest of food and service to create a warm and welcoming atmosphere for locals and tourists alike.

B&B from €39.00 to €60.00

JOHN MCHUGH

American Express
Diners
Mastercard
Visa

☺ Weekend specials from €89.00

16 16

Open All Year

YEATS COUNTRY HOTEL AND LEISURE CLUB

ROSSES POINT,
CO. SLIGO

TEL: 071-77211 FAX: 071-77203
EMAIL: yeatscountry@eircom.net
WEB: www.sligoaccommodation.com/yeats

HOTEL ★★★ MAP 10 H 16

A family run, 3*** hotel. All rooms en suite, cable TV, direct dial phone, tea/coffee facilities, hairdryer. Within 3km of sandy beaches and Sligo's 18 hole ch'ship golf courses at concession rates. Amenities include de-luxe leisure club with 18m swimming pool, sauna, jacuzzi, steam room and hi-tech gymnasium. Also available tennis, basketball, indoor bowling. Supervised creche and indoor play areas on bank holiday weekends July/August. Local activities: golf, yachting, fishing, scenic drives.

Member of Brian McEniff Hotels

B&B from €40.00 to €110.00

FIONA MCENIFF
MANAGING DIRECTOR

American Express
Diners
Mastercard
Visa

98 98

Closed 02 January - 02 February

B&B rates are per person sharing per night incl. Breakfast

CLARENCE HOTEL

**WINE STREET,
SLIGO**

TEL: 071-42211 FAX: 071-45823
EMAIL: clarencehotel@eircom.net

HOTEL U   MAP 10 H 16

Listed for its striking architectural design, the hotel is situated in the centre of Sligo. Its location makes it the perfect base to explore one of Ireland's most beautiful counties. You will find all of Sligo's business, shopping and historic centres just steps away with a modern new entertainment complex adjoining the hotel. Our restaurant, a gourmet delight, atmospheric throughout, brings an exciting dimension to wining and dining in Sligo. All rooms en suite with all amenities.

B&B from €44.44 to €63.49

CARMEL FOLEY
MANAGING DIRECTOR

American Express
Diners
Mastercard
Visa

🛏 🐾 ☎ ▢ C 🖊 C M ◡ ♩ ⬛ 🔥 alc
11 11

Open All Year

INNISFREE HOTEL

**HIGH STREET,
SLIGO**

TEL: 071-42014 FAX: 071-45745
EMAIL: innisfreehotelsligo@eircom.net

HOTEL ★★   MAP 10 H 16

Located in the heart of Sligo Town, this comfortable hotel has a special, friendly atmosphere. All rooms are en suite with TV, direct dial phone and tea making facilities. Excellent food served all day or visit the lively Ark Bar with its seafaring theme. Convenient to theatre and shops. Explore W.B. Yeats' breathtaking countryside, the Lake Isle of Innisfree, Glencar, Lisadell, renowned for its golf courses and seaside resorts. Specialising in commercial traveller rates and golf holidays.

B&B from €40.00 to €55.00

GERRY & CATHERINE GURN
OWNERS

American Express
Mastercard
Visa

😊 Midweek specials from €125.00

🛏 🐾 ☎ ▢ T C M ◡ ♩ S ▢ alc ▢
19 19

Closed 23 - 27 December

LISADORN

**DONEGAL ROAD,
SLIGO**

TEL: 071-43417 FAX: 071-46418
EMAIL: cjo'connor@eircom.net

GUESTHOUSE ★★★   MAP 10 H 16

Sligo Town's first and only 3*** guesthouse situated on the N15 within 5 minutes of town centre. Ideal base for North bound traffic. All rooms en suite, remote control colour TVs, direct dial telephones, fax, hairdryers and hospitality tray. Beside pitch & putt and 10 minutes to Rosses Point. Beside Sligo's Tennis & Squash Club. In the heart of Yeats' Country. It's the ultimate in luxury accommodation. A friendly welcome and service is guaranteed.

B&B from €28.00 to €32.00

MARIAN O'CONNOR
PROPRIETOR

Mastercard
Visa

🛏 🐾 ☎ ▢ T C ◡ P 🔥 S ▢
6 6

Closed 01 November - 01 February

Room rates are per room per night

RIVERSIDE HOTEL

MILBROOK,
SLIGO

TEL: 071-914 8080 FAX: 071-914 8060
EMAIL: stay@irishcourthotels.com
WEB: www.irishcourthotels.com

HOTEL U MAP 10 H 16

Opened in October 1999, this 66 bedroomed hotel is situated in the centre of Sligo Town overlooking the River Garavogue. All rooms are en suite with cable TV, direct dial telephone, hair dryer. Indoor swimming pool, gym, jacuzzi, sauna & steam room. The Mill Bar serves food all day or you can dine in the Waterfront Restaurant offering excellent cuisine. Ideal base for touring the North West region.

Member of Irish Court Hotels

B&B from €35.00 to €115.00

TADHG LYNE
PROPRIETOR

American Express
Diners
Mastercard
Visa

66 66

Closed 25 December

SLIGO PARK HOTEL & LEISURE CENTRE

PEARSE ROAD,
SLIGO

TEL: 071-916 0291 FAX: 071-916 9556
EMAIL: sligopk@leehotels.com
WEB: www.leehotels.com

HOTEL ★★★ MAP 10 H 16

Situated one mile south of Sligo on the Dublin Road, the Sligo Park Hotel is set on seven acres of gardens. A 3*** hotel with 110 bedrooms, the hotel has one of the finest leisure centres in the country. In the heart of the Yeats country, the Sligo Park is surrounded by some of the most scenic countryside in Ireland ranging from the majestic Benbulben to the gentle waters of Lough Gill. For that special break, the Sligo Park has all the facilities for your enjoyment.

Member of Lee Hotels

B&B from €61.00 to €97.00

GERARD MOORE
GENERAL MANAGER

American Express
Diners
Mastercard
Visa

Weekend specials from €136.00

110 110

Open All Year

SLIGO'S SOUTHERN HOTEL & LEISURE CENTRE

STRANDHILL ROAD,
SLIGO

TEL: 071-62101 FAX: 071-60328
EMAIL: reservations@sligosouthernhotel.com
WEB: www.sligosouthernhotel.com

HOTEL ★★★ MAP 10 H 16

The Sligo Southern Hotel is situated in the heart of Sligo Town, adjacent to the railway and bus stations. The Sligo Southern Hotel blends old world intimacy with every modern convenience. All 99 rooms are en suite, cable TV, phone, hairdryers, tea/coffee making facilities. Indoor swimming pool, gym, jacuzzi, sauna and steam room. Entertainment most nights in high season. Reservations Tel: 1850 520052 or Free phone NI & UK 0800 783 9024.

Member of Brian McEniff Hotels

B&B from €52.00 to €85.00

KEVIN MCGLYNN
GENERAL MANAGER

American Express
Diners
Mastercard
Visa

Weekend specials from €83.00

99 99

Closed 24 - 26 December

B&B rates are per person sharing per night incl. Breakfast

TOWER HOTEL

**QUAY STREET,
SLIGO**

TEL: 071-914 4000 FAX: 071-914 6888
EMAIL: reservations@ths.ie
WEB: www.towerhotelsligo.com

HOTEL ★★★ MAP 10 H 16

A Tower Group Hotel - located in the heart of Sligo Town, the hotel has immediate access to Sligo's shopping facilities and has a host of lively bars on its doorstep. It also makes an ideal base from which to play the great links courses of the North West. With 60 bedrooms it is small enough to offer a truly personal service. The Links Bar and Lady Eleanor Restaurant offer the perfect relaxation after a busy day touring or a rewarding day's golf.

Member of Tower Hotel Group

B&B from €52.50 to €70.00

ADRIAN HARKINS
GENERAL MANAGER

American Express
Diners
Mastercard
Visa

Weekend specials from €99.00

60 60

Closed 24 - 29 December

OCEAN VIEW HOTEL

**STRANDHILL,
CO. SLIGO**

TEL: 071-68115 FAX: 071-68009
EMAIL: oceanviewhotel@eircom.net
WEB: www.ovhotel.com

HOTEL ★★★ MAP 10 H 16

Ocean View Hotel, nestling at the foot of Knocknarea Mountain, overlooking the Atlantic, is a long established family hotel which offers a unique blend of all modern comforts with old-fashioned courtesy and charm. Its Rollers Restaurant is renowned for its home oak-smoked salmon and fresh local produce. Bar food also available. This picturesque area invites you to stroll its sandy beaches, pony trek, golf, explore the hidden glens, visit the oldest megalithic tombs in Europe.

Member of Irish Country Hotels

B&B from €57.00 to €68.00

SHAY BURKE/JEAN BURKE
PROPRIETORS

American Express
Diners
Mastercard
Visa

12 12

Closed 01 December - 28 February

CAWLEY'S

**EMMET STREET,
TUBBERCURRY,
CO. SLIGO**

TEL: 071-85025 FAX: 071-85963

GUESTHOUSE ★★ MAP 10 G 15

Cawley's, a large 3 storey family run guesthouse. We offer high standards in accommodation with tastefully decorated rooms. Our home cooking and personal service makes this premises your home for the duration of your stay. Private parking, landscaped gardens, easily accessed by air, rail and bus. Local amenities include fishing, 9 hole golf, horse riding. Seaside resorts close by. Major credit cards accepted.

B&B from €25.00 to €32.50

JEAN CAWLEY
PROPRIETOR

American Express
Mastercard
Visa

20 20

Closed 25 - 26 December

Room rates are per room per night

Whether you want to live it up in bustling Belfast or explore more of Northern Ireland, one thing's for sure, it's a holiday you'll never forget

B elfast city is positively bustling! Trendy new pubs and clubs, refined restaurants and café bars and some of the best high street and designer shopping in Europe provides an energy envied by cities everywhere. It's the perfect place for a city break!

Visit Belfast's largest indoor venue, the Odyssey Arena, one of Europe's top ten visitor attractions. Explore W5, an interactive, scientific centre for discovery; see the Belfast Giants in action, currently the UK's Superleague ice-hockey champions or enjoy a world class concert or performance.

The city offers exciting events all year round. In Autumn there's the Belfast Festival at Queen's, second only to the Edinburgh Festival in terms of content and variety. Catch the Cathedral Quarter Arts Festival in May, the Cinemagic Young People's Film Festival in December or get into the Rhythm in the City, Belfast's new summer music festival held in August.

Go back in time at the Ulster Folk and Transport Museum, where bygone days are recaptured and you can relive the excitement of the Titanic. Or browse through the unique collections of art, history and science at the Ulster Museum situated amidst beautiful Botanic Gardens.

As well as Belfast, you can enjoy the big city buzz in historic Londonderry surrounded by its famous 17th Century walls.

Oops! Spent too much, but so many shops, so many bargains!

The food was world class, as was the hospitality.

Londonderry was wall to wall with fun!

es are made.

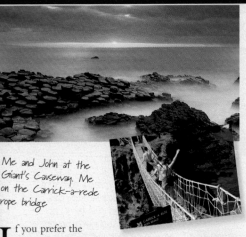

Me and John at the Giant's Causeway. Me on the Carrick-a-rede rope bridge

Spectacular scenery can be found around every corner in Northern Ireland. Take a boat trip on Fermanagh's famous Lakelands. Go walking, cycling or fishing amidst the majestic Mourne Mountains – join us here in August for the Celtic Fusion Festival, the biggest line-up of artists from the Celtic regions of the world. Or head for the Guinness and Oyster Festival in quaint, historic Hillsborough.

Northern Ireland is most famous for the 'craic', the friendly people and a welcome so warm you'll be back time and time again.

If you prefer the countryside, head for the Causeway Coast or the Glens of Antrim - home to sweeping landscapes, rolling hills, lush forest parks and some of Northern Ireland's most beautiful tourist sites. Sample a tipple of whiskey at Old Bushmills, the world's oldest licensed distillery, live the legend of Finn McCool at the world famous Giant's Causeway, test your nerve on the Carrick-a-rede rope bridge, suspended precariously 80ft above the sea, or stroll along the breathtaking European Blue Flag beaches of Ballycastle, Benone and Portrush. Swing by world class Royal Portrush golf course, just one of 30 fine fairways in the area or get on track for the North West 200 Motorcycle races in May.

Northern Ireland. You'll want to stay forever.

Steve & Ann
0131 888665

Had a tipple or two at the Old Bushmills Distillery

The craic was great with our new pals

ADAIR ARMS HOTEL

BALLYMONEY ROAD,
BALLYMENA,
CO. ANTRIM BT43 5BS
TEL: 028-2565 3674 FAX: 028-2564 0436
EMAIL: reservations@adairarms.com
WEB: www.adairarms.com

HOTEL ★★★ MAP 15 O 19

A warm welcome awaits you at the Adair Arms Hotel, which is owned and run by the McLarnon Family. The hotel was built in 1846 by Sir Robert Adair, and designed by the famous architect Charles Lanyon. Situated in the heart of Ballymena, ideally located for touring the romantic Glens of Antrim, Slemish Mountain and North Antrim Coast. The hotel has recently been refurbished and has the added attraction of a new 18 hole golf course within one mile - courtesy transport provided for guests.

B&B from £35.00 to £45.00

G MCLARNON
MANAGER/PROPRIETOR

American Express
Diners
Mastercard
Visa

☺ Weekend specials from £80.00

44 44

Closed 25 - 26 December

GALGORM MANOR HOTEL

136 FENAGHY ROAD,
BALLYMENA,
CO. ANTRIM BT42 1EA
TEL: 028-2588 1001 FAX: 028-2588 0080
EMAIL: mail@galgorm.com
WEB: www.galgorm.com

HOTEL ★★★★ MAP 15 O 19

Galgorm Manor is one of the finest country house hotels in Ireland. An Idyllic location for wedding receptions, business conferences and the perfect venue to get away from it all. The hotel boasts 25 spacious en suite bedrooms, most of which have spectacular views of the River Maine.

B&B from £45.00 to £70.00

IAN THOMPSON
MANAGER

American Express
Diners
Mastercard
Visa

☺ Weekend specials from £140.00

25 25

Open All Year

LEIGHINMOHR HOUSE HOTEL

LEIGHINMOHR AVENUE,
BALLYMENA,
CO. ANTRIM BT42 2AN
TEL: 028-2565 2313 FAX: 028-2565 6669

HOTEL P MAP 15 O 19

In a quiet and convenient location on the prestigious Galgorm Road area, with an unrivalled reputation for its food & service, Leighinmohr House Hotel is owned and run by the Mc Larnon family. Our 3★★★ standard hotel has 20 en suite bedrooms with all newly refurbished facilities.

B&B from £35.00 to £42.50

J. MCLARNON
MANAGER

American Express
Diners
Mastercard
Visa

20 20

Open All Year

B&B rates are Stg£ per person sharing per night incl. Breakfast

BAYVIEW HOTEL

2 BAYHEAD ROAD,
PORTBALLINTRAE,
BUSHMILLS, BT57 8RZ
TEL: 028-2073 4100 FAX: 028-2073 4330
EMAIL: info@bayviewhotelni.com
WEB: www.bayviewhotelni.com

HOTEL ★★★ MAP 14 N 21

Opened 2001, the Bayview Hotel is situated in the heart of the picturesque village of Portballintrae, one mile from Bushmills. Overlooking the Atlantic Ocean and close to the Giant's Causeway and Old Bushmills Distillery, with 25 luxurious bedrooms,standard, superior, premier, interlinking and ambulant disabled rooms available. Excellent conference facilities, Porthole Restaurant and Bar. Lift and private car park. This small luxury hotel is the ideal destination for conferencing, golfing, business, incentive travel and leisure.

Member of North Coast Hotels Ltd.

B&B from £40.00 to £70.00

MARY O'NEILL
GROUP MARKETING MANAGER

American Express
Diners
Mastercard
Visa

Weekend specials from £115.00

25 25

Open All Year

BUSHMILLS INN

9 DUNLUCE ROAD,
BUSHMILLS,
CO. ANTRIM BT57 8QG
TEL: 028-2073 2339 FAX: 028-2073 2048
EMAIL: mail@bushmillsinn.com
WEB: www.bushmillsinn.com

HOTEL ★★★ MAP 14 N 21

"A living museum of Ulster Hospitality" This mulit award winning hotel with turf fires, gas lights, nooks, crannies and even a secret room has been outstandingly successful in recreating its coaching inn origins. There's an atmospheric restaurant (new Irish cuisine), Victorian bar, turf fire 'snugs' and 32 captivating en suite bedrooms. Location: at the world's oldest distillery, by the River Bush between the Giant's Causeway and Royal Portrush Golf Club. "You're Welcome".

Member of Ireland's Blue Book

B&B from £49.00 to £74.00

ALAN DUNLOP & STELLA MINOGUE
MANAGERS

American Express
Mastercard
Visa

32 32

Open All Year

Room rates are Stg£ per room per night

CAUSEWAY HOTEL

40 CAUSEWAY ROAD,
BUSHMILLS,
CO. ANTRIM BT57 8SU

TEL: 028-2073 1226 FAX: 028-2073 2552

EMAIL: reception@giants-causeway-hotel.com
WEB: www.giants-causeway-hotel.com

HOTEL ★★ MAP 14 N 21

Situated on the North Antrim Coast at the entrance to the world famous Giant's Causeway and the new visitors' centre, this old family hotel established in 1836 has been tastefully renovated and restored to provide modern facilities while retaining its old grandeur and charm. The 28 centrally heated bedrooms have TV, telephone, tea/coffee making facilities and bathrooms en suite.

B&B from £32.50 to £32.50

JOHANNA ARMSTRONG
MANAGER

Mastercard
Visa

🙂 2 nights Dinner, +B&B weekend specials from £85.00 pps

28 28

Open All Year

LONDONDERRY ARMS HOTEL

GLENS OF ANTRIM, 20 HARBOUR ROAD,
CARNLOUGH,
CO. ANTRIM BT44 0EU

TEL: 028-2888 5255 FAX: 028-2888 5263

EMAIL: lda@glensofantrim.com
WEB: www.glensofantrim.com

HOTEL ★★★ MAP 15 P 20

This beautiful Georgian hotel was built in 1847. Once owned by Sir Winston Churchill, it is now owned and managed by Mr Frank O'Neill. With its open log fires, private lounges and award-winning restaurant this premier hotel in the Glens of Antrim is the perfect place to stay and discover the north eastern part of Ireland. Member of Irish Country Hotels.

Member of Irish Country Hotels

B&B from £40.00 to £50.00

FRANK O'NEILL
PROPRIETOR

American Express
Diners
Mastercard
Visa

🙂 Weekend specials from £70.00

35 35

Open All Year

DOBBINS INN HOTEL

6/8 HIGH STREET,
CARRICKFERGUS,
CO. ANTRIM BT38 7AF

TEL: 028-9335 1905 FAX: 028-9335 1905

EMAIL: info@dobbinsinnhotel.co.uk
WEB: www.dobbinsinnhotel.co.uk

HOTEL ★★ MAP 15 P 18

A family run hotel, built in the 15th century and with its own ghost 'Maud', the hotel has 15 en suite rooms with tea/coffee facilities, colour TV and trouser press. Meals are served all day in the Paul Jones Lounge or the de Courcy Restaurant. Recently refurbished, the hotel has regular evening entertainment. Well located for a pleasant drive to the Giants Causeway or for a day's shopping in Belfast.

B&B from £32.00 to £34.00

MR & MRS FALLIS

American Express
Mastercard
Visa

15 15

Closed 25 - 27 December

B&B rates are Stg£ per person sharing per night incl. Breakfast

QUALITY HOTEL

75 BELFAST ROAD,
CARRICKFERGUS,
CO. ANTRIM BT38 8PH
TEL: 028-9336 4556 FAX: 028-9335 1620
EMAIL: info@qualitycarrick.com
WEB: www.choicehotels.com

HOTEL ★★★ MAP 15 P 18

On a main coastal road, the Quality Hotel is of modern construction with 64 king size bedrooms and 4 suites with jacuzzi. Excellent conference and banqueting facilities. The perfect base for holidaying or business travel. Convenient to sea ferries and airports (12 -18 miles) and Belfast City 10 miles. Superb menus in main restaurant and bars.

B&B from £30.00 to £62.00

TOM BOYD
GENERAL MANAGER

American Express
Mastercard
Visa

Weekend specials from £65.00

68 68

Closed 25 - 26 December

KEEF HALLA COUNTRY HOUSE

20 TULLY ROAD,
NUTTS CORNER, CRUMLIN,
CO. ANTRIM BT29 4SW
TEL: 028-9082 5491 FAX: 028-9082 5940
EMAIL: info@keefhalla.com
WEB: www.keefhalla.com

GUESTHOUSE ★★★★ MAP 15 P 18

Keef Halla Country House is the nearest 4**** guesthouse to Belfast International Airport. All 7 bedrooms are elegantly decorated and include satellite TV, direct dial phone, trouser press, tea/coffee and refreshments. It is ideal for business people and holiday travellers requiring a central base for visiting Northern Ireland. We are conviently located to Antrim, Belfast, Crumlin, Dunadry, Lisburn and Templepatrick. Excellent value for money. Located on A26.

B&B from £25.00 to £25.00

CHARLES & SIOBHAN KELLY
OWNERS

American Express
Mastercard
Visa

7 7

Open All Year

ALEXANDRA TOWN HOUSE

11 LANDSDOWNE CRESCENT,
PORTRUSH,
CO. ANTRIM
TEL: 028-7082 2284 FAX: 028-7082 2284
EMAIL: mary@alexandratownhouse.com
WEB: www.alexandratownhouse.com

GUESTHOUSE ★★ MAP 14 N 21

The Alexandra, a charming period town-house, traditionally furnished but with modern day facilities offers the discerning visitor an ideal base to explore the surrounding countryside. Royal Portrush golf club five minutes by car is one of seven golf courses situated within half an hour's drive from the Alexandra. Your choice of room will range from cosy and charming to spacious and gracious with uninterrupted sea views to take your breath away.

B&B from £22.50 to £30.00

MARY MCALLISTER

7 7

Open All Year

Room rates are Stg£ per room per night

CLARMONT

10 LANSDOWNE CRESCENT,
PORTRUSH,
CO. ANTRIM BT56 8AY
TEL: 028-7082 2397 FAX: 028-7082 2397
EMAIL: clarmont10@hotmail.com
WEB: www.clarmont.com

GUESTHOUSE ★★ MAP 14 N 21

Clarmont, a spacious period townhouse, situated on Lansdowne Crescent, an award winning Victorian stucco-style resort terrace, designed to take maximum advantage of its seafront position on the famous Causeway Coast. With the renowned Royal Portrush Golf Club on its doorstep, the Clarmont enjoys an international golfing clientele. Also an ideal base for enjoying the many splendours & attractions of Ireland's North Coast. Convenient to pubs & restaurants. Ample parking.

B&B from £20.00 to £25.00

DECLAN PAUL CORMACK
OWNER

Mastercard
Visa

10 10

Open All Year

COMFORT HOTEL PORTRUSH

73 MAIN STREET,
PORTRUSH,
CO. ANTRIM BT56 8BN
TEL: 028-7082 6100 FAX: 028-7082 6160
EMAIL: info@comforthotelportrush.com
WEB: www.comforthotelportrush.com

HOTEL ★★★ MAP 14 N 21

The award winning 3*** Comfort Hotel Portrush opened 2001, situated overlooking the Atlantic Ocean in the centre of Portrush. 50 en suite bedrooms with interlinking and ambulant disabled rooms. Lift and private car park. Ideal base for golfing, walking, cycling, angling, sightseeing, families, tour parties and conferences. Golf at Royal Portrush, Portstewart, Castlerock, Ballycastle and Galgorm Golf Courses. Sister hotel "Bayview Hotel Portballintrae, Bushmills".

Member of Choice Hotels Europe

B&B from £35.00 to £40.00

MARY O'NEILL
GROUP MARKETING MANAGER

American Express
Diners
Mastercard
Visa

50 50

Inet

Open All Year

EGLINTON HOTEL

49 EGLINTON STREET,
PORTRUSH,
CO. ANTRIM BT56 8DZ
TEL: 028-7082 2371 FAX: 028-7082 3155
EMAIL: reservations@eglintonhotel.com
WEB: www.eglintonhotel.com

HOTEL ★★ MAP 14 N 21

The Eglinton Hotel, situated in the centre of Portrush, is ideally situated to allow you to enjoy famous landmarks, beaches, golf courses, watersports, or indeed any adventure sports. The hotel has lounges and a grill room. All rooms are en suite with colour TV, tea/coffee facility, DD phone and also a number of large family rooms are available.

B&B from £30.00 to £35.00

RAYMOND GRAY
PROPRIETOR

American Express
Mastercard
Visa

29 29

Open All Year

B&B rates are Stg£ per person sharing per night incl. Breakfast

MAGHERABUOY HOUSE HOTEL

41 MAGHERABOY ROAD,
PORTRUSH,
CO. ANTRIM BT56 8NX
TEL: 028-7082 3507 FAX: 028-7082 4687
EMAIL: admin@magherabuoy.co.uk
WEB: www.magherabuoy.co.uk

HOTEL ★★★   MAP 14 N 21

Quietly located hotel 1 mile from Portrush Town and central to the Causeway Coast's wonderful attractions - Giants Causeway, Dunluce Castle. The Maherabuoy is only a short driving time to the Royal Portrush, Portstewart and Castlerock golf clubs making it an ideal base for a relaxing or active break. A major renovation schedule is due for completion in 2003, offering a brand new product.

B&B from £40.00 to £50.00

T. CLARKE
GENERAL MANAGER

American Express
Diners
Mastercard
Visa

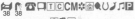
38   38

Closed 24 - 25 December

PENINSULA HOTEL

15 EGLINTON STREET,
PORTRUSH,
CO. ANTRIM BT56 8DX
TEL: 028-7082 2293 FAX: 028-7082 4315
EMAIL: reservations@peninsulahotel.co.uk
WEB: www.peninsulahotel.co.uk

HOTEL ★★   MAP 14 N 21

The Peninsula Hotel, situated in the centre of Portrush is ideally located to allow you to enjoy the delights of the Causeway Coast including the world famous Giant's Causeway. Our bedrooms are warmly decorated with the finest of fittings to ensure comfort for all our guests. The hotel is wheelchair friendly throughout with a passenger lift to all floors. Excellent food served in our Galley Bistro. Less than 10 min walk to Royal Portrush Golf Club.

B&B from £35.00 to £50.00

KADE WADE
GENERAL MANAGER

American Express
Mastercard
Visa

25   25

Inet

Open All Year

Room rates are Stg£ per room per night

ROYAL COURT HOTEL

233 BALLYBOGY ROAD,
PORTRUSH,
CO. ANTRIM BT56 8NF
TEL: 028-7082 2236 FAX: 028-7082 3176
EMAIL: royalcourthotel@aol.com
WEB: www.royalcourthotel.co.uk

HOTEL ★★★   MAP 14 N 21

Occupying one of the best positions on Northern Ireland's most famous coastline is the Royal Court Hotel. Situated overlooking the harbour town of Portrush and its famous Royal Portrush Golf Club with panoramic views of County Donegal and the Scottish Isles. A must of any visitor's schedule is the legendary Giant's Causeway, just 10 minutes drive away from the hotel.

Member of Causeway Coast and Glens

B&B from £35.00 to £45.00

BARRY DUFFY
MANAGER

American Express
Mastercard
Visa

18 18

Closed 26 December

BALLYMAC

7A ROCK ROAD,
STONEYFORD,
CO. ANTRIM BT28 3SU
TEL: 028-9264 8313 FAX: 028-9264 8312
EMAIL: info@ballymachotel.co.uk
WEB: www.ballymachotel.co.uk

HOTEL ★★   MAP 15 O 18

The Ballymac Hotel set amid tranquil surroundings. Spectacularly reincarnated, the contemporary designed 15 en suite bedrooms with excellent facilities including DD phones, modem facilities, hairdryers, TVs and hospitality trays. Our Grill Bar/Lounge and à la carte restaurant feature outstanding cuisine along with an extensive wine list. The Ballymac also boasts well-equipped function suites suitable for weddings, parties, trade shows and conferences. Extensive private parking is available in our grounds.

B&B from £35.00 to £45.00

CATHY MULDOON
GENERAL MANAGER

American Express
Mastercard
Visa

15 15

Closed 25 December

HILTON TEMPLEPATRICK

CASTLE UPTON ESTATE,
TEMPLEPATRICK,
CO. ANTRIM BT39 0DD
TEL: 028-9443 5500 FAX: 028-9443 5511
EMAIL: hilton_templepatrick@hilton.com
WEB: www.hilton.com

HOTEL ★★★★   MAP 15 O 18

Hilton Templepatrick, set in 220 acres of parkland, just 10 mins from Belfast International Airport is the perfect retreat for a short break. 130 en suite rooms offering views of the surrounding countryside. All rooms are equipped with satellite TV, phone, trouser press, hairdryer and hospitality tray. Dine in style in one of the hotel's restaurants or bars. Play a round of golf on the hotel's own 18 hole championship course or relax in the LivingWell Health Club.

B&B from £39.50 to £72.50

SEAN MURRAY
HOTEL MANAGER

American Express
Diners
Mastercard
Visa

130 130
18

Open All Year

B&B rates are Stg£ per person sharing per night incl. Breakfast

TEMPLETON HOTEL

882 ANTRIM RD, TEMPLEPATRICK,
BALLYCLARE,
CO. ANTRIM BT39 0AH
TEL: 028-9443 2984 FAX: 028-9443 3406

HOTEL ★★★ MAP 15 O 18

This luxury hotel is in a prime location close to Belfast International Airport, Belfast City Centre and Larne Harbour. Mixing the best of modern facilities with the appeal of yesterday, the hotel offers total quality for all tastes and needs. Upton Grill Room serving lunch and dinner daily, Raffles à la carte restaurant, spacious lounge, 24 bedrooms including executive suites and family rooms, Sam's Bar with pub grub. Late bar on Friday and Saturday evenings.

B&B from £37.50 to £55.00

ALISON MCCOURT/CLAIRE KERR
GEN MANAGER/MRKTG MANAGER

American Express
Diners
Mastercard
Visa

24 24

Closed 25 - 26 December

O'NEILL ARMS HOTEL

20-22 MAIN STREET,
TOOMEBRIDGE,
CO. ANTRIM. BT41 3TQ
TEL: 028-7965 0202 FAX: 028-7965 0970
EMAIL: enquiries@oneillarmshotel.co.uk

HOTEL ★ MAP 14 N 18

Situated on the main road from Belfast (28 miles) to Derry (43 miles) via the International Airport (15 miles) and less than 40 mins from the North Coast. The O'Neill Arms is ideally located for the exploration of Northern Ireland. Nearby there is a championship golf course, forest walks and excellent coarse fishing. The hotel itself provides extensive carparking and beautiful gardens; and good food is served daily in our restaurant. The O'Neill Arms Hotel awaits you with a warm welcome all year round.

B&B from £35.00 to £40.00

DERMOT MCLARNON
PROPRIETOR

Mastercard
Visa

11 11

Closed 25 December

Room rates are Stg£ per room per night

ARMAGH CITY HOTEL

2 FRIARY ROAD,
ARMAGH CITY,
CO. ARMAGH
TEL: 028-3751 8888 FAX: 027-3751 2777
EMAIL: mooneyhotelgroup@talk21.com
WEB: www.mooneyhotelgroup.com

HOTEL N   MAP 14 N 16

The 4* standard Armagh City Hotel is
the latest addition to the Mooney
Hotel Group and the largest Hotel
Conference facility in Northern Ireland.
The 82 luxurious bedrooms overlook
the County Armagh Golf Club, the
Palace Stables and the magnificent
City of Armagh. Our guests can relax
in the spacious and comfortable
foyer, sample the delightful fine
cuisine of the Friary Restaurant, or
alternatively, experience the ultimate
in Health and Fitness in our Country
Club (managed by LA Fitness).

B&B from £35.00 to £55.00

MALACHY TONER
GENERAL MANAGER

American Express
Diners
Mastercard
Visa

Weekend specials from £90.00

99 99

S ⓐ alc 🍴 Inet FAX

Closed 24 - 26 December

CHARLEMONT ARMS HOTEL

57-65 ENGLISH STREET,
ARMAGH CITY,
CO. ARMAGH BT 61 7LB
TEL: 028-3752 2028 FAX: 028-3752 6979
EMAIL: info@charlemontarmshotel.com
WEB: www.charlemontarmshotel.com

HOTEL ★   MAP 14 N 16

A family run hotel set in the city centre
which has completed major
refurbishment. Convenient to shops,
18-hole golf course, leisure centre
and all major tourist attractions
including the 2 Cathedrals and other
places of historic interest. 30 en suite
bedrooms including one for the
disabled, a 60 seat restaurant, 80
seat lounge bar, Turner's theme bar
and Basement Café / Winebar that
offers a unique dining experience for
Armagh.

B&B from £32.50 to £35.00

THE FORSTER FAMILY

American Express
Mastercard
Visa

😊 Midweek specials from €70.00

30 30

Closed 25 - 26 December

ASHBURN HOTEL

81 WILLIAM STREET,
LURGAN,
CO. ARMAGH BT66 6JB
TEL: 028-3832 5711 FAX: 028-3834 7194
EMAIL: info@theashburnhotel.com
WEB: www.theashburnhotel.com

HOTEL ★   MAP 15 O 17

Owned and managed by the
McConaghy Family, the Ashburn Hotel
is friendly and efficient. Conveniently
situated with easy access to the
motorway (M1), rail network and
town centre. An ideal base for angling
or golfing trips - 5 miles from the
River Bann and 1 mile from local golf
course. All bedrooms are en suite
with colour TV, direct dial telephone
and hospitality tray. Entertainment
each weekend in our popular
nightclub.

B&B from £30.00 to £30.00

JOHN F. MCCONAGHY

Mastercard
Visa

12 12

Closed 24 - 26 December

B&B rates are Stg£ per person sharing per night incl. Breakfast

BALMORAL HOTEL

BLACKS ROAD,
DUNMURRY,
BELFAST BT10 0NF
TEL: 028-9030 1234 FAX: 028-9060 1455
EMAIL: info@balmoralhotelbelfast.co.uk

HOTEL ★★ MAP 15 P 18

Situated 4 miles via motorway from Belfast City Centre the Balmoral Hotel offers 43 en suite rooms, 8 of which are equipped with disabled facilities. All rooms have been designed with the guest in mind, each featuring remote control TV, radio, DD phone and hospitality tray. From the moment you arrive at the Balmoral Hotel you can expect the warmest of welcomes. The hotel offers spacious lounges inviting you to sit and relax. Food served all day in the Lady Anne, to fine dining in the hotel restaurant. A member of McKeever Hotels.

B&B from £25.00 to £40.00

CATHERINE & EUGENE MCKEEVER

American Express
Diners
Mastercard
Visa

43 43

Closed 25 - 26 December

CORR'S CORNER HOTEL

315 BALLYCLARE ROAD,
NEWTOWNABBEY,
CO. ANTRIM BT36 4TQ
TEL: 028-9084 9221 FAX: 028-9083 2118
EMAIL: info@corrscorner.com
WEB: www.corrscorner.com

HOTEL ★★ MAP 15 P 18

Corr's Corner is a family-run business located 7 miles north of Belfast at the M2 and A8 junction, 14 miles from Larne Harbour and Belfast International Airport. The hotel has 30 en suite rooms with 2 rooms specifically designed for guests with disabilities. Meals are served all day in the Lady R Bar and the Corriander Room Restaurant. The Ballyhenry Lounge is open every evening and the Cedar Room caters for meetings and private parties up to 60 persons. A member of McKeever Hotels.

Room Rate from £50.00 to £60.00

CATHERINE & EUGENE MCKEEVER

American Express
Diners
Mastercard
Visa

30 30

Inet

Closed 25 - 27 December

DUKES HOTEL

65/67 UNIVERSITY STREET,
BELFAST BT7 1HL
TEL: 028-9023 6666 FAX: 028-9023 7177
EMAIL: info@dukes-hotel-belfast.co.uk
WEB: www.dukeshotelbelfast.com

HOTEL ★★★ MAP 15 P 18

A bright new modern hotel constructed within one of Belfast's more distinguished Victorian buildings. Beside Queen's University, Ulster Museum, Botanic Gardens and less than 1 mile from the city centre. Golf courses only minutes away. 20 luxury en suite bedrooms, all with satellite TV, hairdryers and direct dial telephones. Gymnasium and saunas also available. Glassroom Restaurant serving local cuisine. Popular bar for the smart set. A friendly welcome and service is guaranteed.

B&B from £36.00 to £55.00

MICHAEL CAFOLLA
DIRECTOR

American Express
Diners
Mastercard
Visa

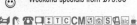
Weekend specials from £79.00

20 20

Open All Year

Room rates are Stg£ per room per night

DUNADRY HOTEL AND COUNTRY CLUB

2 ISLANDREAGH DRIVE,
DUNADRY,
CO. ANTRIM BT41 2HA

TEL: 028-9443 4343 FAX: 028-9443 3389
EMAIL: mooneyhotelgroup@talk21.com
WEB: www.mooneyhotelgroup.com

HOTEL ★★★★   MAP 15 O 18

The place to stay if you're looking for warm hospitality, comfort, charm, relaxation, imaginative gourmet cuisine. Cycling, fishing, country walking, golf & horse riding all available on site or upon request. Luxurious bedrooms, beautiful food in Mill Race Bistro & fine dining in the Linen Mill Restaurant. Modern, fully equipped country club incl. heated indoor swimming pool, steam room & sauna. Conference facilities for up to 400 delegates & free parking. Only 15 mins from Belfast City Centre. Previous 'Les Routiers Hotel of the Year' award winner.

B&B from £42.50 to £80.00

ROBERT MOONEY
GENERAL MANAGER

American Express
Diners
Mastercard
Visa

😊 Weekend specials from £105.00

83 83

Closed 24 - 26 December

HILTON BELFAST

4 LANYON PLACE,
BELFAST BT1 3LP

TEL: 028-9027 7000 FAX: 028-9027 7277
EMAIL: hilton_belfast@hilton.com
WEB: www.hilton.com

HOTEL ★★★★★   MAP 15 P 18

Along with the magnificent Waterfront Hall, you will find Hilton Belfast, a contemporary 5★★★★★ hotel in an enviable location. The hotel has been designed to offer the discerning guest every level of comfort and convenience and is within easy reach of many of Belfast's most famous attractions, including the Odyssey, an exciting new entertainment complex, just 5 minutes walk from the hotel.

Room Rate from £79.00 to £145.00

PATRICK STAPLETON
GENERAL MANAGER

American Express
Diners
Mastercard
Visa

195 195

Open All Year

HOLIDAY INN BELFAST

22 ORMEAU AVENUE,
BELFAST BT2 8HS

TEL: 028-9027 1706 FAX: 028-9062 6546
EMAIL: belfast@6c.com
WEB: www.belfast.holiday-inn.com

HOTEL ★★★★   MAP 15 P 18

A modern hotel situated in the heart of Belfast's City centre, and ideally located for city centre shops, restaurants, Odyssey Centre, Opera House, Belfast Zoo, Botanic Gardens/Ulster Museum, City Hall & the Waterfront Hall. This newly built hotel offers residents superior air-conditioned bedrooms, the contemporary Junction Restaurant and Bar, a superb Health and Leisure Centre. There is also a Pay Car Park on site & an NCP car park behind the hotel.

Member of Bass Hotels & Resorts

B&B from £40.00 to £77.45

ADRIAN MCLAUGHLIN
GENERAL MANAGER

American Express
Diners
Mastercard
Visa

😊 Weekend specials from £89.00

170 170

Open All Year

B&B rates are Stg£ per person sharing per night incl. Breakfast

BELFAST CITY
a kaleidescope of activity

Some city's are just good for adults, some just for kids, Belfast was made for families. Biggest of the many attractions, down by the waterfront, is the amazing new Odyssey Complex. Northern Ireland's multi-million pound Millennium project is several days out in one.

At Odyssey you will find **whowhatwherewhenwhy - W5**, the incredible new interactive discovery centre that has over 140 exciting interactive exhibits - make your own cartoons, build a bridge or play a laser harp. There's also the **Odyssey Pavilion** of bars, cinemas and restaurants, which includes Ireland's very own Hard Rock Cafe, and arriving soon ten-pin bowling, or you can experience **Sheridan IMAX® Cinema** featuring 2D and fabulous 3D presentations on a screen towering six stories tall!

For a great day out for the family, choose.......

ODYSSEY

For further information on where to stay in Belfast contact:
the Belfast Welcome Centre
47 Donegall Place, Belfast
Tel: +44 (0)28 9024 6609
or visit www.gotobelfast.com

Belfast ☺ *City*
...touch the spirit, feel the welcome

whowhatwherewhenwhy-**W5**
+44 (0)28 9046 7700
www.w5online.co.uk

Sheridan IMAX Cinema
+44 (0)28 9046 7000
www.belfastimax.com

Odyssey Pavilion
+44 (0)28 9046 7013
www.odysseypavilion.com

JURYS INN BELFAST

FISHERWICK PLACE,
GREAT VICTORIA ST,
BELFAST BT2 7AP

TEL: 028-9053 3500 FAX: 028-9053 3511
EMAIL: jurysinnbelfast@jurysdoyle.com
WEB: www.jurysdoyle.com

HOTEL ★★★ MAP 15 P 18

Located in the centre of Belfast,
adjacent to the Opera House, the City
Hall and the city's main commercial
district. Just two minute's walk away
are the prime shopping areas of
Donegall Place and the Castlecourt
Centre, while the city's golden mile,
with its myriad lively bars and
restaurants, is also within walking
distance.

Room Rate from £71.00 to £75.00

MARGARET NAGLE
GENERAL MANAGER

American Express
Diners
Mastercard
Visa

190 190

Closed 24 - 26 December

LA MON HOTEL & COUNTRY CLUB

41 GRANSHA ROAD,
CASTLEREAGH,
BELFAST BT23 5RF

TEL: 028-9044 8631 FAX: 028-9044 8026
EMAIL: info@lamon.co.uk
WEB: www.lamon.co.uk

HOTEL ★★★ MAP 15 P 18

This modern family-run hotel offers
70 en suite bedrooms, excellent
banqueting & conference facilities in a
tranquil setting just 8 miles south-
east of Belfast city centre. Guests will
enjoy the superb leisure facilities
including 15 metre swimming pool,
children's pool, sauna, jacuzzi, steam
room, gymnasium, hair studio &
beauty salon. A wide range of dining
options is available with table d'hôte
and à la carte menus in the
Shakespeare Restaurant. Casual
dining with a cosmopolitan flavour is
also available in our lively bistro. An
ideal venue for business or leisure.

B&B from £40.00 to £55.00

FRANCIS BRADY
MANAGING DIRECTOR

American Express
Diners
Mastercard
Visa

☺ Weekend specials from £79.00

70 70

Open All Year

LANSDOWNE HOTEL

657-659 ANTRIM ROAD,
BELFAST BT15 4EF

TEL: 028-9077 3317 FAX: 028-9078 1588
EMAIL: info@the-lansdowne.co.uk
WEB: www.the-lansdowne.co.uk

HOTEL ★★★ MAP 15 P 18

The Lansdowne Hotel. Located 2.5
miles north of the city centre. Belfast
Castle, Fortwilliam Golf Course, Cave
Hill Country Park and Belfast Zoo are
but a stone's throw away. The bar
and restaurant co-exist in a fusion of
modern and contemporary design.
With wonderfully landscaped gardens
and childrens' play area, our
Conservatory Restaurant is not to be
missed, or relax and have a drink in
our lounge bar.

B&B from £30.00 to £37.50

MICHAEL CAFOLLA
GENERAL MANAGER

American Express
Diners
Mastercard
Visa

25 25

Open All Year

B&B rates are Stg£ per person sharing per night incl. Breakfast

MCCAUSLAND HOTEL

34-38 VICTORIA STREET,
BELFAST BT1 3GH

TEL: 028-9022 0200 FAX: 028-9022 0220
EMAIL: info@mccauslandhotel.com
WEB: www.mccauslandhotel.com

HOTEL ★★★★ MAP 15 P 18

An architectural masterpiece, this city centre luxury hotel is of Italianate classical style. A wonderful base to explore Belfast. Each bedroom luxuriously appointed with colour multi channel TV, tea/coffee making facilities and exclusive toiletries. Café style bar & restaurant at hotel. Car parking available. Close to museums, theatres, shopping, Odyssey Arena & Waterfront Hall. Sister hotels Hibernian, Dublin & Woodstock, Ennis, Co. Clare. GDS Acc code: LX. UK Toll free: 00 800 525 48000.

Member of Small Luxury Hotels of the World

B&B from £70.00 to £90.00

NIALL COFFEY
GENERAL MANAGER

American Express
Diners
Mastercard
Visa

Weekend specials from £99.00

61 61

Closed 24 - 26 December

PARK AVENUE HOTEL

158 HOLYWOOD ROAD,
BELFAST BT4 1PB

TEL: 028-9065 6520 FAX: 028-9047 1417
EMAIL: frontdesk@parkavenuehotel.co.uk
WEB: www.parkavenuehotel.co.uk

HOTEL ★★★ MAP 15 P 18

The Park Avenue Hotel has recently been refurbished. 55 rooms with en suite facilities, including TV with satellite channels. Disabled facilities. Free parking. The Griffin Restaurant offers an extensive menu to suit all tastebuds. Alternatively our bistro menu is served daily in Gelston's Corner Bar. 5 minutes from Belfast City Airport. 10 minutes from city centre. Also in close proximity to the Odyssey Arena and Waterfront Hall. Excellent links to outer ring roads and all transport stations and ferry terminals.

B&B from £30.00 to £39.50

ANGELA REID
FRONT OFFICE/CONFERENCE MANAGER

American Express
Mastercard
Visa

55 55

Closed 25 December

WELLINGTON PARK HOTEL

21 MALONE ROAD,
BELFAST BT9 6RU

TEL: 028-9038 1111 FAX: 028-9066 5410
EMAIL: mooneyhotelgroup@talk21.com
WEB: www.mooneyhotelgroup.com

HOTEL ★★★★ MAP 15 P 18

The ideal place to stay when you come to Belfast. 5 minutes from the city centre, in the fashionable Malone Road area. The city's most popular venues are at our doorstep: The Waterfront Hall, King's Hall, the Odyssey complex, museums & theatres. We offer conference facilities for up to 400 delegates. Designed to international standards, the hotel is renowned for its elegant & relaxed atmosphere & luxurious suites. You can enjoy fine cuisine in the Piper's Bistro & there is free parking for residents. Call Central Reservations on +44 (0)28 9038 5050.

Member of Best Western Hotels

B&B from £40.00 to £75.00

ARTHUR MOONEY
GENERAL MANAGER

American Express
Diners
Mastercard
Visa

Weekend specials from £95.00

75 75

Closed 24 - 26 December

Room rates are Stg£ per room per night

BROWN TROUT GOLF & COUNTRY INN

209 AGIVEY ROAD,
AGHADOWEY, COLERAINE,
CO. DERRY BT51 4AD
TEL: 028-7086 8209 FAX: 028-7086 8878
EMAIL: bill@browntroutinn.com
WEB: www.browntroutinn.com

HOTEL ★★★ MAP 14 N 20

The Brown Trout Golf and Country Inn nestles near the River Bann only 12.8km from the picturesque Causeway Coast. This old inn with 15 rooms, and four 5 star cottages, is Northern Ireland's first golf hotel. Bill, Gerry, Jane or Joanna will happily organise golf, horseriding and fishing packages with professional tuition if required or you can just enjoy a relaxing break and the craic with the locals. The warm hospitality and 'Taste of Ulster' restaurant will make your stay enjoyable.

Member of Irish Country Hotels

B&B from £30.00 to £42.50

BILL O'HARA
OWNER

American Express
Diners
Mastercard
Visa

15 15

Open All Year

LODGE HOTEL

LODGE ROAD,
COLERAINE,
CO. LONDONDERRY BT52 1NF
TEL: 028-7034 4848 FAX: 028-7035 4555
EMAIL: info@thelodgehotel.com
WEB: www.thelodgehotel.com

HOTEL ★★★ MAP 14 M 20

Centrally located, the Lodge Hotel boasts 3*** standard en suite rooms, superb food, friendly staff, two restaurants, buffet lunch, Sunday carvery, weekend entertainment, plenty of 'craic', award winning disabled facilities and much much more!! Local amenities include shopping, golfing, horse riding, beach & fun parks. "We think its simply the best and can't wait to stay again!!" Signed Mr. & Mrs Keeps Returning.

B&B from £32.50 to £37.50

NORMA WILKINSON
MANAGING DIRECTOR

American Express
Mastercard
Visa

56 56

Open All Year

BEECH HILL COUNTRY HOUSE HOTEL

32 ARDMORE ROAD,
DERRY BT47 3QP

TEL: 028-7134 9279 FAX: 028-7134 5366
EMAIL: info@beech-hill.com
WEB: www.beech-hill.com

HOTEL ★★★★ MAP 14 L 20

Beech Hill is a privately owned country house hotel, 2mls from Londonderry. It retains the elegance of country living, restored to create a hotel of charm, character & style. Its ambience is complemented by the surrounding grounds, planted with a myriad trees, including beech - after which the hotel is named. Winners of British Airways Best Catering 1994. Manor House Hotels 00353 1 295 8900. Best Kept Secrets of Northern Ireland. Sauna, Steamroom, jacuzzi & fitness suites. Relaxation weekends, aromatherapy, Reiki, massage & beauty therapies. Booking advisable.

Member of Manor House Hotels

B&B from £50.00 to £75.00

SEAMUS DONNELLY
PROPRIETOR

American Express
Mastercard
Visa

27 27

Closed 24 - 26 December

B&B rates are Stg£ per person sharing per night incl. Breakfast

BEST WESTERN WHITE HORSE HOTEL

68 CLOONEY ROAD,
DERRY BT47 3PA

TEL: 028-7186 0606 FAX: 028-7186 0371
EMAIL: info@whitehorsehotel.biz
WEB: www.whitehorse-hotel.com

HOTEL ★★★ MAP 14 L 20

A luxury family-run hotel with 57
bedrooms including 3 executive
suites and new (2001) leisure centre.
The hotel is ideal for pleasure and
business with 4 conference centres,
22m pool with childrens' section,
gymnasium, aerobics studio, sauna
and steam rooms, spa, jacuzzi and
beauty. Only 10 minutes from the
airport and city centre and on the
main route to the Giant's Causeway.
Award winning restaurant and bar
and keen room rates. AA Selected
♦♦♦.

Member of Best Western Hotels

B&B from £35.00 to £50.00

SHEILA HUNTER
GENERAL MANAGER

American Express
Diners
Mastercard
Visa

57 57

Open All Year

CITY HOTEL

QUEENS QUAY,
DERRY BT48 7AS

TEL: 028-7136 5800 FAX: 028-7136 5801
EMAIL: res@derry-gsh.com
WEB: www.gshotels.com

HOTEL N MAP 14 L 20

The new City Hotel is Derry's first
4**** standard city centre hotel.
Ideally located on Queens Quay it has
magnificent views of the River Foyle
and Guildhall. Leisure facilities
include swimming pool, steam room,
jacuzzi, gym. Enjoy fine food at
Thompsons On The River. The hotel
has conference facilities for up to 450
delegates. A Great Southern Hotel.
Bookable through UTELL International
or Central Reservations on Tel:
01-214 4800.

Member of Great Southern Hotels

Room Rate from £70.00 to £100.00

CLODAGH CUSSEN
GENERAL MANAGER

American Express
Diners
Mastercard
Visa

Weekend specials from £85.00

145 145

Closed 24 - 26 December

DA VINCIS HOTEL COMPLEX

15 CULMORE ROAD,
DERRY BT48 8JB

TEL: 028-7127 9111 FAX: 028-7127 9222
EMAIL: info@davincishotel.com
WEB: www.davincishotel.com

HOTEL ★★★ MAP 14 L 20

Derry's premier hotel located only five
minutes from the city centre. Da
Vinci's Hotel Complex is home of
Quality Hotel Da Vinci's with 70
vibrant and stylish bedrooms, 21
luxuries apartments and penthouses,
an award winning bar, award
winning Grillroom Restaurant, the
funky and fashionable Spirit Bar, not
to mention the exclusive Style Bar.

Member of Choice Hotels Ireland

Room Rate from £63.00 to £97.00

CIARAN O'NEILL
GENERAL MANAGER

American Express
Diners
Mastercard
Visa

Weekend specials from £75.00

70 70

Closed 24 - 26 December

Room rates are Stg£ per room per night

TOWER HOTEL DERRY

OFF THE DIAMOND,
DERRY CITY

TEL: 028-7137 1000 FAX: 028-7137 1234
EMAIL: reservations@thd.ie
WEB: www.towerhotelderry.com

HOTEL U MAP 14 L 20

A Tower Group Hotel - Tower Hotel Derry, located just off the Diamond in the heart of the city, opened in March 2002. The hotel is excellently situated for visiting the many tourist attractions, which include St. Columb's Cathedral as well as being an ideal base to tour the rest of County Derry. Facilities include 93 bedrooms with state of the art amenities, Mediterranean style bistro, café bar, conference and business centre and an in-house fitness facility. RAC ◆◆◆◆ approved.

Member of Tower Hotel Group

B&B from £30.00 to £50.00

IAN HYLAND

American Express
Diners
Mastercard
Visa

☺ Weekend specials from £69.00

93 93

Closed 24 - 27 December

WATERFOOT HOTEL & COUNTRY CLUB

CAW ROUNDABOUT,
14 CLOONEY ROAD,
DERRY BT47 6TB

TEL: 028-7134 5500 FAX: 028-7131 1006
EMAIL: info@thewaterfoothotel.co.uk
WEB: www.thewaterfoothotel.co.uk

HOTEL ★★★ MAP 14 L 20

A superbly appointed family run hotel including indoor leisure centre guaranteeing a luxurious & restful stay. Located on the banks of the River Foyle and only a 5 minute drive to city centre. The hotel restaurant is renowned for its excellent cuisine and this reputation for fine food and drink has been an integral part of the Waterfoot philosophy. Mid-week & weekend breaks available throughout the year.

Member of Holiday Ireland Hotels

B&B from £30.00 to £40.00

JOHANNE FERGUSON
GENERAL MANAGER

American Express
Diners
Mastercard
Visa

☺ Weekend specials from £79.00

48 48

Closed 25 - 27 December

RADISSON ROE PARK HOTEL & GOLF RESORT

ROE PARK,
LIMAVADY,
CO. LONDONDERRY BT49 9LB

TEL: 028-7772 2222 FAX: 028-7772 2313
EMAIL: sales@radissonroepark.com
WEB: www.radissonroepark.com

HOTEL ★★★★ MAP 14 M 20

One of the North Coast's largest 4★★★★ deluxe hotels, leisure & golf resorts. Radisson Roe Park sits on the historic site of St. Columba's address at the Convention of Drumceatt in 575AD and the house, around which the complex springs, dates back to 1710. Old & new blend with 118 bedrooms & suites, an unrivalled leisure spa & golf course, all sitting at the gateway to the championship links course on the North Coast, including Royal Portrush & Portstewart, making Radisson the perfect choice.

B&B from £45.00 to £49.00

IAN WYNNE

American Express
Diners
Mastercard
Visa

☺ Weekend specials from £79.00

118 118

Open All Year

B&B rates are Stg£ per person sharing per night incl. Breakfast

EDGEWATER HOTEL

88 STRAND ROAD,
PORTSTEWART,
CO. DERRY BT55 7LZ
TEL: 028-7083 3314 FAX: 028-7083 2224
EMAIL: edgewater.hotel@virgin.net
WEB: www.edgehotel.com

HOTEL ★★ MAP 14 M 21

Adjacent to Portstewart Golf Club, the hotel is magnificently situated overlooking spectacular views of Portstewart Strand, Hills of Donegal and Atlantic Ocean. All 28 en suite rooms (incl 6 suites with sea views) contain colour TV, radio, direct dial phone and tea/coffee facilities. Indulge in dinner in O'Malleys split level restaurant or relax and enjoy a bar snack in the Inishtrahull Lounge, both with picture windows capturing breathtaking views.

B&B from £30.00 to £50.00

KEVIN O'MALLEY
PROPRIETOR

American Express
Diners
Mastercard
Visa

Weekend specials from £70.00

28 28

Open All Year

CAIRN BAY LODGE

THE CAIRN, 278 SEACLIFF ROAD,
BANGOR,
CO. DOWN BT20 5HS
TEL: 028-9146 7636 FAX: 028-9145 7728
EMAIL: info@cairnbaylodge.com
WEB: www.cairnbaylodge.com

GUESTHOUSE ★★★ MAP 15 Q 18

Award winning guesthouse set in extensive gardens directly overlooking Ballyholme Bay. Bangor Business Award -"Best Tourist Accommodation" - 2nd year in succession. The lodge is family run, offering the highest standards of food accommodation and service in luxurious surroundings. An oasis of calm yet only 5 minutes walk from Bangor Town Centre and marina. 50m from Ballyholme Yacht Club, 5 golf courses within 5 miles, in-house Guinot appointed beauty salon. Off street parking.

Member of Kingdoms of Down

B&B from £27.50 to £30.00

CHRIS & JENNY MULLEN
PROPRIETOR

Mastercard
Visa

3 3

Open All Year

ROYAL HOTEL

26/28 QUAY STREET,
BANGOR,
CO. DOWN BT20 5ED
TEL: 028-9127 1866 FAX: 028-9146 7810
EMAIL: royalhotelbangor@aol.com
WEB: www.the-royal-hotel.com

HOTEL ★★ MAP 15 Q 18

Overlooking Bangor Marina this family run hotel is probably the best known landmark on Bangor's seafront. All 50 rooms are en suite and include 7 executive suites. Satellite TV, direct dial phone, courtesy tray and hairdryer are all standard throughout. Renowned for our food served in a variety of atmospheric restaurants and bars. Nightclub, conference and banqueting facilities. 15 minutes from Belfast City Airport. Direct rail link from Dublin and Derry.

B&B from £30.00 to £40.00

PAUL DONEGAN
PROPRIETOR

American Express
Diners
Mastercard
Visa

50 50

Closed 25 - 26 December

Room rates are Stg£ per room per night

SHELLEVEN HOUSE

61 PRINCETOWN ROAD,
BANGOR BT20 3TA,
CO. DOWN
TEL: 028-9127 1777 FAX: 028-9127 1777
EMAIL: shellevenhouse@aol.com
WEB: www.shellevenhouse.com

GUESTHOUSE ★★★ MAP 15 Q 18

Two large Victorian houses converted into a substantial guesthouse, in a leafy conservation area, 5 mins walk from Bangor Centre. Shelleven has been run by Philip and Mary Weston for the past four years. The comfort & well-being of their guests is most important to them. 11 en suite bedrooms are tastefully decorated, some with sea views. Breakfasts, with a wide choice of dishes, are served in the elegant dining room. Several golf courses nearby, tee-off times can be arranged. Train/Bus station 5 mins away, with direct link to Dublin & Belfast City Airport.

Member of Kingdoms of Down

B&B from £26.00 to £28.00

MARY WESTON

Mastercard
Visa

11 11

Open All Year

TARA GUEST HOUSE

51 PRINCETOWN ROAD,
BANGOR,
CO. DOWN BT20 3TA
TEL: 028-9146 8924 FAX: 028-9146 9870
EMAIL: taraguesthouse@lineone.net
WEB: www.taraguesthouse.co.uk

GUESTHOUSE ★★ MAP 15 Q 18

10 en suite rooms in a quiet area close to all amenities. All rooms are en suite and comfortably furnished with telephone, TV, radio and tea/coffee making facilities. A friendly atmosphere and warm welcome assured.

Member of Kingdoms of Down

B&B from £22.50 to £22.50

WILLIAM SPENCE

American Express
Mastercard
Visa

10 10

Closed 24 - 28 December

CHESTNUT INN

28/34 LOWER SQUARE,
CASTLEWELLAN,
CO. DOWN BT31 9DW
TEL: 028-437 78247 FAX: 028-437 78247

GUESTHOUSE ★ MAP 12 P 16

In the old market town of Castlewellan, the Chestnut Inn (King's Hotel) is ideally situated to take advantage of the Mournes, the seaside town of Newcastle and all the amenities of South Down. Royal County Down is only 5 minutes away as are the forest parks and the beaches of Dundrum Bay. The Inn is renowned for excellent bar food, friendly atmosphere and also boasts a superb à la carte restaurant. World's biggest maze close by.

B&B from £25.00 to £35.00

JOHN & FIONNUALA KING
PROPRIETORS

Mastercard
Visa

7 7

Open All Year

B&B rates are Stg£ per person sharing per night incl. Breakfast

SLIEVE CROOB INN

119 CLANVARAGHAN ROAD,
CASTLEWELLAN,
CO. DOWN BT31 9LA
TEL: 028-4377 1412 FAX: 028-4377 1162
EMAIL: info@slievecroobinn.com
WEB: www.slievecroobinn.com

GUESTHOUSE ★★★ MAP 12 P 16

Set on the slopes of Slieve Croob, the Inn hosts "the best country restaurant in the North of Ireland". This 'gem in the mountains' is an award winning 'Taste of Ulster' restaurant and boasts its own celebrity chef, Patrick Ferris. Know as a golfer's favourite, the Inn is set in an 'area of outstanding natural beauty' just 15 minutes from the main Dublin/Belfast road. Laurence and Patrick welcome you.

B&B from £25.00 to £35.00

LAURENCE KELLY/PATRICK FERRIS
PROPRIETOR/HEAD CHEF

American Express
Mastercard
Visa

☺ Midweek specials from £59.00

8 8

Open All Year

KILMOREY ARMS HOTEL

41-43 GREENCASTLE STREET,
KILKEEL,
CO. DOWN BT34 4BH
TEL: 028-4176 2220 FAX: 028-4176 5399
EMAIL: info@kilmoreyarmshotel.co.uk
WEB: www.kilmoreyarmshotel.co.uk

HOTEL ★★ MAP 12 P 15

Set in the middle of Kilkeel, home to Northern Ireland's largest fishing fleet. We are perfectly placed to allow you to explore the beautiful Mountains of Mourne. If golf is your passion, championship courses are within easy reach including Royal County Down. Only 30 minutes from Newry and 1 hour from Belfast by car. We can also be reached by regular bus service.

Member of Mourne Activity Breaks

B&B from £23.50 to £23.50

PETER HOUSTON

Mastercard
Visa

26 26

Open All Year

Stunning beauty with contrasting landscapes, charming villages and bustling towns

Newry & Mourne invites you to experience the many different aspects of our area. Located in the south eastern corner of Northern Ireland, this region has unspoiled and special charm, a land with infinite variety.

NEWRY AND MOURNE
DISTRICT COUNCIL

For Further information contact:
Newry Tourist Office,
Newry. Co. Down
Tel: 028 30268877.
Fax: 028 30268833
email: info@newryandmourne.gov.uk
Website: seenewryandmourne.com

Room rates are Stg£ per room per night

BURRENDALE HOTEL AND COUNTRY CLUB

51 CASTLEWELLAN ROAD,
NEWCASTLE,
CO. DOWN BT33 0JY
TEL: 028-4372 2599 FAX: 028-4372 2328
EMAIL: reservations@burrendale.com
WEB: www.burrendale.com

HOTEL ★★★ MAP 12 P 16

At the foot of the Mournes, the Burrendale is the ideal location for your family, golfing holiday or short break. The hotel comprises a Country Club, Beauty Salon, à la carte Vine Restaurant, bistro style Cottage Kitchen Restaurant, Cottage Bar and excellent banqueting / conference facilities. In close proximity are 15 golf courses including Royal County Down, golden beaches, nature walks, forest parks and pony trekking. Superb hospitality awaits you.

B&B from £50.00 to £65.00

KEM AKKARI
GENERAL MANAGER

American Express
Diners
Mastercard
Visa

Weekend specials from £97.00

Open All Year

HASTINGS SLIEVE DONARD HOTEL

DOWNS ROAD,
NEWCASTLE,
CO. DOWN BT33 0AH
TEL: 028-4372 1066 FAX: 028-4372 1166
EMAIL: res@sdh.hastingshotels.com
WEB: www.hastingshotels.com

HOTEL ★★★★ MAP 12 P 16

Nestling at the foot of the Mourne Mountains the Slieve Donard is Northern Ireland's favourite holiday hotel. On 6 acres of private grounds overlooking an extensive golden strand & next door to the world famous Royal County Down golf course. Offering deluxe accommodation, health & leisure facilities in the exclusive Elysium Spa, luxurious surroundings & excellent facilities for holidays & weekend breaks, we provide the ideal setting for every occasion. The Percy French Restaurant provides an ideal option for informal dining.

B&B from £55.00 to £55.00

RICHARD ROBINSON
GENERAL MANAGER

American Express
Diners
Mastercard
Visa

Open All Year

CANAL COURT HOTEL

MERCHANTS QUAY,
NEWRY,
CO. DOWN BT35 8HF
TEL: 028-3025 1234 FAX: 028-3025 1177
EMAIL: manager@canalcourthotel.com
WEB: www.canalcourthotel.com

HOTEL ★★★★ MAP 12 O 15

Newry City's finest four star hotel; The Canal Court Hotel boasts 51 en suite bedrooms and suites. All rooms include satellite TV, hospitality tray, hairdryer, direct dial phone and ironing facilities; with suites incorporating mini bar and private jacuzzi bath. The Old Mill Restaurant is one of the finest in the area, the Granary Bar serves carvery and bar snacks daily. Conference & banqueting facilities for up to 500 and a fully equipped health and leisure complex.

B&B from £55.00 to £65.00

MICHELLE BARRETT
GENERAL MANAGER

American Express
Diners
Mastercard
Visa

Closed 25 December

B&B rates are Stg£ per person sharing per night incl. Breakfast

NARROWS (THE)

8 SHORE ROAD,
PORTAFERRY,
CO. DOWN BT22 1JY
TEL: 028-4272 8148 FAX: 028-4272 8105
EMAIL: reservations@narrows.co.uk
WEB: www.narrows.co.uk

GUESTHOUSE ★★★ MAP 15 Q 17

In the six years since it opened, The Narrows has taken the Northern Ireland hospitality industry by storm. With numerous awards and reviews for its architecture, cuisine, accommodation, accessibility and conference facilities, you will see why our guests keep coming back. Our 13 en suite rooms, restaurant and conference room all have stunning views of Strangford Lough. British Airways Tourism Award for Best Catering in Northern Ireland. AA 2 Rosettes. Residents' bar and walled garden for your relaxation.

Member of Kingdoms of Down

B&B from £39.00 to £45.00

WILL & JAMES BROWN

American Express
Mastercard
Visa

🏠 🛏 ☎ 🖥 📅 T C M ❄ 🛥 🅿 🛗
13 13
alc 🍴 ♿ inet FAX

Open All Year

PORTAFERRY HOTEL

10 THE STRAND,
PORTAFERRY,
CO.DOWN BT22 1PE
TEL: 028-4272 8231 FAX: 028-4272 8999
EMAIL: info@portaferryhotel.com
WEB: www.portaferryhotel.com

HOTEL ★★★ MAP 15 Q 17

Loughside hotel in spectacular setting. Award winning cuisine and fine wines. Explore or simply relax and do nothing; just peace and tranquillity. BA Tourism Endeavour Award, RAC Restaurant of the Year Award, AA rosette, Taste of Ulster, Good Hotel Guide. 29 miles from Belfast.

Member of Northern Ireland's Best Kept Secrets

B&B from £45.00 to £52.50

JOHN & MARY HERLIHY
PROPRIETORS

American Express
Diners
Mastercard
Visa

🏠 🛏 ☎ 🖥 T C 🛥 C M U 🅿 🛗 alc 🍴
14 14

Closed 23 - 26 December

CUAN (THE)

STRANGFORD VILLAGE,
CO. DOWN,
BT30 7ND
TEL: 028-4488 1222 FAX: 028-4488 1770
EMAIL: info@thecuan.com
WEB: www.thecuan.com

GUESTHOUSE ★★★ MAP 15 Q 17

Located in the conservation village of Strangford, The Cuan is a family run licenced guest inn with nine superbly finished en suite bedrooms. All rooms have direct dial telephone, colour TV and tea/coffee making facilities. The Cuan is renowned for superb food and excellent wines, food is available all day. This is the ideal base for activity or leisure. Full disabled access. Private car parking.

B&B from £34.95 to £39.95

PETER & CAROLINE MCERLEAN

American Express
Diners
Mastercard
Visa

☺ Weekend specials from £79.95

🏠 🛏 ☎ 🖥 T C ❄ C M P 🅿 alc 🍴 ♿ 🛥 inet
9 9

Closed 25 - 26 December

Room rates are Stg£ per room per night

HOTEL CARLTON

2 MAIN STREET,
BELLEEK,
CO. FERMANAGH BT93 3FX
TEL: 028-6865 8282 FAX: 028-6865 9005
EMAIL: reception@hotelcarlton.co.uk
WEB: www.hotelcarlton.co.uk

HOTEL ★★ MAP 13 I 17

The Hotel Carlton's setting on the banks of the River Erne in the heart of the Irish lake district is quite simply breathtaking. Also on the steps of one of Ireland's most famous landmarks, Belleek Pottery, Ireland's oldest pottery. Ideally situated for visitors who wish to tour the nearby counties of Donegal, Sligo, Tyrone and Leitrim. The Hotel Carlton has recently been completely rebuilt in a traditional style and boasts 19 luxurious well appointed en suite rooms.

Member of MinOtel Ireland Hotel Group

B&B from £30.00 to £37.50

THE GALLAGHER & ROONEY FAMILY

American Express
Mastercard
Visa

😊 Weekend specials from £75.00

19 19

Closed 24 - 25 December

KILLYHEVLIN HOTEL

DUBLIN ROAD,
ENNISKILLEN,
CO. FERMANAGH BT74 6RW
TEL: 028-6632 3481 FAX: 028-6632 4726
EMAIL: info@killyhevlin.com
WEB: www.killyhevlin.com

HOTEL ★★★★ MAP 11 K 16

Killyhevlin Hotel and chalets are situated on the shores of beautiful Lough Erne, making it a terrific location at the gateway to the West and an ideal base for exploring the many sights of Fermanagh. All 43 bedrooms plus the Belmore Suite are fitted to a high standard, all en suite, with satellite TV, direct dial phone, radio and tea facilities. Our scenic lounge and restaurant offer a wide variety of menus. Lunchtime buffet, bar snacks all day. Evenings, table d'hôte or à la carte.

B&B from £45.00 to £57.50

RODNEY J. WATSON
MANAGING DIRECTOR

American Express
Diners
Mastercard
Visa

😊 Weekend specials from £95.00

43 43

Closed 24 - 26 December

MANOR HOUSE COUNTRY HOTEL

KILLADEAS,
ENNISKILLEN,
CO. FERMANAGH BT94 1NY
TEL: 028-6862 2211 FAX: 028-6862 1545
EMAIL: info@manor-house-hotel.com
WEB: www.manor-house-hotel.com

HOTEL ★★★★ MAP 14 K 16

Overlooking Lough Erne, this fine Manor is a blend of 19th century elegance combined with premier hotel facilities. Ideally situated for touring many nearby attractions, the hotel offers the use of our luxurious leisure complex and beauty salon. With four poster and executive rooms available, our accommodation, voted the Best Hotel Accommodation in 2002 by Northern Ireland Tourist Board and excellent restaurants provide for a memorable stay.

B&B from £55.00 to £120.00

DAVID BEGLEY
GENERAL MANAGER

American Express
Mastercard
Visa

😊 Weekend specials from £95.00

81 81

Open All Year

B&B rates are Stg£ per person sharing per night incl. Breakfast

RAILWAY HOTEL

34 FORTHILL STREET,
ENNISKILLEN,
CO. FERMANAGH BT74 6AJ
TEL: 028-6632 2084 FAX: 028-6632 7480
EMAIL: enquiries@railwayhotelenniskillen.com
WEB: www.railwayhotelenniskillen.com

HOTEL ★ MAP 11 K 16

James Crozier and Owen McKenna take pride in maintaining the Railway Hotel's reputation for good food, hospitality and service which has been established through 150 years of trading. Guests have the choice of 19 well appointed bedrooms, all en suite, with Sky TV and telephone. A full range of meals is available, in style in the Dining Car Restaurant, which has an excellent reputation for food. Friendly staff and cosy atmosphere ensure a memorable breakaway for everyone.

B&B from £25.00 to £32.50

JAMES CROZIER/OWEN McKENNA
OWNERS

Mastercard
Visa

🖐📶☎🖥TC CMU♪🎵P🔲alc🔌
19 19

Closed 25 - 26 December

MAHONS HOTEL

ENNISKILLEN ROAD,
IRVINESTOWN,
CO. FERMANAGH BT94 1GS
TEL: 028-6862 1656 FAX: 028-6862 8344
EMAIL: info@mahonshotel.co.uk
WEB: www.mahonshotel.co.uk

HOTEL ★★ MAP 13 K 17

Situated in the heart of the Fermanagh Lakeland. Ideal base for visiting all major tourist attractions - Belleek Pottery 20 minutes, Marble Arch Caves 30 minutes, Necarne Equestrian Centre 5 minutes, Lough Erne 5 minutes, Donegal 20 minutes. All rooms en suite, TV, tea making facilities. Bushmills Bar of the Year winner, entertainment at weekends, private car park. Family run from 1883. Visit us in our second century. Cycling, horseriding, tennis and golf all available.

Member of Fermanagh Lakeland Hotels

B&B from £27.50 to £32.50

JOE MAHON
MANAGER

American Express
Mastercard
Visa

✓

☺ Midweek specials from £75.00

🖐📶☎🖥TC🖥CM✎🔌U♪🎵P
🖐7🔲alc🔌
18 18

Open All Year

SILVERBIRCH HOTEL

5 GORTIN ROAD,
OMAGH,
CO. TYRONE BT79 7DH
TEL: 028-8224 2520 FAX: 028-8224 9061
EMAIL: info@silverbirchhotel.com
WEB: www.silverbirchhotel.com

HOTEL ★★★ MAP 14 L 18

The hotel is situated on the outskirts of Omagh on the B48 leading to the Gortin Glens, Ulster History Park, Sperrins and the Ulster American Folk Park. Set in its own spacious and mature grounds, the hotel now has 46 new en suite bedrooms to 3*** standard. Other facilities include Buttery Grill all day, newly refurbished dining room, function suite for 250 guests for weddings, dinners or conferences. Award winning leisure centre 300 metres away.

B&B from £38.00 to £48.00

ALLAN DUNCAN
MANAGER

American Express
Diners
Mastercard
Visa

☺ Weekend specials from £79.00

🖐📶☎🖥🖥TC CM✱🔌U♪🎵P📶
🔲alc🔌&♿
46 46

Closed 25 December

Room rates are Stg£ per room per night

IRELAND FOR

Golf

HOTELS & GUESTHOUSES

Golfing in Ireland is not quite like
golfing any other place else on earth.

Here the game has become part of
the national culture and is for
everyone. That includes you.

Ireland's rugged landscape, perched on the
edge of the Atlantic ocean, has provided
many great golf courses.

And they are relatively uncrowded.
So get in the swing - come golfing in Ireland.

WHERE TO STAY WHEN YOU PLAY!

We invite you to sample the golf, the countryside and the friendship of the Irish people and then to stay in some of Ireland's most charming accommodation. We have listed a range of hotels and guesthouses which are either situated on or close to a golf course. Your host will assist you if necessary in arranging your golfing requirements including tee reservations and green fee charges. A full description of the hotels and guesthouses can be had by looking up the appropriate page number. Premises are listed in alphabetical order in each county.

ACCOMMODATION	COURSES	BE OUR GUEST PAGE NUMBER	GOLF ON SITE	ALL INCLUSIVE PACKAGE	TUITION AVAILABLE	CART AVAILABLE	ARRANGE TEE OFF TIMES	ADVANCE RESERVATIONS	CLUBS FOR HIRE	TRANSPORT	PREFERENTIAL GREEN FEES	CADDY AVAILABLE
East Coast												
DUBLIN												
Aberdeen Lodge	St. Margarets, Portmarnock, Woodbrook, Dun Laoghaire, Sea Point, Druids Glen	35		•	•	•	•	•	•	•	•	•
Airport View	Donabate Golf Club, Island Links Donabate, Swords Open, Hollywood Lakes, Rush Golf Club, Skerries Golf	32		•	•	•	•	•	•		•	•
Bracken Court Hotel	Balbriggan, Seapoint, Baltray, The Island, Donabate, Malahide, St. Margarets	31		•	•	•	•	•	•		•	
Carriage House	St. Margarets, Portmarnock, Skerries, Balbriggan, Hollywood, Luttrellstown, The Island	91		•	•		•	•	•		•	
Cassidys Hotel	Royal Dublin, Luttrellstown, St. Anne's, Clontarf, Portmarnock, St. Margaret's Golf and Country Club	47			•	•	•	•	•		•	•
Charleville Lodge	St. Margarets, Luttrellstown, The Links, Portmarnock, The Island Golf Links	49			•	•	•	•	•		•	
Clarion Stephens Hall Hotel and Suites	St. Margaret's, Portmarnock Links, Citywest, Luttrellstown Castle	51		•	•	•	•	•	•		•	
Deer Park Hotel and Golf Courses		88	▶18	•	•	•	•	•	•			
Georgian Hotel	K Club, Druids Glen, St. Margaret's, Portmarnock	58		•	•	•	•	•	•		•	•
Gresham (The)	Royal Dublin, Portmarnock, St Margarets, The Island, St. Anne's, Malahide	60			•	•	•	•	•		•	•
Gresham Royal Marine	Dun Laoghaire, Woodbrook, Killiney, Greystones, Seapoint, Druids Glen	88			•	•	•	•	•		•	
Holiday Inn Dublin Airport	Hollystown, St. Margaret's, Portmarnock, Malahide, Forest Little, The Island	34		•	•	•	•	•	•		•	
Holiday Inn Dublin City Centre	Elm Park, Clontarf, St.Margarets, Royal Dublin, The Castle, The Island	63		•		•	•	•	•			
King Sitric Fish Restaurant & Accommodation	Deerpark, Howth, Royal Dublin, Portmarnock, St. Margaret's, The Island	89				•	•	•	•			
Le Meridien Shelbourne	Glen-of-the-Downs	68					•	•	•			
Merrion Hall	Portmarnock, Royal Dublin, Elm Park, Castle, Milltown, Druids Glen	71		•	•	•	•	•	•		•	•

▶18 = Full 18 Hole   ▶9 = 9 Hole   ▶3 = Par 3

WHERE TO STAY WHEN YOU PLAY!

ACCOMMODATION	COURSES	BE OUR GUEST PAGE NUMBER	GOLF ON SITE	ALL INCLUSIVE PACKAGE	TUITION AVAILABLE	CART AVAILABLE	ARRANGE TEE OFF TIMES	ADVANCE TEE RESERVATIONS	CLUBS FOR HIRE	TRANSPORT	PREFERENTIAL GREEN FEES	CADDY AVAILABLE
DUBLIN Continued												
Portmarnock Hotel & Golf Links	Portmarnock, St. Margaret's, Royal Dublin, Malahide, The Island	92	18	•			•	•	•	•	•	•
Quality Hotel & Suites	Citywest, K Club, Killeen	79				•	•			•		
Redbank House Guesthouse & Restaurant	Skerries, Laytown, Bettystown, Baltray, Portmarnock, St. Margaret's	93		•		•	•	•		•	•	•
Regency Airport Hotel	Malahide, Contarf, Hollystown, St. Annes, Royal Dublin	80				•	•			•	•	
Spa Hotel	Hermitage, Citywest, Knockanally, Lucan, Luttrellstown, Highfield	90		•		•	•			•	•	•
Stillorgan Park Hotel	Druids Glen, Portmarnock, Woodbrook, Woodenbridge, Powerscourt, European	31		•			•	•		•	•	•
Waterside Hotel	Donabate, Turvey, Beaverstown, Balcarrick, Island, Corballis	32	18	•		•	•	•		•	•	•
White Sands Hotel	Malahide, St. Margarets, Royal Dublin	92		•		•	•	•		•	•	•
LOUTH												
Ballymascanlon House Hotel		97	18	•			•	•	•	•	•	•
Boyne Valley Hotel & Country Club	Baltray-Seapoint, Laytown/Bettystown, Dundalk, Headfort (2 courses), Kells, Ardee	96		•		•	•	•	•	•	•	•
Hotel Imperial	Ballymascanlon, Dundalk, Greenore, Carron Beg	99		•		•	•	•	•	•	•	•
McKevitt's Village Hotel	Greenore	96		•		•	•	•	•	•	•	•
MEATH												
Highfield House	Co. Meath Golf Course, Glebe, Royal Tara	104		•			•	•	•		•	
Neptune Beach Hotel & Leisure Club	Laytown & Bettystown, Sea Point, County Louth/Baltray, Royal Tara	100		•		•	•	•	•	•		
Station House Hotel	Royal Tara, Blackbush, Headfort	102		•		•	•	•	•		•	
Wellington Court Hotel	Trim, Keegans, Glebe	104		•			•	•	•		•	

18 = Full 18 Hole   9 = 9 Hole   3 = Par 3

WHERE TO STAY WHEN YOU PLAY!

ACCOMMODATION	COURSES	BE OUR GUEST PAGE NUMBER	GOLF ON SITE	ALL INCLUSIVE PACKAGE	TUITION AVAILABLE	CART AVAILABLE	ARRANGE TEE OFF TIMES	ADVANCE RESERVATIONS	CLUBS FOR HIRE	TRANSPORT	PREFERENTIAL GREEN FEES	CADDY AVAILABLE
WICKLOW												
Arklow Bay Conference and Leisure Hotel	European, Arklow, Woodenbridge, Blainroe	104		•	•	•	•	•	•	•	•	•
Brooklodge	Woodenbridge, The European Links, Coolattin, Arklow, Druids Glen, Blainroe	107		•	•	•	•	•	•	•	•	•
Charlesland Golf Hotel & Country Club	Druids Glen, Powerscourt, Glen of the Downs, Delgany, Greystones, Woodbrook	112	⚑18	•	•	•	•	•			•	•
Chester Beatty Inn	Druids Glen, Woodenbridge, Blainroe, European, Powerscourt, Charlesland	106					•	•	•	•	•	
Glendalough Hotel	The European Club, Woodenbridge, Charlesland, Druids Glen, Blainroe	112		•			•	•	•	•	•	
Glenview Hotel	Glen O' The Downs, Powerscourt, Druids Glen, The European Club, Charlesland, Delgany	111		•			•	•	•	•	•	•
Gormanstown Manor	Wicklow Golf Club, Blainroe, European, Druids Glen, Arklow, Woodenbridge	114	⚑3	•			•	•		•	•	
Grand Hotel	Blainroe, Wicklow, Druids Glen, European Golf Course	114			•	•	•	•	•	•	•	•
Heather House Hotel	Bray, Woodbrook, Old Conna, Powerscourt, Greystones, Druids Glen	108						•	•	•	•	•
Hunter's Hotel	Druid's Glen, European, Blainroe, Powerscourt, Woodenbridge, Delgany	113		•	•	•	•	•	•	•	•	•
Lawless's Hotel	Woodenbridge, Coolattin, European, Blainroe, Arklow, Druids Glen, Tulfarris	107					•	•	•	•	•	•
Rathsallagh House, Golf and Country Club	Mount Juliet, Carlow, K Club, Mount Wolseley, Druids Glen, Powerscourt	110	⚑18	•		•	•	•	•	•	•	•
Royal Hotel and Leisure Centre	Woodbrook, Charlesland, Delgany, The European Club, Druids Glen	109					•	•	•	•	•	•
Summerhill House Hotel	Powerscourt, Druids Glen, Kilternan, Old Conna	110				•	•	•	•	•	•	•
Tinakilly Country House and Restaurant	European, Druids Glen, Blainroe, Woodenbridge, Wicklow, Delgany	113		•	•	•	•	•	•	•	•	•
Tulfarris Hotel & Golf Resort	K Club, Druids Glen, Citywest, Rathsallagh	108	⚑18					•	•		•	•
Valley Hotel and Restaurant	Woodenbridge, European, Arklow, Courtown, Blainroe	114								•	•	
Woodenbridge Hotel	Woodenbridge, Blainroe, Arklow, European Club, Mill Brook, Glenmalure	115		•			•	•	•	•	•	•
Woodland Court Hotel	Powerscourt, Woodbrook, Druids Glen, Charlesland, Old Conna, Kilternan	109		•			•	•	•	•	•	•

⚑18 = Full 18 Hole   ⚑9 = 9 Hole   ⚑3 = Par 3

WHERE TO STAY WHEN YOU PLAY!

Midlands & Lakelands

Accommodation	Courses	Be Our Guest Page Number	Golf on Site	All Inclusive Package	Tuition Available	Cart Available	Arrange Tee Off Times	Advance Reservations	Clubs for Hire	Transport	Preferential Green Fees	Caddy Available
CAVAN												
Park Hotel	Cavan Golf Club, Headfort Golf Club, Kells	119 [9]	•				•	•			•	
Slieve Russell Hotel, Golf & Country Club		118 [18]	•	•	•	•	•	•	•	•	•	•
KILDARE												
Glenroyal Hotel, Leisure Club & Conference Centre	Knockanally, K Club, Killeen, Castlewarden, Bodenstown, Citywest, Cartan	123	•				•	•			•	
Hazel Hotel	Cill Dara, Portarlington, Curragh, The Heath, Athy	124	•				•	•	•	•	•	
K Club	Luttrellstown Castle, Druids Glen, Portmarnock Links, Rathsallagh, Hermitage	126 [18]	•	•	•	•	•	•	•	•	•	•
LAOIS												
Heritage - Portlaoise (The)	The Heath, Abbeyleix, The Heritage Golf & Country Club - opening Sept. 2003	127	•		•	•	•	•	•	•	•	•
LONGFORD												
Longford Arms Hotel	Longford, Glasson, Ballyconnell, Carrick-on-Shannon	128	•	•	•	•	•	•	•		•	
MONAGHAN												
Four Seasons Hotel & Leisure Club	Rossmore, Nuremore, Armagh, Castleblaney, Slieve Russell	129	•		•		•	•			•	•
Glencarn Hotel and Leisure Centre	Castleblayney, Mannon Castle, Rossmore	129	•			•	•	•			•	•
Nuremore Hotel & Country Club	Nuremore, Baltray, Headfort, Dundalk, Greenore, Royal County Down	129 [18]	•	•	•	•	•	•	•	•	•	•
OFFALY												
Bridge House Hotel & Leisure Club	Esker Hills, Tullamore	133	•		•	•	•	•	•	•	•	•
Brosna Lodge Hotel	Birr, Esker Hills, Tullamore, Glasson, Portumna, Ballinasloe	130	•			•	•	•	•		•	•
County Arms Hotel	Birr, Portumna, Roscrea, Glasson, Tullamore, Esker Hills	130	•		•	•	•	•	•		•	•

[18] = Full 18 Hole   [9] = 9 Hole   [3] = Par 3

WHERE TO STAY WHEN YOU PLAY!

ACCOMMODATION	COURSES	BE OUR GUEST PAGE NUMBER	GOLF ON SITE	ALL INCLUSIVE PACKAGE	TUITION AVAILABLE	CART AVAILABLE	ARRANGE TEE OFF TIMES	ADVANCE RESERVATIONS	CLUBS FOR HIRE	TRANSPORT	PREFERENTIAL GREEN FEES	CADDY AVAILABLE
OFFALY Continued												
Doolys Hotel	Birr, Esker Hills, Roscrea, Portumna	131			•	•	•	•	•	•	•	•
Moorhill House Hotel	Esker Hills, Tullamore, Daingean, Mount Temple, Birr, Glasson	134			•	•	•	•	•	•	•	•
Tullamore Court Hotel Conference & Leisure Centre	Tullamore, Esker Hills, Castle Barna, Mount Temple, Glasson, Birr	134			•	•	•	•	•	•	•	•
WESTMEATH												
Bloomfield House Hotel & Leisure Club	Mullingar, Glasson, Mount Temple, Esker Hills, Athlone, Tullamore	138			•	•	•	•	•	•	•	•
Glasson Golf Hotel and Country Club	Athlone Golf Club, Mount Temple Golf Club, Glasson Golf Hotel & Country Club	135	⚑18		•	•	•	•	•	•	•	•
Greville Arms Hotel	Mullingar, Glasson, Mount Temple, Tullamore, Longford, Esker Hills	138			•	•	•	•	•	•	•	•
Hodson Bay Hotel	Athlone, Glasson, Mountemple, Ballinasloe, Roscommon, Esker Hills	136	⚑18		•	•	•	•	•	•	•	•
Royal Hoey Hotel	Mount Temple, Glasson, Hodson Bay	136					•	•	•	•		
Wineport Lodge	Glasson, Mount Temple, Esker Hills, Athlone, Mullingar, Tullamore	137					•	•	•	•		

South East

ACCOMMODATION	COURSES	BE OUR GUEST PAGE NUMBER	GOLF ON SITE	ALL INCLUSIVE PACKAGE	TUITION AVAILABLE	CART AVAILABLE	ARRANGE TEE OFF TIMES	ADVANCE RESERVATIONS	CLUBS FOR HIRE	TRANSPORT	PREFERENTIAL GREEN FEES	CADDY AVAILABLE
CARLOW												
Dolmen Hotel and River Court Lodges	Mount Wolseley, Kilkea Castle, Carlow	142			•	•	•	•	•	•	•	•
Mount Wolseley Hotel, Golf and Country Club	Carlow, Rathsallagh, Coolattin, Kilkea Castle, Killerig Castle, Mount Juliet	143	⚑18		•	•	•	•	•	•	•	•
Seven Oaks Hotel	Mount Wolseley, Kilkea Castle, Killerig Castle, Carlow	142			•		•	•	•	•		
KILKENNY												
Bambricks Troysgate House	Kilkenny, Callan, Mount Juliet, Castlecomer	144			•					•		
Brannigans Glendine Inn	Kilkenny, Mount Juliet, Callan, Castlecomer, Pococke, Gowran (New 18 hole Golf Course)	145					•	•	•	•		
Butler House	Kilkenny, Mount Juliet, Carlow, Killerig Castle, Waterford, Kilkea Castle	146			•	•	•	•	•	•	•	•

422

⚑18 = Full 18 Hole ⚑9 = 9 Hole ⚑3 = Par 3

WHERE TO STAY
WHEN YOU PLAY!

ACCOMMODATION	COURSES	BE OUR GUEST PAGE NUMBER	GOLF ON SITE	ALL INCLUSIVE PACKAGE	TUITION AVAILABLE	CART AVAILABLE	ARRANGE TEE OFF TIMES	ADVANCE RESERVATIONS	CLUBS FOR HIRE	TRANSPORT	PREFERENTIAL GREEN FEES	CADDY AVAILABLE
KILKENNY Continued												
Club House Hotel	Kilkenny (18), Mount Juliet (18), Callan (18), Castlecomer (9) Gowran Park (18) and Borris (9)	146			•	•	•	•	•	•	•	•
Kilford Arms	Mount Juliet, Kilkenny, Callan, Gowran, Castlecomer, Borris	147		•	•		•		•			
Kilkenny River Court	Mount Juliet, Callan, Castlecomer, Gowran, Kilkenny	148		•	•	•	•	•	•			•
Metropole Hotel	Kilkenny, Callan, Castlecomer and Carrick-on-Suir	150		•	•		•	•	•			•
Mount Juliet Conrad		152	🚩18	•			•	•	•	•	•	•
TIPPERARY SOUTH												
Ach Na Sheen Guesthouse	Tipperary, Ballykisteen, Cahir, Dundrum	159					•	•	•			•
Cahir House Hotel	Cahir Park, Carrick-on-Suir, Clonmel, Ballykisteen, Dundrum, Tipperary, Thurles	153		•	•	•	•	•	•	•	•	•
Carraig	Carrick-on-Suir, Cahir, Waterford, Clonmel, Dungarvan	153									•	
Dundrum House Hotel		155	🚩18	•			•	•	•	•	•	•
Mulcahys	Clonmel, Cahir, Carrick-on-Suir, Slieve na mBan at Lisranagh, Dungarvan	157		•	•		•		•	•		•
Rectory House Hotel	Clonmel, Ballykisteen, Dundrum, Tipperary, Thurles	157		•	•		•		•		•	
WATERFORD												
Ard Ri Hotel	Waterford, Faithleg	167		•		•	•	•	•	•	•	•
Barnawee Bridge Guesthouse	Gold Coast, Dungarvan, West Waterford, Lismore, Youghal, Waterford Castle	162		•	•		•	•	•	•	•	•
Belfry Hotel	Waterford Castle Golf Club, Waterford Golf Club, Faithlegg, Tramore	168		•		•	•	•	•	•	•	•
Clonea Strand Hotel, Golf & Leisure	Gold Coast, West Waterford, Dungarvan, Lismore	162	🚩18	•		•	•	•	•	•	•	•
Dooley's Hotel	Waterford, Tramore, Faithlegg, Waterford Castle, Dunmore, Carrick-on-Suir	169		•		•	•	•	•	•		•
Faithlegg House Hotel	Waterford Castle, Tramore, Waterford Golf Club	165	🚩18	•			•	•	•	•	•	•

🚩18 = Full 18 Hole   🚩9 = 9 Hole   🚩3 = Par 3

WHERE TO STAY WHEN YOU PLAY!

Accommodation	Courses	Be Our Guest Page Number	Golf On Site	All Inclusive Package	Tuition Available	Cart Available	Arrange Tee Off Times	Advance Reservations	Clubs For Hire	Transport	Preferential Green Fees	Caddy Available
WATERFORD Continued												
Grand Hotel	Tramore, Dunmore East, Faithlegg, Waterford Castle, Mount Juliet	166		•		•	•	•	•	•	•	•
Granville Hotel	Waterford, Faithlegg, Waterford Castle, Tramore, Dunmore East	170		•		•	•	•	•	•	•	•
Haven Hotel	Dunmore East, Faithlegg, Tramore, Waterford Castle, Dungarvan	164					•	•	•	•	•	•
Ivory's Hotel	Tramore, Dunmore East, Faithlegg, Waterford, Waterford Castle, Williamstown	170		•		•	•	•	•	•	•	•
Lawlors Hotel	Dungarvan, West Waterford, Gold Coast	163		•		•	•	•	•	•	•	•
Majestic Hotel	Tramore, Waterford, Faithlegg, Waterford Castle, Mount Juliet, Dunmore East	166		•		•	•	•	•	•	•	•
Ocean Hotel	Waterford, Waterford Castle, Faithlegg, Dunmore East, Tramore	165		•		•	•	•	•	•	•	•
O'Shea's Hotel	Tramore, Faithlegg, Waterford Castle, Waterford, Dungarvan	166		•		•	•	•	•	•	•	•
Rhu Glen Country Club Hotel	Waterford Golf Course, Waterford Castle, Faithlegg, Tramore, New Ross	171		•		•	•	•	•	•	•	•
Rice Guesthouse O'Driscoll's Bar	Dunmore East, Faithlegg, Waterford Castle, Tramore, Waterford	171		•		•	•	•	•	•	•	•
Sands Hotel	Tramore, Waterford, Faithlegg	167							•			
Three Rivers Guest House	Faithlegg, Dunmore East, Tramore, Waterford Castle, Waterford, Mount Juliet	161		•		•	•	•	•	•	•	•
Tower Hotel & Leisure Centre	Waterford Castle, Waterford, Faithlegg, Tramore	172		•		•	•	•	•	•	•	•
Waterford Castle Hotel & Golf Club	Waterford Castle Golf Club, Faithlegg, Tramore, Waterford Golf Club	172 ▶18		•		•	•	•	•	•	•	•
Woodlands Hotel	Waterford Castle, Waterford, Faithlegg, Tramore, Dunmore East	173		•		•	•	•	•	•	•	•
WEXFORD												
Ashdown Park Hotel Conference & Leisure Centre	Seafield, Courtown, Ballymoney, Woodenbridge, Coolattin, European Club	177			•		•	•	•			
Bayview Hotel	Courtown Harbour, Ballymoney, Coolattin, Enniscorthy, Woodenbridge, Arklow, Seafield	173			•		•	•	•			
Clarion Brandon House Hotel, Health Club & Spa	New Ross, Mount Juliet, Faithlegg, Rosslare Strand, Waterford, Enniscorthy	178		•			•	•		•		•

▶18 = Full 18 Hole   ▶9 = 9 Hole   ▶3 = Par 3

WHERE TO STAY WHEN YOU PLAY!

Accommodation	Courses	BE OUR GUEST PAGE NUMBER	GOLF ON SITE	ALL INCLUSIVE PACKAGE	TUITION AVAILABLE	CART AVAILABLE	ARRANGE TEE OFF TIMES	ADVANCE RESERVATIONS	CLUBS FOR HIRE	TRANSPORT	PREFERENTIAL GREEN FEES	CADDY AVAILABLE
WEXFORD Continued												
Coral Gables	St. Helens, Rosslare and Wexford	180						•			•	•
Danby Lodge Hotel	St. Helens Bay, Rosslare Strand, Wexford	180		•				•	•	•	•	•
Hotel Rosslare	Rosslare Strand, St. Helens Bay	181		•				•	•	•	•	•
Murphy - Floods Hotel	Enniscorthy, Vinegar Hill (par 3)	175		•		•		•	•	•		
Riverside Park Hotel	Enniscorthy, Rosslare, St. Helens	176		•		•		•	•		•	•
Talbot Hotel Conference and Leisure Centre	St. Helens, Wexford, Rosslare, Enniscorthy and Courtown	184		•	•		•	•	•		•	•
Tuskar House Hotel	St. Helen's, Rosslare Strand, Wexford, Mount Juliet, Waterford, Enniscorthy	182		•		•		•	•		•	•
Whites Hotel	Wexford, Rosslare, St. Helen's Bay, Enniscorthy	184		•	•		•	•	•		•	•
Whitford House Hotel	Enniscorthy, St. Helen's, Wexford, Rosslare, Rathaspeck (par 3 golf)	185		•	•		•	•	•		•	•
South West												
CORK												
Actons Hotel	Kinsale, Old Head of Kinsale, Fota Island, Bandon, Harbour Point, Little Island	217		•		•	•	•	•	•	•	•
Aherne's Townhouse & Seafood Restaurant	Youghal, Waterford Castle, Old Head Kinsale, Little Island, Dungarvan, Fota Island	228			•		•	•	•		•	
Ambassador Hotel	Fota Island, Little Island, Harbour Point, Douglas, Cork, Water Rock	202		•		•	•	•			•	
Ashlee Lodge	Lee Valley, Harbour Point, Fota Island, Muskerry, Cork, Mallow	192		•			•	•			•	
Ashley Hotel	Harbour Point, Water Rock Midleton, Fota Island, Lee Valley, Blarney Golf Club, Kinsale	202		•		•	•	•			•	
Blarney Castle Hotel	Blarney, Muskerry, Lee Valley, Fota Island, Harbour Point, Cork, Mallow	192		•		•	•	•			•	
Blarney Park Hotel	Lee Valley, Harbour Point, Fota, Muskerry, Mallow	193			•	•	•	•			•	
Blarney Woollen Mills Hotel	Muskerry, Lee Valley, Fota Island, Harbour Point, Mallow	193		•	•	•	•	•			•	•

Υ_{18} = Full 18 Hole Υ_9 = 9 Hole Υ_3 = Par 3

ACCOMMODATION	COURSES	BE OUR GUEST PAGE NUMBER	GOLF ON SITE	ALL INCLUSIVE PACKAGE	TUITION AVAILABLE	CART AVAILABLE	ARRANGE TEE OFF TIMES	ADVANCE RESERVATIONS	CLUBS FOR HIRE	TRANSPORT	PREFERENTIAL GREEN FEES	CADDY AVAILABLE
CORK Continued												
Castle Hotel & Leisure Centre	Macroom Golf Course - 18 hole Parklands Course	222		•			•	•			•	
Celtic Ross Hotel Conference & Leisure Centre	Skibbereen, Bandon, Lisselan, Bantry, Kinsale, Dunmore	225		•	•	•	•	•	•	•	•	•
Colla House Hotel	Coosheen, Bantry, Skibbereen	225		•				•		•	•	•
Comfort Inn & Suites Cork	Fota Island, Frankfield (Cork City), Muskerry (Blarney), Lee Valley	204		•	•	•	•	•	•	•	•	•
Commodore Hotel	East Cork, Midleton, Cobh	199		•			•				•	
Devonshire Arms Hotel & Restaurant	Youghal, West Waterford, Fota Island, Harbour Point, Lismore	228		•	•		•	•	•	•	•	•
Dunmore House Hotel	Macroom, Bandon, Skibbereen, Old Head of Kinsale, The Island and Fota Island	196 🏌9		•		•	•	•	•	•	•	•
Eldon Hotel	Skibbereen, Bantry, Glengarriff, Schull, Clonakilty	227		•		•	•	•	•	•	•	•
Fernhill Golf & Country Club	Douglas, Monkstown, Harbour Point, Kinsale - Old Head, Cork, Fota	195 🏌18		•		•	•	•	•	•	•	•
Fernhill House Hotel	Skibbereen, Bandon, Lisselan, Bantry Bay, Lee Valley, Dunmore	197		•			•	•		•	•	•
Glengarriff Eccles Hotel	Bantry Bay, Glengarriff, Ring of Kerry	216		•				•			•	•
Gresham Metropole	Fota Island, Little Island, Harbour Point, Muskerry, Kinsale	207			•	•	•	•	•	•	•	•
Harbour Lodge	Kinsale, Old Head of Kinsale, Bandon, Fota, Cork, Harbour Point	218		•	•	•	•	•	•		•	•
Hibernian Hotel and Leisure Centre	Mallow, Lee Valley, Charleville, Doneraile, Fota Island	223		•			•				•	•
Hotel Isaacs	Lee Valley, Fota Island, Harbour Point, Old Head, Muskerry	208					•	•	•		•	
Imperial Hotel	Fota Island, Douglas, Cork, Muskerry, Lee Valley, Monkstown	208					•	•	•		•	
Kierans Folkhouse Inn	Kinsale, Farrangalway, Fota, Lee Valley, Harbour Point, Old Head of Kinsale	219		•		•	•	•	•	•	•	•
Long Quay House	Kinsale Golf Club, Old Head Golf Links, Ringenane Kinsale	219		•	•	•	•	•			•	•
Lotamore House	Cork, Harbour Point, Fota Island, Water Rock, Lee Valley, Kinsale	211		•			•	•		•	•	•

🏌18 = Full 18 Hole   🏌9 = 9 Hole   🏌3 = Par 3

WHERE TO STAY WHEN YOU PLAY!

ACCOMMODATION	COURSES	BE OUR GUEST PAGE NUMBER	GOLF ON SITE	ALL INCLUSIVE PACKAGE	TUITION AVAILABLE	CART AVAILABLE	ARRANGE TEE OFF TIMES	ADVANCE RESERVATIONS	CLUBS FOR HIRE	TRANSPORT	PREFERENTIAL GREEN FEES	CADDY AVAILABLE
CORK Continued												
Maryborough House Hotel	Douglas, Fota Island, Cork, Kinsale Old Head, Harbour Point, Monkstown	211	•	•	•	•	•	•	•	•	•	•
Midleton Park Hotel & Spa	Fota Island, Cork - Little Island, Harbour Point, Water Rock, East Cork	224	•	•	•	•	•	•	•	•	•	•
Quality Hotel and Leisure Centre	Dunmore, Kinsale, Bandon, Skibbereen, Lisselan	198	•		•	•	•	•	•			
Quayside House	Kinsale Golf Club (18 & 9 hole course)	220		•	•		•	•	•			•
Seven North Mall	Cork, Douglas, Fota Island, Harbour Point, Monkstown, Muskerry	213		•	•	•	•	•	•		•	
Trident Hotel	Kinsale Golf Club, Fota Island, Old Head Golf Links, Lee Valley	221	•	•	•	•	•	•	•			•
Victoria Hotel, Cork City	Fota Island, Cork Golf Club, Monkstown Golf Club, Douglas, Lee Valley	214			•	•	•	•				•
Victoria Hotel, Macroom	Lee Valley, Macroom	222			•	•	•		•			•
Vienna Woods Hotel	Cork, Harbour Point, Fota, Old Head of Kinsale, Water Rock	214	•	•	•	•	•	•	•		•	•
WatersEdge Hotel	Fota Island, Harbour Point, Cobh, Water Rock, East Cork, Old Head of Kinsale	200		•	•	•	•	•	•			•
West Cork Hotel	Skibbereen, West Carbery	228	•		•	•	•	•	•			•
White House	Kinsale (18) and (9), Old Head, Bandon, Carrigaline, Muskerry	221			•	•	•		•			•
White Lady Hotel	Kinsale, Old Head of Kinsale, Farrangalway, Ringenane	221		•	•	•	•	•	•			•
KERRY												
19th Lodge	Ballybunion Old Course, Ballybunion Cashen Course, Tralee Golf Course	229	•		•	•	•	•	•		•	•
Abbey Gate Hotel	Tralee, Ballybunion, Killarney, Dooks, Waterville, Kerries	273	•		•	•	•	•	•		•	•
Aghadoe Heights Hotel	Waterville, Ballybunion, Kenmare, Killarney, Beaufort, Ring of Kerry	249			•	•	•	•			•	•
Arbutus Hotel	Killarney, Ballybunion, Waterville, Dooks, Tralee, Ring of Kerry	250				•	•	•				•
Ard-Na-Sidhe	Dooks, Killorglin, Waterville, Beaufort, Killarney, Tralee	234		•	•	•	•	•	•			•

$\blacktriangleright_{18}$ = Full 18 Hole $\blacktriangleright_{9}$ = 9 Hole $\blacktriangleright_{3}$ = Par 3

WHERE TO STAY
WHEN YOU PLAY!

ACCOMMODATION	COURSES	BE OUR GUEST PAGE NUMBER	GOLF ON SITE	ALL INCLUSIVE PACKAGE	TUITION AVAILABLE	CART AVAILABLE	ARRANGE TEE OFF TIMES	ADVANCE RESERVATIONS	CLUBS FOR HIRE	TRANSPORT	PREFERENTIAL GREEN FEES	CADDY AVAILABLE
KERRY Continued												
Ashville Guesthouse	Killarney, Ross, Dunloe, Beaufort, Waterville, Dooks, Ballybunion	250				•	•	•	•	•	•	•
Ballinskelligs Inn	Waterville, Ring of Kerry	229				•	•	•	•	•	•	•
Ballygarry House Hotel	Ballybunion, Tralee (Barrow), Killarney, Dooks, Killorglin, Castlegregory	273				•	•	•	•		•	•
Bianconi	Killarney, Beaufort, Dunloe, Killorglin, Dooks, Waterville	270	•			•	•	•	•	•	•	•
Brandon Hotel	Tralee, Ballybunion, Waterville, Dooks, Killarney, Ring of Kerry	275	•			•	•	•	•	•	•	•
Brookhaven Country House	Waterville, Dooks, Parknasilla, Tralee, Kenmare, Ballybunion, Ring of Kerry	278				•		•			•	•
Butler Arms Hotel	Waterville, Dooks, Killarney, Tralee, Ballybunion, Ring of Kerry	279	•			•	•	•	•	•	•	•
Carrig House	Dooks, Killarney, Beaufort, Killorglin	234				•		•	•			•
Cashen Course House	Ballybunion Old Course, Ballybunion Cashen Course, Listowel Golf Course	230	•			•	•	•	•	•	•	•
Castlelodge Guesthouse	Killarney Golf Course, Ross Golf Course	251				•		•				•
Castlerosse Hotel & Leisure Centre	Killarney (3 courses), Beaufort	252	▶9		•	•	•	•	•	•	•	•
Coffey's Loch Lein House Hotel	Killarney Golf Club, Beaufort, Dooks, Waterville, Barrow, Ballybunion	252				•	•	•	•	•	•	•
Davitts	Kenmare, Ring of Kerry	243						•	•	•		
Derrynane Hotel	Ring of Kerry, Kenmare, Waterville, Parknasilla, Beaufort, Dooks	233						•	•		•	
Dingle Benners Hotel	Ceann Sibeal (Dingle), Castlegregory	238				•	•	•	•	•	•	
Dingle Skellig Hotel	Ceann Sibeal Dingle, Castlegregory	238				•	•	•	•	•		•
Earls Court House	Killarney, Waterville, Ballybunion, Tralee, Beaufort, Dooks, Old Head	254					•	•	•	•	•	•
Eviston House Hotel	Ballybunion, Beaufort, Killarney, Waterville, Dooks, Tralee	254				•	•	•	•	•	•	•
Fairview Guesthouse	Killarney, Waterville, Tralee, Dooks, Ballybunion, Beaufort	255				•	•	•	•	•	•	•

428   ▶18 = Full 18 Hole   ▶9 = 9 Hole   ▶3 = Par 3

WHERE TO STAY WHEN YOU PLAY!

ACCOMMODATION	COURSES	BE OUR GUEST PAGE NUMBER	GOLF ON SITE	ALL INCLUSIVE PACKAGE	TUITION AVAILABLE	CART AVAILABLE	ARRANGE TEE OFF TIMES	ADVANCE RESERVATIONS	CLUBS FOR HIRE	TRANSPORT	PREFERENTIAL GREEN FEES	CADDY AVAILABLE
KERRY Continued												
Foley's Townhouse	Killarney, Barrow, Beaufort, Dooks, Ballybunion, Waterville	255						•	•			
Friars Glen	Killarney Golf & Fishing Club, Beaufort Golf Club, Dunloe Golf Course & Driving Range, Ross Golf Course	256	•	•	•	•	•	•	•	•		•
Fuchsia House	Killarney, Ballybunion, Waterville, Beaufort, Tralee, Dooks, Old Head	256	•	•	•	•	•	•	•	•		•
Gleann Fia Country House	Killarney, Tralee, Ballybunion, Waterville, Beaufort, Dooks	256	•	•	•	•	•	•	•	•		•
Gormans Clifftop House and Restaurant	Ceann Sibeal	239						•	•			
Grand Hotel	Tralee, Ballybunion, Waterville, Dingle, Dooks, Killarney	277	•	•	•	•	•	•	•		•	•
Grove Lodge Riverside Guesthouse	Killarney, Killorglin, Dooks, Beaufort, Gap of Dunloe, Dingle	271		•	•	•	•	•	•	•		
Harty Costello Town House	Ballybunion, Tralee, Listowel, Ballyheigue, Killarney	231	•	•	•	•	•	•	•	•		•
Hotel Dunloe Castle	Dunloe, Dooks, Beaufort, Killarney, Ross, Killorglin	258	•	•	•	•	•	•	•			•
Hotel Europe	Killarney Mahony's Point, Killeen, Lackabane, Beaufort, Dooks, Killorglin	258	•	•	•	•	•	•	•	•		•
International Best Western Hotel	Killarney, Beaufort, Killorglin, Dooks, Ballybunion, Tralee	259	•	•	•	•	•	•	•	•		•
Kathleens Country House	Killarney, Waterville, Tralee, Dooks, Ballybunion, Beaufort	260		•	•	•	•	•	•	•		•
Kenmare Bay Hotel	Ring of Kerry, Kenmare, Killarney, Tralee, Ballybunion, Waterville	244	•	•	•	•	•	•	•	•	•	•
Killarney Lodge	Killarney, Waterville, Ballybunion, Tralee, Dooks, Beaufort	261		•	•	•	•	•	•	•		•
Killarney Park Hotel	Killarney, Ballybunion, Tralee, Waterville, Dooks, Ring of Kerry	262		•	•	•	•	•	•	•		•
Killarney Royal	Killarney, Tralee, Dooks, Waterville, Beaufort, Ross	262		•	•	•	•	•	•	•		•
Killarney Ryan (The)	Killarney, Beaufort, Waterville, Dooks, Tralee, Ballybunion	263		•	•	•	•	•	•			
Killeen House Hotel	Killarney, Waterville, Tralee, Dooks, Ballybunion, Beaufort	263	•	•	•	•	•	•	•	•		•
Kingfisher Lodge Guesthouse	Beaufort, Dunloe, Castlerosse, Killarney, Ross	264	•	•	•	•	•	•	•		•	•

$\text{\textit{18}}$ = Full 18 Hole $\text{\textit{9}}$ = 9 Hole $\text{\textit{3}}$ = Par 3

429

WHERE TO STAY
WHEN YOU PLAY!

ACCOMMODATION	COURSES	BE OUR GUEST PAGE NUMBER	GOLF ON SITE	ALL INCLUSIVE PACKAGE	TUITION AVAILABLE	CART AVAILABLE	ARRANGE TEE OFF TIMES	ADVANCE RESERVATIONS	CLUBS FOR HIRE	TRANSPORT	PREFERENTIAL GREEN FEES	CADDY AVAILABLE
KERRY Continued												
Lake Hotel	Killarney (3 courses), Beaufort, Dooks, Ballybunion, Waterville, Tralee, Ross, Castlerosse	264		•	•	•	•	•	•	•		•
McSweeney Arms Hotel	Killarney, Waterville, Tralee, Ballybunion, Ring of Kerry, Dooks	265		•	•	•	•	•	•	•		•
Moorings (The)	Waterville Golf Links	272		•	•	•	•	•	•	•	•	•
Muckross Park Hotel	Beaufort, O'Mahony's Point, Killeen, Ross, Tralee, Ballybunion, Waterville, Dooks	265					•	•	•		•	•
Old Weir Lodge	Killarney, Waterville, Ballybunion, Tralee, Dooks, Beaufort	266		•	•	•	•	•	•	•		•
Parknasilla Great Southern Hotel	Ring of Kerry, Waterville, Killarney, Dooks	272 [9]		•				•	•	•		•
Randles Court Clarion Hotel	Killarney, Tralee, Beaufort, Dooks, Ring of Kerry	267		•			•	•			•	•
Rivermere	Killarney (O'Mahony's Point and Killeen), Dooks, Ballybunion, Waterville, Tralee, Ring of Kerry	267			•	•	•	•	•	•		•
Riversdale House Hotel	Kenmare, Killarney, Waterville, Parknasilla, Dooks, Ring of Kerry	246		•	•	•	•	•	•	•		•
Ross Hotel	Killarney, Ballybunion, Tralee, Waterville, Dooks, Beaufort	268			•	•	•	•	•	•		•
Scarriff Inn	Waterville, Kenmare, Sneem, Killorglin, Tralee, Ballybunion	233		•	•	•	•	•	•	•		•
Sheen Falls Lodge	Kenmare, Ring of Kerry	247		•	•	•	•	•	•	•		•
Smerwick Harbour Hotel	Ceann Sibeal (Dingle) - 18 hole links	242		•	•	•	•	•	•	•	•	•
Smugglers Inn	Waterville, Killarney, Dooks, Tralee, Ballybunion, Kenmare, Parknasilla	279		•	•	•	•	•	•	•		•
Southern Hotel	Ballybunion Old & New, Doonbeg, Lahinch, Tralee, Dooks, Castleisland	232		•	•	•	•	•	•		•	•
Tuscar Lodge	Killarney Golf Club, Beaufort, Dooks, Killorglin, Waterville, Tralee	269		•	•	•	•	•	•	•		•
Shannon												
CLARE												
Atlantic Hotel	Lahinch Championship Course and Castle, Woodstock, Ennis, Spanish Point, Doonbeg	296		•	•	•	•	•	•	•	•	•

[18] = Full 18 Hole   [9] = 9 Hole   [3] = Par 3

WHERE TO STAY WHEN YOU PLAY!

ACCOMMODATION	COURSES	BE OUR GUEST PAGE NUMBER	GOLF ON SITE	ALL INCLUSIVE PACKAGE	TUITION AVAILABLE	CART AVAILABLE	ARRANGE TEE OFF TIMES	ADVANCE RESERVATIONS	CLUBS FOR HIRE	TRANSPORT	PREFERENTIAL GREEN FEES	CADDY AVAILABLE
CLARE Continued												
Ballinalacken Castle Country House & Restaurant	Lahinch, Lahinch Castle, Woodstock, Galway Bay, Dromoland Castle, Doonbeg	285				•		•				
Bellbridge House Hotel	Spanish Point, Lahinch, Doonbeg	300		•	•	•	•	•	•	•	•	•
Dough Mor Lodge	Lahinch Golf Club (36 holes), Doonbeg G.C.	296					•	•				
Greenbrier Inn Guesthouse	Lahinch Championship Golf Links, Lahinch Castle Golf Links, Doonbeg Championship Golf Links, Woodstock	296			•	•						•
Grovemount House	Lahinch, Spanish Point	291			•	•	•	•	•	•	•	
Halpin's Townhouse Hotel	Ballybunion, Lahinch, Kilkee, Doonbeg, Woodstock, Shannon	291		•	•	•	•	•	•		•	
Kilkee Bay Hotel	Kilkee, Kilrush, Doonbeg	292		•		•	•	•	•		•	•
Kincora Hall Hotel	East Clare, Lahinch, Limerick County Golf & Country Club, Adare Manor	294		•			•	•	•	•	•	•
Kincora House and Gallery Restaurant	Lahinch, Lahinch Castle, Woodstock, Galway Bay, Dromoland Castle, Ennis, Doonbeg	298			•	•	•	•	•	•		•
Liscannor Bay Hotel	Lahinch (Links), Lahinch (Castle), Spanish Point, Doonbeg	298		•		•	•	•	•	•		•
Magowna House Hotel	Woodstock, Ennis, Lahinch, Dromoland Castle, Shannon, Doonbeg	288		•	•	•	•	•	•			
Old Ground Hotel	Doonbeg, Lahinch, Woodstock, Ennis, Dromoland, Shannon, East Clare	289		•		•	•	•	•	•	•	•
Sancta Maria Hotel	Lahinch Links, Lahinch Castle, Doonbeg, Woodstock, Dromoland, Spanish Point	297		•	•	•	•	•	•	•		•
Shamrock Inn Hotel	Lahinch Championship Course, Spanish Point, Woodstock, Ennis, Doonbeg	297		•	•	•	•	•	•	•	•	•
Temple Gate Hotel	Woodstock, Ennis, Lahinch, East Clare, Doonbeg, Dromoland	290		•	•	•	•	•	•	•	•	•
Waterman's Lodge Country House Hotel	Castletroy, Adare, East Clare, Lahinch, Cloneara, Woodstock	295		•	•	•	•	•	•	•	•	•
Woodstock Hotel		290	18	•	•	•	•	•	•	•		•
LIMERICK												
Adare Manor Hotel & Golf Resort		304	18	•	•	•	•	•	•	•	•	•

18 = Full 18 Hole   9 = 9 Hole   3 = Par 3

WHERE TO STAY WHEN YOU PLAY!

Accommodation	Courses	Be Our Guest Page Number	Golf On Site	All Inclusive Package	Tuition Available	Cart Available	Arrange Tee Off Times	Advance Reservations	Clubs For Hire	Transport	Preferential Green Fees	Caddy Available
LIMERICK Continued												
Carrabawn House	Adare Manor, Adare Golf Club (New), Newcastle West, Charleville, Limerick County (Ballyneety), Dromoland	305						•	•		•	•
Castletroy Park Hotel	Castletroy, Limerick County (Ballyneety), Dromoland, Adare	307			•			•	•	•		•
Clarion Hotel Limerick	Castletroy, Limerick County (Ballyneety), Dromoland, Adare, Shannon	307	•	•			•	•	•	•		•
Courtenay Lodge Hotel	Newcastle West, Adare Manor, Adare Golf Club, Ballybunion, Charleville, Dingle (Ceann Sibeal)	312	•	•		•	•	•	•	•	•	•
Devon Inn Hotel	Newcastle West, Killeline, Ballybunion, Killarney, Tralee	312	•	•		•	•	•	•	•	•	•
Fitzgeralds Woodlands House Hotel and Leisure Spa	Adare Manor Golf Club, Adare Golf Club, Newcastle West, Charleville, Limerick Co. Golf Club	306	•	•		•	•	•	•	•	•	•
Greenhills Hotel Conference/Leisure	Ballyneety, Shannon, Castletroy, Ballykisteen, Dromoland, Limerick	309	•	•		•	•	•	•	•	•	•
Gresham Ardhu	Limerick, Castletroy, Adare, Shannon, Ballykisteen, Limerick County	310		•	•	•	•	•	•	•		•
Leens Hotel	Ballybunion, Adare, Ardagh, Killenane	304						•				
Rathkeale House Hotel	Adare, Adare Manor, Killeline, Newcastle West, Charleville, Ballybunion	313	•	•		•	•	•	•	•	•	•
TIPPERARY NORTH												
Anner Hotel & Leisure Centre	Thurles, Dundrum, Templemore	315	•	•		•	•	•	•	•	•	•
Dromineer Bay Hotel	Nenagh, Roscrea, Dundrum, Birr, Portumna	313	•					•				
Grant's Hotel	Roscrea, Birr, Nenagh, Mountrath, Esker Hills	314	•	•		•	•	•	•	•	•	•
West												
GALWAY												
Abbey House	Barna, Galway, Galway Bay, Athenry, Oughterard	330	•					•				
Adare Guest House	Galway Bay, Oughterard	330	•	•		•	•	•	•	•	•	•
Alcock and Brown Hotel	Connemara	322	•	•		•	•	•	•	•	•	•

$\blacktriangleright_{18}$ = Full 18 Hole $\blacktriangleright_{9}$ = 9 Hole $\blacktriangleright_{3}$ = Par 3

WHERE TO STAY WHEN YOU PLAY!

Accommodation	Courses	Be Our Guest Page Number	Golf On Site	All Inclusive Package	Tuition Available	Cart Available	Arrange Tee Off Times	Advance Reservations	Clubs For Hire	Transport	Preferential Green Fees	Caddy Available
GALWAY Continued												
Anno Santo Hotel	Glenlo, Athenry, Galway, Oughterard, Galway Bay	330		•				•	•		•	
Ardagh Hotel & Restaurant	Connemara	322		•	•	•	•	•		•		
Ardilaun House Hotel, Conference Centre & Leisure Club	Galway, Oughterard, Galway Bay Golf & Country, Athenry, Lahinch, Connemara, Barna Golf Club	331		•		•	•	•	•	•	•	•
Ben View House	Connemara	322				•	•	•		•		
Boat Inn	Oughterard, Barna, Ballyconneely	349		•		•	•	•			•	•
Brennans Yard Hotel	Galway Golf Club, Galway Bay Golf & Country Club, Bearna Golf Club	332					•	•				
Byrne's Mal Dua House	Connemara Golf Club, Oughterard Golf Club	324		•	•	•	•	•	•		•	
Connemara Coast Hotel	Barna, Oughterard, Galway Bay	329		•	•			•	•		•	•
Connemara Gateway Hotel	Oughterard, Barna Golf and Country Club	349		•	•		•	•	•		•	
Corrib Wave Guest House	Oughterard	350		•	•	•	•	•		•	•	•
Forster Court Hotel	Galway, Barna, Galway Golf & Country, Athenry	334					•	•				
Galway Bay Hotel, Conference & Leisure Centre	Galway, Galway Bay, Athenry, Bearna, Gort	334		•	•	•	•	•	•	•	•	•
Galway Ryan (The)	Galway Bay, Galway, Athenry, Oughterard, Roscam, Rosshill	335				•	•	•	•		•	
Glenlo Abbey Hotel	Glenlo Abbey, Galway, Bearna, Oughterard, Galway Bay, Connemara	335 ₉		•	•	•	•	•	•		•	
Inishmore Guesthouse	Barna, Galway Bay, Oughterard, Athenry, Salthill	337		•	•	•	•	•	•		•	•
Lady Gregory Hotel	Gort	344		•	•	•	•	•			•	
Lake Hotel	Oughterard Golf Club and other local championship courses	350		•	•	•	•	•	•		•	•
Lochlurgain Hotel	Bearna, Galway, Athenry, Gort, Oughterard and Galway Bay	339		•	•	•	•	•	•		•	•
Menlo Park Hotel and Conference Centre	Barna, Galway Bay, Galway, Athenry, Oughterard, Connemara	339		•	•	•	•	•	•		•	•

 ₁₈ = Full 18 Hole   ₉ = 9 Hole   ₃ = Par 3

WHERE TO STAY WHEN YOU PLAY!

ACCOMMODATION	COURSES	BE OUR GUEST PAGE NUMBER	GOLF ON SITE	ALL INCLUSIVE PACKAGE	TUITION AVAILABLE	CART AVAILABLE	ARRANGE TEE OFF TIMES	ADVANCE RESERVATIONS	CLUBS FOR HIRE	TRANSPORT	PREFERENTIAL GREEN FEES	CADDY AVAILABLE
GALWAY Continued												
Mountain View Guest House	Oughterard, Galway, Connemara, Westport	351		•	•	•	•	•	•	•	•	
O'Deas Hotel	Loughrea, Curragh, Gort, Galway Bay	347		•			•	•	•	•	•	
Peacockes Hotel & Complex	Oughterard, Ballyconneely, Glenlo Abbey, Barna, Westport	348		•			•	•	•	•	•	•
Renvyle House Hotel	Connemara, Westport, Oughterard, Renvyle Golf Course	353 ▶9	•	•	•		•	•	•	•	•	
River Run Lodge	Oughterard	351		•	•	•	•	•	•	•	•	
Rosleague Manor Hotel	Connemara, Westport	347		•			•	•	•	•	•	
Ross Lake House Hotel	Oughterard, Barna, Galway Bay, Connemara	351		•			•	•	•	•	•	
Shannon Oaks Hotel & Country Club	Portumna, Galway Bay, Birr, Glasson, Gort, Lahinch	352		•	•		•	•	•	•	•	•
Sunrise Lodge	Galway Golf Club, Galway Bay Golf & Country Club, Connemara Golf Club, Barna Golf & Country Club	342		•			•	•	•	•	•	
Westwood House Hotel	Barna, Oughterard, Ballyconneely, Galway Bay Golf and Country Club	344		•		•	•	•	•	•	•	
Zetland Country House Hotel	Connemara Golf Club	320		•			•	•	•	•	•	•
MAYO												
Atlantic Coast Hotel	Westport, Enniscrone, Carne, Ballyconneely, Castlebar, Ballinrobe	363		•	•		•	•	•	•	•	•
Belmont Hotel	Claremorris, Ballinrobe, Castlebar and Ballyhaunis	361		•			•	•		•	•	
Castlecourt Hotel Conference and Leisure Centre	Westport, Ballinrobe, Castlebar, Belmullet, Clew Bay, Enniscrone	364		•	•		•	•	•	•	•	
Downhill House Hotel	Ballina, Enniscrone, Carne (Belmullet), Rosses Point, Strandhill, Westport	356		•			•	•	•	•	•	•
Healys Restaurant & Country House Hotel	Castlebar, Ballina, Westport, Enniscrone, Carne, Swinford, Ballinrobe, Mulranny	362		•			•	•	•	•	•	
Hotel Westport, Conference & Leisure Centre	Westport, Castlebar, Ballinrobe, Carne	364		•			•	•	•	•	•	
Knockranny House Hotel	Westport, Castlebar, Ballinrobe, Clew Bay, Mulranny	365		•			•	•	•	•	•	•

▶18 = Full 18 Hole   ▶9 = 9 Hole   ▶3 = Par 3

WHERE TO STAY
WHEN YOU PLAY!

ACCOMMODATION	COURSES	BE OUR GUEST PAGE NUMBER	GOLF ON SITE	ALL INCLUSIVE PACKAGE	TUITION AVAILABLE	CART AVAILABLE	ARRANGE TEE OFF TIMES	ADVANCE RESERVATIONS	CLUBS FOR HIRE	TRANSPORT	PREFERENTIAL GREEN FEES	CADDY AVAILABLE
MAYO Continued												
Ostan Oilean Acla	Achill, Mulranny, Westport, Castlebar, Ballinrobe, Carne	355			•		•	•	•	•	•	•
Regans Bartra House Hotel	Enniscrone, Ballina, Carne, Rosses Point, Strandhill	357					•	•	•	•	•	•
Ryan's Hotel	Westport, Clifden (Ballyconneely), Galway, Ballinrobe	360	•		•	•	•	•	•	•	•	•
Stella Maris Hotel	Carne, Belmullet, Enniscrone, Ballina, Rosses Point	357	•		•		•	•	•	•	•	•
Teach Iorrais	Carne Links Golf Course	360	•				•	•		•		•
TF Royal Hotel & Theatre	Castlebar, Westport, Three Oaks, Ballinrobe, Belmullet, Enniscrone	358	•		•		•	•	•	•	•	•
Westport Woods Hotel & Leisure Centre	Westport, Castlebar, Ballinrobe, Clew Bay, Carne (Belmullet)	366	•		•		•	•	•	•	•	•
Wyatt Hotel	Westport Golf Club, Castlebar Golf Club, Clew Bay, Mulranny	367	•		•	•	•	•	•	•	•	•
ROSCOMMON												
Gleesons Townhouse & Restaurant	Roscommon, Athlone, Glasson, Strokestown, Castlerea	368			•	•	•	•	•	•	•	•
O'Gara's Royal Hotel	Roscommon, Glasson, Longford, Athlone	368	•				•	•		•		•
Royal Hotel	Roscommon, County Sligo, Strandhill, Carrick-on-Shannon, Woodbrook	367								•		
North West												
DONEGAL												
Arnolds Hotel	Dunfanaghy 18 Hole Links, Cloughaneely 9 Hole Parkland	377	•			•	•	•	•	•	•	•
Bay View Hotel & Leisure Centre	Donegal Murvagh, Nairn, Portnoo	379	•			•	•	•		•	•	•
Castle Grove Country House Hotel	Portsalon, Letterkenny, Rosapenna, Ballyliffin	379	•				•	•		•	•	•
Dorrians Imperial Hotel	Donegal, Murvagh, Bundoran	372			•	•	•	•		•		
Great Northern Hotel	Donegal, Strandhill, Rosses Point	374	▶18	•	•	•	•	•	•	•	•	•

▶18 = Full 18 Hole   ▶9 = 9 Hole   ▶3 = Par 3

WHERE TO STAY WHEN YOU PLAY!

ACCOMMODATION	COURSES	BE OUR GUEST PAGE NUMBER	GOLF ON SITE	ALL INCLUSIVE PACKAGE	TUITION AVAILABLE	CART AVAILABLE	ARRANGE TEE OFF TIMES	ADVANCE RESERVATIONS	CLUBS FOR HIRE	TRANSPORT	PREFERENTIAL GREEN FEES	CADDY AVAILABLE
DONEGAL Continued												
Harvey's Point Country Hotel	Murvagh, Ballybofey, Bundoran, Portnoo, Ballyliffin	376	•		•	•	•	•	•	•	•	•
Highlands Hotel	Nairn, Portnoo	378	•			•	•	•	•		•	
Holyrood Hotel	Bundoran, Murvagh, Strandhill, Rosses Point, Castle Hume, Enniscrone	375	•		•	•	•	•	•		•	•
Jackson's Hotel	Ballybofey, Stranorlar	371	•				•	•	•			
McGrorys of Culdaff	Ballyliffin Golf Club	375	•		•	•	•	•	•		•	•
Ostan Na Tra (Beach Hotel)	Rosapenna Golf Club, St. Patricks, Carrigart	377					•	•				
Rosapenna Hotel	Rosapenna, Portsalon, Dunfanaghy	377 ▶18	•		•	•	•	•	•		•	•
Sandhouse Hotel	Donegal Murvagh, Bundoran, Rosses Point	382	•		•	•	•	•	•	•	•	•
SLIGO												
Castle Arms Hotel	Enniscrone, Ballina, Strandhill, Rosses Point	385			•	•	•	•	•		•	•
Ocean View Hotel	Strandhill, Sligo, Co. Sligo Golf Club	389				•	•	•	•			•
Sligo Park Hotel & Leisure Centre	Rosses Point Links Course, Strandhill Links Course	388	•			•	•	•			•	
Sligo's Southern Hotel & Leisure Centre	Rosses Point, Strandhill, Bundoran, Enniscrone	388	•			•	•	•				
Tower Hotel	Co.Sligo (Rosses Point), Strandhill, Enniscrone, Donegal	389	•			•	•	•				•
Yeats Country Hotel and Leisure Club	Co. Sligo, Strandhill, Enniscrone, Bundoran	386	•		•	•	•	•			•	•
North												
ANTRIM												
Bayview Hotel	Royal Portrush, Portstewart, Castlerock, Ballycastle, Bushfoot, Gracehill	393	•		•	•	•	•				•
Bushmills Inn	Royal Portrush, Portstewart, Castlerock, Ballycastle, Bushfoot, Gracehill	393	•		•	•	•	•	•			•

▶18 = Full 18 Hole   ▶9 = 9 Hole   ▶3 = Par 3

WHERE TO STAY WHEN YOU PLAY!

Accommodation	Courses	BE OUR GUEST PAGE NUMBER	GOLF ON SITE	ALL INCLUSIVE PACKAGE	TUITION AVAILABLE	CART AVAILABLE	ARRANGE TEE OFF TIMES	ADVANCE RESERVATIONS	CLUBS FOR HIRE	TRANSPORT	PREFERENTIAL GREEN FEES	CADDY AVAILABLE
ANTRIM Continued												
Comfort Hotel Portrush	Royal Portrush, Portstewart, Castlerock, Ballycastle, Bushfoot, Gracehill	396		•	•	•	•	•	•	•	•	•
Hilton Templepatrick		398	⛳18	•	•	•	•	•	•	•	•	•
Magherabuoy House Hotel	Royal Portrush, Valley, Portstewart, Castlerock, Bushfoot, Ballycastle, Gracehill	397		•	•	•	•	•	•	•	•	•
ARMAGH												
Charlemont Arms Hotel	Co. Armagh Golf Club, Loughgall Country Park & Golf Club, Tandragee, Portadown	400		•		•		•	•			
DERRY												
Brown Trout Golf & Country Inn	Royal Portrush, Portstewart, Castlerock	406	⛳9	•	•	•	•	•	•	•	•	•
Edgewater Hotel	Portstewart, Royal Portrush	409		•	•	•	•	•	•	•	•	•
Radisson Roe Park Hotel & Golf Resort		408	⛳18	•	•	•	•	•	•	•	•	•
DOWN												
Burrendale Hotel and Country Club	Royal County Down, Kilkeel, Downpatrick, Ardglass, Spa	412						•	•			
Royal Hotel	Bangor, Clandeboye, Blackwood	409		•								
FERMANAGH												
Mahons Hotel	Castle Hume, Enniskillen Golf Club, Murvagh Golf Club (Donegal)	415		•	•	•	•	•	•	•	•	•

⛳18 = Full 18 Hole   ⛳9 = 9 Hole   ⛳3 = Par 3

IRELAND FOR

Fishing

HOTELS & GUESTHOUSES

Ireland is accepted as being the outstanding angling holiday resort in Europe. Whether you are a competition angler, a serious specimen hunter, or just fishing while on holiday, you are sure to enjoy yourself here. With over 14,000km of rivers feeding over 4,000 lakes and with no part of Ireland over 112km from sea. Ireland can, in truth, be called an angler's dream.

So come on and get hooked!

ANGLING FOR A PLACE TO STAY!

We invite you to sample the fishing, the countryside and the friendship of the Irish people and then to stay in some of Ireland's most charming accommodation. We have listed a range of hotels and guesthouses which are either situated with or near angling facilities. Your host will assist you in arranging your angling itinerary. A full description of the hotels and guesthouses can be had by looking up the appropriate page number. Premises are listed in alphabetical order in each county.

ACCOMMODATION	TYPES OF FISH	BE OUR GUEST PAGE NUMBER	COARSE FISHING	GAME FISHING	SEA FISHING	BAIT AND TACKLE	BOATS FOR HIRE	DRYING ROOM	PACKED LUNCHES	GILLIE	TACKLE ROOM	FREEZER	PERMITS REQUIRED
East Coast													
DUBLIN													
Bracken Court Hotel	Pike, Perch, Roach, Tench, Bream, Salmon, Brown Trout, Rainbow Trout, Sea Trout, Mackerel	31	•	•					•	•			•
Gresham Royal Marine	Cod, Plaice, Pollock, Ling, Dab	88			•	•	•				•	•	
MEATH													
Wellington Court Hotel	Trout, Salmon	104		•					•		•	•	•
WICKLOW													
Lawless's Hotel	Wild Brown Trout, Rainbow Trout, Codling, Dab, Bass, Dogfish	107		•	•	•					•	•	•
Royal Hotel and Leisure Centre	Trout, Salmon, Cod, Plaice, Pollock	109		•	•	•	•						
Valley Hotel and Restaurant	Brown Trout, Pike, Perch, Roach, Rainbow Trout	114	•	•		•			•	•		•	•
Midlands & Lakelands													
KILDARE													
Hazel Hotel	Pike, Rudd, Roach, Eel, Tench, Perch, Salmon, Trout	124	•	•		•			•			•	•
K Club	Salmon, Trout, Carp, Tench, Bream, Rudd	126	•	•		•	•	•	•	•	•	•	•
LAOIS													
Heritage - Portlaoise (The)	Trout, Salmon	127		•		•	•	•		•	•		•
LONGFORD													
Longford Arms Hotel	Perch, Pike, Eel, Bream, Salmon, Trout	128	•	•		•	•		•	•		•	•

ANGLING FOR A PLACE TO STAY!

ACCOMMODATION	TYPES OF FISH	BE OUR GUEST PAGE NUMBER	COARSE FISHING	GAME FISHING	SEA FISHING	BAIT AND TACKLE	BOATS FOR HIRE	DRYING ROOM	PACKED LUNCHES	GILLIE	TACKLE ROOM	FREEZER	PERMITS REQUIRED
MONAGHAN													
Glencarn Hotel and Leisure Centre	Perch, Bream, Pike, Trout	129	•	•							•		
OFFALY													
Brosna Lodge Hotel	Bream, Tench, Rudd, Roach, Perch, Brown Trout, Pike, Salmon	130	•	•		•	•	•	•		•	•	•
County Arms Hotel	Bream, Tench, Rudd, Roach, Brown Trout, Perch, Salmon	130	•	•		•	•				•	•	•
Doolys Hotel	Trout, Salmon	131		•							•	•	•
WESTMEATH													
An Tintain Guesthouse	Roach, Rudd, Bream, Tench, Carp, Trout, Pike	139	•	•						•			
Austin Friar Hotel	Pike, Trout	137	•	•			•	•		•		•	•
Glasson Golf Hotel and Country Club	Pike, Perch, Roach, Bream, Brown Trout	135	•	•				•	•	•			•
Greville Arms Hotel	Pike, Trout	138	•	•				•			•	•	•
Hodson Bay Hotel	Bream, Perch, Pike, Brown Trout	136	•	•				•			•	•	•
Royal Hoey Hotel	Pike, Bream, Perch, Salmon, Trout, Cod, Mackerel	136	•	•	•	•		•		•		•	•
South East													
CARLOW													
Dolmen Hotel and River Court Lodges	Pike, Salmon, Trout	142	•	•			•			•	•	•	•
Seven Oaks Hotel	Bream, Perch, Roach, Pike, Eel, Salmon, Trout	142	•	•			•		•	•		•	•
KILKENNY													
Bambricks Troysgate House	Pike, Bream, Tench, Salmon, Brown Trout	144	•	•			•				•		•
Butler House	Brown Trout, Salmon	146		•					•	•	•	•	•

ANGLING FOR A PLACE TO STAY!

Accommodation	Types of Fish	Be Our Guest Page Number	Coarse Fishing	Game Fishing	Sea Fishing	Bait and Tackle	Boats for Hire	Drying Room	Packed Lunches	Gillie	Tackle Room	Freezer	Permits Required
KILKENNY Continued													
Kilford Arms	Salmon, Brown Trout, Trout	147		•		•				•		•	•
Kilkenny River Court	Trout, Salmon	148		•		•				•			•
Mount Juliet Conrad	Salmon, Trout	152		•		•			•	•	•	•	•
TIPPERARY SOUTH													
Cashel Palace Hotel	Perch, Salmon, Brown Trout, Grilse	154	•	•		•	•	•	•	•	•	•	•
Rectory House Hotel	Pike, Trout, Salmon	157	•	•						•	•	•	•
WATERFORD													
Grand Hotel	Trout, Salmon	166			•	•	•	•	•			•	•
Lismore Hotel	Salmon, Trout	165		•		•	•	•	•			•	•
WEXFORD													
Danby Lodge Hotel	Sea Trout, Bass, Cod	180		•	•		•					•	•
Quay House	Bass, Pollock, Coalfish, Tope, Spurdog, Ballan, Wrasse, Cod, Ray	178			•	•	•	•			•	•	
Talbot Hotel Conference and Leisure Centre	Salmon, Trout, Roach, Bass, Cod, Pollock, Ling	184	•	•	•	•	•	•	•	•			
Whites Hotel	Sea Bass, Salmon, Trout, Bream, Roach	184	•	•	•	•	•	•	•				•
South West													
CORK													
Ashley Hotel	Pike, Perch, Carp, Bream, Salmon, Sea Trout, Rainbow Trout, Cod, Ling, Plaice, Turbot, Pollock	202	•	•	•	•	•	•	•	•	•	•	•
Celtic Ross Hotel Conference & Leisure Centre	Bream, Roach, Tench, Trout, Salmon, Cod, Shark, Wrasse, Flat Fish	225	•	•	•	•	•			•			•
Colla House Hotel	Shark, Conger Eel, Cod, Mackerel, Ling, Flat Fish	225			•	•			•				•

ANGLING FOR A PLACE TO STAY!

ACCOMMODATION	TYPES OF FISH	BE OUR GUEST PAGE NUMBER	COARSE FISHING	GAME FISHING	SEA FISHING	BAIT AND TACKLE	BOATS FOR HIRE	DRYING ROOM	PACKED LUNCHES	GILLIE	TACKLE ROOM	FREEZER	PERMITS REQUIRED
CORK Continued													
Commodore Hotel	Ling, Cod, Pollock, Conger, Blue Shark	199			•	•	•	•				•	
Coolcower House	Bream, Rudd, Pike, Perch, Trout	222	•	•		•	•		•	•		•	•
Dunmore House Hotel	Bass, Cod, Mackerel, Skate, Whiting, Ling	196			•	•	•	•				•	
Eldon Hotel	Pike, Bream, Tench, Trout, Salmon, Shark, Ray, Mackerel	227	•	•	•	•	•		•	•		•	•
Fernhill Golf & Country Club	Salmon, Brown Trout	195		•			•	•	•	•	•	•	•
Hibernian Hotel and Leisure Centre	Bream, Pike, Perch, Tench, Trout, Salmon	223	•	•		•	•		•	•		•	•
Innishannon House Hotel	Salmon, Sea Trout, Brown Trout, Shark, Cod, Ling, Skate, etc.	216		•	•	•	•		•	•		•	•
Kierans Folkhouse Inn	Ling, Cod, Conger, Blue Shark, Sea Bass, Pollock	219			•	•	•		•				
Maryborough House Hotel	Bream, Perch, Pike, Trout, Rudd, Eel, Salmon, Shark, Ling, Conger, Pollock, Cod, Ray, Wrasse	211	•	•	•	•	•		•	•		•	•
Midleton Park Hotel & Spa	Rainbow Trout, Brown Trout, Salmon, Roach, Shark, Cod	224	•	•	•	•	•			•		•	•
Quality Hotel and Leisure Centre	Salmon, White Trout, Rainbow Trout, Cod, Ling, Pollock, Ray, Blue Shark	198	•	•	•	•	•		•	•			•
Trident Hotel	Ling, Cod, Conger, Wrasse, Pollock, Mackerel, Blue Shark	221			•	•	•		•				
Victoria Hotel	Bream, Pike, Perch	222	•						•		•	•	
Whispering Pines Hotel	Blue Shark, Conger, Ling, Pollock, Coalfish	215			•	•	•		•			•	
White Lady Hotel	Shark fishing our speciality, Cod, Pollock, etc.	221			•	•	•		•				
KERRY													
Abbey Gate Hotel	Salmon, Sea Trout, Brown Trout, Mackerel, Pollock, Dog Fish, etc.	273	•	•	•	•	•		•	•	•	•	•
Aghadoe Heights Hotel	Salmon, Sea Trout, Brown Trout, Mackerel, Pollock, Cod	249		•	•	•	•		•	•		•	•
Ard-Na-Sidhe	Salmon, Trout	234		•		•	•		•	•		•	•

ANGLING FOR A PLACE TO STAY!

ACCOMMODATION	TYPES OF FISH	BE OUR GUEST PAGE NUMBER	GAME FISHING	COARSE FISHING	SEA FISHING	BAIT AND TACKLE	BOATS FOR HIRE	DRYING ROOM	PACKED LUNCHES	GILLIE	TACKLE ROOM	FREEZER	PERMITS REQUIRED
KERRY Continued													
Ballygarry House Hotel	Pollock, Salmon, Trout, Cod	273	•		•	•		•				•	•
Brandon Hotel	Cod, Sea Trout, Salmon, Pollock, Mackerel, Brown Trout	275	•		•	•		•	•			•	•
Brookhaven Country House	Bream, Pike, Chub, Rudd, Roach, Tench, Salmon, Trout, Pollock, Mackerel, Whiting	278	•	•	•	•		•	•	•	•	•	•
Butler Arms Hotel	Salmon, Trout, Bass, Pollock, Cod, Shark, Mackerel, Whiting	279	•		•	•	•	•	•			•	•
Castlelodge Guesthouse	Trout, Salmon	251	•			•	•						•
Castlerosse Hotel & Leisure Centre	Trout, Salmon	252	•			•	•	•				•	•
Derrynane Hotel	Mackerel, Pollock, Shark, Salmon, Bass, Cod, Whiting, Wrasse	233	•		•	•	•	•	•			•	•
Dingle Skellig Hotel	Pollock, Garfish, Blue Shark, Tope, Dogfish, Ling, Whiting, Ray	238			•	•	•	•	•		•	•	•
Earls Court House	Salmon, Trout	254	•			•	•						•
Glencar House Hotel	Salmon, Trout, Sea Trout, Tope, Pollock, Cod, Mackerel, Ray, Shark	242	•		•	•	•	•	•			•	•
Grand Hotel	Perch, Trout, Pike, Salmon, Dog Fish, Pollock, Ray, Monkfish	277	•	•	•	•	•	•	•			•	•
Hotel Dunloe Castle	Salmon, Trout	258	•		•	•	•	•				•	•
Hotel Europe	Salmon, Trout	258	•		•	•	•	•				•	•
Inveraray Farm Guesthouse	Salmon, Brown Trout, Perch, Peel	259	•	•			•	•				•	•
Killarney Park Hotel	Brown Trout, Salmon, Sea Trout	262	•		•	•	•	•	•	•	•	•	•
Killarney Royal	Brown Trout, Salmon	262	•		•	•	•	•	•			•	•
Kingfisher Lodge Guesthouse	Salmon, Trout, Sea Trout, Pollock, Ling, Coalfish, Mackerel, Wrasse, Shark	264	•		•	•	•	•	•			•	•
Lake Hotel	Salmon, Trout	264	•		•	•	•	•				•	•
Moorings (The)	Salmon, Trout, Cod, Pollock, Mackerel, Shark, Turbot, Sea Trout, Plaice	272	•		•	•	•	•	•			•	•

44.

ANGLING FOR A PLACE TO STAY!

ACCOMMODATION	TYPES OF FISH	BE OUR GUEST PAGE NUMBER	COARSE FISHING	GAME FISHING	SEA FISHING	BAIT AND TACKLE	BOATS FOR HIRE	DRYING ROOM	PACKED LUNCHES	GILLIE	TACKLE ROOM	FREEZER	PERMITS REQUIRED
KERRY Continued													
Muckross Park Hotel	Salmon, Brown Trout, Tench, Rainbow Trout	265	•	•		•	•					•	•
O'Connor's Guesthouse	Salmon, Trout, Bass, Ray, Plaice, Cod, Mackerel	235		•	•	•	•					•	•
Riversdale House Hotel	Bream, Chub, Dab, Eel, Roach, Rudd, Tench, Brown Trout, Rainbow Trout, Salmon, Bass, Cod	246	•	•	•	•	•	•	•	•		•	•
Scarriff Inn	Mackerel, Pollock, Salmon, Pike, Bass	233	•	•	•	•	•		•	•		•	•
Sheen Falls Lodge	Salmon, Trout, Shark, Mackerel, Pollock, Skate, Conger Eel, Dogfish	247		•	•	•	•	•	•	•	•	•	•
Smerwick Harbour Hotel	Plaice, Turbot, Sole, Mackerel, Cod, Pollock, Conger, Shark	242			•	•	•		•	•		•	•
Tuscar Lodge	Salmon, Trout, Pike, Perch	269	•	•		•	•		•	•		•	•
Shannon													
CLARE													
Ardilaun Guesthouse	Pike, Perch, Trout, Salmon	286	•	•		•			•			•	•
Grovemount House	Roach, Trout	291	•	•		•	•						•
Kilkee Bay Hotel	Salmon, Cod, Mackerel	292	•		•	•						•	•
Kincora Hall Hotel	Tench, Bream, Roach, Perch, Pike, Wild Brown Trout	294	•	•	•	•	•	•	•	•	•	•	•
Waterman's Lodge Country House Hotel	Salmon, Trout, Pike	295	•	•		•	•		•	•		•	•
LIMERICK													
Adare Manor Hotel & Golf Resort	Salmon, Trout	304		•		•				•		•	•
Castle Oaks House Hotel & Country Club	Pike, Bream, Tench, Eel, Trout, Salmon	306	•	•	•	•	•		•	•	•	•	•
Fitzgeralds Woodlands House Hotel and Leisure Spa	Pike, Trout, Salmon	306	•	•		•			•	•		•	•
Gresham Ardhu	Pike, Perch, Roach, Trout, Salmon	310	•	•		•			•	•	•		•

ANGLING FOR A PLACE TO STAY!

Accommodation	Types of Fish	Be Our Guest Page Number	Coarse Fishing	Game Fishing	Sea Fishing	Bait and Tackle	Boats for Hire	Drying Room	Packed Lunches	Gillie	Tackle Room	Freezer	Permits Required
LIMERICK Continued													
Leens Hotel	Salmon, Trout, Ray, Bass, Pollock, Cod, Monkfish	304	•	•	•	•	•		•	•		•	•
Rathkeale House Hotel	Pike, Perch, Roach, Trout, Salmon	313	•	•		•	•					•	•
TIPPERARY NORTH													
Dromineer Bay Hotel	Bream, Roach, Perch, Pike, Brown Trout	313	•	•			•		•			•	•
West													
GALWAY													
Anglers Rest Hotel	Pike, Perch, Rudd, Bream, Trout, Salmon	345	•	•		•	•		•			•	•
Ardilaun House Hotel, Conference Centre & Leisure Club	Salmon, Brown Trout, Sea Trout, Rainbow Trout	331		•	•	•	•		•	•		•	•
Ballindiff Bay Lodge	Pike, Perch, Browntrout	328	•	•								•	•
Ballynahinch Castle Hotel	Salmon, Sea Trout, Brown Trout	318		•		•	•		•	•	•	•	•
Ben View House	Salmon, Trout, Cod, Herring, Whiting, Pollock, Plaice	322		•	•	•	•		•			•	•
Boat Inn	Perch, Pike, Salmon, Trout, Mackerel	349	•	•	•		•		•			•	•
Connemara Gateway Hotel	Brown Trout, Salmon	349		•					•			•	•
Corrib Wave Guest House	Pike, Perch, Brown Trout, Salmon	350	•	•		•	•		•	•	•	•	•
Eldons Hotel	Shark, Pollock, Cod, Mackerel	353			•							•	
Galway Bay Hotel, Conference & Leisure Centre	Bream, Roach, Perch, Rudd, Salmon, Brown Trout, Blue Shark, Cod, Ling, Pollock, Ray	334	•	•	•	•						•	•
Galway Ryan (The)	Pike, Perch, Bream, Roach, Salmon, Brown Trout	335	•	•		•	•					•	•
Glenlo Abbey Hotel	Pike, Bream, Roach, Trout, Salmon, Shark, Cod, Mackerel	335	•	•	•		•		•			•	•
Lake Hotel	Pike, Perch, Trout, Salmon	350	•	•			•		•	•	•	•	•

ANGLING FOR A PLACE TO STAY!

ACCOMMODATION

TYPES OF FISH

GALWAY Continued

Accommodation	Types of Fish	Be Our Guest Page Number	Coarse Fishing	Game Fishing	Sea Fishing	Bait and Tackle	Boats for Hire	Drying Room	Packed Lunches	Gillie	Tackle Room	Freezer	Permits Required
Lough Inagh Lodge	Salmon, Sea Trout, Brown Trout	352		•	•	•	•	•	•	•		•	•
Menlo Park Hotel and Conference Centre	Perch, Pike, Trout, Salmon, Mackerel, Pollock, Ray, Tope, Bullhuss, Wrasse	339	•	•	•	•	•	•	•	•	•	•	•
Mountain View Guest House	Salmon, Trout, Pike, Perch, Bream	351	•	•		•			•		•	•	•
O'Deas Hotel	Trout, Pike, Perch	347	•	•		•			•		•	•	•
Peacockes Hotel & Complex	Salmon, Sea Trout, Shark, Cod, Pollock, Mackerel, Ray	348		•	•	•	•	•	•	•	•	•	•
Renvyle House Hotel	Brown Trout, Salmon, Sea Trout, Cod, Shark, Eel, Mackerel, Pollock	353		•	•	•	•	•	•	•	•	•	•
River Run Lodge	Pike, Perch, Roach, Salmon, Trout	351	•	•		•			•		•	•	•
Rosleague Manor Hotel	Salmon, Sea Trout, Brown Trout, Shark, Mackerel, Pollock	347		•	•	•	•	•	•	•	•	•	•
Sunrise Lodge	Bream, Pike, Trout, Salmon, Mackerel, Shark, Tope, Sea Bass	342	•	•	•	•	•	•	•	•	•	•	•
Zetland Country House Hotel	Perch, Pike, Salmon, Trout, Shark, Cod, Gurning, Mackerel, Pollock	320	•	•	•	•	•	•	•	•	•	•	•

MAYO

Accommodation	Types of Fish	Be Our Guest Page Number	Coarse Fishing	Game Fishing	Sea Fishing	Bait and Tackle	Boats for Hire	Drying Room	Packed Lunches	Gillie	Tackle Room	Freezer	Permits Required
Achill Cliff House Hotel	Dog Fish, Bass, Conger Eel, Skate, Gurnard	355			•	•	•	•		•		•	•
Atlantic Coast Hotel	Eel, Pike, Perch, Salmon, Trout, Sea Trout, Brill, Mackerel, Ling, Pollock, Ray, Shark, Herring	363	•	•	•	•	•	•	•	•	•	•	•
Healys Restaurant & Country House Hotel	Salmon, Brown Trout, Sea Trout, Rainbow Trout, Shark, Pollock, Mackerel, Herring, Cod, Sole	362	•	•	•	•	•	•	•	•	•	•	•
Hotel Westport, Conference & Leisure Centre	Pike, Perch, Bream, Salmon, Trout, Pollock, Dog Fish, Cod, Whiting, Blue Shark, Ling, Tope, Skate	364	•	•	•	•	•	•	•	•	•	•	•
Knockranny House Hotel	Salmon, Trout, Sea Trout, Cod, Whiting, Skate, Ray, Monkfish	365		•	•	•	•	•	•	•		•	•
Ostan Oilean Acla	Cod, Ling, Conger, Shark, Mackerel, Trout, Brill, Whiting, Ray	355		•	•	•			•		•	•	•
Ryan's Hotel	Brown Trout, Salmon - also Pike, Perch and Roach, Hake, Mackerel, Plaice, Pollock, Ray	360	•	•	•	•	•	•	•			•	•
Teach Iorrais	Salmon, Trout, Cod, Mackerel	360		•	•	•	•	•	•			•	•

ANGLING FOR A PLACE TO STAY!

Accommodation	Types of Fish	Be Our Guest Page Number	Coarse Fishing	Game Fishing	Sea Fishing	Bait and Tackle	Boats for Hire	Drying Room	Packed Lunches	Gillie	Tackle Room	Freezer Room	Permits Required
ROSCOMMON													
Gleesons Townhouse & Restaurant	Pike, Perch, Roach, Tench, Hybrids	368	•				•	•	•	•		•	
Royal Hotel	Trout, Pike, Perch, Eel, Bream	367	•	•		•			•			•	•
Whitehouse Hotel	Pike, Perch, Rudd, Bream, Tench, Brown Trout	367	•	•			•	•	•	•			•
North West													
DONEGAL													
Arnolds Hotel	Brown Trout, Salmon, Sea Trout	377		•	•		•		•			•	•
Bay View Hotel & Leisure Centre	Salmon, Seatrout, Brown Trout, Tuna, Shark, Pollock, Cod, Ling	379	•	•	•	•			•			•	•
Dorrians Imperial Hotel	Bream, Pike, Eel, Trout, Salmon, Cod, Sea Trout, Sole	372	•	•	•		•		•	•			•
Great Northern Hotel	Pike, Perch, Salmon, Trout, Pollock, Cod, Ling, Plaice, Shark, Sole	374	•	•	•	•	•		•	•	•	•	•
Ostan Na Tra (Beach Hotel)	Shark, Cod, Haddock, Ling, Conger, Gurnard, Pollock	377			•	•			•			•	
North													
ANTRIM													
Bushmills Inn	Roach, Bream, Haddock, Salmon, Cod, Plaice, Whiting, Sea Trout	393	•	•	•	•	•	•	•	•		•	•
DERRY													
Brown Trout Golf & Country Inn	Salmon, Trout, Pike, Bream	406	•	•		•			•	•		•	•
DOWN													
Royal Hotel	Cod, Skate, Mackerel, Haddock, Whiting	409			•	•		•				•	
FERMANAGH													
Killyhevlin Hotel	Roach, Bream, Pike, Salmon, Trout, Mackerel, Pollock, Ling, Cod	414	•	•	•	•	•	•	•	•			•

IRELAND FOR
Conferences
HOTELS & GUESTHOUSES

Small meetings or large conferences are part
and parcel of life in Irish hotels and guesthouses.

What makes Ireland special as a venue
is the warmth of the welcome you will receive,
coupled with excellent facilities
which can be tailored to your needs.

If you have an agenda, we can supply
the venue.

SELECT A VENUE FOR YOUR AGENDA

We will be glad to see you and work with you to make your meeting or conference a successful one. Choose from the wide selection of special facilities throughout the country as shown here. A full description of the hotels and guesthouses can be had by looking up the appropriate page number. Premises are listed in alphabetical order in each county.

ACCOMMODATION	CONTACT PERSON	BE OUR GUEST PAGE NUMBER	NUMBER OF ROOMS OF VARIOUS SEATING CAPACITIES							BLACK OUT FACILITIES	AIR CONDITIONING	INTERPRETING EQUIPMENT	AUDIO VISUAL EQUIPMENT
			500+	400+	300+	200+	100+	50+	3-				
East Coast													
DUBLIN													
Academy Hotel	Peter Collins	36							5	•	•	H	O
Alexander Hotel	Siobhan O'Hare	37		1	1	2	4	5	1	•	•	H	O
Ashling Hotel	Zaira Gil	40				1	1	1	5	•	•	H	H
Becketts Country House Hotel	Emma Mandler	89							1	•		H	O
Bracken Court Hotel	Stephen O'Donoghue / Bryan O'Sullivan, General Manager	31				1		1	2		•	H	O
Buswells Hotel	Aileen Mangan	46						1	3	•	•	H	O
Carnegie Court Hotel	Sharon Caffrey	94				1		1	2	•	•	H	O
Cassidys Hotel	Carol/Karen	47						1	3	•	•		H
Citywest Hotel Conference, Leisure & Golf Resort	Fiona Killilea	92	6	6	7	8	25	26	20	•	•	H	H
Clarion Hotel Dublin IFSC	Jane Hurley	50					2	2	7	•	•		O
Clontarf Castle Hotel	Judith Graham	52		1			3	2	1	•	•	H	H
Conrad Dublin	Fiona Keys	53				1	1	4	6	•	•	H	H
Davenport Hotel	Siobhan O'Hare	53			1	2	2	2	4	•	•	H	O
Finnstown Country House Hotel	Jenny Holmes	90				1	1	2	4		•	H	O
Fitzpatrick Castle Dublin	Sharon Joyce	89			1	1		3	6	•	•	H	O
Four Seasons Hotel Dublin	Robin Stewart	58	1			1		3	1	•	•	H	H
Georgian Hotel	Lorraine Loughnane	58							3			H	H

H = Can Arrange Hire   O = Available On Premises

SELECT A VENUE FOR YOUR AGENDA

ACCOMMODATION	CONTACT PERSON	BE OUR GUEST PAGE NUMBER	500+	400+	300+	200+	100+	50+	30-	BLACK OUT FACILITIES	AIR CONDITIONING	INTERPRETING EQUIPMENT	AUDIO VISUAL EQUIPMENT
DUBLIN Continued													
Grand Hotel	Avril Clarke	91	1			1	1	6	6	•	•	H	O
Great Southern Hotel	Louise Maguire	33			1	1	3		8	•	•	H	H
Gresham (The)	Ian Craig	60			1	2	3	8	22	•	•	H	H
Gresham Royal Marine	Banqueting Manager	88	1			1	1	2	4	•		H	H
Herbert Park Hotel	Orla McLoughlin	62					2	1	2	•	•	H	H
Hilton Dublin	Karen O'Sullivan	63			1			4	7		•	H	O
Holiday Inn Dublin Airport	Valerie Markey	34						1	7	•	•	H	H
Holiday Inn Dublin City Centre	Sabrina Guida	63				1	2	5	6	•	•	H	O
Lansdowne Hotel	Margaret English	68					1	1	1	•	•	H	O
Le Meridien Shelbourne	Ray Mulligan	68	1				2	2	6	•		H	H
Marine Hotel	Sheila Baird	94					1	4	2	•	•	H	H
Mercer Hotel	Caroline Fahy	71					1	1	3	•	•	H	O
Merrion Hall	Pat Halpin	71							2	•	•	H	H
North Star Hotel	Hazel Rigler	74					1	1	1	•	•	H	H
Ormond Quay Hotel	Helen McManus	75						1	3	•		H	H
Orwell Lodge Hotel	Reception	75						1	2				
Portmarnock Hotel & Golf Links	Lisa Butler	92				1	2	2	2	•	•	H	H
Red Cow Moran Hotel	Karen Moran	80	1	1	1	2	5	10	16	•	•	H	O
Regency Airport Hotel	Catherine McGettigan	80			2			1	3	•	•	H	O

H = Can Arrange Hire   O = Available On Premises

SELECT A VENUE FOR YOUR AGENDA

	BE OUR GUEST PAGE NUMBER	**NUMBER OF ROOMS OF VARIOUS SEATING CAPACITIES**							**BLACK OUT FACILITIES**	**AIR CONDITIONING**	**INTERPRETING EQUIPMENT**	**AUDIO VISUAL EQUIPMENT**
ACCOMMODATION / **CONTACT PERSON**		500+	400+	300+	200+	100+	50+	30+				
DUBLIN Continued												
Sheldon Park Hotel & Leisure Centre — John Gannon	82	1	1	1	2	3	2	9	•	•	H	O
Spa Hotel — Betty Dolan	90	1	1	1	1	1	1	1	•	•		H
Stephen's Green Hotel — Tina Ward	83							6	•	•	H	O
Stillorgan Park Hotel — Sharon Power	31	1	1	1	2	5	6	10	•	•	H	H
Temple Bar Hotel — Danny Harrington	84						1	4	•		H	H
West County Hotel — Rachel Walshe	86					1	1	2	•	•	H	
Westin Dublin — Sheila O'Sullivan	87				1	2	2	8	•	•	H	O
LOUTH												
Boyne Valley Hotel & Country Club — Noel Comer	96	2	2	1	2	1	2	3	•	•	H	H
Carrickdale Hotel & Leisure Complex — Breige Savage/Declan O'Neill/Fiona Clerkin	97	1			1	1	1	4	•	•	H	O
Derryhale Hotel — Liam Sexton	98				1			2	•		H	H
Fairways Hotel & Conference Centre — Killian O'Grady/Dara McCarthy	98	1	1	2	2	2	5	10	•	•	H	O
Hotel Imperial — Peter Quinn	99				1	2	2		•			O
McKevitt's Village Hotel — Terry and Kay McKevitt	96					1		1	•			H
Westcourt Hotel — Valerie Sherlock	97			1	1	2	3	5	•	•		O
MEATH												
Ardboyne Hotel — Mary Fitzsimons	102			1		2	3	4	•	•	H	O
Johnstown House Hotel — Denise Kenny	101	1	1	1	2	2	4	14				H
Neptune Beach Hotel & Leisure Club — Patrick Reilly	100				1			2	•		H	O

H = Can Arrange Hire   O = Available On Premises

SELECT A VENUE FOR YOUR AGENDA

Accommodation	Contact Person	Be Our Guest Page Number	500+	400+	300+	200+	100+	50+	30+	Air Conditioning	Black Out Facilities	Interpreting Equipment	Audio Visual Equipment
MEATH Continued													
Newgrange Hotel	Lorraine Cunningham	103	1			1	1	1	1	•	•	H	O
Station House Hotel	Chris Slattery	102		1		1	1	1	1	•	•	H	O
WICKLOW													
Arklow Bay Conference and Leisure Hotel	Monique Freeman	104	1	1	1	2	2	4	5	•	•	H	O
Glendalough Hotel	Patrick Casey	112					1		2	•	•	H	O
Glenview Hotel	Marie O'Halloran	111				1	1	2	2	•	•	H	O
Grand Hotel	Michelle Tyrell	114				1	2		3			H	O
Heather House Hotel	John Lyng/ Frances Lamb	108						1			•	H	H
Hunter's Hotel	Tom Gelletlie	113							3	•			
Lawless's Hotel	Seoirse or Maeve O'Toole	107					1		1	•		H	O
Rathsallagh House, Golf and Country Club	Catherine Lawlor	110						1	4	•		H	O
Royal Hotel and Leisure Centre	Stephanie Curran	109			1				1	•	•	H	O
Tinakilly Country House and Restaurant	Brenda Gilmore	113						1	3	•	•	H	O
Woodenbridge Hotel	Esther and Bill O'Brien	115					1		1	•	•		O
Woodland Court Hotel	Ruth Connolly	109						1	4	•	•	H	O
Midlands & Lakelands													
CAVAN													
Hotel Kilmore	Sharon Crowe	119	1			2	3	3	4	•	•	H	O
Park Hotel	Mary McMillan	119						2	2	•	•	H	O

H = Can Arrange Hire   O = Available On Premises

SELECT A VENUE FOR YOUR AGENDA

ACCOMMODATION	CONTACT PERSON	BE OUR GUEST PAGE NUMBER	500+	400+	300+	200+	100+	50+	50-	BLACK OUT FACILITIES	AIR CONDITIONING	INTERPRETING EQUIPMENT	AUDIO VISUAL EQUIPMENT
CAVAN Continued													
Slieve Russell Hotel, Golf & Country Club	Bridie Gallagher	118	1	1	3	3	3	4	7	•	•	H	O
KILDARE													
Glenroyal Hotel, Leisure Club & Conference Centre	Clare Lyons	123	1	2	4	4	6	6	12	•	•	H	O
Hazel Hotel	John Kelly	124			1	1	1	1	1	•	•		O
K Club	Kerri Wells	126					1	1	3	•	•	H	O
Keadeen Hotel	Pauline Barry	126	1	1	1	1	3	4	7	•	•	H	O
Killashee House Hotel	Anne-Marie Hayes	124	1	2	2	2	3	4	20	•	•	H	O
Standhouse Hotel Leisure & Conference Centre	Shane D'Arcy	121	1	1	2	3	4	4	7	•	•	H	O
LAOIS													
Heritage - Portlaoise (The)	Trish Murphy	127	1			1		1	5	•	•	H	O
LONGFORD													
Longford Arms Hotel	Siobhan Symth	128	1			2	3			•	•	H	H
MONAGHAN													
Glencarn Hotel and Leisure Centre	Patrick McFadden/Fiona Dooley/Kathleen Lavelle	129	1	1	1	3	3	3	5	•	•	H	O
Hillgrove Hotel	Roisin McFadden	130	1	1	2	2	2	4			•	H	H
Nuremore Hotel & Country Club	Lisa Sinclair	129	1			2	3	4		•	•	H	O
OFFALY													
Bridge House Hotel & Leisure Club	Colm McCabe	133	1	1	2	2	3	4	9	•	•	H	O
County Arms Hotel	Barry Loughnane	130			1	1	1	4	6	•			O

NUMBER OF ROOMS OF VARIOUS SEATING CAPACITIES

H = Can Arrange Hire   O = Available On Premises

SELECT A VENUE FOR YOUR AGENDA

ACCOMMODATION	CONTACT PERSON	BE OUR GUEST PAGE NUMBER	500+	400+	300+	200+	100+	50+	50-	BLACK OUT FACILITIES	AIR CONDITIONING	INTERPRETING EQUIPMENT	AUDIO VISUAL EQUIPMENT
OFFALY Continued													
Doolys Hotel	Jo Duignan	131				1		1				•	O
Kinnitty Castle Demesne	Enda McDonagh / Fiona Comerford	131				1	1	2	2	•		H	H
Moorhill House Hotel	David or Alan Duffy	134						1	3	•		H	H
Tullamore Court Hotel Conference & Leisure Centre	Ann Lynch	134	1	1	2	2	3	4	8	•	•	H	O
WESTMEATH													
Austin Friar Hotel	Patrina Mullen	137						1		•	•	H	O
Bloomfield House Hotel & Leisure Club	Ita Kerrigan	138			1	2	4	5	8	•	•	H	O
Glasson Golf Hotel and Country Club	Gareth Jones/Fidelma Reid	135					1	1	1	•	•	H	H
Greville Arms Hotel	John Cochrane	138				1	2	1	2	•		H	H
Hodson Bay Hotel	Christina Melican	136	1	1	1	2	3	4	4	•	•	H	O
Royal Hoey Hotel	M. Hoey	136					1	2	3	•	•		O
Wineport Lodge	Ray Byrne	137							2	•	•	H	O

South East

ACCOMMODATION	CONTACT PERSON	BE OUR GUEST PAGE NUMBER	500+	400+	300+	200+	100+	50+	50-	BLACK OUT FACILITIES	AIR CONDITIONING	INTERPRETING EQUIPMENT	AUDIO VISUAL EQUIPMENT
CARLOW													
Dolmen Hotel and River Court Lodges	Nora Duggan	142	1	2	2	2	2	3	8	•	•	H	O
Mount Wolseley Hotel, Golf and Country Club	Kathy Walsh	143						1	3	•	•	H	H
Seven Oaks Hotel	Kathleen Dooley	142		1		1		1	2	•	•		H
KILKENNY													
Butler House	Gabrielle Hickey	146					1	2	2			H	O

454

H = Can Arrange Hire   O = Available On Premises

ACCOMMODATION	CONTACT PERSON	BE OUR GUEST PAGE NUMBER	500+	400+	300+	200+	100+	50+	50-	AIR CONDITIONING	BLACK OUT FACILITIES	INTERPRETING EQUIPMENT	AUDIO VISUAL EQUIPMENT
KILKENNY Continued													
Hotel Kilkenny	Fiona Fields	147		1	1	2	3	4	7	•	•	H	H
Kilford Arms	Pius Phelan	147			1	1	2	3	5			H	H
Kilkenny Ormonde Hotel	Sheena McCanny	148	1		1			2	6	•	•	H	O
Kilkenny River Court	Breda Kehoe	148			1				4	•	•	H	H
Mount Juliet Conrad	Aine O'Hare	152					1	3	2	•	•	H	O
Newpark Hotel	Orla Gray	150		1	1	1	2	2	7	•	•	H	O
Springhill Court Hotel	Suzanne Palmer	151	1	1	1		2	2	3	•	•	H	O
TIPPERARY SOUTH													
Cahir House Hotel	Liam Duffy	153			1	1	1	1	3	•	•	H	H
Carraig	Pat Power	153					1						O
Cashel Palace Hotel	Susan Murphy	154						1			•	H	H
Dundrum House Hotel	Dolores Thornton	155		1						•	•	H	O
Hotel Minella & Leisure Centre	Elizabeth Nallen	156	1			2	2	4	5	•	•	H	O
Kilcoran Lodge Hotel	Joanne Morrisey	153				1	1	1	1	•	•	H	O
Mulcahys	Ros Donaghue	157							1		•	H	H
WATERFORD													
Ard Ri Hotel	Susie Molloy	167	1				2	2	2	•	•	H	H
Clonea Strand Hotel, Golf & Leisure	Mark Knowles or Ann McGrath	162			2	2	3	4	5	•	•	H	H
Dooley's Hotel	Margaret Darrer	169			1	1	2	1	3	•	•	H	O

H = Can Arrange Hire   O = Available On Premises

SELECT A VENUE FOR YOUR AGENDA

Accommodation	Contact Person	BE OUR GUEST PAGE NUMBER	500+	400+	300+	200+	100+	50+	30-	BLACK OUT FACILITIES	AIR CONDITIONING	INTERPRETING EQUIPMENT	AUDIO VISUAL EQUIPMENT
WATERFORD Continued													
Faithlegg House Hotel	Tracy McDaid	165				1		1	3	•	•	H	O
Grand Hotel	Irene Treacy	166				1				•	•	H	H
Granville Hotel	Richard Hurley	170					1	2	1	•		H	H
Lawlors Hotel	William Buckley & Lucy McEwry	163		1		2	3	4	5	•	•	H	O
Rhu Glen Country Club Hotel	Rita Fitzgerald	171		1	1	1	1	1	1	•	•	H	H
Tower Hotel & Leisure Centre	Alicia Maguire	172		1			3	1	2	•	•		H
Woodlands Hotel	Marguerite Fitzgerald	173	1			1		1	3	•	•	H	H
WEXFORD													
Ashdown Park Hotel Conference & Leisure Centre	Catherine Byrne / Liam Moran	177	1					1	2	•	•	H	O
Clarion Brandon House Hotel, Health Club & Spa	Billy Brenner	178			1			2	1	•	•	H	O
Danby Lodge Hotel	Margaret Parle	180							1	•		H	H
Ferrycarrig Hotel	Caroline Roche	183		1	1	1	1	1	2	•	•	H	H
Hotel Rosslare	James Kelly	181					1				•	H	H
Marlfield House Hotel	Margaret Bowe	177							1	•		H	O
Riverside Park Hotel	Jim Maher	176	1			2		4	1	•	•	H	O
Rosslare Great Southern Hotel	Roisin Buckley	182			1				1	•	•	H	H
Talbot Hotel Conference and Leisure Centre	Niamh Lambert	184		1	1	2	3	4		•	•	H	O

H = Can Arrange Hire   *O = Available On Premises*

SELECT A VENUE FOR YOUR AGENDA

South West

CORK

ACCOMMODATION	CONTACT PERSON	Be Our Guest Page Number	Number of Rooms of Various Seating Capacities							Air Conditioning	Black Out Facilities	Interpreting Equipment	Audio Visual Equipment
			500+	400+	300+	200+	100+	50+	5+				
Actons Hotel	Anne Marie Cross	217			1				2	•	•	H	H
Aherne's Townhouse & Seafood Restaurant	John Fitzgibbon	228							2	•	•	H	H
Ambassador Hotel	Sile Ni Dhonaile	202						2	2			O	O
Blarney Park Hotel	David Harney / Josephine Noonan	193					1	3	2	•	•	H	H
Celtic Ross Hotel Conference & Leisure Centre	Kate Wycherley	225				1		1	1	•	•	H	H
Commodore Hotel	Robert Fitzpatrick	199			1				1			H	O
Glengarriff Eccles Hotel	Geraldine Owens	216				1		1	1	•		H	H
Great Southern Hotel	Pat Cussen	200				1			5	•	•	H	O
Gresham Metropole	Fiona Keohane	207	1	1	1	2	2	6	11	•	•	H	H
Hibernian Hotel and Leisure Centre	Catherine Gyves	223				1		2	4	•			O
Hotel Isaacs	Paula Lynch/Victoria Smith	208							2	•	•		O
Imperial Hotel	Elaine Gantly	208			1		1	1	4	•	•	H	H
Lodge & Spa at Inchydoney Island	Claire O'Connor	198		1					4	•	•	H	O
Maryborough House Hotel	Mary Motherway	211		1	1		2	2	5	•	•	H	O
Midleton Park Hotel & Spa	Daphne Spillane	224			1		1		3	•		H	H
Quality Hotel and Leisure Centre	Raymond Kelleher	198				1	3	4	1	•	•	H	H
Quality Hotel Cork	Shane McShortall	212					1	3	4	•		H	H
Rochestown Park Hotel	Liam Lally/Claire Cullinane	212	1	1	2	2	3	5	9	•	•	H	H

H = Can Arrange Hire   O = Available On Premises

SELECT A VENUE FOR YOUR AGENDA

Accommodation	Contact Person	BE OUR GUEST PAGE NUMBER	500+	400+	300+	200+	100+	50+	5+	AIR CONDITIONING	BLACK OUT FACILITIES	INTERPRETING EQUIPMENT	AUDIO VISUAL EQUIPMENT
CORK Continued													
Silversprings Moran Hotel	Tracey Moran	214	2		4	4	7	11	6	•	•	H	O
Springfort Hall Hotel	Paul Walsh	224				1	1	2	3	•			O
Trident Hotel	Hal McElroy/Una Wren	221				1			4	•	•	H	O
Victoria Hotel, Cork City	Paul / Eamonn King	214						1		•		H	H
Victoria Hotel, Macroom	Sabrina	222				1				•	•		O
KERRY													
Abbey Gate Hotel	Patrick Dillon	273		1	1	1	2	3	3	•	•	H	O
Aghadoe Heights Hotel	Emma Phillips	249					1		2	•	•		H
Brandon Hotel	Karina Dunne	275	1	1	2	2	3	4	4	•	•	H	O
Castlerosse Hotel & Leisure Centre	Michael O'Sullivan	252				1		1		•		H	H
Dingle Skellig Hotel	Colin Aherne	238				1		2		•	•	H	O
Dromhall Hotel	Andrew Joy	253			1	1	1	1	1	•	•	H	H
Gleneagle Hotel	Cara Fuller	257	2	2	3	3	4	4	4	•	•	H	O
Grand Hotel	Dick Boyle	277	1					3	6	•	•	O	O
Hotel Dunloe Castle	Suzanne Ennis	258			1	3	2	2		•		H	H
Hotel Europe	Suzanne Ennis	258	1	1	1	3	2			•			O
Kenmare Bay Hotel	Terry O'Doherty	244	1			1				•		H	O
Killarney Great Southern Hotel	Michele King	261	1			1		2	2	•	•	H	H
Killarney Park Hotel	Niamh O'Shea	262				1		1	3	•	•	H	O

H = Can Arrange Hire   O = Available On Premise

SELECT A VENUE FOR YOUR AGENDA

Column groups: **NUMBER OF ROOMS OF VARIOUS SEATING CAPACITIES** (500+, 400+, 300+, 200+, 100+, 50+, 50-), **BLACK OUT FACILITIES**, **AIR CONDITIONING**, **INTERPRETING EQUIPMENT**, **AUDIO VISUAL EQUIPMENT**

Accommodation	Contact Person	Be Our Guest Page Number	500+	400+	300+	200+	100+	50+	50-	Black Out Facilities	Air Conditioning	Interpreting Equipment	Audio Visual Equipment
KERRY Continued													
Lake Hotel	Tony Huggard/Marie O'Shea/Majella Steinbeck	264						1	2		•	H	O
Meadowlands Hotel	Carol Kennelly	277				1	1	1	2	•	•	H	H
Muckross Park Hotel	Lisa Cronin	265			1			1	1		•	H	H
Parknasilla Great Southern Hotel	Jim Feeney	272						1	1		•	H	H
Randles Court Clarion Hotel	Tom Randles	267							1	•	•	H	O
Riversdale House Hotel	Joanne O'Sullivan	246	1						1	•	•	H	H
Sheen Falls Lodge	Carmel Flynn	247					1	1	2	•	•	H	O
Shannon — CLARE													
Bunratty Castle Hotel	Kathleen McLoughlin	283					1	1	2	•	•	H	H
Falls Hotel	Lourda Roche	291		1					2		•	H	H
Great Southern Hotel	Clodagh Cussen	303				1			3	•	•	H	O
Kilkee Bay Hotel	Sandra Doherty	292					1		1	•	•	H	H
Kincora Hall Hotel	Matt Sherlock	294					1			•	•	H	O
Liscannor Bay Hotel	Brian J O'Higgins	298				1	1			•	•	H	H
Magowna House Hotel	Gay Murphy	288					1			•	•	H	O
Old Ground Hotel	Clara Clarke	289		1				1	1	•	•	H	O
Temple Gate Hotel	John Madden	290				1	1	2	1	•	•	H	O
Waterman's Lodge Country House Hotel	John Downes	295							1	•	•	H	H

H = *Can Arrange Hire*   O = *Available On Premises*

SELECT A VENUE FOR YOUR AGENDA

ACCOMMODATION	CONTACT PERSON	BE OUR GUEST PAGE NUMBER	500+	400+	300+	200+	100+	50+	50-	BLACK OUT FACILITIES	AIR CONDITIONING	INTERPRETING EQUIPMENT	AUDIO VISUAL EQUIPMENT
CLARE Continued													
Woodstock Hotel	Therese O'Connor	290				1	1	1	2	•	•	H	O
LIMERICK													
Adare Manor Hotel & Golf Resort	Yvette Kennedy	304				1	1	1	1	•		H	O
Castletroy Park Hotel	Ursula Cullen, Sales Manager	307		1	2	2	2	2	9	•	•	H	O
Clarion Hotel Limerick	Veronica Edwards	307					1	2	9	•	•	H	H
Fitzgeralds Woodlands House Hotel and Leisure Spa	David or Karen	306		1	1	1	2	3	3	•	•	H	H
Greenhills Hotel Conference/Leisure	Roger Beck	309	1	1	1	1	2	3	4	•	•	H	O
Gresham Ardhu	Claire Kennedy	310					1	5	6	•		H	H
Radisson SAS Hotel	Suzanne O'Dwyer	311	1	1					4	•		H	O
Rathkeale House Hotel	Gerry O'Connor	313			1		1		1	•	•	H	O
Woodfield House Hotel	Austin/Mary	312						1	1	•	•		O
TIPPERARY NORTH													
Anner Hotel & Leisure Centre	Joan Brett-Moloney	315		1	1	1	2	3			•	H	O
Dromineer Bay Hotel	Mary Guilfoyle	313				1	1				•	H	H
Grant's Hotel	Mary Deegan	314			1	1	1	2	2				O
West													
GALWAY													
Ardilaun House Hotel, Conference Centre & Leisure Club	John Ryan	331		1	1	1	2	3		•	•	H	H
Byrne's Mal Dua House	Peter & Aideen Byrne	324							1			H	H

NUMBER OF ROOMS OF VARIOUS SEATING CAPACITIES

H = Can Arrange Hire   O = Available On Premises

SELECT A VENUE FOR YOUR AGENDA

ACCOMMODATION	CONTACT PERSON	BE OUR GUEST PAGE NUMBER	500+	400+	300+	200+	100+	50+	5-	BLACK OUT FACILITIES	AIR CONDITIONING	INTERPRETING EQUIPMENT	AUDIO VISUAL EQUIPMENT
GALWAY Continued													
Connemara Coast Hotel	Paul O'Meara/Michelle Cremin	329		1	1	2	2	5	8	•		H	O
Corrib Great Southern Hotel	Micheal Cunningham	332	1			2		1	3	•	•	H	O
Galway Bay Hotel, Conference & Leisure Centre	Virginia Connolly	334	1	1	2	2	2	5	5	•	•	H	O
Galway Great Southern Hotel	Fergal O'Connell	334				1	1		3	•	•	H	O
Galway Radisson SAS Hotel	Marie Carmody	335	1	2	2	4	4	4	12	•	•	H	O
Galway Ryan (The)	Duty Manager	335							2		•	H	H
Glenlo Abbey Hotel	Eimear O'Farrell	335					1	2	9	•		H	H
Harbour Hotel	Amanda O' Farrell	336						3		•		H	O
Lady Gregory Hotel	Brian Morrissey/Yvonne McNamara	344			1					•		H	O
Meadow Court Hotel	Tom Corbett Jnr	347			1			1		•	•		H
Menlo Park Hotel and Conference Centre	Martina McKee	339		1	1	2	3	2		•	•	H	O
Oranmore Lodge Hotel, Conference & Leisure Centre	Mary O'Higgins	348		1		1	1	1		•	•	H	H
Park Lodge Hotel	Jane Marie Foyle	354					1	1	1	•	•	H	H
Peacockes Hotel & Complex	Eimear Killian	348	1			1	1			•	•	H	H
Renvyle House Hotel	Mairead McManamon	353					1	1	1	•	•	H	O
Salthill Court Hotel	Pauline Griffin	341					1			•	•		
Shannon Oaks Hotel & Country Club	Barry Maher	352	1				1	1	2	•	•	H	O
Victoria Hotel	Mary King	342						1		•	•	O	O
Westwood House Hotel	Nicola Jones	344			1	1	1	3	3	•	•	H	O

H = Can Arrange Hire   O = Available On Premises

SELECT A VENUE FOR YOUR AGENDA

ACCOMMODATION	CONTACT PERSON	BE OUR GUEST PAGE NUMBER	500+	400+	300+	200+	100+	50+	50-	BLACK OUT FACILITIES	AIR CONDITIONING	INTERPRETING EQUIPMENT	AUDIO VISUAL EQUIPMENT
GALWAY Continued													
Zetland Country House Hotel	Rory Prendergast	320							1				H
MAYO													
Atlantic Coast Hotel	Suzanne O'Brien	363					1		3	•	•	H	O
Castlecourt Hotel Conference and Leisure Centre	Cynthia Doyle	364	1	1	1	2	2	3	3	•	•	H	O
Downhill House Hotel	Kay Devine & Rachel Moylett	356	1		1	1	1	2	4	•	•	H	O
Hotel Westport, Conference & Leisure Centre	Gerry Walshe & Ruth Farrell & Rhona Chambers	364			1		1	3	1	•	•	H	O
Knock House Hotel	Brian Crowley	361					1	1	1				O
Knockranny House Hotel	Elaine Joyce/Patricia Crowley	365	1	1	1	1	2	3	3	•	•	H	O
Ostan Oilean Acla	Michael McLoughlin	355			1			1	1	•	•	O	O
Teach Iorrais	Carmel Gallagher	360				2				•	•	H	H
TF Royal Hotel & Theatre	David McManus	358	1	1	2	2	3	3	4	•	•	H	O
Westport Woods Hotel & Leisure Centre	Margaret Mulchrone	366		1	1	1	2	1	2	•	•	H	H
Wyatt Hotel	Brian Fahy	367			1			2	3	•	•		O
ROSCOMMON													
O'Gara's Royal Hotel	Larry O'Gara	368					1	2	1	•	•		O
Regans	Mary Regan/Dominic Regan	369						1			•		H
Royal Hotel	Adrian Bouchier	367						1		•	•	O	O

NUMBER OF ROOMS OF VARIOUS SEATING CAPACITIES

H = Can Arrange Hire   O = Available On Premises

SELECT A VENUE FOR YOUR AGENDA

ACCOMMODATION	CONTACT PERSON	BE OUR GUEST PAGE NUMBER	NUMBER OF ROOMS OF VARIOUS SEATING CAPACITIES							BLACK OUT FACILITIES	AIR CONDITIONING	INTERPRETING EQUIPMENT	AUDIO VISUAL EQUIPMENT
			500+	400+	300+	200+	100+	50+	50-				
North West													
DONEGAL													
Bay View Hotel & Leisure Centre	Aidan McHugh	379			1			1		•	•		O
Central Hotel, Conference & Leisure Centre	Michael Naughton	375			1	1	1	1	1	•	•	H	O
Dorrians Imperial Hotel	Mary Dorrian	372				1		1	1	•	•		H
Great Northern Hotel	Philip McGlynn	374	1	1	1	1	1	1	1	•	•	H	O
Harvey's Point Country Hotel	Siobhan McNulty	376					1	2	2			H	
Sandhouse Hotel	Paul Diver - Manager	382						1	3	•	•	H	H
LEITRIM													
Bush Hotel	Joseph Dolan	384		1		2		3	5	•			O
Landmark Hotel	Mary Stillman	384		1	1	2		2		•	•	H	O
Shannon Key West Hotel	Margaret Mitchell-Devlin	385		1				1		•	•		O
SLIGO													
Beach Hotel and Leisure Club	Audri Herron	386				1	2				•	H	H
Sligo Park Hotel & Leisure Centre	Bernadette Coffey	388		1				3	3	•	•	H	O
Sligo's Southern Hotel & Leisure Centre	Kevin McGlynn/Jackie McLoughlin	388			1	1	1	2	4			H	H
Tower Hotel	Adrian Harkins	389					1	1	2	•		H	H
North													
ANTRIM													
Ballymac	Cathy Muldoon	398				1		1		•			O

H = Can Arrange Hire   O = Available On Premises

SELECT A VENUE FOR YOUR AGENDA

Accommodation	Contact Person	Be Our Guest Page Number	500+	400+	300+	200+	100+	50+	50-	Black Out Facilities	Air Conditioning	Interpreting Equipment	Audio Visual Equipment
ANTRIM Continued													
Bayview Hotel	Mary O'Neill	393						1	1	•	•	H	H
Bushmills Inn	Stella Minogue	393							3	•	•	H	O
Comfort Hotel Portrush	Mary O'Neill	396						1	1	•	•	H	H
Galgorm Manor Hotel	Martin Boon	392	1		1			1	1	•	•	O	H
Hilton Templepatrick	Sinead Burns	398	1			2	5	7	3	•	•	H	O
Londonderry Arms Hotel	Frank O'Neill	394					1	2	2	•		H	H
Magherabuoy House Hotel	Anna Conn	397		1	1	2	2	2	3	•		H	O
Quality Hotel	Tom Boyd	395		1				1	2	•	•	H	O
ARMAGH													
Armagh City Hotel	Gary Hynes	400	2	2	2	4	4	5	10	•	•	H	O
BELFAST													
Dukes Hotel	Yvonne McNally	401					1	2	3	•	•	H	H
Dunadry Hotel and Country Club	Sheree Davis	402			1	1	2	4	5	•	•		O
Hilton Belfast	Kelly-Ann Smiley	402	1			1	1	6		•	•	H	O
Lansdowne Hotel	Jeanette McIntyre	404					1	1	1	•	•	H	O
McCausland Hotel	Adrianne Carr	405						1	2	•	•	H	O
Park Avenue Hotel	Angela Reid	405		1	1	3	4	8	11	•	•	H	O
Wellington Park Hotel	Gerardo Jimenez	405		1	1	2	3	4	9	•	•	H	O

H = Can Arrange Hire   O = Available On Premises

SELECT A VENUE FOR YOUR AGENDA

Accommodation	Contact Person	Be Our Guest Page Number	Number of Rooms of Various Seating Capacities							Black Out Facilities	Air Conditioning	Interpreting Equipment	Audio Visual Equipment
			500+	400+	300+	200+	100+	50+	5-				
DERRY													
Brown Trout Golf & Country Inn	Bill O'Hara	406							2	•	•		
City Hotel	Averil Clarke	407		1	1	1				•	•	H	H
Tower Hotel Derry	Ian Hyland	408				1			3	•	•	H	H
DOWN													
Burrendale Hotel and Country Club	Fiona O'Hare	412					1	1	6	•	•	H	O
Royal Hotel	Martin Newell	409							1	•			O
Slieve Croob Inn	Laurence Kelly	411						1	1	•	•		O
FERMANAGH													
Killyhevlin Hotel	David Morrison	414	1			2		2	3	•	•	H	H
Manor House Country Hotel	David Begley	414			1	1		2	5	•	•	H	O

H = Can Arrange Hire   O = Available On Premises

KEY TO MAPS

Grid rows: 22, 21, 20, 19, 18, 17, 16, 15, 14, 13, 12, 11, 10, 9, 8, 7, 6, 5, 4, 3, 2, 1

Grid columns: A B C D E F G H I J K L M N O P Q R

Map labels: COLERAINE, LETTERKENNY, DERRY, BALLYMENA, 13-14, 15, LARNE, COOKSTOWN, DONEGAL, BELFAST, SLIGO, ENNISKILLEN, ARMAGH, NEWRY, BALLINA, MONAGHAN, DUNDALK, CAVAN, 11-12, CASTLEBAR, 9-10, DROGHEDA, WESTPORT, ATHLONE, GALWAY, DUBLIN, TULLAMORE, PORTLAOISE, ARKLOW, 5-6, 7-8, ENNIS, CARLOW, KILKENNY, LIMERICK, TIPPERARY, WEXFORD, TRALEE, CLONMEL, WATERFORD, KILLARNEY, CORK, BANTRY, 3-4, 1-2

LEGEND

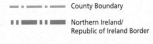

- M50 — Motorway
- N7 — Dual Carriageway
- N2 — National Primary Routes
- N69 — National Secondary Routes
- Regional Routes
- Other Roads
- 14 — Distances Between Centres (in Kilometres)
- County Boundary
- Northern Ireland/ Republic of Ireland Border
- SHANNON AIRPORT — Airports
- Holyhead ----- Ferries
- Hill of Tara ◆ Heritage Sites

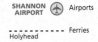

DISTANCE CHART
in Kilometres

ARMAGH	ATHLONE	BELFAST	CARLOW	CLIFDEN	CORK	DERRY	DUBLIN	DUNDALK	ENNISKILLEN	GALWAY	KILKENNY	KILLARNEY	LARNE	LIMERICK	PORTLAOISE	ROSSLARE HARBOUR	SHANNON AIRPORT	SLIGO	TRALEE	WATERFORD	WEXFORD	WICKLOW
159																						
66	224																					
211	108	248																				
316	171	370	256																			
380	219	423	187	287																		
114	225	118	309	303	460																	
129	124	167	82	296	256	233																
45	142	82	166	314	340	158	84															
81	127	135	240	237	346	98	175	101														
238	92	303	177	79	206	277	216	233	192													
245	121	282	39	248	148	335	114	200	242	169												
388	229	430	235	295	89	480	303	348	356	214	196											
105	264	40	287	411	462	122	206	121	174	343	320	470										
279	119	320	138	184	101	369	192	238	245	105	114	109	356									
208	71	250	37	229	174	287	82	167	192	150	50	221	285	109								
282	201	320	93	348	206	385	151	237	324	269	100	272	356	204	130							
293	134	345	163	172	126	357	216	261	261	93	138	134	380	24	134	229						
148	116	203	224	167	336	134	213	171	68	142	237	345	240	235	187	319	224					
382	222	423	242	288	121	472	296	341	349	208	216	32	460	103	213	291	127	338				
285	167	324	74	296	126	383	156	240	290	217	48	192	359	124	97	81	148	283	211			
264	184	301	76	330	187	365	132	219	306	250	81	254	338	187	113	19	209	299	272	61		
185	138	222	61	311	256	293	56	140	221	232	100	303	259	193	82	118	216	238	296	135	100	

N

MAGNETIC

Variation 10°45' (1990)

```
0     5     10     15     20     25km
0          5               10      15miles
```

SCALE 1 : 625 000

MAPS

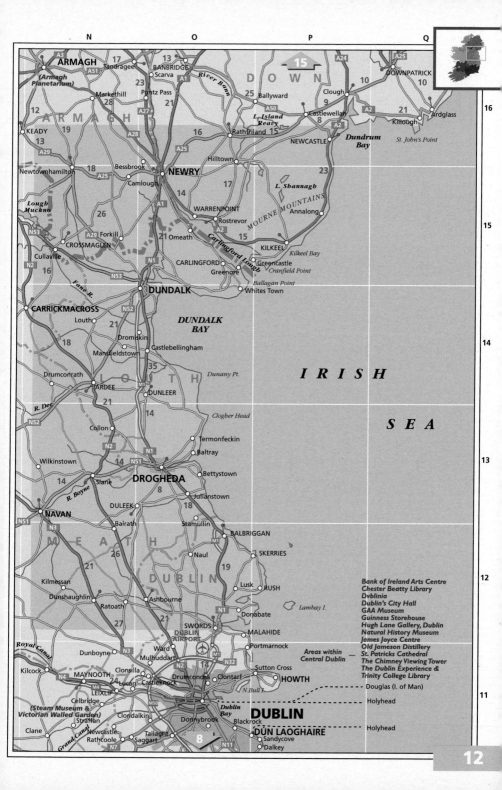

ARMAGH 17 Tandragee 13 **BANBRIDGE**
(Armagh Planetarium) Scarva A1
23 Markethill Puntz Pass
28 21 **DOWN** 15 A24
A51 25 Ballyward 10 **DOWNPATRICK** 10
A3
12 19 A27 A50 Castlewellan Clough 9 A2 21 Ardglass
A28 L. Island Ready 8 Kiltough
KEADY Rathfriland **NEWCASTLE** A2
13 A29 18 Bessbrook 16 15 **Dundrum** St. John's Point
Newtownhamilton Camlough **NEWRY** Hilltown **Bay**
A25
14 17 23
A1
Lough 26 **WARRENPOINT** L. Shannagh
Muckno Rostrevor Annalong
A29 Forkill 21 Omeath 15 **MOURNE MOUNTAINS**
CROSSMAGLEN Carlingford Lough **KILKEEL**
Cullaville N1 **CARLINGFORD** Greencastle Kilkeel Bay
N2 16 N53 Greenore Cranfield Point
Fane R. **DUNDALK** Ballagan Point
Whites Town
CARRICKMACROSS N52 21 **DUNDALK**
Louth **BAY**
18 Dromiskin
Mansfieldstown Castlebellingham
Drumconrath 35 Dunany Pt. **I R I S H**
ARDEE **DUNLEER**
N52 21 14 Clogher Head **S E A**
Collon
Wilkinstown 14 N51 Termonfeckin
14 Slane Baltray
R. Boyne Bettystown
DROGHEDA Julianstown
NAVAN DULEEK 8
N51 N3 Balrath 18 Stamullin
M E A T H BALBRIGGAN
26 M1
Naul SKERRIES
21 19
Kilmessan Lusk RUSH
Dunshaughlin **DUBLIN** Lambay I.
Ratoath Ashbourne Donabate
27 N1 **Bank of Ireland Arts Centre**
Dunboyne **SWORDS** MALAHIDE **Chester Beatty Library**
Ward **AIRPORT** Portmarnock **Dvblinia**
Kilcock N4 **MAYNOOTH** Mulhuddart M1 **Dublin's City Hall**
N3 N2 Sutton Cross **GAA Museum**
Clonsilla N32 Areas within **Guinness Storehouse**
LEIXLIP Lucan Castleknock Drumcondra Clontarf **HOWTH** Central Dublin **Hugh Lane Gallery, Dublin**
Celbridge M50 N. Bull I. **Natural History Museum**
(Steam Museum & Clondalkin **James Joyce Centre**
Victorian Walled Garden) Straffan Dublin **Old Jameson Distillery**
Clane Newcastle Donnybrook Bay **DUBLIN** **St. Patricks Cathedral**
Grand Canal Rathcoole Tallaght Blackrock **The Chimney Viewing Tower**
N7 Saggart 8 **DÚN LAOGHAIRE** **The Dublin Experience &**
Sandycove **Trinity College Library**
Dalkey Douglas (I. of Man)
Holyhead

Holyhead

16

15

14

13

12

11

GUINNESS®

Holiday Competition

Guinness invite you to Be Our Guest in any of the hotels or guesthouses featured in Ireland's favourite and most successful accommodation guide. (Value of prize €1,250).

[Excluding peak periods and subject to availability]

Simply complete the sentence below in 10 words or less:

I would like to win this wonderful prize because

_____

_____

Replies clearly marked Holiday Competition to:

Irish Hotels Federation, 13 Northbrook Road, Dublin 6, Ireland.

Closing Date for Entries 31st August 2003

(Photocopies not accepted)

Name: _____

Address: _____

irelandhotels.com
log on and book in

IRISH HOTELS FEDERATION

Throughout the year, Ireland has a great range of social, cultural and sporting events. The big cities and even the smallest villages have festivals, whether in honour of a goat, as at Puck Fair, or to celebrate the oysters in Galway.

Listed below is a small selection of well known events/festivals which take place. There are, of course, many others, whether music or sport. **Please contact your nearest Irish Tourist Board office for confirmation of dates and a full calendar of events. (TBC = Dates to be Confirmed)**

FEBRUARY

16 February	Dublin Toy & Train Fair

MARCH

11 - 17 March	St. Patrick's Festival 2003, Dublin
22 March	Ireland v France (6 Nations) Rugby International, Lansdowne Road, Dublin
25 March - 01 April	Kerry Arts Easter Weekend Festival, Tralee, Co. Kerry
30 March	Ireland v England Rugby International, Lansdowne Road, Dublin

APRIL

25 March - 01 April	Kerry Arts Easter Weekend Festival, Tralee, Co. Kerry
22 April - 27 April	Pan - Celtic Festival, Kilkenny City
T.B.C.	Circuit of Ireland Rally, Enniskillen, Co. Fermanagh & Bundoran, Co. Donegal
27 April - 05 May	Dundalk Maytime Festival, Dundalk, Co. Louth

MAY

T.B.C.	Cork International Choral Festival, Cork
27 April - 05 May	Dundalk Maytime Festival, Dundalk, Co. Louth
02 - 05 May	Bray Jazz Festival, Bray, Co. Wicklow
02 - 05 May	Newbridge Bealtine Festival, Newbridge, Co. Kildare
02 - 05 May	Carlsberg Kilkenny Roots Festival, Kilkenny
08 - 11 May	International Mussel Fair, Bantry, Co. Cork

MAY (CONTINUED)

7 - 18 May	A.I.M.S. Choral Festival, New Ross, Co. Wexford
8 May - 05 June	Writers' Week, Listowel, Co. Kerry
0 May - 02 June	Guinness Castlebar Blues Festival, Castlebar, Co. Mayo
0 May - 02 June	Guinness Bandon Humours Music Festival, Bandon, Co. Cork

JUNE

8 May - 05 June	Writers' Week, Listowel, Co. Kerry
0 May - 02 June	Guinness Castlebar Blues Festival, Castlebar, Co. Mayo
0 May - 02 June	Guinness Bandon Humours Music Festival, Bandon, Co. Cork
2 June T.B.C	Tesco/Evening Herald Women's Mini Marathon, Dublin City
7 June	Ireland v Albania (Soccer International), Lansdowne Road, Dublin
1 June	Ireland v Georgia (Soccer International), Lansdowne Road, Dublin
6 June	Bloomsday Festival, Dublin
.B.C	Murphy's Irish Open, Fota Island, Cork
0 June -22 June	Portnoo Seafood Festival, Portnoo, Co. Donegal
7 - 29 June	Budweiser Irish Derby Weekend, The Curragh Racecourse, Co. Kildare

JULY

3 - 06 July	The Smurfit European Open, K Club, Co. Kildare
.B.C	Willie Clancy Summer School, Miltown Malbay, Co. Clare
.B.C	Bard Summer School, Clare Island, Co. Mayo
.B.C	Galway Film Fleadh, Galway City
1 July - 20 July	Ballina Arts Festival, Ballina, Co. Mayo
5 - 27 July	Galway Arts Festival, Galway City
8 July - 20 July	Carlsberg Arklow Seabreeze, Arklow, Co. Wicklow

JULY (CONTINUED)

21 July - 27 July	Buncrana Festival, Buncrana, Co. Donegal
T.B.C	Yeats International Summer School, Sligo
26 July - 04 August	Mary from Dungloe International Festival, Dungloe, Co. Donegal
27 July - 04 August	Wicklow Regatta, Wicklow
27 July - 04 August	Carlsbery Kilkenny Roots Festival, Kilkenny
28 July - 03 August	Guinness Galway Race Meeting, Galway

AUGUST

T.B.C	Yeats International Summer School, Sligo
26 July - 04 August	Mary from Dungloe International Festival, Dungloe, Co. Donegal
27 July - 04 August	Wicklow Regatta, Wicklow
27 July - 04 August	Carlsbery Kilkenny Roots Festival, Kilkenny
28 July - 03 August	Guinness Galway Race Meeting, Galway
01 August - 04 August	Guinness Mitchelstown Music Festival, Mitchelstown, Co. Cork
01 August - 04 August	Smithwicks Ballyshannon Folk Festival, Ballyshannon, Co. Donegal
01 August - 04 August	Waterford Spraoi, Waterford City
T.B.C	Birr Vintage Week, Birr, Co. Offaly
06 - 10 August	Kerrygold Horse Show 2003, Royal Dublin Society, Dublin
08 - 17 August	Kilkenny Arts Festival, Kilkenny City
10 - 12 August	Guinness Puck Fair, Killorglin, Co. Kerry
21 August	Connemara Pony Show, Clifden, Co. Galway
T.B.C	Fleadh Ceoil Na hEireann, Listowel, Co. Kerry
22 August	Rose of Tralee International Festival, Tralee, Co. Kerry
23 August - 24 August	Dunmore East Bluegrass Festival, Dunmore East, Co. Waterford
T.B.C	Matchmaking Festival, Lisdoonvarna, Co. Clare

CALENDAR OF EVENTS

SEPTEMBER

T.B.C	Matchmaking Festival, Lisdoonvarna, Co. Clare
05 September	Cape Clear Island International Storytelling Festival, Cape Clear Island, West Cork
06 September	Ireland v Russia (Soccer International), Lansdowne Road, Dublin
12 - 14 September	Guinness Clarenbridge Oyster Festival, Clarenbridge, Co. Galway
14 September	Guinness All Ireland Hurling Championship Final, Croke Park, Dublin
15 - 21 September	Listowel Racing Festival, Listowel, Co. Kerry
17 - 28 September	Waterford International Festival of Light Opera, Waterford
28 September	Bank of Ireland All Ireland Football Championship Final, Croke Park, Dublin
26 - 28 September	Guinness Galway International Oyster Festival, Galway City
27 September - 05 October	Ballinasloe International Horse Fair and Festival, Ballinasloe, Co. Galway

OCTOBER

T.B.C	Matchmaking Festival, Lisdoonvarna, Co. Clare
T.B.C.	Dublin Theatre Festival, Dublin
T.B.C.	27th International Gourmet Festival, Kinsale, Co. Cork
T.B.C.	Cork Film Festival, Cork City
18 October - 05 November	Wexford Festival Opera, Wexford
24 - 27 October	Guinness Cork Jazz Festival, Cork City
27 October	Dublin City Marathon, Dublin City

HOTEL

whether you're offering...

bedrooms & ballrooms

saunas & swimming pools

cabaret & craic...

to brighten up your brochure

pick up the phone

and have a word with **'the wood'**.

wood **printcraft** *group*

for the full package in brochure production

contact stanley crawford
sales director
greencastle parade clonshaugh dublin 17
telephone 847 0011 facsimile 847 5570
e-mail s.crawford@wpg.ie

INDEX OF HOTELS & GUESTHOUSES   GUINNESS

A

19TH GREEN (THE)
Killarney, Kerry....................248
☎ 064-32868

19TH LODGE
Ballybunion, Kerry 229
☎ 068-27592

A STAR OF THE SEA
Galway City, Galway............329
☎ 091-525900

AARONMOR GUESTHOUSE
Dublin City, Dublin 34
☎ 01-668 7972

ABBERLEY COURT HOTEL
Dublin City, Dublin 34
☎ 01-459 6000

ABBEY COURT HOTEL AND TRINITY LEISURE CLUB
Nenagh, Tipperary North 313
☎ 067-41111

ABBEY GATE HOTEL
Tralee, Kerry........................273
☎ 066-712 9888

ABBEY HOTEL
Ballyvourney, Cork 188
☎ 026-45324

ABBEY HOTEL
Dublin City, Dublin 35
☎ 01-872 8188

ABBEY HOTEL, LEISURE & CONFERENCE CENTRE
Roscommon Town, Roscommon 368
☎ 0903-26240

ABBEY HOUSE
Galway City, Galway............330
☎ 091-524394

ABBEY LODGE
Killarney, Kerry....................248
☎ 064-34193

ABBEYGLEN CASTLE HOTEL
Clifden, Galway 321
☎ 095-22832

ABBEYLEIX MANOR HOTEL
Abbeyleix, Laois....................126
☎ 0502-30111

ABERDEEN LODGE
Dublin City, Dublin 35
☎ 01-283 8155

ABRAE COURT
Dublin City, Dublin 36
☎ 01-492 2242

ACADEMY HOTEL
Dublin City, Dublin 36
☎ 01-878 0666

ACH NA SHEEN GUESTHOUSE
Tipperary Town, Tipperary South 159
☎ 062-51298

ACHILL CLIFF HOUSE HOTEL
Achill Island, Mayo...............355
☎ 098-43400

ACHILL HOUSE
Cork City, Cork 201
☎ 021-427 9447

ACORN HOUSE
Cork City, Cork 201
☎ 021-450 2474

ACTONS HOTEL
Kinsale, Cork 217
☎ 021-477 2135

ADAIR ARMS HOTEL
Ballymena, Antrim 392
☎ 028-2565 3674

ADAMS TRINITY HOTEL
Dublin City, Dublin 36
☎ 01-670 7100

ADARE GUEST HOUSE
Galway City, Galway............330
☎ 091-582638

ADARE MANOR HOTEL & GOLF RESORT
Adare, Limerick 304
☎ 061-396566

AGHADOE HEIGHTS HOTEL
Killarney, Kerry....................249
☎ 064-31766

AHERLOW HOUSE HOTEL
Glen Of Aherlow, Tipperary South 157
☎ 062-56153

AHERNE'S TOWNHOUSE & SEAFOOD RESTAURANT
Youghal, Cork......................228
☎ 024-92424

AIRPORT LODGE
Cork Airport, Cork 200
☎ 021-431 6920

AIRPORT MANOR
Swords, Dublin.....................94
☎ 01-840 1818

AIRPORT VIEW
Blakes Cross, Dublin 32
☎ 01-843 8756

AISHLING HOUSE
Dublin City, Dublin 37
☎ 01-833 9097

AISLEIGH GUEST HOUSE
Carrick-on-Shannon, Leitrim 383
☎ 078-20313

AISLING HOUSE
Ashbourne, Meath 99
☎ 01-835 0359

AISLING HOUSE
Killarney, Kerry....................249
☎ 064-31112

ALCOCK AND BROWN HOTEL
Clifden, Galway 322
☎ 095-21206

ALEXANDER HOTEL
Dublin City, Dublin 37
☎ 01-607 3700

ALEXANDRA GUEST HOUSE
Limerick City, Limerick 306
☎ 061-318472

ALEXANDRA TOWN HOUSE
Portrush, Antrim...................395
☎ 028-7082 2284

ALPINE HOUSE
Dingle, Kerry 236
☎ 066-915 1250

AMBASSADOR HOTEL
Cork City, Cork....................202
☎ 021-455 1996

AMBASSADOR HOTEL
Kill, Kildare..........................122
☎ 045-877064

AN CRUISCIN LAN HOTEL
Spiddal, Galway 354
☎ 091-553148

AN CUIRT GEORGIAN GEORGIAN COURT
Dublin City, Dublin 38
☎ 01-855 7872

AN TINTAIN GUESTHOUSE
Multyfarnham, Westmeath 139
☎ 044-71411

ANCHOR GUEST HOUSE
Dublin City, Dublin 38
☎ 01-878 6913

ANGLERS REST HOTEL
Headford, Galway................345
☎ 093-35528

ANGLESEA TOWN HOUSE
Dublin City, Dublin 38
☎ 01-668 3877

ANNAGH LODGE GUESTHOUSE
Newbridge, Kildare 125
☎ 045-433518

ANNER HOTEL & LEISURE CENTRE
Thurles, Tipperary North 315
☎ 0504-21799

ANNO SANTO HOTEL
Galway City, Galway............330
☎ 091-523011

ANTOINE HOUSE
Cork City, Cork 202
☎ 021-427 3494

ARAN VIEW HOUSE HOTEL & RESTAURANT
Doolin, Clare 285
☎ 065-707 4061

ARBUTUS HOTEL
Killarney, Kerry....................250
☎ 064-31037

ARD EINNE GUESTHOUSE
Aran Islands, Galway 317
☎ 099-61126

ARD RI HOTEL
Waterford City, Waterford 167
☎ 051-832111

INDEX OF HOTELS & GUESTHOUSES GUINNESS

ARDAGH HOTEL & RESTAURANT
Clifden, Galway 322
☎ 095-21384

ARDAGH HOUSE
Killenaule, Tipperary South 158
☎ 052-56224

ARDAGH HOUSE
Dublin City, Dublin 39
☎ 01-497 7068

ARDAWN HOUSE
Galway City, Galway...........................331
☎ 091-568833

ARDBOYNE HOTEL
Navan, Meath.......................................102
☎ 046-23119

ARDENODE HOTEL
Ballymore Eustace, Kildare 120
☎ 045-864198

ARDILAUN GUESTHOUSE
Ennis, Clare 286
☎ 065-682 2311

**ARDILAUN HOUSE HOTEL, CONFERENCE
CENTRE & LEISURE CLUB**
Galway City, Galway...........................331
☎ 091-521433

**ARDMORE COUNTRY HOUSE HOTEL AND
RESTAURANT**
Westport, Mayo 362
☎ 098-25994

ARD-NA-SIDHE
Caragh Lake, Kerry 234
☎ 066-976 9105

ARIEL HOUSE
Dublin City, Dublin 39
☎ 01-668 5512

**ARKLOW BAY CONFERENCE AND LEISURE
HOTEL**
Arklow, Wicklow 104
☎ 0402-32309

ARLINGTON HOTEL
Dublin City, Dublin 40
☎ 01-804 9100

**ARLINGTON LODGE
COUNTRY HOUSE HOTEL**
Waterford City, Waterford 167
☎ 051-878584

ARMAGH CITY HOTEL
Armagh City, Armagh 400
☎ 028-3751 8888

ARNOLDS HOTEL
Dunfanaghy, Donegal 377
☎ 074-913 6208

ASHBERRY LODGE
Kenmare, Kerry 243
☎ 064-42720

ASHBOURNE COURT HOTEL
Ashbourne, Meath 99
☎ 01-835 9300

ASHBURN HOTEL
Lurgan, Armagh 400
☎ 028-3832 5711

**ASHDOWN PARK HOTEL CONFERENCE &
LEISURE CENTRE**
Gorey, Wexford 177
☎ 055-80500

ASHFIELD HOUSE
Dublin City, Dublin 40
☎ 01-260 3680

ASHFORD CASTLE
Cong, Mayo 359
☎ 094-954 6003

ASHFORD MANOR
Galway City, Galway...........................331
☎ 091-563941

ASHLEE LODGE
Blarney, Cork 192
☎ 021-438 5346

ASHLEY HOTEL
Cork City, Cork 202
☎ 021-450 1518

ASHLING HOTEL
Dublin City, Dublin 40
☎ 01-677 2324

ASHVILLE GUESTHOUSE
Killarney, Kerry...................................250
☎ 064-36405

ASTON HOTEL
Dublin City, Dublin 41
☎ 01-677 9300

ATLANTA HOUSE
Bantry, Cork 190
☎ 027-50237

ATLANTIC COAST HOTEL
Westport, Mayo 363
☎ 098-29000

ATLANTIC HOTEL
Lahinch, Clare.....................................296
☎ 065-708 1049

ATLANTIC HOUSE
Dungloe, Donegal 378
☎ 074-952 1061

ATLANTIC VIEW HOUSE
Galway City, Galway...........................332
☎ 091-582109

AUBURN GUESTHOUSE
Dublin City, Dublin 41
☎ 01-822 3535

AUBURN LODGE HOTEL
Ennis, Clare 287
☎ 065-682 1247

AUGUSTA LODGE
Westport, Mayo 363
☎ 098-28900

AULBER HOUSE
Cashel, Tipperary South 154
☎ 062-63713

AUSTIN FRIAR HOTEL
Mullingar, Westmeath 137
☎ 044-45777

AVONBRAE GUESTHOUSE
Rathdrum, Wicklow 113
☎ 0404-46198

B

BAGGOT COURT
Dublin City, Dublin 42
☎ 01-661 2819

BAILEYS OF CASHEL
Cashel, Tipperary South 154
☎ 062-61937

BAILIE HOTEL
Bailieborough, Cavan 117
☎ 042-966 5334

**BALLINALACKEN CASTLE COUNTRY
HOUSE & RESTAURANT**
Doolin, Clare 285
☎ 065-707 4025

BALLINDIFF BAY LODGE
Corrandulla, Galway 328
☎ 091-791195

BALLINSKELLIGS INN
Ballinskelligs, Kerry.............................229
☎ 066-947 9104

BALLYGARRY HOUSE HOTEL
Tralee, Kerry 273
☎ 066-712 3322

BALLYGLASS COUNTRY HOUSE
Tipperary Town, Tipperary South 159
☎ 062-52104

BALLYKNOCKEN COUNTRY HOUSE
Ashford, Wicklow................................106
☎ 0404-44627

**BALLYLICKEY MANOR HOUSE
AND RESTAURANT**
Ballylickey, Cork 188
☎ 027-50071

BALLYMAC
Stoneyford, Antrim..............................398
☎ 028-9264 8313

BALLYMALOE HOUSE
Shanagarry, Cork 226
☎ 021-465 2531

BALLYMASCANLON HOUSE HOTEL
Dundalk, Louth.....................................97
☎ 042-9358200

BALLYNAHINCH CASTLE HOTEL
Ballynahinch, Galway 318
☎ 095-31006

BALLYROE HEIGHTS HOTEL
Tralee, Kerry 274
☎ 066-712 6796

BALLYSEEDE CASTLE HOTEL
Tralee, Kerry 274
☎ 066-712 5799

Notes

Notes

irelandhotels.com
log on and book in

Notes